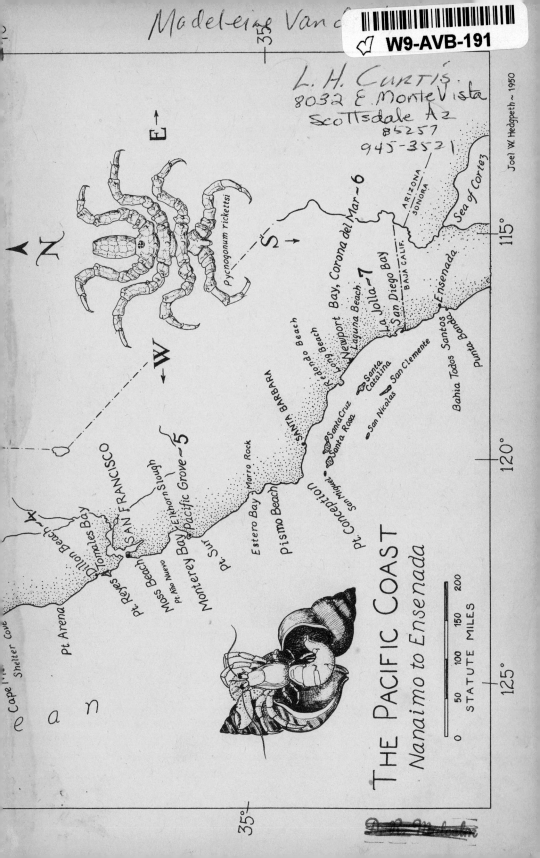

Madeleine Van d...

L. H. Curtis
8032 E. Monte Vista
Scottsdale Az
85257
945-3521

Joel W. Hedgpeth ~ 1950

E ↑

N

S →

W ↓

Pycnogonum rickettsi

Cape ...
Shelter Cove
Pt. Arena
Dillon Beach
Tomales Bay
Pt. Reyes
SAN FRANCISCO
Moss Beach
Pt. Año Nuevo
Elkhorn Slough
Monterey Bay
Pacific Grove ~ 5
Pt. Sur

Estero Bay / Morro Rock
Pismo Beach
Pt. Concepcion
San Simeon
SANTA BARBARA

Redondo Beach
Long Beach
Newport Bay, Corona del Mar ~ 6
Laguna Beach ~ 7
La Jolla
San Diego Bay
Ensenada
Santos Santos
Punta Banda
Bahia Todos
Santa Cruz
Santa Rosa
Santa Catalina
San Clemente
San Nicolas

ARIZONA
SONORA
BAJA CALIF.
Sea of Cortez

115°
120°
125°

35°

o c e a n

THE PACIFIC COAST
Nanaimo to Ensenada

0 50 100 150 200
STATUTE MILES

BETWEEN PACIFIC TIDES

CHITONS (SEA CRADLES)
(See §127, pp. 88–89, 448.)

Names of chitons shown on the plate opposite are given below, by rows, left to right. Those indicated as "sp." are uncertain varieties which have not yet been clearly determined.

First row: (1) *Mopalia ciliata* (Sowerby); (2) *Lepidozona mertensii* (von Middendorf); (3) and (4) *Mopalia* sp. (near *wosnessenskii* von Middendorf).

Second row: (1) *Cyanoplax hartwegii* (Carpenter); (2) *Tonicella lineata* (Wood); (3) *Stenoplax fallax* (Carpenter); (4) *Tonicella lineata* (Wood).

Third row: (1) *Lepidozona mertensii* (von Middendorf); (2) *Stenoplax heathiana* Berry; (3) *Mopalia* sp.; (4) *Placiphorella velata* Dall.

Fourth row: (1) *Mopalia lignosa* (Gould); (2) *Mopalia* sp. (near *wosnessenskii*); (3) *Ischnochiton (Rhombochiton) regularis* Carpenter; (4) *Mopalia lignosa* (Gould).

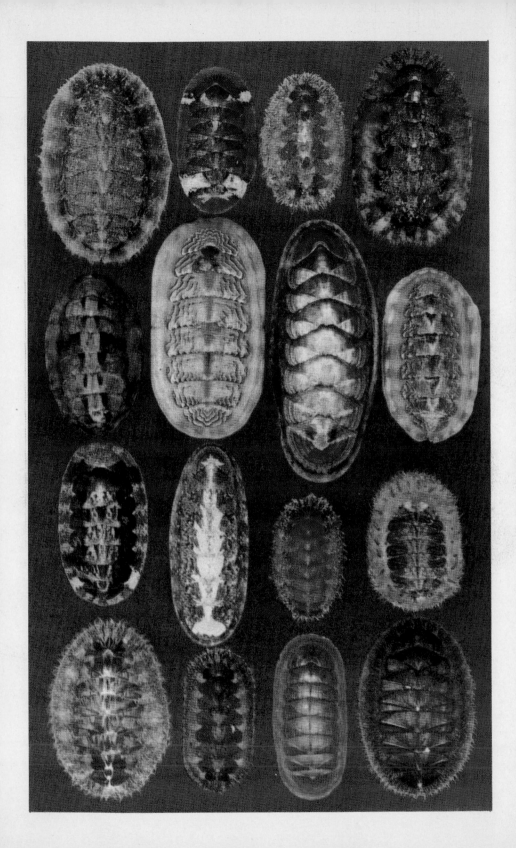

STANFORD UNIVERSITY PRESS
STANFORD, CALIFORNIA

London : Geoffrey Cumberlege
Oxford University Press

———

THE BAKER AND TAYLOR COMPANY
HILLSIDE, NEW JERSEY

HENRY M. SNYDER & COMPANY
440 FOURTH AVENUE, NEW YORK 16

W. S. HALL & COMPANY
457 MADISON AVENUE, NEW YORK 22

———

First edition, April 1939
Revised edition, August 1948
Third edition, September 1952

Library of Congress Catalog Card No. 52-6351

EDWARD F. RICKETTS and JACK CALVIN

BETWEEN PACIFIC TIDES

*An account of the habits and habitats of some
five hundred of the common, conspicuous seashore invertebrates of the Pacific Coast between
Sitka, Alaska, and northern Mexico*

THIRD EDITION
Revised by
JOEL W. HEDGPETH

Foreword by
JOHN STEINBECK

Line drawings by
RITCHIE LOVEJOY

STANFORD UNIVERSITY · PRESS
STANFORD, CALIFORNIA

FOREWORD

PERIODICALLY in the history of human observation the world of external reality has been rediscovered, reclassified, and redescribed. It is difficult for us to understand the reality of Democritus, of Aristotle, of Pliny, for they did not see what we see and yet we know them to have been careful observers. We must concede then that their universe was different from ours or that they warped it and to a certain extent created their own realities. And if they did, there is no reason to suppose that we do not. Possibly our warp is less, owing to our use of precise measuring devices. But, in immeasurables, we probably create our own world.

The process of rediscovery might be as follows: a young, inquisitive, and original man might one morning find a fissure in the traditional technique of thinking. Through this fissure he might look out and find a new external world about him. In his excitement a few disciples would cluster about him and look again at the world they knew and find it fresh. From this nucleus there would develop a frantic new seeing and a cult of new seers who, finding some traditional knowledge incorrect, would throw out the whole structure and start afresh. Then, the human mind being what it is, evaluation, taxonomy, arrangement, pattern making would succeed the first excited seeing. Gradually the structure would become complete, and men would go to this structure rather than to the external world until eventually something like but not identical with the earlier picture would have been built. From such architectures or patterns of knowledge, disciplines, ethics, even manners exude. The building would be complete again and no one would look beyond it—until one day a young, inquisitive, and original man might find a fissure in the pattern and look through it and find a new world. This seems to have happened again and again in the slow history of human thought and knowledge.

There is in our community an elderly painter of seascapes who knows the sea so well that he no longer goes to look at it while he paints. He dislikes intensely the work of a young painter who sets his easel on the beach and paints things his elder does not remember having seen.

Modern science, or the method of Roger Bacon, has attempted by measuring and rechecking to admit as little warp as possible, but still some warp must be there. And in many fields young, inquisitive men are seeing new worlds. And from their seeing will emerge not only new patterns but new ethics, disciplines, and manners. The upheaval of the present world may stimulate restive minds to new speculations -and evaluations. The new eyes will see, will break off new facets of reality. The excitements of the chase are already felt in the fields of biochemistry, medicine, and biology. The world is being broken down to be built up again, and eventually the sense of the new worlds will come out of the laboratory and penetrate into the smallest living techniques and habits of the whole people.

This book of Ricketts and Calvin is designed more to stir curiosity than to answer questions. It says in effect: look at the animals, this is what we seem to know about them but the knowledge is not final, and any clear eye and sharp intelligence may see something we have never seen. These things, it says, you will see, but you may see much more. This is a book for laymen, for beginners, and, as such, its main purpose is to stimulate curiosity, not to answer finally questions which are only temporarily answerable.

In the laboratories, fissures are appearing in the structure of our knowledge and many young men are peering excitedly through at a new world. There are answers to the world questions which every man must ask, in the little animals of tidepools, in their relations one to another, in their color phases, their reproducing methods. Finally, one can live in a prefabricated world, smugly and without question, or one can indulge perhaps the greatest human excitement: that of observation to speculation to hypothesis. This is a creative process, probably the highest and most satisfactory we know. If only in the process one could keep the brake of humor in operation, it would be even more satisfactory. One has always to keep in mind his own contribution to the world of reality. Aristotle built a world and we are building one. His was a true world, and ours is. And the two need not meet and quarrel. His world worked for him and for his people and ours works for us. A Greek thinker built a world that operated, and, given that man and that society, it would still work. We build a motor and it runs. It will always run if the principle involved is followed correctly, but it is not now impossible to imagine a world wherein the principle of the internal-combustion engine will become inoperative because it is no longer important.

This book then says: "There are good things to see in the tidepools and there are exciting and interesting thoughts to be generated from the seeing. Every new eye applied to the peep hole which looks out at the world may fish in some new beauty and some new pattern, and the world of the human mind must be enriched by such fishing."

JOHN STEINBECK

PREFACE: ABOUT THIS BOOK AND ED RICKETTS

When a cannery fire spread to the Pacific Biological Laboratories in 1936, Ed Ricketts bounded out just ahead of the flames with the only two items he had had time to save—a pair of pants and the bulky type-script of *Between Pacific Tides*. Later he regretted the pants, remembering more important things that he might have grabbed as he ran, but it was characteristic of him that he shrugged off the loss of the biological supply house that was his means of livelihood and cheerfully went on with the job that really mattered. *Between Pacific Tides* was almost ready for the printer.

Obviously many people have helped to shape this book, supplying knowledge, assistance, criticism, encouragement. But the qualities that make the book truly unique in its field came from the lively intellectual curiosity, the warm humanness and, quite possibly, the touch of genius, that constituted the mind of Ed Ricketts. The junior author, Jack Calvin, was the literary collaborator and photographer for the original edition. He emerges now from his happy obscurity in southeastern Alaska long enough to help to write this preface, and to explain that, being no zoölogist, he could not, if he would, do the work of preparing this new edition for the press. This task has fallen to one who has undertaken it, not as a zoölogist, but as a friend.

The revised edition of 1948 was admittedly an interim printing, since a large amount of wartime research was not yet accessible. The editor of this edition has tried to bring things up to date and to make as many corrections and necessary changes as possible. Some of the photographs and drawings have been replaced, and some new illustrations added. The appendix has been overhauled. The text remains essentially unchanged, though new paragraphs have been added here and there, and some old ones have been rewritten. As with previous editions, there have been many helping hands, and for their work acknowledgment will be found on page 404.

Edward F. Ricketts was a fine example of the idea that naturalists are born, not made. A less-promising environment, especially for a seashore biologist, could scarcely be imagined than the streets of west-side Chicago, where Ed was born on May 14, 1897. His parents were staunch pillars of the Episcopal Church near Garfield Park and his father had studied for holy orders, but Ed's interests lay elsewhere. He spent many hours in the city parks whetting his taste for biology, and many hours roaming the city at night studying that subspecies of Homo sapiens, the city man.

Ed was never much of a conformist, and his education in zoölogy was informal and haphazard: a year at Illinois State Normal and two or three years at Chicago, where the zoölogy courses were the only ones that mattered. He did not complete his Bachelor of Arts degree but, what is more important, he came under the influence of W. C. Allee. He became one of a group of "Ishmaelites," as Dr. Allee remembers them, "who tended sometimes to be disturbing, but were always stimulating."

Ed came to the Pacific coast in 1923 as a partner in a biological supply business—a business admirably adapted to his talents and temperament, for it offered a variety of work, working hours determined by the tide, or the mood, periods of tranquillity alternated with periods of intense activity. Best of all, it enabled him to work constantly with his beloved animals of the seashore, to travel up and down the Pacific coast, seeing more of its tide pools and beaches than any other single person. Standing in a tide pool, watching some small animal, or dropping it tenderly into a collecting jar (see Plate IV), telling his companions something of the creature's habits or accomplishments, he glowed with happiness.

And there were nearly always companions, for Ed possessed to a rare degree the ability not only to make friends but to draw them along with him, whether it was physically, as on collecting trips, or spiritually, as on his flights into philosophy, mysticism, or science. But he was as ready to follow as to lead if a companion had an idea that promised to develop into a brain-teasing discussion, a pleasant trip, or an amusing party.

In the things that were important to him—music, literature, automobiles, women, and, in the days when he wore one, his beard—Ed insisted gently and very firmly on having the finest quality available. He would drive the hundred and forty miles from Pacific Grove to San Francisco because he knew a posh barber there who was an artist at beard trimming. Many a time he made that drive, with a car full of friends, to hear the singing of midnight Mass at the Russian Orthodox Church, although buying gasoline for the trip might take some doing. The things that were unimportant to him might as well not have existed, except as the law or other circumstance beyond his control forced him to give them a bare minimum of attention. His own clothing was a notable example. He usually dressed like a tramp, sometimes in nothing more than a tattered shirt, a pair of pants held together inadequately with safety pins, and shoes that weren't held together at all. In towns away from the Monterey peninsula the contrast between Ed's fine car and informal clothes sometimes startled cops into making inquiries.

In the friends who accompanied him on his collecting trips, Ed stirred something of his own interest in the luxuriant seashore life, and soon they began urging him to put some of his thumbnail sketches of the tide-pool dwellers into writing. Just a little pocket-size handbook for the casually curious. . . .

At first he was diffident. Writing was for the Carmel long hairs, not for him. But the idea took root, or perhaps it had been growing there for some time, and his "no" became "well, maybe," if he had help and somebody to make him apply the seat of his pants to the seat of his typewriter chair. But once started he needed no prodding. His enthusiasm grew, and so did the book, which quickly ceased to bear any resemblance to a pocket-size handbook. There was just too much material in scattered papers and in Ed's own fund of tide-pool lore. The urge to communicate to others the things that he knew, or believed, or surmised, kept him going during the years that it took to write the book and see it through the frustrating delays of its first publication.

By the time *Between Pacific Tides* was published, Ed was less interested in the moderately profitable business of selling bits and pieces of beautifully preserved seashore life to school laboratories (he had long since bought out his partner) than in the unprofitable pastime of writing about it. At the time of his death the supply business had a very poor Dun & Bradstreet rating, but its owner was working on a book on the Queen Charlotte Islands.

Ed died on May 11, 1948, after his car was struck by a train almost in front of his laboratory. As he was being extricated from the wreckage he told the policeman that the accident was not the engineer's fault. At the hospital he complimented the nurse on duty on the new way she was doing her hair. No one with his health and vitality (he looked ten years younger than his almost fifty-one years) gives up life easily, but few have done so more gracefully.

This is not the place for literary criticism, but one book that Ed did not write will have to be mentioned, because it was written about him. How much of John Steinbeck's *Cannery Row* is true? Was Ed really like Doc? To avoid an irritating yes and no answer as far as possible, we might say, Yes, *Cannery Row* is a true story, but it is not the whole truth. The laboratory, the phonograph records, the beer milkshake, and the establishment across the street—these details are true. And Ed was really like Doc, but Doc is only a one-dimensional portrait of Ed. Who would know from *Cannery Row* that Ed was the devoted father of three children, and that he was a hard-working biologist who managed to get a great deal done between his records and that solemn procession—Ed would have called it a lovely procession—of wine jugs? We mean no criticism of John in suggesting that the Doc of *Can-*

nery Row is half Ricketts the man and half Steinbeck the author. Doc remains a delightful character, and people who did not know Ed can achieve a considerable acquaintance with him by reading the lusty story of Doc of *Cannery Row*.

However, if Ed Ricketts has achieved a trace of immortality, we believe that it is because of his ability to plant in the minds of others not facts, since many can do that, but the essential truths beyond facts: the shadowy half-truths, the profoundly disturbing questions that thinking men must face and try to answer. This ability was the mature fruit of the quality that Dr. Allee saw when he noted that Ed tended sometimes to be disturbing, but was always stimulating.

JACK CALVIN
JOEL W. HEDGPETH

CONTENTS

CONTENTS

LIST OF ILLUSTRATIONS

BETWEEN PACIFIC TIDES

INTRODUCTION

THE shore topography of the Pacific coast differs considerably from that of the Atlantic coast, and this factor, since it determines the conditions of life of the shore animals, often produces animal communities that seem strange to Eastern students. More obviously on the Pacific coast than on the Atlantic coast, the three co-ordinate and interlocking factors that determine the distribution of shore invertebrates are: (a) the degree of wave shock, (b) the type of bottom (whether rock, sand, mud, or some combination of these), and (c) the tidal exposure.

Considering these in turn:

(a) On the Pacific coast the degree of wave shock is of particular importance. According to the physics of wave motion, the size of the unbroken water area (and to a limited extent the depth) plus the velocity and direction of the wind determines the size of waves. Assuming that wind velocities are the same in the Atlantic and the Pacific, the great unobstructed expanses of the latter ocean make for larger wave possibilities. When, in addition, there is bluff unprotected coast with few islands or high submarine ridges for thousands of miles, as from Cape Flattery to Point Conception, with prevailing northwesterly to westerly winds, wave shock is probably more powerful than in any other part of the Northern Hemisphere.

Nevertheless there are various factors, as will be noted later, which modify the force of the waves in particular regions and bring about correlative changes in the animal assemblages. The extreme modification comes in closed bays, sounds, and estuaries where there is almost no surf at all. Given all gradations in wave shock from the pounding surf of 20-foot groundswells to the quiet waters of Puget Sound, where the waves barely lap the shore, one could enumerate an indefinite number of gradient stages. For the purposes of this book, however, we use only three, although even in Puget Sound it is quite possible to recognize sheltered and exposed positions and to note corresponding faunal distinctions. Ours is a classification of convenience. It is as though we divided the numbers from 1 to 100 into three parts, calling the divisions I, II, and III. Notwithstanding the arbitrariness of the divisions, however, the collector will find that there is often a reasonably sharp dividing line, as where the surf beats

3

against a jutting point which protects a relatively quiet bay; and that there is a fairly high degree of correlation between these divisions and the animal communities. There is often overlapping of the animals, of course, but if test counts show that 75 per cent of the total observed number of a certain starfish are found to occur on surf-swept rocky points, then we feel no hesitation in classifying it as an animal that belongs predominantly in that environment, noting also that some individuals stray to more protected shores and to wharf piling.

These qualifying statements apply with equal force to the other two factors—type of bottom and tidal exposure—on which we base our classification. It must be understood that infinite variations exist, that few regions belong purely to one or the other of our divisions, and that any animal, even the most characteristic "horizon marker," may occasionally be found in totally unexpected associations.

(b) In considering the types of bottom this intergradation is too obvious to stress beyond remarking that in the cases of the innumerable variations between sand, muddy sand, sandy mud, and mud we have begged the question somewhat by using only two headings—sand flats and mud flats—leaving it to the judgment of the collector to decide where one merges into the other.

(c) The third important aspect of habitat, tidal exposure, has to do with the zoning of animals according to the relative lengths of exposure to air and water (bathymetrical zoning)—in other words, the level at which the animals occur. A glance at Figure 1, opposite, and Figure 112 (page 339) will lend more weight than would much discussion to an understanding of the extreme variations that exist between the uppermost region at and above the line of high spring tides, where the animals are wetted only a few times in each month by waves and spray, and the line of low spring tides, where the animals are uncovered only a few hours in each month. Many animals adhere closely to one particular level, and all have their preferences; but again the overlapping of one zone with another should be taken for granted. Also local conditions may affect the animals' level, as along the coast of Lower California where the high summer temperatures force the animals down to a lower level than they would normally assume. Even there, however, the animals' relative positions remain the same. There is merely a compressing of the life zone into something less than the actual intertidal zone. With these provisos, then, our system of zonation (Fig. 1) is equally applicable to San Quintin Bay, where the extreme range of tides is less than eight feet, and to Juneau, where it is more than twenty-three feet.

These three aspects of habitat—wave shock, type of bottom, and

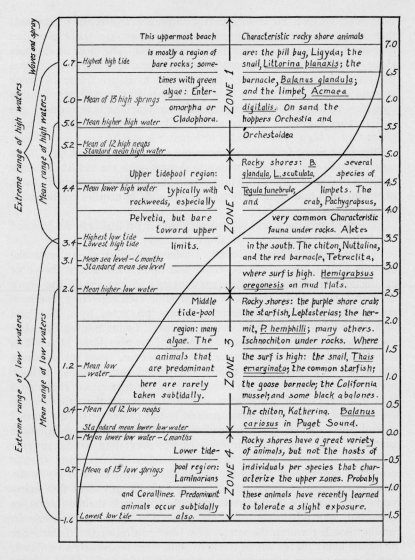

FIG. 1.—A diagram to illustrate the vertical zoning of animals according to relative lengths of exposure to air and water. The height figures apply to Crissy Wharf in San Francisco Bay, but the relative heights and the character of the exposure curve are the same for any point on the open Pacific coast. The data shown at the left-hand margin and the data from which the curve is drawn are from tide predictions and recordings for a six-months period.

tidal level—which so tremendously influence the types of animals that occur, suggest the classification herein used, a classification that may sound more cumbersome than it actually is. The most unscientific shore visitor will know whether he is observing a surf-swept or a protected shore, and whether the substratum is predominantly rock or sand or mud, although he probably will not know the classification by which zoölogists arrange the animals in which he is interested. He will further know, or he can easily find out, whether the tide at a given time is high or low ; and if or when it is low he can easily visualize the four zones or levels of the bared area to be defined later. The observer possessing this information should, with the aid of the illustrations and descriptions in this handbook, be able to identify most of the animals that he is likely to find and thus to acquire considerable information about each.

Users of this book will accordingly find it profitable to fix in mind the following classification of shore habitats :

I. Protected Outer Coast. Under this division we treat the animals of the semi-sheltered coast and open bays where the force of the surf is somewhat dissipated before it can crush the more delicate forms. Such shores, which provide rich collecting, are generally concave, and characteristically are protected by a headland or a close-lying island (Fig. 2, *a,* opposite). Todos Santos Bay, Laguna, Santa Barbara, much of Monterey Bay, also Half Moon Bay, and Point Arena are good examples. However, stretches of shore which, at first glance, appear to be entirely open to the sea may actually belong in this category. An offshore reef of submerged rocks or a long gradually sloping strand is sufficient to break the full force of the waves and to modify very materially the character of the animal assemblages. Even distant headlands, outlying bars, or offshore islands, if they are in the direction of the prevailing winds, provide a degree of protection that makes the animals correspond to our protected outer-coast division. An offshore kelp bed will serve the same purpose, smoothing out the water to such an extent that many years ago small coasting vessels used often to seek shelter inside the beds and take advantage of their protection whenever possible in landing goods through the surf. The 1889 edition of the *Coast Pilot* mentions many places where the kelp beds were frequently so utilized, and in recent years fishermen, rum-runners, and an occasional yachtsman have kept the tradition alive.

Here on the Pacific we have only two types of shore within this division. They are: A. Rocky shores. B. Sandy beaches.

II. Open Coast. Entirely unprotected, surf-swept shores, while by no means as rich in animals as the partially protected shores of

Division I, support a distinctive and characteristic assemblage of animals that either require surf or have learned to tolerate it. This type of shore is generally convex (Fig. 2, *b*, below), varying from bold headlands to gently out-sweeping stretches, and there will be fairly deep water close offshore.* Obviously there are no muddy shores in this division; so again we have only: A. Rocky shores. B. Sandy beaches.

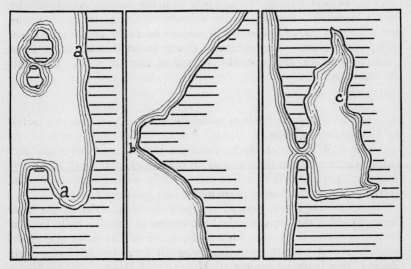

Fɪɢ. 2.—Typical examples of a shore classified as Protected Outer Coast are shown at *a—a.* A characteristic bold headland of the Open Coast is shown at *b,* and an enclosed bay of the Bay and Estuary classification at *c.*

III. Bay and Estuary. Animals of the sloughs, enclosed bays, sounds, and estuaries, where the rise and fall of the tides is not complicated by surf, enjoy the ultimate in wave protection and commonly differ correspondingly in species from the animals inhabiting the open coast and the protected outer coast. Where the same species occur they frequently differ in habit and in habitat. The shores embraced in this division are sharply concave; that is, they have great protected area with a relatively small and often indirect opening to the sea (Fig. 2, *c,* above). San Quintín Bay in Lower California is an example, and moving northward we find other such areas in San Diego, Newport, Morro, San Francisco, Tomales, and Coos bays, in

---

* Pismo Beach, the Point Sur and Point Lobos outer rocks, and the outer reefs of Cypress Point and Point Pinos are all good examples from the central California coast.

Puget Sound, and in all the inside waters of British Columbia and southeastern Alaska. This time we have a greater variety of types of shore, including: A. Rocky shores, as in the San Juan Islands and north. B. Sand flats, found in quiet waterways throughout the entire coast line. C. Eelgrass, growing on many types of completely protected shore along the entire range of coast herein considered. D. Mud flats, found in nearly all protected waterways.

IV. Wharf Piling. In addition to many animals which will be found elsewhere, wooden pilings support numerous species, such as the infamous *Teredo,* which will seldom or never be found in any other environment. The nature of piling fauna justifies its division (for convenience, and probably in point of fact) into: A. Exposed. B. Protected.

Each of the above habitats is subdivided into zones by the factor of tidal exposure, thus:

Zone 1. Uppermost beach: from the highest reach of spray and storm waves to about the mean of all high tides, plus 5′ at Monterey (see Fig. 1, p. 5). Within this infrequently wetted zone, only such forms as the land-aspiring periwinkles and pill bugs occur.

Zone 2. High-tide region, or upper horizon: from mean high water to about the mean flood of the higher of the two daily lows, a bit below mean sea level. This is the home of barnacles and other animals accustomed to tolerating more air than water. Along with Zone 1, this is the equivalent of Murray and Hjort's (1912) "Bare Rock Area" and the "Upper Beach" of Davenport and others. On the central California coast, this comprises the 5′ to 2½′ belt.

Zone 3. Mid-tide region, or middle horizon: from about mean higher low water to mean lower low water—the zero of the tide tables. Typically covered and uncovered twice each day, this belt extends from plus 2½′ to 0 on the California coast, and is the equivalent of Murray and Hjort's "Fucoid Zone" in part at least and of the "Lower Beach" of Davenport and others. The animals found here have accustomed themselves to, and often require, the rhythm of the tides.

Zone 4. Low-tide region or lower horizon: normally uncovered by "minus" tides only, extending from 0 to −1.8′ or so at Pacific Grove, corresponding to the upper parts of the "Laminarian Zone" of Murray and Hjort, the "Submerged Beach" of Davenport, and the "Sublittoral" of others. This zone is available for examination during only a few hours in each month, and is peopled by animals working up as far as possible from deep water. Most of them remain in this zone, foregoing the advantages of the less crowded conditions higher up, because they are unable to stand more than the minimum of exposure incident to minus tides. The air-water relations of this and the other zones are illustrated graphically in Figure 112 (page 339), derived from data in an unpublished study of tidal levels on the California coast.

In the bibliography we cite, from the widely scattered literature, the following only: (1) the most recent general taxonomic papers covering the region; (2) smaller papers likely to be overlooked because of publication in obscure or foreign journals; (3) important references to the natural history, embryology, life history, and occasionally even the physiology, of common Pacific types or of comparable forms occurring elsewhere under supposedly similar circumstances.

The final choices therefore represent the pick of some seven or eight hundred references, practically all of which were consulted directly. Papers treating exclusively of pelagic, dredged, parasitic, or very minute species, however common, have rarely been cited unless they carry information on related common forms as well. This is a book for the observer or student limited to the shore, and without equipment. The scope had to be limited in some way, and this fits it for the largest field. While we have attempted to give a fair showing to the entire coast from Mexico to Alaska, it may very well be that the central California area has received undue attention. Expediency has dictated that this should be so, despite summer trips into Puget Sound, British Columbia, and even into southeastern Alaska, and frequent winter excursions south. The writers have themselves captured and observed practically all the animals listed—all except as otherwise stated—but some we may not have identified correctly.

One more word of explanation is necessary before we begin to consider the animals themselves. It would have been desirable in some respects to depend on scientific names less frequently than we have been forced to do in this account. Certainly it would make pleasanter reading for the layman if a common name were provided in each case and if he did not have to read, or to skip over, long, tongue-twisting names compounded of Latin and Greek words and the Latinized names of scientists and even of boats that have carried scientific expeditions. Unfortunately, however, few of the marine animals have popular names that are of any diagnostic value. Seldom do such names have more than local significance, and often the same name is applied to different animals in different regions. Just as often a particular animal goes by a different name in each region where it occurs. We have accordingly given, for what they are worth, any popular name already in use, along with its scientific equivalent; as for the rest, persons who believe that magnetos, carburetors, cams, and valves are all "gadgets" are free to designate them, indifferently, as bugs, worms, critters, and beasties.

The table of contents may be consulted as a summary of the Divisions and Zones within which the living creatures here described are classified.

Absolute beginners will do well to devote their primary attention to large, common, and spectacular animals which may easily be identified merely by reference to the group of illustrations concerned with the given type of shore. For instance, the beginner who for any reason would familiarize himself with a starfish found on surf-swept rocks can refer almost instantly to the illustrations of open-coast animals, all of which are grouped together in Division II. Here approximate identification can be ascertained and reference will be found to a fairly comprehensive statement of habits and natural history of the indicated starfish in the main text; citations of more complete and detailed accounts may subsequently be looked up in the bibliography and systematic index.

I. PROTECTED OUTER COAST

A. Rocky Shores

FROM the standpoint of the shore collector the rocky tide flats of the protected outer coast comprise the most important of all regions. Rocky-shore animals are abundant, easy to find, and frequently spectacular in their bright colors and unexpected shapes. So keen is the struggle for existence here that not only is every square inch of shore surface likely to be utilized but the holdfasts and stipes of kelp also are occupied, and many such forms as sponges, tube worms, and barnacles occupy positions on the shells of larger animals.

Rocky-intertidal animals are characterized by interesting physiological processes which offer methods of attachment, ways and means of surviving wave shock or of coping with an alternate exposure to air and water, and techniques of offense and defense, all intensely specialized to meet the crowded environment. Obviously there is no need for the elaborate devices developed by sand- and mud-flat animals to avoid suffocation or to retain orientation. But the rocky shore presents its own special problems. Perhaps the most interesting process, highly developed in this environment, is that by which a captured crab or brittle star deliberately breaks off an appendage in order to free itself. Losses occasioned by this process, called autotomy, are usually replaced by subsequent growth, or regeneration. This is a trait of great survival value to animals that may be imprisoned by loose rocks overturned by wave action.

Rocky-shore collecting is best managed by turning over small rocks by hand and lifting big ones with a bar. Moreover, it is highly important that the collector, in the interests of conservation, replace carefully all such rocks in their depressions; otherwise many of the delicate bottom animals are exposed to fatal drying, sunlight, or wave action. Whoever doubts the necessity for such care should examine a familiar intertidal area directly after and again a few days after it has been combed by a biology class that has failed to observe the precaution of replacing overturned rocks. At first the rocks will simply look strange and scarred. In a few days whole colonies of tunicates and solitary corals and tube worms will be found dead, and

11

a noticeable line of demarcation will set off the desolate area from its natural surroundings. It takes weeks or months for such a spot to recover.

ZONE 1. *Animals of the uppermost rocky beach, wetted in its upper reaches by waves and spray only and in its lower part by high tides only.*

This is a bare rock area in the main, but sometimes there are sparse growths of green algae. It is inhabited by hardy semi–land-dwellers. At Pacific Grove the range is from plus 7' or 8' to plus 5'.

§1. The small dingy snails that litter the highest rocks are not easy to see until one has accustomed one's eyes to distinguishing the dry, dirty-gray shells from their rocky background of the same tone. Their habitat, higher on the occasionally wetted rocks than that of almost any other animal, gives them their Latin name of *Littorina,* shore-dwellers—a more diagnostic term than the popular "periwinkle." Marine animals though they are, the littorines keep as far as possible away from the sea, staying barely close enough to wet their gills occasionally. In regions of moderate surf they may be several feet above the high-tide line, scattered over the rock face by the thousand or clustered around crevices. Specimens placed in an aquarium show their distaste for sea water by immediately crawling up the sides until they reach the air, and if forced to remain under water they will ultimately drown.

It seems probable that some species of *Littorina* are well along in the process of changing from sea-dwellers to land-dwellers, and they have, in consequence, an extraordinary resistance to un-marine conditions. European littorines have been kept dry experimentally for 42 days without being damaged, and they can stand immersion in fresh water, which kills all true marine animals, for 11 days. We recently subjected *Littorina planaxis* (Fig. 3), the commonest species on these high rocks, to a shorter but even more severe test: we fed it to a sea anemone (*Metridium*). There was no intention, however, of testing *Littorina*'s endurance; we merely wished to feed the anemone so as to keep it alive in captivity, assuming that its powerful digestive juices would circumvent the difficulty of the shell. The anemone swallowed the snail promptly, and our expectation was that in due time the empty shell would be disgorged. But it was an intact and healthy *Littorina* that emerged, like Jonah, after a residence of from 12 to 20 hours in the anemone's stomach. When first discovered, the disgorged snail was lying on the bottom of the dish and, since it must have been in some doubt as to just where it was, its shell was still tightly closed. When it was picked up for examination, however, it showed signs of life, and on being returned to the dish it crawled away at its liveliest pace. It had apparently suffered no harm whatever, but its shell was beautifully cleaned and polished.

Such resistance to distinctly unfavorable conditions is made possible by a horny door, the operculum, with which *Littorina,* like other marine snails, closes its shell. This door serves the double purpose of retaining moisture in the gills and keeping out fresh water and desiccating wind. That it can also exclude the digestive enzymes of an anemone is a considerable tribute to its efficiency.

Like other marine snails, *Littorina* possesses a wicked food-getting instrument, the radula—a hard ribbon armed with rows of file-like teeth. The radula of this particular animal is unoffendingly used to scrape detritus and microscopic plants from almost bare rock—an operation that necessitates continual renewal by growth—but the radulae of several other snails are used to drill holes through the hard shells of oysters, mussels, and other snails.

The sexes of the littorines are separate. In central California, at least, some specimens may be found copulating at almost any time of the year; but reproduction in mass seems to be confined to the spring and summer months, when it is difficult to find, among thousands, a dozen specimens that are not copulating. The Pacific coast forms have not been studied specifically, but the female of a European species is known to lay in the neighborhood of 5,000 eggs in a month after one act of fertilization, the eggs being laid singly or in pairs in tiny transparent capsules shaped "like a soldier's tin hat." It is probable that the female of *L. planaxis* lays her eggs in a simlar manner.

Along with this extreme high-tide form, which ranges from Puget Sound to southern Lower California, may be found the similar *Littorina scutulata* (Fig. 4), which finds its optimum conditions, however, farther down in the intertidal zone (see §10).

§2. In some places specimens of the large pill bug,* *Ligyda†* *occidentalis* (Fig. 5), up to 1½" long, can be found scurrying around on the rocks at distances so far removed from the water that one is led to believe it is another animal in the very act of changing from a marine to a terrestrial habitat. *Ligyda* (including a more northern, open-coast species, §162) is very careful to avoid wetting its feet, and if kept under water will drown in a short time. When the tide

---

* The name "pill bug" properly applies only to isopods that curl up into "pills," but is here used as a convenient term for the whole group.

† *Lygia?* disputed; U.S.N.M. and Abbott use *Lygida.*

is out it may venture down into the intertidal area, but when there is any surf it will be found just above the spray line. Specimens rarely occur singly; there will be hundreds or none. This species is recognized by the presence of two long forked spines projecting behind—the spines being used, apparently, as a rudder to help the animal to steer its rapid and circuitous course over the rocks. We have taken specimens at Pacific Grove early in March that had the incubatory pouch on the under side of the abdomen turgid with developing eggs. The range is from the Sacramento River, where it occurs in almost fresh water, to the Gulf of California.

Still another child of the ocean that has taken to living on land is the sand flea or beach hopper, *Orchestia traskiana*. Along the steep cliffs west of Santa Cruz we have found it more than 20 feet above tidewater and above the usual spray line, living practically in the irrigated fields. It is known at Laguna from a brackish water slough that runs through marshy fields and rarely receives an influx of tidewater. Like the other hoppers it is a scavenger, and may often be found about decaying seaweed that has been thrown high up on the shore. The animal's body color is dull green or gray-brown, with the legs slightly blue. Except for its small size (½″ or a little more in length) and its short antennae, this form is similar in appearance to the handsome hopper, *Orchestoidea californiana*, shown in Plate XXIX.

§3. Another conspicuous rocky-shore animal that keeps a considerable distance above mean sea level is the large flatworm, *Planocera californica* (Fig. 6), which is up to 1½″ long. Thick-bodied and firm, almost round in outline, these animals are rather beautiful with their markings of blue-green, black, and white. They are relatively abundant, near Monterey at least, but are not often seen, since their habitat is restricted, when the tide is out, to the under sides of large boulders on gravel that is damp but seldom wet. The casual observer should feel properly thrilled at finding the several specimens that usually turn up, and will easily remember them from their size and beauty. As a matter of fact, they richly reward any layman who undertakes the labor involved in clearing the surroundings and rolling over one of these huge boulders.

Like most of the flatworms, *Planocera* is hermaphroditic, each animal developing first male and then female gonads. The egg masses, found almost throughout the year, form round encrusting bodies up to ¼″ in diameter under boulders and in rock crevices. *Planocera* is known to feed on minute snails, since portions of snails' radulae or grinding organs have been found in its digestive tract. As far as we know, this flatworm has been recorded from the Monterey Bay

region only, but it will surely be found elsewhere. We have taken
an identical or similar form in Lower California.

§4. Small acorn barnacles and, interspersed among them, small
limpets, occur abundantly near the extreme upper limit of the intertidal zone. Except at extreme high tide both have dried, dead-looking
shells of the dingy gray color so common to high-tide rocks. The
barnacles, *Balanus glandula* (Pl. I), are actually crustaceans, more
nearly related to the crabs and shrimps than to the shelled mollusks
with which the tyro associates them. The sharp projecting shells, ½″
or less in diameter, often cover the sloping or vertical rock faces,
sometimes crowded together like cells in a honeycomb. They are
necessarily exposed, a great deal of the time, to sun, rain, or wind;
but at such times they keep carefully closed the hinged double doors
that protect the delicate internal anatomy. At extreme high tide, sometimes for only a few hours in a week, each animal throws open its
operculum and rhythmically sweeps the water with its brightly colored
appendages, respiring and searching for the minute animals that constitute its food. A dry cluster of barnacles will "come to" very quickly
if immersed in a jar of fresh sea water, and they live well in aquaria.

Balanus glandula is one of the most abundant single animals on
the coast, being the high intertidal representative on the Pacific of a
group of animals distributed throughout all oceans and in all depths.
It is also one of the beautifully generalized (that is, unspecialized,
hence adapted to meet unexpected conditions) animals that range all
the way from the Aleutian Islands to Ensenada, Lower California,
and probably still farther south. This generalization offers the only
obvious means of accounting for a wide and peculiar variation in
glandula's habitat. It thrives not only in the constantly aerated ocean
waters along the protected outer coast (and even on violently surf-
swept points), but in the quiet waters of Puget Sound, where according to Shelford *et al.* it actually prefers estuarine conditions—enclosed
bays, poor circulation of water, little wave action, and low salinity.

The reproductive habits of barnacles are noteworthy. Eggs and
larvae are retained within the shell of the parent, to be discharged as
free-swimming animals called nauplii. A nauplius (Fig. 7) is a one-
eyed, one-shelled, microscopic animal with three pairs of legs. After
undergoing several intermediate transformations it becomes a cypris
(Fig. 8)—an animal with two eyes, two shells, six pairs of legs, and
an inclination to give up the roving habits of its youth and settle down.
Accordingly its antennae turn to suckers, with which it attaches itself
to a rock or other object, whereupon it secretes a cement and begins
to build the limy protective shell of an adult barnacle. Now it is a
blind animal, fastened by its head, and feeding with its curled feathery

legs. It has been supposed that during its free-swimming stages the animal was unable to take food; but one investigator, Hertz, has seen diatoms in the body cavity. The mouth, however, remains hidden from the prying eye of the microscope.

Like their relatives, the crabs, barnacles moult at regular intervals, shedding the thin, skin-like covering of the animal itself rather than the familiar jagged shell. In the quiet waterways of Puget Sound and British Columbia their almost transparent casts may be seen floating on the water in incalculable numbers.

It should be mentioned in passing that occasionally we may have mistaken *Balanus hesperius* for *B. glandula,* although no specimen from our random shore collections has been so identified. We have taken undoubted specimens of *hesperius* from boat bottoms and from deep water only. In any case it makes extremely little difference, for the two are so similar that only specialists are thoroughly competent to tell them apart.

§5. Ranging southward from the neighborhood of Santa Barbara is the much smaller gray or brown barnacle, *Chthamalus fissus,* recognizable in that the shell has less than half the diameter of *Balanus.* Everything else being equal, this tiny barnacle will be found gradually but evenly replacing its larger relative as one moves southward, until, in northern Lower California, it becomes the predominant form. In some sheltered localities, or on gradually sloping beaches, it is the only barnacle to be found; but where there is a bit of surf the larger *Balanus* steps in again. There is one wave-pounded cliff on a jutting headland about 35 miles below the Mexican border that has *Balanus* only, although the smaller form is found within a few miles both north and south.

An Italian investigator has recently experimented with another species of *Chthamalus.* He found that they prefer atmospheric respiration, using the air dissolved in the water, and that consequently they thrive best on wave-battered reefs. While water remains on the rock the cirri or feeding legs are frequently protruded into the air. This investigator kept 100 individuals on his laboratory table for three years, immersing them for from one to two days about every three months. They were immersed a total of only 59 days out of the 1,036, and yet only ten to twelve individuals died each year. Other lots lived as long as four months continually immersed in fresh water, which kills nearly all marine animals. Some lived two months completely immersed in vaseline! Under either natural or artificial conditions, periods of drying are as necessary to them as periods of immersion.

§6. *Acmaea,* the limpet, is a gastropod (stomach-foot), related to the common marine snails, however little its lopsidedly conical shell resembles theirs. It occurs in great abundance plastered so tightly against the rocks that specimens can be removed undamaged only by slipping a knife blade under them unawares. If the animal receives any warning of an impending attack it draws its shell into such firm contact with the rock that a determined attempt to remove it by force will result in breaking the shell, hard as it is. So powerful is the suction foot, once it has taken hold, that an estimated 70-pound pull is required to remove a limpet having a basal area of one square inch. The sexes of limpets are separate, and fertilization occurs in the sea, since the eggs and sperm are shed freely into the sea.

Our limpets, except *Acmaea persona,* stay pretty much at home at night. The other species will move about in daylight as long as they are covered with water. Much can be learned, however, from a night trip to the shore. A single excursion into the tidelands with a flashlight will often reveal more of an animal's habits than a score of daylight trips. Seen in the daytime, a littorine seems as immobile and inactive as a dry barnacle; but at night the foot extends, the shell lifts from the rock, and the animal goes cruising in search of food, which it scrapes from the rock with a broad, file-like ribbon, the radula.

Studies of an Atlantic form indicate that there is a direct connection between the animal's position in the intertidal zone and the height of the shell. Individuals inhabiting relatively low positions have low shells, while the higher (and hence the drier) the habitat the higher the shell. A tentative explanation is that the animals which are least submerged must have the greatest amount of storage space for water. As usual, there are exceptions to every rule; the tallest *Acmaea, A. mitra,* frequents the lowest intertidal, but in general this relation applies. Through the work of Orton, 1929, it is known also that shade and sunlight are the chief factors regulating the distribution of the British *Patella;* position in the littoral with relation to tidal levels is secondary. It seems that the needs of this creature are met in the following order: (*a*) shade, (*b*) moisture, (*c*) food—this last, because even such a slow-moving animal can work out into food-laden areas during the night or when the tide is high.

The commonest species on these high Pacific rocks is *Acmaea digitalis* (Pl. I and Fig. 9), which ranges from the Aleutian Islands to San Diego but abundantly only from Monterey northward. This is the exceedingly common form which has been listed as *A. persona* even in recent accounts. Great colonies occur even where (or especially where) the surf is fairly brisk, extending occasionally clear up to the splash line in areas sheltered from direct sunlight. The average small, dingy-brown specimen found in these high colonies will measure under 25 mm., even under 15 mm.; but the larger, usually solitary, individuals found farther down may be half again as large and more brilliantly marked. *A. digitalis,* apparently preferring rough rocks, notably tolerates conditions such as swirling sand, mud, debris, even sewage and industrial pollution, most of which are disastrous to other limpets, and is therefore possibly the most abundant *Acmaea* numerically on the whole outer coast north of Point Conception. A related, heavily eroded type, the former subspecies *textilis* Gould, is known now simply to be an ordinary *digitalis* the shell of which has been pitted by a parasitic fungus found also on other limpets inhabiting successively lower levels (§§11 and 25) to the accounts of which reference should be made, since some of the ordinarily deeper forms occasionally are taken this high also.

§7. Especially in the southern part of its range, northern California to Cerros Island, Mexico, a giant form, *Lottia gigantea,* the owl limpet (Pl. I), occurs in the high intertidal zone. The largest specimens, however, more than 3″ long, are found in the middle zone, especially on surf-swept rocks. Beside the animal in the photograph is the characteristic scar that marks the normal position of an absent specimen. Work done by European zoölogists indicates that these animals range far afield in search of food, presumably algae, and then return, each to his own scar although a thousand scars in an area of a few square yards seem to be identical.

The Mexicans justly prize the owl limpet as food, for when properly prepared it is delicious, having finer meat and a more delicate flavor than abalone. Each animal provides one steak the size of a silver dollar, which must be pounded between two blocks of wood before it is rolled in egg and flour and fried.

§8. In localities that have spray pools at or above the high-tide line the vivid yellow-green strands of the plant *Enteromorpha* are likely to colonize, especially where there is an admixture of fresh water. In such brackish pools, often having a high temperature through long exposure to the sun, very tiny red "bugs"—crustaceans —may often be seen darting about. These animals, easily visible because of their color, are the copepod *Tigriopus californicus.* We have taken copulating specimens near Santa Cruz in April and have seen, at the same time, thousands of ovigerous females, each carrying its eggs in two long cylindrical sacs, almost like caudal appendages. A similar species occurs on the Norwegian coast, where it was observed in 1867, under like conditions, by the zoölogist Sars.

§9. A few other animals may occur in the high intertidal zone: occasional small clusters of goose barnacles (§160) and even small mussels (§158), but they achieve their greatest development in other zones and are therefore treated elsewhere. All the above are abundant and characteristic; they are fairly well restricted to the uppermost zone, and we should say that all except *Planocera* (which takes searching for) and the uncertain *Ligyda* can be found and identified by the neophyte. They should serve as a pleasant enough introduction to whoever cares to proceed further into the tidelands.

ZONE 2. *Animals of the high-tide region, from mean high water to about mean higher low water.*

In this belt there is a greater variety and a tremendously greater number of individuals of many of the species represented than in the highest zone. Here there are some more or less permanent tide pools with their active fauna of hermit crabs, snails, and crabs. Barnacles occur here also, certainly larger and possibly in greater abundance. Plants begin to appear in the uppermost part of this zone, and grow lush in its lower part. Most of the blue-green algae begin here, and some of the greens, and extend on down into the lower zones. The slim brown rockweed, *Pelvetia,* begins at about the mid part of Zone 2, and cuts off fairly sharply at its lower boundary. In mildly surf-beaten areas the first alga to appear may be the crinkly brown *Endocladia,* covering the granite ledges sparsely with tufted clusters. Below this the more massive *Fucus* appears. These plants not only provide bases of attachment for sessile animals but furnish shelter for others adhering closely to the rock and protect them from desiccation.

In the highest zone one can collect dryshod, but in this zone and downwards wet feet are likely to penalize the un-rubber-booted observer.

§10. *Littorina scutulata* (Fig. 4), one of the periwinkles, takes up the burden here where *planaxis* leaves off and covers the territory down to the lower reaches of the upper tide pool zone where *Tegula* becomes the dominant snail. The two species of *Littorina* may be found side by side, but of a thousand individuals more than 80 per cent will indicate depth zoning as stated. *L. scutulata,* for instance, never occurs more than a few feet above high-tide line, whereas in surfy regions *planaxis* may be found 20 feet above the water. The two may be differentiated easily: *L. planaxis* has an aperture bounded at the inner margin by a large flattened area; it is dingy gray in color, chunky in outline and comparatively large—up to ¾" high. The smaller, daintier *L. scutulata* is slim, has one more whorl to the shell, lacks the flattened area, and may be prettily checkered with white on shining brown or black. The range of *L. scutulata* is from Alaska, and that of *L. planaxis* from Washington, south to Lower California.

Certain of the rockweeds (*Pelvetia* or *Fucus*) serve the young periwinkles as a sort of nursery, for it is on their fronds and stems that the young will nearly always be found.

§11. A number of limpets find in this zone their optimum conditions, and scattered individuals may be found of others, as *A. digitalis* (§6), and types more abundant lower down (§25). A large, high-peaked, spectacular form, the newly rediscovered true *A. persona,* occurs high up, sometimes even in the uppermost zone; but in dark stations, as in deep crevices or (particularly) on the roofs of caverns, it evidences a phototropism so negative that it emerges to feed only at night. Mrs. Grant (MS.)* says of it: "exterior color olivaceous, variegated by numerous fine white dots sprinkled over surface. Larger white dots on antero-lateral area make definite butterfly pattern in anterior view." The range is central and northern California, and an average specimen is 34 × 25 × 16 mm. This species should prove interesting to the local instructor in biology through the report by MacLellan and Connell, 1931, of parasitic protozoa (ciliates), *Eupoterion pernix,* occurring in the intestine.

The dainty and relatively flat *A. scabra* (Fig. 10), the ribbed limpet, ranging from north central California to Socorro Island, Mexico, is regularly and deeply scalloped. It may be locally abundant on "rough rocks otherwise sparsely populated" (Grant) even by other limpets; its average dimensions are 19 × 15 × 7 mm.

The brown and white shield limpet, *A. cassis* (Fig. 11), occurs in this zone also, but around Monterey it may be taken far out. North of Crescent City it occurs high up with *digitalis.* Its distribution probably includes the entire littoral, but the submerged specimens are solitary, although larger than the average run. The range is from the Aleutians south to Point Conception, and a typical specimen measures 38 × 27 × 27 mm. The largest specimens are said to occur on the "large, immovable rocks of the reefs, frequently covered by masses of *Ulva,* the sea lettuce," and on the surf-swept sea palm, *Postelsia.*

All the limpets illustrated (Figs. 10, 11, 15, 16, and 49) are typical and representative specimens of their species, and show such marked characteristics of form and texture that identification, from the illus-

---

* A. R. Grant, "The genus Acmaea," Ph.D. Thesis, Department of Zoölogy, University of California, 1938. Parts of this have also been published under the name, A. R. (Grant) Test, *q.v.*

trations, of equally typical specimens seen in life should be easy. The collector is quite likely, however, to find occasional specimens which seem to have grown up in indecision as to just which species they would favor. It is possible to arrange the shells of a large number of limpets in such a way that it would be difficult to tell where one variety ended and the other began. Dr. (Grant) Test had drawn up definite diagnoses, and the dividing lines, though small, are known to be there; but specimens will still be turned up which can give even the specialist his moments of indecision.

§12. The pleasant and absurd hermit crabs are the clowns of the tide pools. They rush about on the floors and sides of the rock pools, withdrawing instantly into their borrowed or stolen shells at the least sign of danger, and so dropping to the bottom. Picked up, they remain in the shell; but if allowed to rest quietly in the palm of one's hand they quickly protrude and walk about. Among themselves, when they are not busy scavenging or love-making, the gregarious "hermits" fight with tireless enthusiasm tempered with caution. Despite the seeming viciousness of their battles, none, apparently, are ever injured. When the vanquished has been surprised or frightened into withdrawing his soft body from his shell, he is then allowed to dart back into it, or at least to snap his hind quarters into the shell discarded by his conqueror.

It is a moot question whether or not hermit crabs have the grace to wait until a snail is overcome by some fatal calamity before making off with its shell. Many observers suppose that the house-hunting hermit may be the very calamity responsible for the snail's demise, in which case the hermit would obtain a meal and a home by one master stroke.* In the Monterey Bay region a great many small hermits use the shells of *Tegula* of two species, snails that are strong and tough and very ready to retreat inside their shells, closing the entrance with the horny operculum. It would seem that ingress to such a shell occupied by a living animal determined to sell out as dearly as possible would be very difficult, even by the ingestion route. Attacks have actually been observed in which the snail, by sawing the rough edge of its shell back and forth across the hermit's claw, convinced the hermit that that particular shell was not for rent.

But even when the hermit finds a suitable house, his troubles are far from over, for at intervals he must find larger shells to accommodate his growing body. It is a lifelong job and one in which he seems

---

* Orton, however, has determined conclusively that the common British hermits are unable to ingest large food, and that their fare consists entirely of microscopic, or at the most very small particles of macroscopic, food and debris.

never to lose interest. A few hermits and some spare shells in an aquarium will provide hours of amusement. Inspecting a new shell—and every shell or similar object is a prospect—involves an unvarying sacred ritual: touch it, grasp it, rotate it until the orifice is in position to be explored with the antennae, and then, if it seems satisfactory, move in. The actual move is made with such rapidity that only a quick eye can follow it. One experimenter deprived some hermits of their shells and placed them in the presence of shells that had been stopped up with plaster. After much fruitless activity the animals finally became indifferent to the useless shells. But when shells of another kind, likewise closed with plaster, were put in the aquarium, they recommenced their active and systematic efforts to obtain homes.

The food of hermits consists of any available animal matter, living or long dead. In aquaria we have watched them nip the tube feet from living sea urchins until the urchins were practically denuded.

Along the California coast the commonest hermit in the upper tide pools is *Pagurus samuelis* (Pl. II), a small crab, with bright red antennae and brilliant blue bands around the tips of its feet. At Pacific Grove there are ten of these to every one of the granular-handed *P. granosimanus* (§196), but in the north the latter is larger and more abundant, apparently having an efficient or dominant range only in Puget Sound and to the northward, although its total range is from Alaska to Mexico. *P. samuelis,* on the other hand, having about the same total range, finds its dominant range along the California coast. We have taken ovigerous (egg-bearing) specimens of *samuelis* from early May through July, and of *granosimanus* in late May, both in California. Eggs, as shown in the photograph of another hermit (Pl. V), are borne on the female's abdomen—a region always protected by the shell, but provided with a continuous current of water for aeration by the action of the abdominal appendages.

§13. The original residents of the homes so coveted by hermit crabs, the turban snails, *Tegula,* often congregate in great clusters in crevices or on the sides of small boulders, especially at night or during still, cloudy days. The shells are pretty enough when wet; dry, they have the dingy gray color that blends so well with the dry rocks. The black turban, *Tegula funebralis* (Pl. II), ranging from Sitka to Lower California, is the dominant type in this upper level. Lower down it is replaced by the brown turban (§29), which more often than the black turban carries specimens of the commensal slipper shell, *Crepidula.**

* Both of these frequently carry also a small black limpet, *Acmaea asmi,* one of which can be seen in the upper right-hand corner of Plate II. Dr. (Grant) Test records for this a range from Point Arena south, doubtfully from Puget Sound or even from Sitka, and an average size of 8 × 6 × 6 mm.

By Italians these snails are considered fine food. They are cooked in oil and served in the shell, the bodies being removed from the shells with a pin as they are eaten. The lucky Americans who can overcome their food prejudices in this and other respects will at least achieve a greater gastronomic independence and may even develop an epicurean appreciation of many of the intertidal delicacies.

§14. The third obvious and distinctly "visible" animal occurring in this assemblage is the pugnacious little rock crab, *Pachygrapsus crassipes,* without which any rocky beach must seem lonesome and quiet. These dark red or green, square-shelled crabs run sideways or backwards when alarmed, scurrying away before the intruder or rearing up and offering to fight all comers. They may be found on top of the rocks at night and hiding in crevices and pools during the day. To see a group of them attack a discarded apple core is to understand one method by which the rock pools are kept clear of all foreign matter that is to any degree edible. These crabs, which are common in the rocky intertidal from Oregon to the Gulf of California, and the beach hoppers are the most active scavengers in this particular ecological association.

Pachygrapsus females carry their eggs, attached to the under side of the recurved tail, until the late larval stages; just how long is not known. Egg-carrying specimens have been taken in the Monterey region in such divergent seasons as June and February.

§15. Collectors in the La Jolla region will find, along with other limpets on and under fairly bare rocks on the upper shore, the small, cleancut, and rather beautifully marked volcano shell limpet, *Fissurella volcano* (Pl. II). For some obscure reason this animal moves down into the low intertidal as it ranges northward. It has been reported from Crescent City to Panama. The shell is pink between the red or purple ridges that radiate from the small opening at the apex.

§16. In the muddy layer between closely adjacent rocks, or in the substratum, the upper tide pools are characterized by the presence of the hairy-gilled worm, *Cirriformia luxuriosa,* formerly *Cirratulus* (Pl. II), which may be found in bits of the blackest and foulest mud. The gills of this worm, resembling long, thin, pink roundworms,* will often be noticed on the muddy substratum. They are withdrawn immediately when the animal is disturbed. This method of respiration is particularly efficient under the circumstances in that it gives its possessor an opportunity to burrow in the mud in search of food (thus gaining considerable protection also) while leaving its "lungs" behind, at the surface. *Cirriformia* is thus one of the few animals that

---

* See also the autonomous gills of *Terebella* (§53).

can live in an environment of foul mud, the very substratum that repels others serving for its protection from enemies and desiccation. An English species is known to feed on such small food particles as one-celled plants and the spores of algae selected from the mud by the aspiration of very delicate sensory flaps of the mouth. Entrance to the digestive tract proper is effected by means of minute waving hairs.

Our collecting records show that sexually mature specimens have been observed in June under interesting conditions. We quote from a report dated June 21, 1927, time 9:30 to 10:30 P.M.: "For the past several evenings I have noticed that the *Cirriformia* were very active in mud-bottom pools of the upper tide flats. Some of them lie half exposed, whereas only the tentacles are protruded normally. Tonight I have noticed further that the shallow pools containing them were murky and milky. Then I noted some of the worms almost fully out of the substratum, extruding milky fluid or more solid white 'castings.' I took two worms back to the laboratory, examined the exudate, and found it to be spermatic fluid." Eggs were not specifically observed at this time.

§17. Under flat rocks in the upper tide-pool region (but possibly as abundant in the middle tide pools also) are the polyclad flatworms, *Leptoplana acticola* (Fig. 12). They are tan in color, with darker markings about the midline. Large specimens may exceed an inch in length, although the average will be nearer a half inch. By examining the pharynx contents Dr. Heath found that the food of many flatworms consists of one-celled plants, spores of algae, micro-crustacea, and worm larvae. Miss Boone found that captive *L. acticola* fed on the red nudibranch, *Rostanga*.

These worms and small *Planocera* crawl about on the damp under sides of freshly moved rocks much as a drop of glycerine flows down the side of a glass dish. This unique motion, achieved by means of cilia, is so effective as to make difficult the removal of these soft-bodied animals without damage. We use a camel's-hair brush, to which they adhere as firmly as to the rock unless immediately cast into a jar of water.

§18. From British Columbia to the Gulf of California, *Petrolisthes cinctipes,* the porcelain crab (Pl. III), is also a common and characteristic inhabitant of the flat under-rock association, although, like the above, it is almost as characteristic of the middle zone. A large specimen will measure about 9/16″ in carapace width. It is these small flat crabs that scurry about so feverishly for cover when a stone is up-ended. Their excessive flatness makes it easy for them to creep into crevices, and they avoid imprisonment by throwing off (autotomizing) a claw or walking leg at the slightest provocation. Indeed, *Petrolisthes* is one of the champion autotomizers of this coast—no mean distinction, for many animals have this peculiar ability.

In autotomizing, a crab not only casts off the limb voluntarily but by an automatic reaction instantly closes the severed blood vessel to prevent bleeding to death. This breakage, together with the constriction of the blood vessel, takes place at a prearranged breaking point near the base of the limb, marked externally by a ring-like groove. The muscles and tendons are particularly adapted to facilitate breakage, and following autotomy a membrane consisting of two flaps is forced across the stump by the congestion of blood at that point. Regeneration begins at once and a miniature limb is soon formed, which, however, undergoes no further growth until the next moult, when it grows rapidly to several times its previous size.

Female crabs will often be found with large egg masses under their curved and extended abdomens. (We have taken ovigerous *Petrolisthes* in California in March, May, and June.) These eggs do not hatch into young crabs, but into fantastic larval forms which the shore collector, as such, will never see. In the first larval stage, called zoea, the animals are minute transparent organisms swimming at the surface of the sea. So totally unrelated do they seem to their parents and to their own later stages that zoölogists long mistook them for a distinct and independent species of animal. After casting its skin several times as it grows in size the zoea becomes a still different-looking animal, also formerly regarded as a separate genus, known as *Megalopa*. The megalops, bearing to a crab something of the relationship that a tadpole bears to a frog, casts its skin several times, finally emerging into a recognizable young crab. The pelagic zoea of *Petrolisthes* is a wondrous sight under a microscope, somewhat resembling a preposterous unicorn. Projecting from the front of the carapace is an enormous spine, often longer than all the rest of the animal. If this spine has any function, it is, presumably, to make ingestion by its enemies difficult. An enterprising pup that had just attacked its first porcupine would understand the principle involved.

§19. Of the two exceedingly common and shoreward-extending brittle stars the dainty black and white *Amphipholis pugetana* (Pl. III) is the highest, being characteristically an upper tide-pool animal. Since large adults measure only about ¾" in arm spread, it is further distinguished by being the smallest of all Pacific coast ophiurans, although it is a rather hardy form which, unlike many of the brittle stars, does not autotomize readily. *Amphipholis* occurs in great beds, so commonly that it would be difficult to find a suitable rock in this zone that hid no specimens; but it is never found with intertwined arms as is its larger relative, *Amphiodia* (§44). The possible significance of such concentration of population is discussed in connection with the latter form. The recorded range of *Amphipholis* is from Alaska to San Diego, but it extends farther south, for we have taken it or the similar *A. squamata* in northern Lower California also.

§20. Representatives of two related groups of crustaceans, the amphipods and isopods, are found under practically every imbedded rock and boulder in the upper tide-pool zone, and farther down also. The amphipods, a group containing the sand hoppers or beach fleas, are, as their popular names imply, lively animals. Being compressed laterally, so that they seem to stand on edge, they are structurally adapted to the jumping careers that they follow with such seeming enthusiasm. *Melita palmata* (Fig. 13) is almost certain to be present under a high percentage of suitable rocks down to the middle tide pools. The amphipods of the Pacific coast have been worked over very little, so that the collector who would identify his species has before him a weary search through scattered literature unless he enlists the aid of the National Museum.

§21. The isopods, being flattened belly-wise or dorso-ventrally, are crawlers, usually slow ones. These are the pill bugs, so called from their habit of curling up into little balls when disturbed, and known also as sow bugs from their resemblance to swine. Representatives of the group are common on land, where they are found in damp places, as under boards lying on the ground. The drab *Cirolana harfordi* (Fig. 14), a common inhabitant of the entire coastline from British Columbia to at least Ensenada, occurs most abundantly under rocks in the high intertidal, but will be found in other zones as well. The isopods are fairly well known.

§22. Small round boulders which are constantly immersed in the pools are very likely to be covered with the tiny calcareous tubes of a serpulid worm, the sinistral *Spirorbis* (Pl. III). The almost microscopic red gills protrude from the tubes to form dots of color that disappear instantly whenever the stone is disturbed. *Spirorbis* is not unique in being hermaphroditic, but its bisexuality takes an interesting form in that its anterior abdominal segments are female and its posterior segments male. It is thought that the operculum may serve as a brood pouch. The eggs, which are extruded in February at least, develop into free-swimming larvae. In a related form (*Serpula,* §213) the sexes are separate.

§23. Other less common or less characteristic animals will sometimes be found in this belt. The purple snail, *Thais,* may be locally abundant in crevices and along the lower edges of rocks, but larger and more noticeable examples are found on the open coast (§182).

Coincident with the start of beds of algae, and so abundant as to be a feature of the tidal landscape, may be found extensive beds of a warty anemone that is more characteristic, however, of the next lower zone (§24). A very small six-rayed starfish will now and then be seen in the pools (§30), as well as small snails and hosts of red flatworms (§59). Even an occasional ribbon worm may be turned out of its home under some rock, but the ribbon worms too reach their maximum development in other zones and are treated elsewhere.

Animals described in connection with the uppermost beach and the upper tide pools form an assemblage interesting in its resistance to some of the "un-marine" conditions that are a part of the environment. During rainy seasons they are drenched with fresh water. Temperature changes of many degrees suddenly descend on them when the cool tide sweeps in over sun-heated rocks. When the sun beats on isolated pools at low tide, evaporation increases the salinity of the water. All this is in addition to the usual problems of wave shock, respiration, and drying that all the intertidal animals must meet. Animals successfully adjusting themselves to such variants must be hard-boiled indeed, and it is not surprising that successful ones are found throughout ranges of literally thousands of miles of variable coast line.

ZONE 3. *Fauna of the mid-tide region, from about the mean of higher low water to the mean of lower low water, the zero of tide tables (plus 2½' to 0 at Monterey).*

This area is below mean sea level, and is largely uncovered by most lows and covered by most high tides. The higher zones seem relatively barren by comparison with the teeming life of this mid-region, which is exceeded in prolificness only by the outer tidelands. Here plants grow in great profusion. There may be a bit of *Pelvetia* in the upper parts; *Fucus* is more likely to occur; *Gigartina* and *Porphyra* grow lush, with the sea lettuce *Ulva*. These plants, in providing protection from deadly sunlight and drying, are of importance to the animals, which are predominantly intertidal forms, rarely occurring in deep water.

The variety of animals associated in this zone is so great that it seems desirable to consider them according to a further division of habitat, as follows: (*a*) Exposed Rock; (*b*) Protected Rock; (*c*) Under-rock; (*d*) Burrowing; (*e*) Pool; (*f*) Root and Holdfast.

(a) Exposed Rock Habitat. Animals living on the tops and sides of rocks and ledges, exposed to waves, sun, and wind.

§24. Extensive beds of a small verrucose anemone, the aggregated *Bunodactis elegantissima*, which is often considered to be a size and color phase of the great green anemone (§64), occur on the exposed surfaces of rocks, especially where sand is being deposited. It is beds of these hardy animals, certainly the most abundant anemone on the coast, that make the intertidal rocks so "squshy" under foot, the pressure of a step causing myriad jets of water to extrude from the mouth and from pores in the body wall. These anemones commonly cover themselves with bits of gravel or shell, so that when contracted they are part of the background. Many a weary collector has rested upon a bit of innocent-looking rock ledge, only to discover that an inch or so of exceeding and very contagious wetness separated him from the bare rock.

These animals are not restricted to pure water, for they live well where there is industrial pollution or sewage, their hardihood belying their apparent delicacy. They can be kept in marine aquaria, even where there is no running sea water, provided only that the water is aerated or changed once or twice a day. In keeping with its exposed position high in the intertidal zone, this *Bunodactis* fully expands in the brightest sunshine, closing up at night. Contracted it is rarely more than 1½" in diameter; expanded the disc may be more than twice that size and may display rather dainty colors over a groundwork of solid green. The tentacles are often banded with pink or lavender, and lines of color frequently radiate from the mouth to the edges of the transparent disc, marking the position of the partitions (mesenteries) inside. We have found this form abundant from San Luis Obispo northward into British Columbia. South of central California its place is often, but not always, taken by small specimens of the giant green anemone, which typically attains its maximum development farther down in the intertidal zone.

Anemones are voracious feeders and when hungry will ingest almost anything offered, even apparently clean stones. Their tentacles are armed with nettle cells that paralyze any small animals so unfortunate as to touch them. We have many times seen small shore crabs disappearing down the anemone's gullet, and as often seen an anemone spew out bits of the crabs' shells. The surprising rapidity of digestion was illustrated by specimens of a related form *Metridium* (§321), with which we experimented at Pender Harbor, B.C. One half of a small chiton which had been cut in two was placed on the disc of an anemone in a glass dish. The disc was immediately depressed at the

center, so that the food disappeared into the body cavity. Within
fifteen minutes the cleaned shell of the chiton, all the meat completely
digested away, was disgorged through the mouth—a striking tribute
to the potency of *Metridium*'s enzymes.* And this action takes place
at about the temperature of sea water! Those of us troubled with
dyspepsia can very well envy animals so equipped, looking forward
to the time when we may be able to help along an inadequate digestion
with anemone enzymes artificially extracted and properly adminis-
tered.

Not much is known about the rate of growth, which presumably
varies directly with the food supply; but several examples have been
cited of extreme longevity in this group. Professor Ashworth tells
of several anemones that were donated to the University of Edinburgh
in 1900 by a woman who had collected them, already fully grown,
thirty years before. She had kept them throughout that period in a
round glass aquarium, strictly observing a daily rite of aerating the
water with a dipper and a weekly rite of feeding them on fresh liver,
which she believed they preferred to anything else. When they came
into the possession of the University they were fed, possibly not so
regularly, any scraps of protein that came to hand, such as shredded
crab meat or even crass beefsteak. Nevertheless the anemones continued in the best of health, annually producing clouds of sperm and
eggs. Dr. Ashworth expects to bequeath the animals to his successor—
a perpetual heritage, for there seems now to be no good reason for
not believing that in another sixty-nine years observers may be edified
by watching the anemones well into their second century.

§25. Also occurring more or less exposed on the tops and sides
of rocks are a number of forms more properly treated elsewhere.
Occasional acorn barnacles extend their range down into this middle
zone when competition is not too keen, and such open-coast forms as
the red barnacle (§168) and the common tough-skinned starfish
(§157) may be locally plentiful, depending on the exposure. There
may be clusters of mussels and goose barnacles also, and the small
chiton or sea cradle, *Nuttallina,* is occasional.

Three common limpets may be found at this level on the protected
outer coast. The large *Acmaea scutum* (Fig. 15), formerly *patina,* the
plate limpet, is the flattest of the tribe. It is frequently green, often
with long trailers of stringy green algae, *Enteromorpha* and *Ulva,*
attached to its shell, and ranges north from Point Conception clear
into the Bering Sea, being in northern California one of the common-

* See also Edge (1934, "Digestive Rates of Marine Invertebrates," *American
Midland Naturalist,* 15: 187–89), who found that digestion required from two to
twelve and one-half hours in most forms investigated, action taking place most
rapidly in the actively voracious animals.

est large limpets. Southward of Monterey, however, according to Mrs. Grant, it becomes increasingly rare, giving way to, and south of Conception being replaced entirely by, the *limatula* mentioned below, former literary references to the contrary notwithstanding, the southern *scutum* identifications having been incorrect. Both are thin and flat, but *scutum* particularly has a knife-edge shell easily broken in removal and lacks the black sides of the foot so diagnostic of the other. An average specimen is 33 × 25 × 9 mm.

There is in the south a species related to *A. scabra,* recently described by Dr. A. R. (Grant) Test as *Acmaea conus.* It is ivory-colored to brown and, with *A. limatula,* replaces the plate limpet on all reefs south of Point Conception. Its average dimensions are 15 × 23 × 6 mm.

A. limatula (Fig. 16), frequently in the past called *scabra,* is sculptured with coarse and imbricated ribs (hence the name "file limpet") which are sometimes obscured by algae. A diagnostic feature is the characteristic deep black color around the side of the foot, the bottom being contrastingly white. The range is reported from Crescent City to San Diego, becoming increasingly common south of Monterey. The average specimen is 29 × 23 × 9 mm.

Occasional specimens of any of the limpets previously mentioned in §§6 and 11 may be turned up here, or of *fenestrata* and *mitra* of the lowest horizon (§117).

(b) Protected Rock Habitat. Animals attached to, or living on, protected rocks and rockweed.

Many of the commonest inhabitants of this subregion can scarcely be considered obvious, since in order to see them advantageously one must almost lie down in the pools, looking up into the crevices and under ledges.

§26. The large red, yellow, or purple starfish, *Patiria miniata* (Pl. III), called locally "sea bat" on account of its webbed rays, is possibly the most obvious animal in this association, extending downward to deep water. Because it is readily available, because it has an unusually long breeding season, and because it extrudes its sexual products so obligingly, *Patiria* is used extensively for embryological experimentation. A large percentage of male and female specimens, laid out on wet seaweed, discharge their ripe sperm and eggs almost throughout the year, but especially during the winter. With ordinary aseptic precautions the ova can be fertilized by fresh sperm and will develop over night, if spread out in scrupulously clean glass dishes, into minute larvae which swim by vibrating their cilia. The young starfish develop within these larvae, gradually absorbing the larvae as they grow. After the adult specimens have shed their sexual products they should be put back alive into the tide pools to avoid depletion of the race. In the Monterey region, and probably because of collecting activities, this striking and interesting form is no longer to be found in the great congregations that formerly occurred in the middle tide pools, although it still occurs in large numbers in the outermost pools and reefs. The recorded range is from Sitka to San Diego and even to La Paz, but south of Point Conception the specimens are few, small, and stunted, and are found almost invariably under rocks.

§27. The little square-shelled rock crab, *Pachygrapsus,* is still abundant, but the purple shore crab, *Hemigrapsus nudus* (Pl. IV), is the dominant representative of this group in the middle tide-pool region, although it extends into the next lower zone also. *Hemigrapsus* is as characteristic of the zone of the rockweeds as is *Pachygrapsus* of the naked rock zone higher up or *Cancer antennarius* (§105) of the lower tide-pool zone. The purple spots on *Hemigrapsus'* claws, particularly noticeable on their white under sides, will serve to differentiate it from the smaller and slimmer *Pachygrapsus.* Egg-bearing females of *Hemigrapsus* have been taken in November, December, and February in Monterey Bay, but in the Puget Sound area the females are ovigerous in early summer. The range is from Sitka to the Gulf of California.

Hemigrapsus is certainly as belligerent as the smaller rock crab, and it can back up its nasty disposition with a pair of nutcracker claws. Some idea of the strength of the claws of crustacea may be gained through experiments performed with the green European shore crab. The left, or weaker, claw was found capable of supporting a weight of nearly two kilograms, or nearly thirty times the weight of the crab's body. A man's right hand, on the average, is capable of exerting a pull of only fifty kilograms, or a little more than two-thirds of his body weight. Thus, relative to body weight, the crab's claw is something more than forty times as strong as a man's hand.

§28. An abundance of hermit crabs is a feature of this zone also. Specimens of *P. samuelis* larger than those encountered in the upper tide-pool region (§12) can be found, but even the large *samuelis* are small in comparison with the average *Pagurus hemphilli* (Pl. V), characteristic of the middle and lower tide-pool regions. The stalwart and cleancut *hemphilli,* up to 2″ long and colored a fairly uniform straw tan, can be recognized, apart from this size and color, by the laterally compressed wrist of the big claw, which subtends a sharp angle with the upper surface. Other hermits have the top of the wrist more or less rounded. Egg-bearing females of *hemphilli* have been taken in February and March. This hermit ranges from British Columbia to Monterey, occupying the shells of large *Tegula* almost to the exclusion of anything else.

Hermit crabs are sometimes afflicted with a parasite, *Peltogaster,* that produces a long white sac on the abdomen. This is actually a degenerate barnacle that gains access to its host as a free-swimming nauplius larva scarcely distinguishable from the nauplii of other barnacles. Once attached, the animal loses all its appendages, and becomes a sac of generative organs devoted solely to the production of eggs and sperm, food and respiration being provided by the host. Hermit crabs so afflicted are not common on the Pacific coast of North America, and are not easy to find, since the shell must be crushed in a vise to determine whether or not the animal is affected. The collector who locates one of these parasites can make a contribution to science by immediately preserving both host and parasite in 70 per cent alcohol, since there is an opportunity now, through the offices of a specialist, to have the Pacific coast species determined.

§29. In the middle zone the brown turban snail, *Tegula brunnea* (Pl. V), ranging from Mendocino to Lower California, takes the place of its black brother in the upper zone, although each to some extent overlaps the territory of the other. They are definitely larger in the middle zone, however, and more often carry specimens of another snail, the horned slipper shell or boat shell, *Crepidula adunca.* This small dark brown form looks, with its sharply recurved hook, not unlike a limpet, and it affixes itself with limpet-like strength to the *Tegula* that carries it. The boat shell is known to occur from Vancouver to Cape San Lucas. Breeding individuals carry the eggs in the shell cavity, where they can be seen if the animal is pried from its support. With a hand lens the embryos of *Crepidula* can sometimes be seen whirling around in their envelopes in the egg packets. We have taken specimens with the eggs at this stage through the spring months.

Atlantic-coast forms of *Crepidula* have been used for the study of cell lineage, for the development of the animal from the two-celled stage follows, as Wilson has shown, a remarkable mathematical sequence. Ordinarily it is impossible to say which part of a fertilized ovum will develop into a given organ. That is, development seems to be a matter of chance, the pattern being laid out as the form builds up. With *Crepidula,* however, it is possible to trace the ancestry of the cells and then, by reversing the process, map out from the two-celled stage the regions that will develop into the various organs. In other words, the pattern has been laid out in advance, and the mathematical unfolding process can be prophesied and observed. The throwing off of daughter cells is synchronous in the various regions, the cleavages being alternately to the right and to the left. Such a study may ultimately answer the question of why two seemingly identical bits of protoplasm grow into totally different animals.

An Eastern form (*Crepidula fornicata*) was introduced on the English coast, about 1880, along with American oysters, and its habits and natural history have been studied there by Orton. It is considered an enemy of the oyster beds on the Essex coast because it uses the same kind of food in the same way. "Water is drawn in and expelled at the front end of the shell, the in-going current entering on the left side, passing over the back of the animal and out at the right side. . . . . Between the in-going and out-going current the gill of the animal acts as a strainer, which collects all the food material that occurs floating in the water." The food is divided on its way toward the mouth into two main batches—coarse and fine. The fine material, consisting of diatoms, etc., is collected in a cylindrical mass in a groove and ingested at intervals. The coarse particles are stored in a pouch in front of the mouth so that the animal can feed whenever it wishes.

Crepidula fornicata is a protandric hermaphrodite.* It is born as a male, later is bisexual for a time, and finally becomes female. In America it breeds in April and May, but in its new English environment in March. Special care is taken of the spawn. The animal constructs 50 to 60 membranous bags, into each of which it passes some 250 eggs, afterward closing each bag and tying it with a short cord. All the cords are then attached to the surface on which the slipper shell sits (our Pacific form carries them in the mantle cavity, as previously noted), and the 13,000 or so eggs are there carefully protected until, in about a month, they hatch. Thereafter the young are free-swimming for two weeks. (See pages 452–53 for recent information on Pacific coast crepidulas.)

Orton finds the adults sticking together in long chains, one on the back of the other, with the shells partially interlocked by means of projections and grooves. Old individuals sometimes get permanently attached to their support or to each other by a calcareous secretion of the foot. There are as many as 13 individuals in a chain, the lower ones old and female, the middle ones hermaphroditic, and the upper ones young and hence male. Orton allows one year to the individual, so that in such a chain the oldest would be fourteen years old.

§30. *Leptasterias pusilla* (Pl. V), a dainty little six-rayed starfish, with a total arm spread usually under 1 inch, may be very numerous in this zone, crawling about in the sea lettuce or dotting the tide pools.

---

* Orton (*Proc. Malac. Soc. London,* **28** [1950]: 168–84) reports on the recent spread of this species in England, and suggests that self-fertilization may occur, making its continued extension easier.

At night specimens are likely to be seen walking around on top of the rocks that have hidden them during the day. In contradistinction to their larger relative, *L. aequalis,* of the lower tide pools, these are delicate and cleancut, usually light gray in color. The breeding habits are famous. The mother broods the eggs in clusters around the mouth region until the larvae have attained the adult form. Ovigerous females may be found in January and February, and the very minute liberated stars are seen in the tide pools during February and March. This newly described species is found at present only in central California, including San Mateo, Santa Cruz, and Monterey counties, where it is very common; but it will doubtless be found elsewhere.

§31. Encrusting the sides of rocks with gay colors are sponges and tunicates of several types. *Haliclona permollis* (Pl. V), formerly *Reneira cineria,* is the vivid purple, fairly soft, but not slimy encrustation common during some years in this association. It is recognizable as a sponge by the regularly spaced, volcano-like "craters," the oscula, that give the characteristic porousness to all the animals of this group, including the common bath sponge. *Haliclona* (*Reneira*) is a form almost cosmopolitan on north-temperate shores, known from central California, Europe, and the Atlantic coast of the United States. A similar species occurs in Puget Sound (§198).

§32. There are likely to be several types of encrusting red sponges overgrowing narrow crevices and the undersides of overhanging ledges, often *Ophlitaspongia pennata* (Pl. V), a beautifully coral-red form characterized, especially after drying, by starry oscula; the surface is velvety. De Laubenfels remarks that it occurs clear up to the half-tide mark, higher up than any other sponge, especially on vertical rocks under pendent seaweed, hence shaded from direct sunlight.

Plocamia karykina (Pl. V), in layers up to ¾″ thick, bright red, is firm and woody with smooth surface. The oscula are usually large, irregular, and rather far apart. De Laubenfels says it "emits copious quantities of a colorless slime not conspicuous before injury." A common neighbor is the slightly different-looking *Isociona lithophoenix,* more a vermilion red, softer, and with a very lumpy, almost papillate, surface. The oscula are very small and in depressions. The microscopic spicules are straight, spiny rods instead of short, thick, double-headed affairs as in the first-mentioned form. The brilliantly splashed colors of these red sponges are a feature of the rocky caverns and granite rock faces, particularly in the Monterey Bay region; the former ranging from Vancouver to Laguna Beach. Other sponges occasionally occurring up this far are mentioned in §140.

§33. A vivid red nudibranch (shell-less snail), *Rostanga pulchra,* averaging ½″ in length, is found very commonly feeding on red sponges—a good example of protective coloration if there is such a thing. (Two specimens are shown on the photograph of *Ophlita-spongia* [Pl. V].) Even the egg ribbons, which may be found through-out the year attached to the sponge in a loose coil, are vividly red. *Rostanga pulchra* ranges from Monterey Bay to San Diego.

§34. Two other nudibranchs occur this high in the tide pools. One, *Triopha carpenteri* (Pl. VI), which is found in the Monterey Bay region and as far north as Dillon Beach, can be seen walking upside down suspended from the under side of the air-water surface film of pools. As it moves along the animal spins a path of slime which prevents its weight from bending down and finally breaking the surface film. If the film is once broken, the animal sinks to the bottom of the pool, crawls up the side, and climbs to the surface film again—a long slow labor that may be watched to advantage in an aquarium. A good many nudibranchs, even the large ones, have this habit. *T. carpenteri* is seldom more than an inch long, but the brilliant orange-red of its nipple-like appendages against its white body make it very noticeable. Dumpy and sac-shaped in outline, it has none of the firm definiteness of many other sea slugs, and collapses very readily. It might be supposed that so tender-looking a morsel, apparently defenseless, would not last long among the voracious tide-pool animals, but for some reason as yet unknown the nudibranchs are avoided. Obviously this challenge to all enterprising human tasters could not go unanswered indefinitely. Professor Herdman took up the gauntlet by eating a vividly colored nudibranch alive. He reported that it had a pleasant oyster-like flavor; so the question remains open. McFarland says that the bright colors seem to serve as a warning. But more tasters are needed to find out why that warning is heeded. Certain special cases of inedibility among nudibranchs will be mentioned later.

§35. *Diaulula sandiegensis* (Pl. VI) occurs more frequently on the sides of boulders, or sometimes even under them. The colors are dainty rather than spectacular—consisting of as many as a dozen dark circles or spots on a light brown-gray background. In common with other nudibranchs, *Diaulula* is hermaphroditic. At Monterey it has been observed depositing eggs, in broad white spiral bands, almost throughout the year, records being at hand for the summer, early October, January, and February. Apparently here is another of the Monterey Bay animals that has no restricted breeding season—probably a concomitant of the slight annual temperature variation at this point. Specimens 4 to 5″ long are occasionally seen on the flats south of Dillon Beach.

Respiration in this and other dorids is by means of a circlet of retractile gills at the posterior end, which, if the animal is left undisturbed, flower out very beautifully. Never occurring in great numbers, but found steadily and regularly in the proper associations, *Diaulula* ranges from Unalaska to San Diego and probably farther south. The abundant specimens at Sitka are darker in color, gray brown, and larger than the average Monterey examples.

§36. Some of the bolder of the chitons or sea cradles can be considered characteristic members of this zone. Most of them live under rocks, coming out to forage at night; but *Tonicella lineata* (formerly *Lepidochitona lineata*), the lined chiton (Pl. VI), is often in plain sight during the day. Although this is a small species, usually not much over an inch in length, it is the most strikingly beautiful sea cradle found in the Pacific coast intertidal. In semi-sheltered areas it maintains the high station (that is, high for a chiton) that characterizes *Nuttalina* (§169) on the surf-swept open coast. In southeastern Alaska *Tonicella lineata* is the most abundant shore chiton, but it occurs there with the leather chiton, *Katharina*, which on the California coast is restricted to surf-swept areas. The lined chiton ranges from Alaska to San Diego and is common as far south as Monterey.

Another chiton, *Cyanoplax* hartwegii* (§ 237), an oval olive-green form, may be found almost at will, although not in great numbers, by lifting up the clusters of *Pelvetia* on vertical rocks. In such places it spends its days, protected from sunlight and drying winds. It seems more at home, however, in quieter regions like Puget Sound.

The natural history of chitons is discussed in §76.

§37. The small anemone, *Epiactis prolifera* (Pl. VI), is locally abundant, usually on the protected sides of small smooth boulders, sometimes on the fronds of the sea lettuce, *Ulva*. This anemone is notable for its breeding habits. The eggs, instead of being discharged into the water, are retained in brood pits at the base of the body wall, where they develop into young anemones without leaving the parent, forming almost an accretionary colony. A fully expanded adult, with half a dozen flower-like young, is a lovely thing to see. *Epiactis* is capable of considerable independent movement, as anyone can attest who takes the trouble to move to an aquarium a stipe of alga bearing several specimens, only to discover that the anemones will leave the plant for the smooth walls of the aquarium. In the same manner the young, when they are sufficiently mature, glide away from the parent. Four young liberated themselves from the expanded specimen shown in the photograph within three days. Apparently their departure was hastened by the fact that the parent was dying. The range is from Puget Sound to La Jolla. California specimens average perhaps ¾" in diameter; Puget Sound specimens are larger.

* Dr. Berry prefers *Cyanoplax*.

§38. The solitary hydroid, *Tubularia,* treated (in §80) as an outer tide-pool inhabitant, is occasional here also, as are small fern-like colonies of *Abietinaria* (§83).

§39. The vividly orange-red solitary coral, *Balanophyllia elegans* (Pl. VI), is abundant, but must be well sheltered from desiccation and direct sunlight. In the late winter, February and March, at Pacific Grove, the transparent and beautiful cadmium yellow or orange polyps may be seen extending out of the stony, cup-like base until the base comprises only a third of the animal's bulk. Large individuals may be ½″ in diameter unexpanded. The range is from Puget Sound to Monterey Bay.

Another coral, *Caryophyllia alaskensis,* occurs intertidally in the Puget Sound region and, according to Dr. Durham, may be similar in appearance when alive to *B. elegans.* Perhaps some northern records for *B. elegans* should apply to *C. alaskensis.*

Occupying a similar station in the south, *Astrangia lajollaensis,* smaller and with vivid red polyps, is said to occur from Point Conception south. Although we happen never to have found it, reports (Johnson and Snook, 1927, p. 108) indicate its comparative abundance at La Jolla.

In fact as well as in appearance these corals are related to the anemones, and their method of food-getting is similar. Working with a related East-coast species, *Astrangia danae,* Dr. Boschma found that in the natural state the coral fed on diatoms, small larvae of crustaceans, etc., and that in captivity it would take almost anything offered, including coarse sand. In an average of less than an hour, however, the sand, covered with mucus, was regurgitated on the disc. The tentacles then bent down on one side, allowing the sand to slip off. Living copepods coming into contact with a tentacle remained affixed, probably paralyzed by stinging nematocysts, and were carried to the center of the mouth disc by the tentacle, the mouth disc rising at the same time to meet the morsel. Larger animals struggle when they come in contact with the tentacles, but other tentacles then bend over to help hold the captive until it quiets.

§40. A form similar in appearance to the above, but having white-tipped tentacles and of course lacking the hard skeleton, is the small red anemone, *Corynactis californica,* often clustered under the overhang of rocks. *Corynactis* does not like sunshine, hence the most fully expanded specimens are seen at night. It seems to have been recorded from Monterey Bay only, where it is very common; but it probably occurs elsewhere (Pl. VI).

§41. The purple sea urchin is found frequently here, but not in great beds that characterize the outer pools and reefs (see §174).

§42. Living on and in the rockweed itself, especially in *Pelvetia,* are several diminutive forms rarely found elsewhere. By shaking a mass of freshly gathered rockweed over a dishpan, one can easily dislodge and capture hosts of tiny amphipods (beach fleas) whose colors match perfectly the slaty green of the weed. *Atylopsis* (probably a new species) is the commoner of two abundant forms. The other, *Ampithoë* (of unknown species), is noticeable because of its saddle-shaped marking in white. Other amphipods will be found in *Pelvetia;* these seem to be characteristic. To enable them to cling to plants and other objects, both amphipods and isopods have the last joint of the legs in-curved to form a claw. The shape of isopods (flattened horizontally) adapts them for crawling over rocks rather than over weeds, while amphipods (flattened vertically, or laterally) seem better adapted for balancing on vegetation. The leaps of the latter constitute a sort of "flapping" motion. Driving power for the leap is obtained by suddenly snapping backward the bent posterior portion of the abdomen—a spring strong enough to send them several feet at a leap and make them adept at avoiding the specimen jar. In appearance they are scarcely distinguishable from *Melita* (§20).

§43. It is in this area also that one is likely first to see examples of the roundworms, a group of animals which also includes such well-known forms as the hookworm and the eelworm. Referring to the abundance and widespread distribution of these worms, Dr. Cobb has said that if everything else in the world were to be removed there still would remain the ghost or shadowy outline, made up of roundworms, of mountains, rivers, plants, soil, and forests, and even of animals in which they are parasitic. Their characteristically wiggling bodies are very noticeable to the keen-eyed collector who pulls loose a bit of alga, especially where decay has set in. Some forms writhe so rapidly that they seem almost to snap themselves back and forth.

(c) Under-rock Habitat. Animals found on the under side of loosely imbedded rocks, but not in the substratum, or between adjacent rocks and boulders where there is no accumulation of substratum.

Having here the maximum of protection from wave shock, sunlight, and desiccation, a characteristic group of animals occurs. Some of the brittle stars (*Ophioplocus,* §45) are diagnostic of this association and rarely found elsewhere, but such widely ranging and generalized forms as the flatworms (*Leptoplana,* §17) may be the most abundant as to number of individuals. Members of this group must be considered as even less obvious than those mentioned in the protected rock habitat, but they are there plainly enough for the collector who will turn over a few rocks.

§44. The fragile and beautiful brittle stars, whose delicacy requires the protection incident to the under-rock habitat, are the most striking of all animals to be found there. They are bountifully represented, as to both number of individuals and number of species. In Monterey Bay six shore species occur in this habitat and there are still others in the south, most of them restricted to the lower intertidal.

The tiny *Amphipholis pugetana,* already treated (§19) as an inhabitant of the upper tide-pool region, is almost as plentiful here in the middle zone. A much larger and hence more conspicuous form, ranging from Alaska to Monterey Bay, is *Amphiodia occidentalis* (Pl. VII), an annoyingly "brittle" brittle star with long snaky arms bearing spines that take off at right angles. An interested observer who places a specimen in the palm of his hand to examine it is likely to see the arms shed, piece by piece, until nothing is left but the disc, possibly bearing a few short stumps. Normally regeneration takes place quickly; but experiments have shown that if the radial nerve is injured, little or no new growth will appear. During October the disc of the female, up to ½" in diameter, is greatly swollen with eggs, and at such times it becomes detached on slight provocation, possibly in a kind of autotomy; but whether or not the remaining part of the body, which is little more than the intersection of the arms, will regenerate a new disc is not known.

Although closely restricted to the under side of rocks, especially where the rocks are imbedded in fine sand with detritus, and even occurring in the substratum, these animals, like many others which hide away during the day, may be seen on calm nights crawling about, at ebb tide, on top of the rocks. In their under-rock retreat they are almost invariably found in aggregations of from several to several dozen, so closely associated that their arms are intertwined; recent studies of this intertwining habit, by Dr. Allee, lead us to the borderline of the metaphysical.

Working with Atlantic brittle stars, isopods, and planarians, Dr. Allee has found that social units of this type have distinct survival value for their members, bringing about a degree of resistance to untoward conditions that is not attainable by isolated individuals. By treating individual animals and also naturally and spontaneously formed aggregations with toxic substances he found not only that the mass had greater resistance to the action of the poisons (partly because of absorption by secreted slime and the bodies of the outermost animals) but that an actual protective material was given off by the aggregations. This subtle material, which "once in solution passes through ordinary filter paper and persists after the filtrate is boiled," is apparently similar to antibodies, such as are familiar to the general public in vaccine. Solutions containing these protective units are capable of conferring protection from poisons—fresh water or colloidal silver, for instance—to isolated animals which could not otherwise survive. Furthermore, certain animals can confer immunity on other taxonomically unrelated animals.

This rather astounding discovery opens new and unexplored vistas to students of biology. It will certainly throw some interesting light on animal communities in general, and may conceivably make understandable the evolutionary background behind the gregariousness of animals, even human beings. Specifically, it explains a phenomenon regarding anemones that has puzzled us for some time. A single anemone may be very easily anesthetized for preservation, but a large number in a tray show a tremendous degree of resistance, even though the amount of anesthetic employed per individual is greater for the group than for the single specimen. Furthermore the pans in which anemones are anesthetized become increasingly unsuitable; that is, each successive batch of animals is more resistant than the batch before. We finally took to scrubbing out the pans with hot water and washing powder and then revarnishing them.

Several animals, such as *Nereis* and *Amphitrite*, which do not form aggregations in their natural habitat, do so under artificial conditions, as when placed in trays. Since *Amphiodia* aggregates in its natural state, however, it may be assumed that it is for protection against some usual environmental factor, probably oxygen suffocation. It is not known whether or not the aggregations disband when the tide is in, but this is probably the case.

Some more tangible aspects of brittle stars in general are their feeding habits and methods of locomotion. The locomotion is peculiar—quite different from that of starfish and very rapid as compared with the snail-like pace of even the fastest starfish. Most that we have observed pull with two arms, pushing with the other three arms behind, apparently exerting the power in jerky muscular movements. Their very flexible arms take advantage of even slight inequalities in the surface.

Of the feeding habits not a great deal is known. The hard parts, called jaws, surrounding the mouth, can be rotated downwards, thus greatly enlarging the mouth, and then rotated upwards and inwards, so that they form a strainer. The digestive tract is restricted to the disc, not extending into the arms as is the case with starfish, and again unlike starfish it cannot be everted, or projected outside the body to envelop food. Apparently brittle stars simply crawl along, mouth downwards, over the gravel, sand, or mud, and scoop bits of food into the mouth with the first two pairs of tube feet on each arm.

Any area colonized by animals is continually full of organic debris and continually being sorted over by animals of various capacities and with varying requirements, with the Victorian "economy of nature" factor always at work. The whole thing calls to mind the sorting effect of a set of sieves. Certain animals, like crabs, dispose of sizeable chunks of food; others, like beach hoppers, eat minute particles and may, in time, reduce large pieces of edible matter; certain of the sea cucumbers, buried in the substratum, sweep the surface with their tentacles for adherent particles—an office which is performed for rock surfaces by limpets and periwinkles; and other animals, including the brittle stars, pass quantities of dirt and sand through their alimentary canals in order to extract whatever nourishment these may contain. Everything is accounted for, particles so small as to be overlooked by everything else being attacked and reduced by the last sieve of all— the bacteria.

The deep-water brittle stars, and presumably the shore forms also, feed on the most superficial layer, which consists partly of microscopic algae and partly of decaying organic matter and is much more easily digested than the living animals on which the starfish preys. Thus "the simple structure of the alimentary canal seems to be correlated with the exceedingly simple character of the food." Deep-water forms under examination have frequently extruded a dirty-white fluid from the mouth, presumably a mixture of half-digested food, digestive fluid, and waste products, since there is no anus.

§45. *Ophioplocus esmarki* (Pl. VII) is a larger, sand-colored brittle star, common in some regions on a sandy-mud substratum under flat rocks, especially disintegrating granite. It averages ½" to ¾" in disc diameter and has short stubby arms with a spread of 3" to 3½". It is a relatively hardy form that maintains its form well when preserved. Specimens particularly noted during January had the genital bursae, or sacs, swollen with eggs, and young are found in the bursae in July. *Ophioplocus* and *Ophioderma* (§121) differ from most brittle stars in having the spines on the arms extend outward at a sharp angle to the arms instead of being at right angles. The former ranges from Pacific Grove to San Diego.

Two other common brittle stars of this southern range belong in the lower tide-pool zone but often stray up into the middle zone. Both (§121) are large and striking, and neither is found above San Pedro. One, *Ophioderma panamensis,* has a superficial resemblance to *Ophioplocus,* but is larger, richer brown in color, and smoother in texture, and has banded arms. The other, *Ophionereis annulata,* is the southern counterpart of the snaky-armed *Amphiodia.*

§46. The porcelain crab (*Petrolisthes,* §18), discussed with the upper tide-pool animals, is a common and easily noticed member of the middle tide-pool under-rock association also. The pearly chiton and the transparent tunicate (*Clavelina,* §101) are fairly common here, but they belong more characteristically to the lower intertidal. Some serpulid worms occur (§§129, 213), but they too are more common farther down.

Belonging to this zone is a large, slow-crawling pill bug or isopod, *Idothea urotoma* (Fig. 17), that will be found under rocks, especially in the south. It may be recognized by its paddle-shaped tail and somewhat rectangular outline. It is brown in color and about ¾" in length.

Betaeus longidactylus (Fig. 18), the "long-fingered" shrimp, may be found under rocks or in pools. In adult males the nearly equal large claws are extraordinarily long, sometimes more than half as long as the animal's body. (The specimen figured is a female and therefore small-clawed.) The elongated carapace projects somewhat over the eyes, like a porch roof—a peculiarity that is still more exaggerated in a related shrimp that lives on wharf piling (§326). The legs of this form are red, and there is a fringe of yellow hairs on the last segment of the abdomen. The body and the big claws vary in color from blue and blue-green to olive-brown. It occurs from Elkhorn Slough to San Diego at least, but is most plentiful in the south, where it occurs on the outer coast, being restricted in the north to quiet-water conditions.

§47. A feature of the under-rock fauna below Santa Barbara is a great twisted mass of the intertwined tubes of a remarkable snail, *Aletes squamigerus* (Pl. VIII), which occurs at times even on the sides of rocks. For some reason not readily apparent, this animal lost or gave up the power of independent movement and took to lying in wait for its food instead of going after it. Some adaptation to food-getting under these new conditions had of course to be made, and *Aletes* solved the problem by employing the mucus that normally lubricates a snail's path to entangle minute animals and bits of detritus. When a bit of passing food is thus captured, the animal draws the mucus back into its mouth and removes the food.

Aletes is ovoviviparous (that is, lays eggs but retains them within the shell until the young are hatched), and produces offspring that have snail-like, coiled shells. It is only after the young have attached and started to grow that the shell loses all resemblance to a snail's. Calcareous matter is added to the mouth of the shell to produce a long, worm-like tube, that is irregularly coiled or nearly straight. The hinder part of the body is black, the rest mottled with white. When disturbed, *Aletes* retracts slowly, like an anemone—a trait that distinguishes it instantly from the tube worms, for the latter snap back in a flash, often with nothing more than a shadow to alarm them. Even experienced zoölogists, if unfamiliar with the Pacific fauna, may mistake this tubicolous mollusk for a serpulid worm. The range is Monterey to Peru, but they are only occasional in the Monterey Bay region. The specimens shown were photographed in Newport Bay.

§48. More than a hundred species of ribbon worms (nemerteans) are found on the Pacific Coast. One of them, *Emplectonema* (§165), is abundant here, but is treated elsewhere since it occurs even more commonly under mussel beds. The similar but larger *Amphiporus bimaculatus,* however, has possibly its chief center of distribution in this zone. It may be found occasionally as a twisted brown cord, capable of almost indefinite expansion and contraction, but averaging a few inches in length when undisturbed. As suggested by the specific name, there are two dark spots on the head, not unlike great staring eyes, but having no connection with the light-perceptive organs. The "real" eyes are the ocelli—dozens of minute black dots centered in two clusters which are marginal to the dark spots and extend forward from them. Otherwise the head is light in color, a striking contrast to the rather beautiful dark orange of the rest of the body.

Nemerteans are ribbonworms, and have a physical organization much more primitive than that of the segmented worms such as *Cirriformia* and the serpulids. They are unique among lower animals in the possession of a remarkable evertible organ, the proboscis, which, in the case of some mud-living forms (*Cerebratulus,* §312), may be longer than the animal bearing it. The proboscis of *Amphiporus* is armed with a poisonous barb or stylet, not large enough to penetrate human skin but very effective when directed against smaller worms. This form is abundant in its entire range, from Sitka to Monterey Bay.

It is almost impossible to preserve some of the nemerteans, because of their habit of breaking up on the slightest provocation (*Amphiporus,* however, is only moderately fragile). Often they cannot even be picked up whole. If the head fragment of an autotomized specimen is left in the animal's natural environment, or undisturbed in a well-aerated aquarium, it will regenerate a complete new animal. Some interesting experiments in this connection are discussed in §312.

§49. A very common, insignificant-looking inhabitant of this region is the scale worm or polynoid. *Halosydna brevisetosa* (Fig. 19) is the most common form in the Alaska to Monterey region, being replaced south of that point by *H. californica,* which occurs at least to San Diego. Free-living specimens seldom exceed an inch or so in length. Many, however, exchange their freedom for a parasitic but doubtless comfortable residence in the tubes of other worms. In this case, contrary to the more usual run of things, the dependent form is considerably larger and more richly colored than its self-supporting relatives.

The breeding habits are noteworthy. To quote Essenberg: "The eggs, after leaving the body cavity of the worm, are attached by a mucous secretion to each other and to the dorsal surface of the parent's body beneath the scales. There they develop until a preoral band of cilia is formed, when the larvae escape as the well known trochophores swimming freely near the surface of the water. The larvae finally settle to the bottom of the ocean, undergoing there further metamorphosis and assuming gradually the shape of the adult worm."

The polynoid worms are voracious feeders, and in captivity will attack one another with their strongly developed four-jawed probosces, displacing scales or removing entire segments from the after end of their companions' bodies. *H. brevisetosa,* like allied annelids, bears its scales, called *elytra,* in two longitudinal rows on the upper (dorsal) surface, and may autotomize them when roughly handled. This animal has eighteen pairs of scales, which are mottled, with white centers. Other worms, such as *Neanthes virens* (§311), too numerous to mention, are occasional here.

§50. Here, as in the upper tide pools, small isopods and amphipods, pill bugs and beach hoppers, will be found to exceed in numbers any other animals found under rocks. *Melita palmata* (§20) is the commonest hopper in this zone also, but others may occur, including the very active lustrous slaty-green *Orchestia* (of undetermined species), very nearly related to the tiny fresh-water "shrimps." It should be mentioned in extenuation of the hoppers that their variant name of "beach flea" is a libelous misnomer. None of the beach hoppers has the slightest use for man or other warm-blooded animals.

The pill bug, *Cirolana harfordi* (§21), likewise not restricted to any one habitat, occurs also, as do several others.

§51. A long, eel-like fish, one of the blennies (Pl. IX), is very common under boulders in this association from southeastern Alaska to Point Arguello. The young are greenish black, the adults (up to 12″ long) nearly black with only traces of dusky yellowish or whitish mottlings toward the tail fin. This species, *Epigeichthys atro-purpureus,* lives even as an adult in the under-rock habitat, frequently in

places that are merely damp when the tide is out.* Another common
species is the larger *Xiphister mucosus,* only the young of which are
found in the intertidal zone. The young are a pale translucent olive,
their range Alaska to San Simeon Bay. Still a third, less common,
blenny is a representative of an entirely different group which is
usually tropical. It is more compressed laterally than those described
above and not so elongate, but is often brilliantly striped. Two subspecies of this form, *Gibbonsia elegans,* range from British Columbia
to Lower California and probably below. Many people regard the
blennies as excellent fare. However, some that we tried had green
flesh, the cooking smell of which was so reminiscent of defunct kelp
that our research was discontinued.

With the blennies, or in similar situations, the little clingfish,
Sicyogaster meandrica (Pl. IX), is very common, slithering over
smooth damp surfaces or clinging to the rock with limpet-like
strength.

(d) Burrowing Habitat. Animals occurring in the mud, sand, or gravel substratum underlying tide-pool rocks.

A very common situation is to find the surface boulders laid upon
a matrix of muddy gravel bound together by chunks of rock of
varying sizes.

A small stout trowel is a good tool for this zone. Ordinarily,
however, the barring up of a large boulder will disturb the substratum
so that any animals present will be visible. The normal expectancy
would be that the sand or mud under rocks would harbor forms
similar to those burrowing in the sand or mud of estuaries. This
proves true to some extent, although it actually seems to be the case
that the under-rock substratum animals form a fairly specific assemblage.

§52. Foremost of these substratum animals is the sipunculid
worm, *Phascolosoma agassizii* (Pl. VIII), which ranges at least from
Sitka to Monterey Bay, and is replaced in the south by the more
beautifully flowering *Dendrostoma* (§145). These rough-skinned
worms are related to the annelids, although themselves devoid of
segmentation. They have been popularly termed peanut worms, a
name properly applying to the specimens in their contracted state

* Most specimens have three stripes of light brown or white, bordered by darker
colors, radiating backward and upward from the eyes. Not all *Epigeichthys* have
this character, and other blennies may have it also ; but the condition is fairly
diagnostic.

only. *Phascolosoma* is abundant in the muddy crevices between rocks, often associated with terebellids (see next paragraph). A contracted specimen 2″ long (larger than the average) is capable of extending its introvert, which bears a mouth surrounded by stubs of tentacles, to an extreme length of 6″, much as one would blow out the inverted finger of a rubber glove. Under the process of anesthetization, to get them extended for museum preparations, it is a common thing for specimens taken in the spring to extrude eggs and sperm. In the quiet channels of upper British Columbia large representatives of this form are among the most characteristic substratum animals.

§53. The brown or flesh-colored tapering terebellid worms (Pl. VIII), up to 6″ long, very commonly build their parchmenty tubes under rocks or in the substratum between rocks. Several species are involved. *Thelepus crispus* (= *plagiostoma*), *Eupolymnia heterobranchia* (formerly *Lanice*), and possibly some species of *Terebella* seem to prefer the cool oceanic waters of open shores but may be taken also in the quiet waters of Puget Sound. Another form, *Amphitrite robusta* (§232) reaching great size in those quiet waters, may also occur here, "outside." All of these bear a superficial resemblance to *Cirriformia* (Pl. II), but the cirratulids have gills extending almost to the middle of the body, which is tapered at both ends, whereas the terebellids have the long and delicate tentacles restricted to the enlarged head region.

The differentiation of the many species of terebellid worms is a task for the specialist. We have had little success in identifying them by field characters, but the following suggestions supplied by Dr. Hartman will be found useful: *Thelepus* has thread-like and unbranched (cirriform) tentacles, with gills of about the same length. The tentacles of *Amphitrite* and *Terebella* are branching (dendritic) and dark, longer than the white gills; but the latter genus has only 17 thoracic segments, while *Terebella* has more—23 to 28.

A specimen of any of these tube worms, deprived of its home and placed in an aquarium with bits of gravel, will quickly set about remedying the deficiency. In a few hours a makeshift burrow will have been constructed of the gravel, cemented together with mucus and detritus, and the transparent stringy tentacles will be fully extended on the bottom of the container, writhing slowly in search of food, which is transferred to the mouth by means of cilia.

In Bermuda, Welsh (1934), primarily interested in innervation, investigated the autonomy of the tentacles of a similar form. He found that they would live, squirm about, and react normally in most ways up to twelve days after they had been removed from the body. He determined furthermore that new tentacles, in experimentally denuded worms, grew at the rate of 1 to 1½ cm. per day, and that the fully developed tentacle, up to 50 cm. long, acted, through its ciliated groove, as a food-getting organ, collecting the minute particles of detritus and transmitting them to the body.

Most of the tubes of our local forms, when carefully examined, will be found to contain presumably uninvited guests who share the protection of this substantial tube, profiting by its currents of food-laden water. Commensal polynoid worms (§49) are often present, and with them a minute pea crab, *Pinnixa tubicola,* which never occurs living free.

§54. *Amphitrite* is the first-mentioned, though not the most striking, example, of several animals whose breeding time is known to be correlated with the time of spring tides and hence bears a direct or indirect relationship to the phases of the moon. In this case one investigator, Scott, believes that both moon and tides are entirely secondary factors and that the egg-laying is induced by the higher temperatures at the time of spring tides, caused by long exposure to sunlight, and possibly by the changes of pressure brought about by the alternate increase and decrease in the depth of water. The increased food supply may be another inciting factor.

At any rate, both males and females discharge their ripe sexual products into their tubes during spring lows and expel them from the tubes into the water via the respiratory currents. Another possible reason for discharging the eggs and sperm at this time, or at least a result of it, is that these products have a much greater opportunity to mix than if they were voided into the tons of water present at flood tide—a reason that applies equally well, of course, to other animals. At the time of egg-laying the female's wave-like body contractions become stronger and faster—involving the process of separating the ripe eggs which are to be released from the immature eggs which are to be retained.

§55. In sandy and gravelly substrata, extending downward from the middle tide pools, the dirty-white sea cucumber, *Leptosynapta albicans,* the former *inhaerens* (Pl. IX), is common. This and similar forms (the synaptids) lack the respiratory trees that are common to other cucumbers, having instead a delicate semi-transparent skin through which sufficient dissolved oxygen for purposes of respiration can pass. The skin, through which the internal anatomy can be seen vaguely, is slippery, but is armed with numerous white particles, the calcareous anchors that stiffen the body and enable the animal to get better purchase in burrowing. The anchors often come off on one's fingers. Although it lacks the tube feet that are characteristic of most of the other cucumbers and of echinoderms in general, this remarkably efficient little worm-like form is at home along temperate shores almost all over the world. When disturbed it has the habit, also worm-like, of autotomizing by constricting itself into several portions—a trait that makes it difficult to collect and almost impossible to keep in aquaria. It is not known whether all the portions so autotomized will regenerate into new animals, or only the head portion.

Under feeding conditions, that is, when the tide is in, the animal lies fairly well buried but close enough to the surface to protrude its 10 or 12 feathery tentacles, which capture small living animals, minute floating plants, and probably other bits of organic matter, and then transfer the food to the mouth.

Here on the Pacific coast this species is rarely more than an inch or two in length, but the same species is known from other parts of the world up to 10″ long, and a related form of southeastern Alaska, mostly from quiet water, may be 6″ long or more (*Chiridota*, §245).

§56. The brittle star, *Amphiodia* (§44), is possibly more common buried in the substratum than on the under side of rocks, but it is certainly not so easy to see. In little pockets under rocks, where the bottom is soft and oozy but with coarse particles, one may sometimes sift out with the fingers a dozen or more of these snaky, long-armed specimens.

§57. In southern California and northern Mexico the muddy bottom under tide-pool rocks is often riddled with the burrows of a small white crayfish-like animal, the ghost shrimp, *Callianassa affinis* (Pl. IX). A large specimen may be 2½″ long. Although not so feeble and delicate as its relatives of the mud flats, *C. affinis* is one of the softest animals found in the tide pools. There it utilizes the protection of rocks and then burrows deeply into the substratum so as to obtain the maximum shelter. The recorded range is from Santa Monica to San Diego, but we have taken specimens (identified by the National Museum) from Todos Santos Bay. Like its larger mud-flat relatives (in connection with which the natural history of the ghost shrimps is discussed in more detail, §292), this *Callianassa* has the crayfish habit of flipping its tail suddenly so as to swim backward in a rapid and disconcerting manner. Ovigerous specimens have been taken in early May.

§58. Associated with the above is the blind goby or pinkfish *Typhlogobius californiensis* (Fig. 20). It lives in the burrows made by the ghost shrimp and is about 2½″ long, somewhat resembling a very stubby eel. Its eyes are rudimentary and apparently functionless.

(e) Pool Habitat. Free-swimming or actively crawling animals not often found outside pools.

§59. A minute red flatworm, *Polychoerus carmelensis,* only slightly longer than it is wide, may be locally so abundant during spring and summer as to dot the Monterey tide pools with color. This form (a turbellarian) is interesting in that it is one of the few free-living flatworms having no intestine and distinctive in the possession of a tail. These animals are hermaphroditic, with cross-fertilization, the male of one animal fertilizing the female of another. (Self-fertilization rarely or never takes place in hermaphroditic animals except possibly by accident.) At Woods Hole, Massachusetts, it has been found that the eggs are deposited at night in transparent, gelatinous capsules. *Polychoerus* is a member of the order Acoela, which are reported to feed on copepods, other flatworms, or diatoms, but little is known of the habits of our local form.

§60. Those who examine tide pools bordered with red algae in the early evening, about the time total darkness sets in, will probably be rewarded with an exhibition of phosphorescence from another flatworm (a rhabdocoele), *Monocelis.* These little dots of light can be seen crawling rapidly along the under side of the air-water film or swimming about at the surface. Certain small annelid worms, likewise luminescent, may be found also under similar circumstances, but they swim about more rapidly, change direction quickly in darting movements, and are generally somewhat larger. Like *Polychoerus, Monocelis* is hermaphroditic, with cross-fertilization. It forms hard-shelled eggs.

§61. During late winter or early spring (in February 1930, at Laguna Beach, for example), but unfortunately not every year, the middle and upper tide pools are temporarily inhabited by hordes of very small crustaceans, *Acanthomysis costata* (Pl. IX), in countless numbers. These mysids, called "opossum shrimps" because the eggs are carried in thoracic pouches, are very transparent and delicate, with a slender body up to ½″ long, enormous eyes, and long delicate legs on the thorax. The thoracic legs have outer branches, or exopodites. A large species is common in beds of eelgrass on the Atlantic coast, where it is well known and famous for its phosphorescence. The Pacific-coast *Acanthomysis* is a different animal, very evidently a truly pelagic, or oceanic, form that just happens to drift inshore occasionally in vast numbers.

§62. Especially at night, the transparent shrimp, *Spirontocaris picta,* pale green, often with red bands, is likely to be seen darting about in the pools or quiescent, until found, in bits of sea lettuce or in rocky crevices. There is such a fairy-like beauty to this ephemeral creature that the newly fledged collector will be certain that he has taken a rare form. The elusive animal is likely to lead him a lively chase, too, for it darts backward in a disconcerting manner by suddenly flexing its tail. When at rest it is difficult to see against the vivid colors of a tide pool. Once captured, the living specimen should be confined in a glass vial not much larger than itself and examined with a hand lens. The beating heart and all the other internal organs can be seen very plainly through the transparent body.

About 95 per cent of the transparent shrimps found in rock pools will be of the species named (*S. picta*), but in getting a specimen for illustration we chanced to capture the very similar *S. paludicola* which is shown in Plate IX. The latter is much more common on mud flats and in eelgrass beds, but it does occur in rock pools, as this experience attests.

In the lower tide pools other species of *Spirontocaris* will be found, not transparent, but all striking, and all having the tail bent under the body in a characteristic manner.

There are no roots or holdfasts in the mid-tide region large enough to support a specific assemblage.

ZONE 4. *Low-tide region: Normally uncovered by "minus" tides only, and extending from 0 to −1.8′ or so at Pacific Grove.*

This is the zone par excellence for the collector. It is here that he finds his most treasured prizes, since the region, bared only by the minus tides, is not often available for examination. In its lower ranges, the region of the outer tide pools is uncovered only a few times each month, sometimes not at all. Many of the middle-horizon animals occur here also, but much of the population consists of animals unable to exist higher up and not so accustomed to the rhythm of the tides. This tremendously crowded environment contributes a greater number of species than the sum of the other tidal levels. Triton is a fruitful deity, and here if anywhere is his shrine. Not only do the waters teem but there is no rock so small but harbors some living thing, usually many, and no single cluster of algae without its inhabitants. Since these creatures live and thrive in an environment that seems utterly strange to us, it is no wonder that we find interesting their ways of feeding, of breathing, of holding on, of insuring the continuity of their kind—their strangely different weapons and methods of attack and escape.

(a) Exposed Rock Habitat.

Of the animals exposed to wave action, sun, and wind on unprotected faces of rocks there are very few, except on open coasts where the surf is high. Almost every square inch in the lower tide-pool area is covered with protecting rockweeds, corallines, or laminarians. The animals found often on bare rocks—purple starfish, mussels, and goose barnacles—are treated in Division II with the fauna of the surf-swept open coast.

§63. Where there are limestone reefs however, a black, tube-building cirratulid worm may colonize—*Dodecaceria fistulicola,* originally described, on account of its appearance in tubed masses, as a sabellid. Compact colonies of these may be found occasionally on the shells of the red abalone (§74).

In the south another bare-rock form will be found, *Chama pellucida* (§126), in some regions amounting practically to a reef builder but achieving its maximum development in quiet waters.

(b) Fauna of protected rock surfaces, wide crevices, the underhang of ledges, rockweed, etc.

A rich and varied population can be seen in such stations in this low zone without disturbing the rocks.

§64. The other horizons exhibit a few characteristic and striking animals that occur in great numbers, but it would be hard to pick out of the lower tide-pool life any highly dominant forms. Perhaps the solitary great green anemone, called *Anthopleura* (or *Bunodactis*) *xanthogrammica* (Pl. X), is the most obvious; certainly it is the form most frequently observed by the layman. This surf-loving animal might have been included as justly with the open-coast fauna, but since it is here in the tide-pool region that the casual observer is likely first to see it the inductive method of this book justifies its treatment here. So far as is known, the huge specimens of *xanthogrammica* that are found in the deep pools and channels are exceeded in size only by the giant anemones of the Australian Barrier Reef, specimens of which have been reported over a foot in diameter* with stinging capacities as great as the stinging nettle. Although our form sometimes attains a diameter of 10″, a bare hand placed in contact with its "petals" will feel a slight tingling sensation only, in addition to a highly disagreeable stickiness. This stickiness is possibly in part a function of suction, such as has been investigated at La Jolla by Parker (1917). In addition to recording a tentacular suction power-

---

* MacGinitie writes, March 12, 1947, "There are some anemones on the little rock island in Carmel Bay that will measure a good 16″ when expanded."

ful enough to enable the animal to capture small fish, Parker finds that a suction of 15.6 pounds per square inch was exhibited by the tubercles in retaining pieces of shell and stone.

Typically a West-coast animal, this magnificent anemone has the enormous range of Unalaska and Sitka to Panama, and it has been the subject of observation and experimentation since Brandt first observed Alaska specimens in 1835. It is a more or less solitary animal, typically of great size and a uniform green in color, and is restricted to the very low tide zone, or lower in areas where surf and currents provide continually a fresh supply of water. Unlike the smaller colonial species which occurs in great beds high in the intertidal zone, *xanthogrammica* cannot survive where there is sewage, industrial polution, or depositing sand. The vivid green color of specimens living in sunlight is produced by symbiotic green algae which live actually in the tissues of the animal in a mutually beneficial arrangement, as mosses and algae live together to form lichens. Hence the paleness of specimens found in caves and other places sheltered from direct sunlight.

In its preference for brilliant light, as in many other physiological traits, this giant green anemone is similar to the colonial species of *Cribrina* (treated in §24, to which the reader is referred for an account of anemones in general), and the one has often been considered to be only a size- and color-phase of the other.

A sea spider, *Pycnogonum stearnsi* (§319), will be found commonly associated with the large green anemone, apparently forming some such relationship as most of the other sea spiders form with the hydroids on which their young live. Nor are sea spiders the only animals appreciative of *Anthopleura's* society. A giant amoeba, *Trichamoeba schaefferi,* which is visible to the naked eye if the specimen is in a strong light and which was described by Radir in 1927, has been taken from about the base of the anemone.

§65. *Tealia felina* is another large beaded anemone, beautifully red in color, usually with green blotches, and up to 4″ in diameter, that may be found only at the most extreme of the low tides. It attaches to rocks, but is often half buried in the sand and gravel and, like *Anthopleura,* has bits of shell and gravel attached to its body wall. *Tealia* (also known as *Urticina*) is common also on the coasts of Europe and, through circumpolar distribution, occurs on the east coast of America as far as Maine, where it is called the thick-petalled rose anemone. Thus we have, as far south as Monterey at least, another cosmopolitan species to keep company with the sponge *Haliclona,* the cucumber *Leptosynapta,* and the flatworm *Polychoerus.*

Other anemones, *Epiactis prolifera* and *Corynactis* (§§37, 40), and the solitary coral *Balanophyllia* (§39) may be found abundantly in this zone.

§66. Starfish are likely to be common and noticeable in this prolific zone. In most well-known regions on the Pacific, *Patiria* (§26) may be larger and more plentiful than in the middle tide-pool region, but an examination of virgin areas indicates that the center of distribution is in the higher zones. Where surf keeps the rocks bare of large algae, *Pisaster* (§157), the common starfish, may occur abundantly also. There are a number of sea stars, however, that are characteristic inhabitants of the low intertidal.

The many-rayed sunflower star, *Pycnopodia helianthoides* (Pl. X), is possibly the largest starfish known, examples having a spread of more than 2′ being not uncommon. Certainly it is the most active of our Pacific asteroids; and while all starfish can and do move, they are scarcely to be classed in general as active animals. Probably they possess the most highly specialized form of locomotion to be found in the intertidal zones. Locomotion is effected, in some debatable manner, by the sensory tube feet, which cling so strongly that many will be broken when a starfish is forcibly removed from a rock. The formerly accepted theory was that the tube feet were swung in the direction of motion, taking hold of the substratum as vacuum cups (the vacuum being created by the animal's highly effective water-vascular system), thereupon the starfish drew itself forward, destroyed the vacuum by readmitting water to the tube feet, and repeated the cycle. Jennings, however, has demonstrated that the animal can walk equally well on a greased surface or on sand, and concludes that the tube feet act very much like the legs of higher animals, since they could not exert an effective suction pull on either grease or sand. He believes that the adhesive action of the tube feet serves ordinarily merely to give the animal a firm foothold, and becomes of primary importance only when the starfish is climbing a steep surface or hanging inverted. It of course serves the additional purpose of holding the animal against wave shock.

Pycnopodia is readily distinguished from all other starfish in this zone by its soft delicate skin, often colored in lively pinks and purples, and the bunches of minute pincers (pedicelleriae) on its upper surface. It also has the greatest number of rays—up to twenty-four. It is often called popularly "the twenty-one pointer," but the number of its rays is apparently dependent on its age, since it starts out in life with only six. Unless carefully supported when lifted from its tide pool, *Pycnopodia* indicates its attitude toward the human race by shedding an arm or two, and persistent ill treatment will leave it in a very dilapidated condition. The range is from Unalaska to Monterey Bay, and less frequently below there to San Diego.

The unique feeding habits of starfish are discussed in the account of *Pisaster* (§157).

§67. A less common multi-rayed starfish, rare in the intertidal of central California but slightly more common to the northward, is the often twelve-armed sunstar, *Solaster dawsoni* (Pl. XI). The number of arms varies, however, from 8 to 15. A similar form, *S. stimpsoni,* usually has ten rays, very slim and uniformly tapering to a point. Both have a less webbed appearance than *Pycnopodia,* having discs smaller in proportion to the size of the animal, and both are found only at or below the extreme low-tide mark. The colors range from purple-gray to orange, and the skin, which is harder than *Pycnopodia*'s and softer than *Pisaster*'s, is rough to the touch. *S. dawsoni,* ranging from the Aleutian Islands to Monterey (at the latter place found in deep water only), is larger than *stimpsoni* (up to 14″) but occurs very rarely inshore, whereas *stimpsoni,* ranging from the Bering Sea to Oregon, is not infrequent in the low intertidal.

§68. Two ovigerous starfish occur in this zone, one, *Leptasterias aequalis,* very commonly. This little six-rayed form, up to 2½″ in spread and hence considerably larger than the delicate *L. pusilla* of the middle pools (Pl. V), is a feature of the low intertidal fauna throughout its range of Puget Sound to Newport Bay. The madreporite, or perforated plate, through which water is admitted to the water-vascular system, is conspicuous, and the rays are slightly swollen at the base, giving this dull pink, green, or olive species a bulky, unwieldy appearance. Eggs are carried from February on, and are discharged as minute starfish in April or May. Incubating females are likely to be humped up over the eggs and to keep fairly well hidden in rock crevices.

§69. *Henricia leviuscula* (Pl. XII), not nearly as common as the above, resembles *Leptasterias* in its usually small size, although 5″ individuals have been seen, but differs in its usual vivid blood-red color. The rays are long and sharply tapering. The females of this species brood their eggs in January, keeping absolutely in the dark, and hence well hidden, during this period. *Henricia* ranges from the Aleutian Islands to Monterey Bay, and is related to an East-coast species (*sanguinolenta*) that is circumpolar in distribution but does not range as far south as Monterey. The definitely outlined but gawky shape and vivid color of this animal make it a form that will stand out in the mind of the collector who finds it.

§70. The leather star, *Dermasterias imbricata* (§211), may be found occasionally in the lowest rock pools of the protected outer coast, but it is far more common in completely sheltered bays and sounds.

§71. Southern California has two characteristic rocky-shore star-fish, both semitropical forms: *Linckia columbiae* (Pl. XI) and *Astrometis*. A symmetrical *Linckia* might be mistaken for *Henricia* were it not for the former's mottled gray and red colors and for the difference in the range. *Linckia,* however, a typical nonconformist, rarely falls into the bourgeois error of remaining symmetrical. This grotesque little species, which may have a spread of 4 inches, is most famous among all starfish for autotomy and variability. Dr. Monks says of them: "In over 400 specimens examined not more than four were symmetrical, and no two were alike . . . . The normal number of rays is five, but some specimens have only one, while others have four, six, seven, or even nine . . . .

"Single living rays without any external sign of disk are not uncommon . . . . I have been fortunate in a series of experiments . . . . . in having a number of single rays, cut at various places, regenerate the disc and other rays . . . ."

Referring to autotomy she says, "The cause of breaking is obscure. . . . . If any external force bears a part in breaking the animal, it is probably that the creature is surprised when limp and relaxed, but I am inclined to think that *Phataria* [*Linckia*] . . . . always breaks itself, no matter what may be the impulse. They may break when conditions are changed, sometimes within a few hours after being placed in jars. . . . . Some never break, but stand all kinds of inconvenience . . . . Whatever may be the stimulus, the animal can and does break of itself. . . . . The ordinary method is for the main portion of the starfish to remain fixed and passive with the tube feet set on the side of the departing ray, and for this ray to walk slowly away at right angles to the body, to change position, twist, and do all the active labor necessary to the breakage . . . . I have found that rays cut at various distances from the disk make disks, mouths and new rays in about six months."

Other anomalies recorded are that the animals may have from one to several mouths; the usual number of madreporites is two, but there may be from one to five; some of the rays may be young, while others are sexually mature; comet forms, in which there is one large ray surmounted by a minute disc with from one to six tiny rays are of common occurrence. Here is poly-vitality (if one is permitted to use such a word) with a vengeance. How the single arm of an animal normally constituted of a disc and five arms, can live, regenerate, and grow must remain as a striking example of the flexibility and persistence of what might have been termed a generation back "vital purpose." In the matter of autotomy also it would seem that in an animal that deliberately pulls itself apart we have the very acme of something. One is tempted to speculate as to the internal stimuli effecting disorganizations so radical.

Linckia columbiae reaches its furthest north extension in the southermost part of our territory, at San Pedro and San Diego, extending thence to the Galapagos Islands.

§72. *Astrometis sertulifera* (Pl. XII), compensating in symmetry for *Linckia's* temperamental ways, still clings to a mild autotomy. Specimens roughly handled reward their collector by making him the custodian of a flexible three- or four-rayed animal. The rich ground color of the slightly slimy skin is brown or green-brown. The spines are purple, orange, or blue, with red tips, and the conspicuous tube feet are white or yellow. This active and noticeable starfish, having an arm spread up to 5 or 6 inches, ranges from Santa Barbara to the Gulf of California, but never occurs in central or northern California.

§73. *Strongylocentrotus franciscanus* (Pl. XII), radiating spines like a porcupine, is the largest sea urchin found in this section, which is fitting in view of the length of its name. This giant brick-red or purple form often has a total diameter exceeding 7 inches. The gonads are considered a delicacy by the Italians, who come from a land where such sea food is highly valued, a smaller urchin being commonly marketed for food at Naples. Both the writers have sampled these gonads, eaten à l'Italienne (raw) with French bread, and found them very good—extremely rich, and possibly more subtle than caviar. If it were not for the fact that the race is already being depleted by the appreciative Italians, urchins could be highly recommended as a table delicacy.

Sea urchins are related, not very distantly, to starfish and brittle stars. Whoever examines the test or shell of an urchin that has been denuded of spines will recognize this relationship in the pentamerous design and in the holes through which the sensory tube feet protrude. Urchins and starfish have three kinds of projecting appendages: spines, tube feet, and pedicellariae. In the urchins the movable spines are the most conspicuous of the three. When an urchin's test or shell is prodded with a sharp instrument, the spines converge toward the point touched so as to offer a strictly mechanical defense. If, however, a blunt instrument be used, the spines turn away from the point of attack in order to give the pedicellariae free play. The heads of these peculiar appendages consist of three jaws, each provided with a poison gland and a sensory organ in the form of a stiff hair. Against the attack of a predatory starfish, for instance, the urchin can maintain a stout defense with its pedicellariae, but if the attack is long-continued the urchin is likely to succumb because of the loss of its weapons, as each pedicellaria is sacrificed after inflicting one wound.

Like the starfish, urchins make auxiliary use of the movable spines, crawling about on their tips by depressing the forward and pushing with the backward spines. Locomotion is relatively slow, the fixed algae (such as sea lettuce) on which the urchin feeds not being famous for their speed of retreat. Movable jaw parts, forming a structure called, from its design, "Aristotle's Lantern," cut the seaweed into portions small enough for ingestion in the huge, coiled intestine.

Urchins reproduce in the manner already related for the starfish *Patiria* (§26), by pouring out eggs and sperm into the water for chance fertilization, the embryonic development by free-swimming stages being very similar also. The sexes are separate, and the extrusion of eggs and sperm has been observed in February and March along the California coast. Like *Patiria,* again, *Strongylocentrotus* has become an important object of embryological research.* The range of the species *franciscanus* is from Alaska to Cedros Island off the coast of Lower California, but it is common only as far south as Laguna. It characteristically inhabits only the deeper pools and the rocky shores extending downward from the low-tide line.

An interesting phase of the digestive tract of *franciscanus* is the almost invariable presence of a small rhabdocoele flatworm, *Syndisyrinx franciscanus*. This commensal or parasitic worm, up to ¼" in length, usually reveals itself by sluggish movements when the intestine of its host is opened. Sometime in the past few thousand years *Syndisyrinx* presumably discovered that food-getting conditions on the inside of urchins were much superior to those on the outside, and forthwith gave up free-living habits permanently.

Often occurring with the giant red urchin, but preferring strongly aerated waters with violent surf (and hence treated in that habitat), is a smaller urchin, *Strongylocentrotus purpuratus* (§174), with a larger number of spines which are vividly purple and closer cropped than those in the bristling panoply of *franciscanus*.

§74. To the Californian who has accustomed himself to steaks from this delicious shellfish the very word "abalone" (the final "e" is pronounced) conjures up a host of associations. Still more vivid memories of foggy dawns will be recalled by the sportsman who has captured the huge, limpet-like snail from the low-tide rocks and reefs. By prohibiting the shipping of even the shells to points outside the

---

* The larval development has been investigated at Puget Sound by Johnson (1930), who finds the metamorphosis similar in form to that of the other urchins and not complete even after 62 days, and who reports sexual maturity in March and April both in Puget Sound and at Monterey.

state, an often wise Fish and Game Commission has decreed that only
California residents and tourists may enjoy this finest of all mollusks.
Even with only local consumption, however, abalones of legal size are
becoming increasingly rare and probably ninety-nine per cent of those
that the casual collector sees will be undersize and therefore protected
by law. Abalones for market are taken by divers in 20 to 50 feet of
water, but the original center of distribution was probably the low
intertidal zone. Even in deep water, divers tell us, the supply has
become greatly depleted. Years ago, when the price was fifty cents
a dozen, it would not have been worth while to bring them in, according to one diver, except for the fact that a man could sit down on a
ledge and, without changing his position, fill his basket from a single
rock. Now a diver must walk along the bottom and, if fortunate, may
fill his basket in half an hour.

Haliotis rufescens, the red abalone (Pl. XII), may grow to be 10
or even 12″ long, but 7″ is the minimum approved by the present law
for sportsmen, and larger specimens are rare near shore. Since their
discovery by human beings with an eye for iridescent colors, the shells
have been valued, and abalone pearls, formed when the animal secretes
a covering of concentric layers of pearly shell over parasites or irritating particles of gravel, have in times past been fashionable in jewelry.
One of the common instigators of abalone pearls is a relative of the
Teredo, the minute, boring clam, *Pholadidea parva,* which, except for
the great difference in size, looks much like the rock-boring clam
illustrated in Plate XXXIV.

Haliotis occurs most frequently on the under sides of rock ledges,
where it clings, limpet-fashion, by its great muscle foot. If taken
unawares, specimens may be loosened from their support easily; but
once they have taken hold, it requires the leverage of a pinch bar to
dislodge them. Some of this clinging force, according to Crofts, is
probably the result of a vacuum. The copious secretion of mucus on
which the animal "slides" would certainly be an aid in perfecting a
vacuum beneath the foot. Stories of abalones holding people until
the incoming tide drowns them are probably fictitious, but it is nevertheless inadvisable to try to take them by slipping one's fingers under
the shell and giving a sudden pull. We have captured them in this
manner when no bar was available, but there is always danger of a
severe pinch.

Chiefly in connection with commercial fishery legislation, the life
history of the abalone has been carefully investigated. The red abalone, which is the only one that is marketed extensively, reaches the
breeding age at six years, at which time it is about 4″ in diameter.
One specimen known to be thirteen years old was 8″ long. During

her first breeding season a female produces in the neighborhood of 100,000 eggs, but a 7″ specimen will produce nearly 2½ million. Crofts says "the genital products are shot out in successive clouds," the sperm white, and the eggs gray-green. "All five naturally spawning *Haliotis* observed were stationary during spawning, which occurred as the tide commenced to flow, and on a warm sunny day." Spawning takes place between the middle of February and the first of April. The animal's diet is strictly vegetarian. It crawls about slowly in the forests of algae, filling up an enormous gut with such fixed forms as sea lettuce and kelps.

Abalones are known to have occurred as long ago as the Upper Cretaceous Age. They occur now in the Mediterranean and even on the coast of England, but it is only in the Pacific that they attain great size, the centers of distribution being California, Japan, and Australia. The red abalone, distinguished by its great size, the (usually) three or four open and elevated apertures through which water used in the gills is discharged, and by the fact that whole forests of hydroids, bryozoans, and plants frequently grow on its shell, ranges from the San Francisco area to northern Lower California, reaching its greatest development in Monterey County.

When an abalone is to be eaten, its shell is removed, the entrails are cut away, and the huge foot is cut into several steaks about ⅜″ thick. Commercial fish houses pound these steaks with heavy wooden mallets. Amateurs use rolling pins or short pieces of two-by-four. Whatever the instrument, the pounding must be thorough, so as to break up the tough muscle fibers. Preferably the meat should then be kept in a cool place for twenty-four hours before cooking. When properly prepared and cooked, abalone steak can be cut with a fork; otherwise it is scarcely fit to eat.

In similar stations on the outside Alaska coast, as at Sitka, the small and dainty *H. kamtschatkana* (not a close relative of the very large Japanese *H. gigantea*) may be taken sometimes in abundance, since it, like *rufescens*, occurs gregariously. Rarely has it been taken so far south as Monterey. Our specimens from Sitka Sound were up to 4½″ long. The flesh was butterscotch-colored, and the sides were pigmented with deep brown and gray. Steaks of this small abalone are said to require no pounding, but it is probably well to work over any abalone a bit before frying it.

§75. Below Point Conception, and as far south as we have collected along the coast of Lower California, *H. fulgens* (Pl. XII), the smaller green abalone, is the common form. It may be distinguished by its flatter and cleaner shell with its fine corrugations, and by the presence of six open holes, having only slightly elevated rims. Some are taken commercially and we have often seen Mexicans gathering them for their own use.

Still another *Haliotis,* the black abalone (§179), may occur with either of the above, but it prefers vertical crevices in surf-swept regions.

§76. The collector who, from seeing *Tonicella* (§36) and an occasional *Nuttallina,* has become familiar with the chitons for which the Pacific is famous will surprise himself some day by turning up a perfectly enormous sea cradle without any apparent shell, dull brick-red in color. This giant *Cryptochiton stelleri* (Pl. XIII), sometimes called the "gum boot," is the largest chiton in the world, being as much as 13″ long. It is reputed to have been used for food by the coast Indians, and was eaten by the Russian settlers in southeastern Alaska. After one experiment the writers decided to reserve the animals for times of famine; one tough, paper-thin steak was all that could be obtained from a large cryptochiton, and it radiated such a penetrating fishy odor that it was discarded before it reached the frying pan.

Although it is sensitive to light and feeds mostly at night, as do the other chitons, this giant form may remain out in the tide pools and on the rocks all day when there is fog. *Cryptochiton* feeds on fixed algae, rasping its food into small particles, snail fashion, with a large radula, which may be examined by reaching into the mouth with a pair of blunt forceps and drawing out the file-like ribbon.

Chitons, although usually placed in a separate class, are at least closely related to snails. Like snails they have a long flat foot, with the internal organs between it and the shell; but chitons retain the symmetrical double gills, one on each side of the foot, whereas most snails have their anatomy so convoluted and twisted that only one gill remains. The shell consists of eight articulated plates, which allow the animal to curl up almost into a ball when disturbed. In *Cryptochiton,* however, the plates are not visible externally, the fleshy girdle having completely overgrown them. The hard white disarticulated plates of dead specimens are often cast up on the beach as "butterfly shells."

Sometimes in the spring great congregations of *Cryptochiton* gather on rocky beaches, having presumably come in from deep water to spawn. The range is from Alaska westward to Japan and southward to San Nicolas Island off southern California, although specimens are not numerous below Monterey Bay. An account of the breeding habits of a related chiton (*Ischnochiton magdalenensis*) is given in §127.

More than twenty-five per cent of the cryptochitons examined will be found to have a commensal scale worm, *Arctonoë vittata* (Pl. XXVIII), formerly *Halosydna* (*Polynoe*) *lordi,* living on the gills. These worms, with 25 or more pairs of scales, sometimes shed them when disturbed; length may attain 3 or 4 inches; they are pale to light yellow in color. The same worm may be found in the gill groove of the keyhole limpet, *Diodora aspersa* (§181), or even free-living, under stones.

Another guest which may be found clinging to the gills of *Cryptochiton* is the pea crab, *Opisthopus transversus* (Pl. XIII). This tiny crab, likewise never free-living, takes to a variety of homes, for it is found regularly in the California cucumber (see next §), frequently in the mantle cavities of the quiet water mussel and the gaper (*Schizothaerus*), occasionally in the giant keyhole limpet (*Megathura*), and even in the siphon tubes of rock-boring clams.

§77. Tourists to Monterey who go out in the glass-bottomed sightseeing boats are often shown "sea slugs," more correctly sea cucumbers. These rather spectacular animals, *Stichopus californicus* (Pl. XIII), are usually subtidal, but will often come to the attention of the shore collector. In the south—from Laguna Beach to Lower California—a similar-looking *Stichopus* occurs, *S. parvimensis,* which is definitely intertidal, living as high as the middle tide pools. The cylindrical, highly contractile bodies of these cucumbers, black, dull brown, or red, are up to 18″ long, and are covered above with elongated warts and below with tube feet with which they attach themselves and crawl. The body shape is variable. The animals may be flaccid when unmolested, but they immediately become stiff and turgid when annoyed—shorter in length and very thick.

In considering the urchins it was pointed out that the non-technical observer must tax his credulity before grasping the fact that urchins are closely related to starfish and brittle stars. Sea cucumbers tax one's credulity still further, for they are related to all three of these, despite their worm-like bodies, their possession of tentacles, and their apparent lack of skeleton. Their pentamerous symmetry is much less obvious than in urchins. It can be seen readily, however, in *Cucumaria miniata* (Pl. XXXIII). The water-vascular system is manifest in the tube feet, which, with worm-like wrigglings of the body wall, serve for locomotion. The tentacles around the mouth are actually modified tube feet. Like other echinoderms (spiny-skins), cucumbers have a calcareous skeleton, but in their case a vestigial one only, of plates and spicules of lime buried in the skin and serving merely to stiffen the body wall.

Stichopus and cucumbers in general have a specialized form of respiration that is unique among the echinoderms. Water is pumped

in and out of the anus, distending two great water lungs, the respiratory trees, that extend almost the full length of the body. As would
be expected, this hollow space, protected from the inclemencies of a
survival-of-the-fittest habitat, attracts smaller animals as commensals
and parasites. The respiratory tree is a regularly cited repository of
certain microscopic, one-celled animals, *Licnophora* and *Boveria,* each
of which clings by means of a ciliated sucking disc at the end of a
posterior fleshy stalk. In aquaria the same pea crab that occurs with
Cryptochiton, Opisthopus transversus, may be found in and about the
posterior end of *Stichopus.* When cucumbers are being relaxed for
preservation, the crab will often leave his heretofore dependable home
in the interior to cling to the outside. A scale worm, *Arctonoë* (formerly *Acholoë, Halosydna,* or *Polynoe) pulchra,* distinguishable by
the fact that the scales have dark centers that are lacking from *A. vittata,*
may often occur with the crab.

In general, cucumbers lie half buried in the soft substratum, passing through the intestinal tract quantities of sand and mud from which
the food is extracted. *Stichopus,* however, is a rock-loving form.
Considering its habitat and the nature of its tentacles, it seems likely
that this cucumber brushes its stumpy appendages along the surface
of the substratum as a related English form is known to do, sweeping
into the mouth minute organisms and bits of debris.

The collector who insists on taking away from the tide pools living
specimens of these animals for subsequent observation is sure to be
provided, if the water gets stale, with first-hand information on the
general subject of evisceration, a cucumber trait which has been
termed "disgusting" by unacclimated collectors. When annoyed,
Stichopus spews out its internal anatomy in a kind of autotomy. The
organs thus lost are regenerated if the animal is put back into the
ocean. In the usual evisceration the anus is ruptured by the pressure
of water caused by a sudden contraction of body-wall muscles. This
contraction voids first the respiratory trees and subsequently the remainder of the internal organs. In one or two well-known examples
this trait has protective value. An English form is called "the cotton
spinner" from its habit of spewing out tubes which secrete a mucus
so sticky when mixed with sea water that it entangles predatory animals as large as lobsters to the point where they are helpless.

The sexes are separate. As with many other marine animals, hosts
of ova and sperm are discharged into the water, fertilization being
pretty much a matter of chance. Courtney has shown that in Puget
Sound spawning takes place in late July and August, and that the
animals come into shallow water to spawn, or at least that their migration into shallow water is coincident with the ripening of the sexual

products. Conversely, however, it was found that temperatures of 14° C. (about 59° F.) or above—temperatures often encountered in Puget Sound shallow water—mean death to the animals. The safe temperature for developing eggs is only 10° C.—a temperature to be found only where there is oceanic water with strong currents.

Stichopus californicus and its related species have a wide distribution on the Pacific coast, ranging down into Mexico.

Visitors to San Francisco's Chinatown (and probably visitors to other American Chinatowns) have seen *Stichopus* and a similar cucumber in the food shops. The body wall, first boiled and then dried, is a greatly relished delicacy. On the coast of Australia the production of this "trepang" or "bêche-de-mer" is an important fisheries industry. The very cheapest grades of trepang are sold by Chinese merchants in this country at upward of a dollar a pound. It has the reputation, along with ginseng and bird's-nest soup, of being an efficient aphrodisiac.

§78. In rocky clefts and tide pools where currents of pure water sweep by, delicate sprays of hydroids will be found, often in conspicuous abundance. Until their peculiarities are pointed out to him, the uninitiated collector is quite likely to consider them seaweeds, for only on very close inspection, preferably with a microscope, does their animal nature become apparent. They may occur, like *Eudendrium californicum,* in great bushy colonies, sometimes 6″ tall, or, like *Eucopella everta* and various species of *Halecium* and *Campanularia,* as solitary animals about 1/16″ high, forming a fuzz about the stems of larger hydroids.

Whether large or small, the hydroids are likely to be first noticed for their delicate beauty and often exquisite design. Few things in the exotic tide-pool regions will bring forth more ecstatic "Oh's" and "Ah's" when first examined than these hydroids, and one cannot but wonder why their fragile patterns have never been used as the motif for conventional designs. *Plumularia setacea* (Fig. 21), one of the plume hydroids, is possibly the most delicate of all intertidal animals. Under water, and against many backgrounds, it positively cannot be seen, so perfect is the glassy consistency of the living specimen. This is all the more remarkable when it is remembered that there is a covering of skeletal material over the stems and over the bud-like individual animals or hydranths. When removed from the water, or seen against certain backgrounds, the tiny sprays, ½″ or so long, are plainly visible and well worth examination.*

* *P. setacea* extends from Vancouver Island to California. In the north, the larger and more robust *P. lagenifera,* which occurs sparsely on the central California coast, largely replaces *setacea,* until north of Vancouver Island, and clear up at least to Sitka, it becomes the commonest plume hydroid.

In their alternation of generation, hydroids have a rather startling life history. It is a grotesque business, as bewildering to the average man as if he were asked to believe that rosebushes give birth to hummingbirds, and that the hummingbirds' progeny become rosebushes again. The plant-like hydroid which the shore collector sees gives rise by budding to male and female jellyfish, whose united sexual products develop into free-swimming larvae, the planulae, which attach and become hydroids, like their grandparents. The life cycle, then, is hydroid-jellyfish-larva-hydroid.

Unfortunately for the efficiency of this account, few or none of the rocky tide-pool hydroids of the open coast produce free-swimming jellyfish. The reason is apparent. A jellyfish budded-off from a rock-pool hydroid would begin its independent life in such a dangerous neighborhood that its chances of survival would be almost nil as compared to its chances of being dashed against the rocks and destroyed. Accordingly the jellyfish generation, among the rock-pool species, is usually passed in sac-like gonangia distributed about the hydroid stem. In some cases, as with the sertularians and the plumularians, the gonangia have degenerated into little more than testes and ovaries, but the medusae of *Tubularia marina,* although attached, actually have tentacles and look like the tiny jellyfish that they are. Species like *Obelia* (§316), which inhabit more protected waters or the pilings of wharves, commonly have a conspicuous, free-swimming jellyfish generation. It should be mentioned that not all jellyfish are born of hydroids. All of the hydromedusae come from hydroids, however, and most of the scyphomedusae, or large jellyfish, are budded from a stalked, attached, vase-like animal (the scyphistoma), although some reproduce themselves in the more usual manner.

Hydroids are interesting for a third reason—because they provide a protective forest for many other small animals, some of them, like the skeleton shrimp, absurd beyond belief. These dependents will be mentioned in detail later.

With the aid of the accompanying photographs and drawings the collector should be able to identify the hydroids listed in the following paragraphs. These are, we believe, the commonest forms, but there are innumerable others, and an attempt to list them would only lead us into confusion worse confounded.

§79. *Eudendrium californicum* (Pl. XIII), mentioned above, is one of the most conspicuous of the hydroids, its bushy colonies being sometimes 6″ tall. The brown and slender but hard stem by which the spirally branching colony attaches to the rock is stiff and surprisingly strong, and the roots are very firmly attached. The zooids—the individual animals in the composite group—look like bits of pink cotton on some lovely sea plant. The minute white tentacles surmounting them can be seen readily if the colony is held to the light in a jar of sea water. They retract slowly if touched, lacking the protective hydranth cups (thecae) into which so many of the hydroids snap back their tentacles.

Hydroids belong in the same great group with jellyfish, anemones, and corals, all characterized by the lack of a specialized digestive tract, food simply being dumped indiscriminately into the body cavity where it is digested. The stem must be regarded as part of the colony, since through it runs part of the system of minute tubes which connects with all the zooids, or individual animals, and serves for the transmission of dissolved food. A good-sized cluster of *Eudendrium* may have thousands of living zooids, all with tentacles outstretched for the capture of passers-by smaller than themselves. The prey is stung by the nettling cells and carried into the body cavity through the central mouth. During the winter this hydroid bears fixed jellyfish in the form of orange (female) and green-centered pink (male) gonophores. The female gonangia, borne at the base of the cup-like hydranths, may be so turgid and may invest the zooid so completely as to hide all but the tips of the tentacles.

Except on very low spring tides, colonies of *Eudendrium* are rarely exposed. They occur, even in regions of high surf, from Sitka to San Diego.

§80. *Tubularia marina,* differing from its common and clustered brother, *T. crocea* of boat bottoms and wharf pilings, is strictly solitary. Individuals may be spaced evenly a few inches apart in rocky crevices or under ledges. The stem, usually not more than an inch long, bears a relatively large but dainty hydranth, often vividly orange. The medusoids are red, with pink centers, and have two very noticeable long tentacles. Specimens that were sexually mature, that is, with sessile medusae present, have been taken at Pacific Grove early in February. The range is from Trinidad (near Eureka) to Pacific Grove.

§81. The hydroid *Garveia annulata* (Fig. 22), sometimes 2″ high, with 20 or 30 zooids similar in size and appearance to those of *Eudendrium,* is recognizable by its brilliant and uniform color—orange —root, stem, and hydranth, but with lighter tentacles. The colonies are likely to be seen at their best during the winter and spring months, when they commonly appear growing through or on a sponge. They also grow on coralline algae or at the base of other hydroids, and they themselves are likely to be overgrown with still other hydroids. The range is from Alaska to southern California.

§82. *Hydractinia milleri* (Fig. 23), occurring in pink fuzzy masses on the sides of rocks, is interesting because it illustrates one of the most primitive divisions of labor—nutrition, defense, and reproduction being carried on by specialized zooids. It is known from the outside coast of Vancouver Island and it ranges at least as far south as Carmel.

§83. The hydroids considered above are characterized by naked hydranths (or nutritive zooids). Those that follow have hydranths housed in tough skeletal cups (the thecae), and most of them withdraw their tentacles into these protective cups very rapidly at the slightest sign of danger. The fern-like colonies of *Abietinaria anguina* (Fig. 24) have the skeletal cups well developed, and the obvious skeleton is all that one ordinarily sees. During the winter or spring months one of the cleancut sprays should be placed in a dish of sea water, left unmolested for a few minutes, and then observed. The transparent zooids will be seen fairly popped out of the hard cups, forming a total pattern that is amazingly beautiful. At other times the dead branches will be furred with other smaller hydroids, and with the suctorian protozoan, *Ephelota gemmipara,* and covered with brown particles—diatoms.

With a smaller, undetermined relative, possibly the *A. amphora* also reported from the outer shores of Vancouver Island, *anguina* sometimes carpets the under sides of ledges or loosely imbedded rocks. The bushy-colonied *greenei* (Fig. 25), another of the numerous Pacific intertidal species of *Abietinaria,* will be taken for a totally different animal. The various species range well up the coast and south to San Diego, *anguina* and *greenei* being fairly well restricted to oceanic waters.

§84. The Pacific coast is famous for its ostrich-plume hydroids of the genus *Aglaophenia.* Giant specimens (*A. struthionides*) are more common in violently surf-swept clefts of rock (§173) or in deep water, but they may be found here also. In the habitat considered here, however, occur at least two species so similar in appearance that only the larger form is illustrated. They are *A. inconspicua,* occurring as one-inch bristling plumes foxtailing over eelgrass or corallines or at the base of larger species of the same genus, and *A. latirostris* (Pl. XIV), a clustered form with dainty dark brown plumes as long as 3 inches. The latter, surprisingly enough, was originally described from Brazil, but has since been recorded from Puget Sound, while the former is restricted to central and southern California.

§85. Several other skeletal-cupped forms, all beautiful, turn up very frequently in the lower tide pools. *Eucopella caliculata* (formerly *Orthopyxis*) (Fig. 26) forms a creeping network on the "stems" and fronds of algae that grow just at or below the extreme low-tide line. This network and the stalked solitary zooids that arise from it are opaque white and easily seen. Even the extended tentacles are visible against the proper background. Authorities disagree as to whether or not *Eucopella* liberates its medusae to a free-swimming life. Certainly, however, conditions of surf in this habitat are such that free-swimming jellyfish would be at a disadvantage at least. Several species of *Eucopella* are widely distributed on the Pacific coast, and *caliculata* is almost cosmopolitan in both hemispheres.

§86. *Sertularia furcata* (Pl. XIV) is a small hydroid, known from the outer coast of British Columbia to San Diego, that forms a furry growth on blades of eelgrass and, occasionally, on algae. The related *Sertularella turgida* is one of the most common and widespread hydroids on the coast. It is recorded from many points between Vancouver Island and San Diego, from both the protected outer coast and the fully protected inner coast, and from deep water as well as intertidal. The stout and robust stalks of *turgida* have the zooids, which are swollen to turgidity, arranged alternately on the stem, rather than opposite as in *Sertularia furcata.*

Especially in the north, the coppinia masses (compact fuzzy encrustations of gonangia concentrated about the stems of the hydranths) and the strangely irregular creeping or mildly erect hydroid colonies of *Lafoea* spp. will be seen; these are very characteristic and, once recognized, are not likely to be confused. Unfortunately no illustrations are at hand; possibly the most available figures are in Fraser (1914), Plates 23 and 24. Both species range from Alaska to San Diego, but will be found intertidally only in the north.

§87. The hydrocoral *Allopora porphyra* (Fig. 27) is related to the hydroids, and not to the corals it resembles. Distinct and vividly purple colonies may be found encrusting rocky ledges at very low tide levels where the surf is fairly powerful but where no sediment occurs. In some of the semi-protected regions south of Monterey, *Allopora* colonies cover many square feet of continuous rock surface. Deep-water colonies of similar forms, on the Pacific coast and elsewhere, form huge erect masses, bristling with branches and the sharp points of the colorful lime skeleton. In the Caribbean they make up some of the "coral" reefs.

Many hydrocorals expand only at night, but our California shore form is even more conservative—it never expands at all. Occasionally, however, one gets a glimpse of a white polyp down in the tiny craters that protect the feeding zooids.

§88. As would be expected in a haunt so prolific as the lower tide-pool zone, the shelter of these hydroid forests attracts a great many smaller animals, both sessile and active. It is difficult to draw the line in this work, and say at just what point animals become too inconspicuous to be considered, for in the tidelands it is almost literally true that

> Great fleas have little fleas
> Upon their backs to bite 'em,
> And little fleas have lesser fleas,
> And so *ad infinitum.*

A hydroid colony no bigger than can be contained in one's cupped hands may be almost a whole universe all to itself—a complete unit of life with possibly dozens of units in one tide pool, each little universe including amphipods, isopods, sea spiders (grotesque and impossible "poor relations" of the crustacea and not spiders at all except in appearance), roundworms, other hydroids, bryozoa, and attached protozoa, with a possible number of individuals that is almost uncountable. While all of these animals are at least visible to the naked eye, and are abundant, characteristic, and certainly not lacking in interest, they are minute—too small to be seen in detail without a hand lens or microscope—and hence cannot be included in this handbook. It is impossible, however, to pass over some of the larger of these fantastic creatures without more detailed mention.

§89. Caprellids, amphipods very aptly known as skeleton shrimps, may be present in such multitudes as to transform a hydroid colony into a writhing mass, and the tyro will insist that it is the hydroids themselves that do the wiggling, so perfect is the resemblance between the thin gangly crustacea and the stems they inhabit. If caprellids were a few feet tall instead of, as in the case of the relatively gigantic *Caprella kennerlyi* (Fig. 28), around an inch, no zoo would be without them, and their quarters would surpass those of the monkeys in popularity. Specimens seen under a hand lens seem actually to be bowing slowly, with ceremonial dignity; clasping their palm-like claws they strike an attitude of prayer. Often they sway from side to side without any apparent reason, attached to the hydroid stem by the clinging hooks that terminate the body, scraping off diatoms and bits of debris, or possibly eating the living zooids of the host. As a counterbalance to the animal's preposterous appearance, it evidences great maternal solicitude; the female carries her eggs and larvae in a brood pouch on her thorax. This prettily pink-banded amphipod, most commonly found in *Abietinaria* colonies, ranges from Alaska to southern California. A number of smaller species, e.g., *Caprella equilibra* and several now incorrectly grouped in the species, *C. "acutifrons,"* will be found in *Aglaophenia* and elsewhere.

Caprellids can, when they wish, climb rather actively about on the branches of their hydroid homes in a manner suggestive of measuring worms. They take hold with their front appendages and, releasing the hold of their hind legs, bend the body into a loop, moving the clinging hind legs forward for a new hold. The body is extended forward again and the motion repeated until the desired destination is reached.

§90. Among the sea spiders, the pycnogonids, the male carries the eggs, a pair of his legs being modified for that purpose. Sometimes the thin-bodied, gangly-legged animal will be seen weighted down with a white mass of eggs that must be as heavy as he is. The bodies of sea spiders are not large enough to contain all of the internal anatomy, so that, as with the starfish, the stomach extends into the legs. Few large clusters of *Aglaophenia latirostris* are without these weird creatures, and usually the comparatively large *Lecythorhynchus marginatus* (Fig. 29), with a leg spread up to ¾", is the most conspicuous species. It is well disguised by its color—amber, with darker bands on the legs—and by its sluggish habits, so that often specimens may not be seen until the hydroids on which they live are placed in a tray and carefully examined. One of the larval stages, not even faintly resembling the adult (if the life history of this form resembles that of similar types that have been investigated), lives actually within the hydroid, entering by means of sharply pointed appendages and feeding on the body juices of the host. The recurved hooks that terminate the legs make the sea spiders admirably adapted to crawling about on vegetation and hydroids. *L. marginatus* has been reported from the vicinity of Vladivostok on Zostera, and occurs on the California coast southward to Cedros Island. It is found on sponges and similar encrusting growths in sheltered niches.

Another much smaller sea spider occurs on *Aglaophenia, Tanystylum intermedium*. It is rounder and more symmetrical than its larger fellow lodger, and its legs are banded with white instead of light yellow, in a color pattern that matches its host and which effectively conceals it.

A. latirostris is for some reason a very suitable pycnogonid habitat, and most of the sea spiders mentioned herein have been collected at one time or another on this hydroid. Particularly common along the California coast during some years (possibly alternating in abundance with *L. marginatus,* according to Hedgpeth) is the thin and gangly *Phoxichilidium femoratum,* reminiscent of the *Anoplodactylus* (§333) taken with *Tubularia* and *Corymorpha. P. femoratum* is known to range from Dutch Harbor, Alaska, to Laguna Beach.

§91. Sponges of many kinds are features of the low intertidal landscape. Simpler by far in organization than any of the hydroids and near the bottom of the scale in the animal kingdom, some of the sponges seem to be more or less loose aggregations of one-celled animals—colonies of protozoa, one might say—banded together for mutual advantages. This loose organization has been the subject of recent experiments with West Indies sponges. Bits of carefully dissociated tissue were strained through silk mesh and allowed to stand in dishes of sea water under proper conditions. In a few days the separated pieces were found to have united to form new individuals. Different-colored species of sponges have united in this manner to form a mosaic colony.

While the sponges have no mouth, stomach, or other specialized internal organs, they do have flagella, or lashing "tails," which induce a continual current of water through the colony, bringing in food particles and expelling waste products. The incoming, food-bearing current passes through innumerable fine pores, and the outgoing, waste-bearing current through characteristic crater-like vents (oscula). The observer who would see for himself the currents of water that mark these plant-like encrustations as animals, may do so by transferring one of the large-pored sponges from its tide pool to a clean dish containing fresh sea water and adding a little carmine to the water.

Notwithstanding the ease of making this simple experiment, there has long been a popular belief that sponges are plants. English observers once supposed, the *Cambridge Natural History* notes, that sponge colonies were the homes of worms which built them as wasps build nests and as mud wasps build crater-like holes. The sharp-eyed and sharper-witted Ellis disproved this theory when he stated, in 1765, that sponges must be alive, since they sucked in and threw out currents of water. It is pleasant to note that the mighty intellect of Aristotle, far on the other side of the foggy Middle Ages, knew them for animals.

A modern investigator, Parker, remarks that in the vicinity of large tropical sponges, as at Bermuda, the "water often wells up so abundantly from the sponges as to deform the surface of the sea much as a vigorous spring deforms that of a pool into which it issues." Laboratory tests indicate that a single such sponge colony, with a score of "fingers," will circulate more than 400 gallons of water in a day.

Reproduction is at least sometimes by eggs and sperm, the latter being liberated into the water. Again it may be asexual. In any case, free-swimming larvae emerge from the oscula of the parent and swim away by numerous flagella on the *outside* of the body. When these larvae attach to rocks, the cells move about among each other, which eventually results in those with cilia being on the *inside* of the animal, where they serve the purpose, already mentioned, of creating currents of water.

§92. The giant *Spheciospongia confoederata* is related to a West Indies sponge which is the largest in the world. The Pacific intertidal form occurs at the lowest tidal level in great, slaty clusters on which several people could be seated. On close inspection they are recognizable as sponges by the presence of numerous pores and oscula, the openings of canals by which the circulation of water for respiration and food is maintained. At a distance of a few feet, however, there is nothing to distinguish them from a hundred boulders that may be scattered about in the same acre of tide flat. *Spheciospongia* is known from Monterey Bay, and we have seen a similar or identical form along the shore in northern Lower California.

§93. Masses of the cream-colored *Leucosolenia eleanor* (Pl. XIV), one of the most primitive of sponges, are common at the lowest intertidal horizon in crevices and at the bases of rocks. A similar "antler sponge" has been observed, at Plymouth, England, to attain its complete growth as a massive cluster, several inches in diameter, in six or eight months. Growth of the Pacific species seems to start in the spring with delicate colonies of branching tubes which, late in the fall, have become clusters of rank, connecting growth; hence it is presumed to be an annual here also. It is common in Monterey Bay, and a similar species occurs in Puget Sound (§229).

§94. The urn-shaped *Rhabdodermella nuttingi* (Pl. XIV) may be found growing suspended in crevices and under ledges at the extreme low-tide mark, where it is seldom exposed to the air. Large individuals, creamy white in color, may reach a length of two inches. Visitors from other regions commonly take this form to be *Grantia,* a simple sponge which it closely resembles but to which it is not intimately related. Like *Leucosolenia,* the *Grantia* at Plymouth, England, is known to become adult in from six to eight months. At Pacific Grove large specimens of *Rhabdodermella* have been taken at all times of the year, so it is supposed that they have no regular growing season.

§95. *Leuconia (Leucandra) heathi* (Pl. XIV), a very sharp-spined, cream-colored sponge with a large central volcano-like osculum, occurs typically as a dome-shaped individual but accommodates its shape to that of the crevice it occupies. The average size is small, but large specimens may be several inches in diameter. The large osculum is fringed with spines longer than those which bristle formidably over the rest of the body, and constitutes a centralized excurrent pore. The dangerous-looking spicules are calcareous, however, and so crumble easily—quite the opposite of the really dangerous silicious spicules of *Stelletta* (§96).

§96. It is amusing to note the controversies centering about sponges a few hundred years ago while their structure was still imperfectly known. The herbalist Gerard wrote in 1636: "There is found growing upon the rocks neer unto the sea, a certaine matter wrought togither, of the forme [foam] or froth of the sea, which we call spunges . . . . whereof to write at large woulde greatly increase our volume, and little profite the Reader." The tactful Gerard might have been describing some of our white sponges. Possibly the most obvious of these are species of *Stelletta,* a felt-like, stinging sponge that encrusts the sides of low-tide caves. Certainly this form is the most obvious to the collector who handles it carelessly and spends the rest of the day extracting the spicules from his hands with a pair of fine forceps. The spicules are glassy and have about the same effect on one's fingers as so much finely splintered glass. There are other white sponges, most of them smooth and harmless, but any uniformly white sponge with bristling spicules had best be pried from its support with knife and forceps. On one of the harmless varieties a small white nudibranch may be found, *Aegires albopunctatus,* matching the color of its home just as the red *Rostanga* matches its red sponge.

§97. A good many other sponges occur in the low rocky intertidal, but to consider them in detail would defeat the purpose of this work. Several others, however, must be mentioned.

Lissodendoryx noxiosa, a strong and foul-smelling cluster, up to 8 cm. thick and 15 cm. in diameter, has a lumpy yellow surface like a dried bath sponge, and is malodorously familiar to all prowlers in the Monterey Bay tide pools. Broken open, the interior is found to be semi-cavernous and to harbor hosts of symbionts, nematodes, annelids, and amphipods. This is one of the few sponges which may be found actually in contact with the substratum, on the under sides of rocks.

The famous and cosmopolitan "crumb of bread" sponge, *Halichondria panicea,* may also occur spottily up and down the coast; the University of California zoölogists report it commonly in their findings. Encrustations are orange to green, amorphous, up to 6 mm. thick and 3 cm. in diameter, of fragile consistency, and with the oscula raised 1 mm. above the superficially smooth to tuberculate surface.

Purple colonies of *Haliclona* (§31) occasionally extend into the low-tide zone from the middle tide pools, but these are rare compared to the red sponges. *Plocamia* and *Ophlitaspongia* (§32) and other red encrusting forms are often common here, splashing the sides of rocks with delightful bits of color, some species finding their optimum in this zone. See also §140, under-rock forms, in this connection. Near relatives of the familiar bath sponges are represented here only by small and rare specimens; these grow luxuriantly only in warm to tropic waters, their habitat being correlated in some little-understood way with their food supply.

§98. Under overhanging ledges in the La Jolla–Laguna region, and on the sides of rocks in the completely sheltered Newport Bay, occur clusters of the coarse-textured yellow sponge, *Verongia thiona,* known as the sulphur sponge. It is shown in Plate VIII growing pretty well up in the tide pools, with the tubed snail, *Aletes.* Clusters that fit one's cupped hands have from two to four raised oscula. This animal turns purple or black after being removed from the water, even if immediately preserved. This trait distinguishes it from *Hymeniacidon* (§183), another sponge occasionally abundant in the same habitat and similar superficially, although very different internally.

Living on *Verongia* clusters is another animal, actually related to the sea hares but more nearly resembling a soft-shelled limpet. This little-known creature, *Tylodina fungina* (Fig. 30), is colored the same yellow as the sponge—another of the many examples of apparent protective coloration. Such examples ought never to be accepted without reservations, for very often animals which are "protectively colored" in one environment may turn up commonly in other habitats where their coloring makes them conspicuous.

§99. Encrusting colonies of compound tunicates can be distinguished from sponges by their texture. Most sponge colonies, even the soft ones, have a gritty feeling, due to the presence of lime or glass spicules. Most tunicates are slippery to the touch. Colonies of compound tunicates, *Amaroucium californicum* and similar species, which encrust the sides of rocks in yellows, reds, and browns, are actually the degenerate adults of free-swimming "tadpole larvae" which have a bit of notochord, the structure around which the backbone of the vertebrates is formed. These tunicate colonies are a shining example of the error of judging the position of an animal in the evolutionary scale by its external appearance, since, belonging to the group that contains the vertebrates—most specialized of all animals—they most nearly resemble sponges, one of the lowest and least specialized groups.

A number of species occur, and they are difficult to differentiate, or at least they have been for us. Through the kindness of Dr. Berrill of McGill University, we have some of them—the commonest—cleared up to our own satisfaction. The following notes, based on Dr. Berrill's identifications, may serve as field characters to differentiate these often side-by-side colonies, among the commonest sessile forms of the outer coast.

Amaroucium californicum comprises amorphous but usually sheet-like masses, with a gelatinous light-colored (creamy, yellow, or pink) cover through which the long, pin-headed, white zooids may be seen. The colony is exceedingly soft, almost mushy. The base may be sandy, but the surface is smooth to the point of slipperiness and gives a feeling of flabbiness. This is one of the commonest tunicates of the region.

Eudistoma psammion is the compact, sand-covered, very dark, hard, and firm-textured form, with zooids often raised slightly above the surface. It grows in great and coherent sheets which may be an inch thick. It is probably the commonest Monterey Bay compound tunicate, especially in such regions as the cave area near Santa Cruz, where great beds carpet the ledges within the cave.

E. diaphanes more nearly resembles *Amaroucium* except that the whole colony is much firmer, both in texture and on the surface. Whereas *Amaroucium* cannot easily be pried away unbroken from its support, sheets of *E. diaphanes* can be pulled off without breaking. The test is more opaque, and whiter, with a blue rather than the red tinge of *A. californicum;* the surface is hard, and the zooids are more closely packed together and less noticeable. Colonies may be thin or (usually) thick sheets, or pedunculated. A cross-section shows cave-like areas, with the rest stiff and springy.

Distaplia occidentalis forms mushroom-like, flat, or pedunculated colonies, which show stratification in that the closely packed zooids loom up more clearly at the top of the colony, forming (in cross-section) a superficial layer of differentiated tissue concentrated at the top surface. The richly brown zooids are arranged in rosettes around a common, raised, excurrent pore like a crater.

§100. The peculiar habits of the almost sessile amphipod, *Polycheria osborni* (Fig. 31), living in *Amaroucium* colonies, have been described recently by Skogsberg and Vansell. *Polycheria* will usually be found in its burrow, but, whether swimming, walking awkwardly, or lying in its burrow, it always stays on its back. Females only have been observed, and they are about $\frac{3}{16}''$ long. Nothing but *Amaroucium* will satisfy them for a home. When placed for observation in an aquarium lacking it, they hunt it until they die, apparently from exhaustion. Finding it, they burrow in by grasping the surface of the tunicate and slowly pressing their backs into it. Once satisfactorily settled, *Polycheria* lies there, with antennae protruding, and waits for the currents to bring its food. Its utmost exertion consists in creating currents with its legs and in bending its antennae down occasionally to scrape off and eat their accumulation of diatoms and other food particles. This mode of life is reminiscent of that permanently adopted by the barnacles. When danger impends, the animal draws the edges of its burrow together with its legs, leaving the burrow only when temperature or water conditions become unfavorable.

The female carries her eggs (as many as 70 to 80) and young in a brood pouch throughout the summer, forcing the young out a few at a time, although they cling tenaciously to her hairs. The young, already moving on their backs, immediately begin to search for a lodging place, preferring for their first burrow a slight depression in the surface of the tunicate.

Polycheria was first reported from Puget Sound, but it is fairly common in Monterey Bay also and a careful search will probably reveal it elsewhere, in the intermediate area at least.

§101. A solitary stalked tunicate, *Styela montereyensis,* may be found in this zone, in crevices or on the protected sides of rocks exposed to fairly heavy surf, but more and larger specimens are features of the wharf-piling fauna (§322).* Other obvious solitary and semi-colonial tunicates are characteristic of the lower rocky tide pools, notably great colonies of the club-shaped zooids of *Clavelina huntsmani* (Fig. 32). The individuals are ½″ to 1½″ long, closely connected to one another at the base only. The covering, or tunic, is transparent and never heavily encrusted with sand, so that the pink internal organs can be seen plainly. In adaptation to their sessile lives, tunicates have incurrent and excurrent siphons not unlike those of clams, and in *Clavelina* these siphons are fairly visible, although they do not protrude from the tunic as happens with *Cnemidocarpa* (§216) of the Puget Sound region. *Clavelina* is apparently an annual, as fresh sparkling colonies are found during the summer, which later in the fall become dirty and degenerate, finally disappearing completely in the late fall. Although it is tremendously abundant at Monterey Bay, where next to *Amaroucium* it is the most common tunicate, we have not seen it elsewhere on the California coast.

§102. Like the above, but with longer, slimmer individuals that are more loosely adherent in the completely sand-covered colony, is the semi-compound *Euherdmania claviformis* (Fig. 33). We have found this tunicate to be very plentiful in the sea caves west of Santa Cruz, and it is common at La Jolla. The dull-green zooids of *Euherdmania* are useful for embryological work, since the long oviduct is swollen during the summer with a series of embryos progressing in size from the free end of the parent to the attached end.

§103. A tunicate not uncommon especially south of Point Conception is the stalked *Polyclinum* (formerly *Glossophorum*) *planum*

* The large *Halocynthia johnsoni* will occur occasionally in such situations south of Point Conception, but it seems to be more highly developed in sheltered bay waters, and will be considered in §216.

(Fig. 34). This consists of a definite, usually somewhat flattened, bulb some 2″ or 3″ long by two-thirds as wide, mounted on a thick stalk or peduncle. The zooids give the bulbous colony a flowery wall-paper effect.

As was the case with hydroids and sponges, many more species of tunicates are likely to be turned up in the lower tide pools than can profitably be treated here. At the risk of being misunderstood we might quote the excellent Gerard and say, "whereof to write at large woulde greatly increase our volume, and little profite the Reader." Another semi-compound tunicate, *Perophora annectens,* must be con-sidered, however, because it illustrates a still more adherent stage in the evolutionary series from the simple, completely separated indi-viduals, such as *Styela,* to the completely colonial *Amaroucium.* The dull-green matrix of the colony is closely adherent to the rocks. When the animal is seen unmolested, the bright orange zooids will be well extended, but it has powers of retraction most amazing for a tunicate. If disturbed, *Perophora* pulls its delicate zooids away from danger, withdrawing them into the tough tunic of the matrix and thus almost instantly changing the color of the whole colony. The covering of the extended zooids is more transparent even than that of *Clavelina,* and through a good hand lens the internal anatomy is quite apparent. *Perophora* ranges from British Columbia to San Diego.

§104. The sea hare, *Tethys californica* (Fig. 35), occurs in vari-ous environments—on completely sheltered mud flats and on fairly exposed rocky shores. It occurs below the low-tide line and is also a common feature of the intertidal zone almost up to the upper pools. We have found great numbers of small specimens with the under-rock fauna in northern Lower California in February, and hosts of me-dium-sized specimens—about 5″ long—at Laguna Beach in May. These tectibranch (covered-gill) mollusks belong most characteristi-cally, however, in the low rocky intertidal, where possibly throughout the year at Pacific Grove adults may be found depositing their eggs in yellow stringy masses larger than one's two fists. From a test count of a portion of such a mass MacGinitie estimated that the total number of eggs in the single mass was in the neighborhood of 86,000,000.*

This uniformity of breeding, common among central Pacific coast

---

* MacGinitie (1934) records also a ±5% computation to the effect that a cap-tive sea hare weighing under 6 pounds laid 478 million eggs in less than 5 months. The largest of the 27 layings (totaling 60,565 cm., about ⅓ mile!) amounted to 17,520 cm., at an average rate of 5.9 cm. or 41,000 eggs per minute, each egg averaging 55 microns in diameter (a micron is 1-1000th of a millimeter). The larvae become free-swimming in twelve days, to contribute their mite of food toward appeasing a marine world of hungry, plankton-seeking forms. Presumably few more than the biblical two from one such litter can run the gantlet into adulthood, long before which their flesh will have become distasteful to predacious forms.

invertebrates, is very possibly the result of the even temperature throughout the year—especially likely when it is remembered that on the northern Atlantic coast, where there is great seasonal temperature change, the animals have definite and short reproductive periods.

Tethys is hermaphroditic, having both testes and ovaries and both male and female organs of copulation. It may thus play female during one copulation and male during the next, as its whims happen to dictate, or it may play both roles at the same time. At Elkhorn Slough in the spring of 1931, seven or eight *Tethys* were seen copulating in a "Roman circle," each animal having its penis inserted in the vaginal orifice of the animal ahead. Copulation continues for from several hours to several days.

There are other miscellaneous points of interest. *Tethys* has an internal shell, which it has tremendously outgrown, and a more complicated digestive system than almost any other alga-feeding invertebrate. The food is first cut up by the radula and then passed through a series of three stomachs, the second and third of which are lined with teeth that continue the grinding process begun by the radula. Breathing is assisted by two flaps—extensions of the fleshy mantle—that extend up over the back and are used to create currents of water for the gills, so that the animal may be said to breathe by "flapping its wings." When disturbed, *Tethys* extrudes a fluid comparable to that of the octopus except that it is deep purple instead of sepia. A handkerchief dipped into a diluted solution will be dyed a beautiful purple, but the color rinses out readily. Possibly the addition of lemon juice or some other fixative would make the color fast. The color of the sea hare itself is an inconspicuous olive-green or olive-brown, often with darker blotches. The range does not extend north of Monterey Bay.

§105. Another obvious animal in this zone, with hosts of less obvious relatives, is the large crab, *Cancer antennarius* (Pl. XV), that snaps and bubbles at the collector who disturbs it. The carapace of *antennarius* is rarely more than 5″ wide, but its large claws provide food quite as good from the human point of view as those of its big brother, *C. magister,* the "edible crab" of the Pacific fish markets (which occurs rarely in the intertidal). *C. antennarius* can be identified easily by the red spots on its light undersurface, especially in front.

Here another word anent popular names is necessary, for to many people *antennarius* is known as "the rock crab," whereas the present writers have given that name to the bustling little *Pachygrapsus*. The reason is that the vastly more numerous and obvious *Pachygrapsus* seemed to be in dire need of a non-technical name. It has been called "the striped shore crab," but except in occasional specimens the stripes are not particularly conspicuous. The predominant green color is a more striking characteristic, but the name "green shore crab" designates a European form.

To return to *Cancer antennarius*—female specimens carrying eggs are seen from November to January, with the embryos well advanced by the latter month. The range is from British Columbia to Lower California. *Antennarius* is a rather delicate animal that does not live well in aquaria—a direct corollary of its habitat. It is interesting to contrast it in this respect with the much hardier purple shore crab (*Hemigrapsus*) of the middle zone and with the extremely tough and resistant *Pachygrapsus* of the upper zone. It is an almost invariable rule that the lower down in the tidal area an animal lives, the less resistance it has to unfavorable conditions.

§106. *Cancer productus* (Pl. XVI), related to the above, may be considerably larger and therefore more useful for food, but it is not plentiful enough to be commercially important. Adults are uniformly brick red above. The young exhibit striking color patterns, stripes, as in the accompanying illustration, being common. Like *antennarius, productus* may often be found half buried in the sandy substratum under rocks. At night it stalks about in the tide pools, so large and powerful that it is the Great Mogul of its immediate vicinity unless predatory man happens along. *Productus* is a good example of an animal that is pretty well restricted by its physiological make-up to this rocky habitat, for it lacks equipment for straining fine debris, such as would be encountered on bottoms of mud or pure sand, out of its stream of respiratory water. It ranges from Kodiak to Lower California.

§107. A dark, olive-green, spider crab, *Pugettia producta* (Pl. XV), occurs so frequently on strands of the seaweed *Egregia* and others that it is commonly called the kelp crab. The points on the carapace and the spines on the legs are sharp, the latter adapting the animal to holding to seaweed in the face of wave shock; and the strong claws are rather versatile. The collector who is experienced in the ways of kelp crabs will catch and hold them very cautiously, and the inexperienced collector is likely to find that he has caught a Tartar. Even a little fellow will cling to one's fingers so strongly as to puncture the skin, and a kelp crab large enough to wrap itself about a bare forearm had best be left to follow the normal course of its life.

Most spider crabs are sluggish, and pile their carapaces with bits of sponge, tunicates, and hydroids that effectively hide them; but *Pugettia* is moderately active and keeps its carapace relatively clean. Limited observation on this point suggests that specimens from rocky tide pools are more intolerant of foreign growth than specimens occurring on wharf piling, where the animals are very common. We have examined many wharf-piling crabs that had barnacles and anemones growing on their backs and even on their legs and pincher claws.

Pugettia, which is often parasitized by the degenerate barnacle-like *Sacculina* (§327), is recorded from British Columbia to Lower California, but below Point Conception it is pretty largely replaced by the southern kelp crab, *Taliepus* (formerly *Epialtus*) *nuttallii* (Fig. 36), which ranges from there to Ballenas Bay, Lower California. The carapace of *Taliepus,* also usually fairly clean, is rounder than that of *Pugettia,* and is often purple with blotches of lighter colors.

§108. Our friends, *Hemigrapsus nudus* and *Pagurus hemphilli,* the pugnacious purple shore crab and the retiring hermit, are frequent visitors in the lower tide-pool region, *hemphilli* being the only hermit found this far down, at least in the California area. There are many other crabs, some of which are almost certain to be turned up by the ambitious collector, but they are not sufficiently common to justify their inclusion in this account.

§109. The north Pacific coast is noted for its nudibranchs, for there are probably greater numbers here, of both species and individuals, than in any other several regions combined. Several already have been mentioned, but it is in this lower horizon that these spectacular, brilliantly colored, naked snails come into their own. It would be difficult for any careful observer to visit any good rocky area, especially in central California, without seeing several specimens. Their reds and purples and golds belie their prosaic name, "sea slugs," so often imposed by people who have seen, presumably, only the dead and dingy remains. No animals will retain their color when exposed to the light after preservation, and a colorless, collapsed nudibranch is certainly not an inspiring object. Their appearance "before and after" is one of the strongest arguments against preserving animals unless they are to be used specifically for study or dissection.

Nudibranchs breathe by means of "crepe paper" appendages that are clustered at the rear end, or by delicate nipple-like protuberances that cover the back. Those having centralized gills in a single cluster which may be withdrawn into a circular sheath are the dorids, represented on the Pacific by such striking forms as *Anisodoris, Archidoris,* and *Cadlina. Anisodoris,* the sea lemon, is fairly common in this zone but occurs more frequently on the open coast (§178).* Many

---

* The following notes will help to distinguish them: *Archidoris* is less brilliantly yellow than *Anisodoris,* and has seven branchial plumes, whereas the latter has six, in both much branched, and joined in a circle at the base. The papillae on *Anisodoris* may be circled with black, but are never themselves black, while those on *Archidoris* are black if they occur in a black area.

nudibranchs, the dorids especially, have a penetrating fruity odor that is pleasant when mild but nauseating when concentrated. Undoubtedly this odor has something to do with the fact that nudibranchs seem to be let strictly alone by predatory animals.*

No attempt will be made to note the various species in any detail, but the drawings (Figs. 37–42) and the color notes accompanying them will serve to distinguish the commoner forms.

§110. On the "leaves" and "stems" of outer tide-pool kelps, one finds almost universally an encrusting white tracery delicate enough to be attributable to our childhood friend, Jack Frost. With a hand lens a beauty of design is revealed more intricate than any ever etched on frosty window panes. These encrustations are usually formed by colonies of the bryozoan, or "moss animal," *Membranipora membranacea* (Fig. 74), so named in the middle of the eighteenth century by Linnaeus, the founder of modern classification. There are many other species, *membranacea* being found in temperate regions all over the world and commonly on this coast at least as far south as northern Lower California. The minute, calcareous cells, visible to the keen naked eye but seen to better advantage with a lens, radiate in irregular rows from the center of the colony. The colony may be irregular and sufficient to cover several square inches, or may be fairly small and round. The minute crown of retractile tentacles (not unlike those of hydroids) by which the animals feed can be seen only with a microscope. As is usually the case with sessile animals, these have free-swimming larvae. The larvae were described nearly a hundred years ago as rotifers, later as worm larvae. Robertson mentions finding the larvae of a related species settling on the kelp at La Jolla during July. When a larva comes in contact with a bit of kelp it opens its shell and settles down; the shell flattens over the flattened larva; and the bit of tissue enlarges rapidly to form a colony of several cells which soon reaches naked-eye size. This whole process has been watched and can be watched again by a careful observer with a good lens.

Living on *Membranipora* colonies, and feeding on them, is a recently described species of nudibranch, *Corambe pacifica*. It reaches a maximum length of ½", but is nearly as wide as it is long. Its ground color is a pale translucent gray that makes it almost indistinguishable from its bryozoan background. Its yellowish liver shows through the center of its back, however, and surrounding this area the white of the foot may be seen. The rest of the back, especially toward the margins, is flecked with irregular, sometimes broken, lines of

---

* Such forms as *Hermissenda crassicornis* have nematocysts, presumably acquired secondarily from feeding on hydroids.

yellow. MacFarland and O'Donoghue, who have described the animal in a recent paper, have taken it at Nanaimo, British Columbia,
and in Monterey Bay.

§111. The lower tide pools contain many other bryozoa. Possibly
the most obvious, though certainly not the most common, is *Flustrella
cervicornis* (Fig. 43), reported from the coast of Alaska and from Vancouver and common enough in sheltered areas along the cliffs west of
Santa Cruz. The colonies, which, although encrusting, are soft rather
than calcareous, form great, dull, gray-brown masses over the erect
seaweeds. Their surface is covered by erect horny branching spines
more than ¼″ tall.

§112. Others of the bryozoa are just as certain to be mistaken for
hydroids—the delicate *Tricellaria occidentalis* (Fig. 44) for example,
whose erect branching colonies resemble those of *Obelia*, although the
two belong to entirely unrelated groups. Probably some lusty fore-
father of *Tricellaria* made the happy discovery, back in an age geologi-
cally remote, that the branching habit of growth was successful for
resisting wave shock and providing plenty of area for waving tentacles—a discovery which the hydroids paralleled somewhat earlier.
Sprays of the white *Tricellaria* will often be found in rock crevices, all
the minute tentacle-bearing colonies facing in one direction so that
the "stem" will be curved slightly downward. The range is from the
Queen Charlotte Islands (and probably Alaska) at least to San Diego.

§113. Branching bryozoa of the genus *Bugula* are found all over
the world, and several species occur on the Pacific. A particularly
handsome form is *Bugula californica* (Fig. 45). The colonies are
large and definite, 3″ or more in height, and have a pleasantly fresh
purple tint. The individual branches are arranged in a distinctly spiral
fashion around the axis. This species has heretofore been recorded
from Dillon Beach to Pacific Grove only, but lush growths have been
seen at Fort Ross and will probably be found to the northward, occurring, however, only at the extreme low-tide line.

The aviculariae, the "bird beaks" of *Bugula,* thought to be defen-
sive in function, are classic objects of interest to the invertebrate
zoölogist. It is a pity that these, like so many other structural features
of marine animals, can be seen only with a microscope. If the movable
beaks of aviculariae were a foot or so long, instead of a fraction of a
millimeter, newspaper photographers and reporters would flock to see
them. The snapping process would be observed excitedly, some enterprising cub would certainly have one of his fingers snipped off, and
the *hoi polloi* would amuse themselves by feeding stray puppies into
the pincers. Aviculariae and similar appendages, situated around the
stems that support the tentacled zooids, probably have a function

similar to that of the pedicellariae of urchins and starfish. Whatever else they do, they certainly keep bryozoan stems clean, as anyone will grant who has observed their vicious action under the microscope.*

§114. A more common *Bugula,* occurring along the whole Pacific coast from Bering Sea at least to Monterey Bay, where it is one of the most common bryozoa, is *B. pacifica* (Fig. 46). It is slightly spiral in form and 3″ tall at its best, the largest specimens being found in the northern part of the range. The northern specimens are usually purple or yellowish in color, while those taken at Monterey Bay are light-colored—almost white—and rarely more than an inch high. At the latter place, however, they occur in profusion at a tide level much higher than that chosen by *californica.* Like hydroid colonies, bryozoa of this sort may provide shelter to hosts of different animals, notably skeleton shrimps and beach hoppers. Bits of *B. pacifica* will often be found attached to the sponge *Rhabdodermella* (§94).

§115. In the rocky caves west of Santa Cruz there are rank clusters of endoprocts forming thick-matted colonies on the rocks—*Barentsia ramosa* (Fig. 47)— that have head-like bunches at the end of ½″ to 1″ stalks. The tentacles contract unlike those of any hydroids or other bryozoa herein considered, being pulled in toward the center like the diaphragm of a camera shutter. The similar *Pedicellina cernua* (*echinata*) may also be taken, furring the stems of plants, hydroids, and other bryozoa.

§116. There are a good many small crustacea in this zone, mostly amphipods and isopods. For the most part they look pretty much alike superficially, and there seems to be no need for enumerating them here, for anyone who is interested in their differentiation will already have passed beyond the unpretentious scope of this handbook. Mention should be made, however, of the hosts and myriads of quarter-inch beach hoppers that populate each cluster of the coralline alga, *Amphiroa.* Whoever likes to deal with numbers of astronomical proportions should estimate the number of these amphipods in a handful of corallines, multiply by a factor large enough to account for the specimens present in one particular tide pool, estimate the probable number of such tide pools per mile of coast, and, finally, consider that this association extends for something more than a thousand miles. One who has done this will have great respect, numeri-

---

* Working with a related Atlantic coast form, Grave (1930) found that during the summer and fall breeding season the embryos emerged at dawn, swam about freely for from 4 to 6 hours before attaching, and became half-grown but sexually mature colonies in about one month and senescent in three. Only the young colonies, that is, those produced toward the end of the breeding season, were able to tide over the winter by hibernation, resuming growth in early May.

cally speaking, for the humble amphipod, and will be willing to agree
with Verrill that "these small crustacea are of great importance in
connection with our fisheries, for we have found that they, together
with the shrimps, constitute a very large part of the food of most of
our more valuable fishes," and that they "occur in such immense
numbers in their favorite localities that they can nearly always be
obtained by the fishes who eat them, for even the smallest of them
are by no means despised or overlooked even by large and powerful
fishes, that could easily capture larger game."

§117. We can hope here to cover a fraction only of even the most
obvious animals that may be found in this tremendously populous
zone. There are a number of shelled snails, *Thais* and *Tegula* (§§182,
29) being fairly common. Larger and more spectacular than either,
but not so common, is the brick-red top shell, *Astraea inaequalis*, ranging from Vancouver to San Diego. It may be 3 inches or more in
diameter, and the larger *A. undosa* (Fig. 48) of southern California
may reach a diameter of 6 inches. Large shells of this type are quite
likely to be overgrown by algae or even hydroids, so that they are not
conspicuous unless the living animal is present to move them along.
The cone-shaped shell is so squatty, and the whorls are so wide and
regular, that identification is very easy.

A murex, known as *Ceratostoma foliatum* (Pl. XVI), related to the
richly ornamented tropical shells so familiar to the conchologist,
occurs on this coast. These large and active snails are carnivorous and
closely related to the oyster drill that plays such havoc with commercial oyster beds on the East coast and has become established on this
coast as well. Specimens 3″ to 4″ long have been taken. Its recorded
range is from Sitka to San Diego, but it is seldom to be found below
Pacific Grove. This avoidance of the southern range is interesting
when it is remembered that the large and famous *Murex* is a strictly
tropical animal. Neither *Astraea* nor *C. foliatum* will be found frequently, and both occur in the lowest of low-tide areas only.

Some of the limpets occur, and at least two are characteristic. The
dunce-cap limpet, *Acmaea mitra* (Fig. 49), is found rarely living
above the line of extreme low tides, however common the empty shells
may be on the beach. Its height and size are diagnostic; the average
specimen will be 26 × 23 × 16 mm., hence the tallest of the limpets.
Individuals up to 43 mm. long have been taken, in bulk probably the
largest limpet, although some of the flat species may cover more surface. The shell is thick and white, but is frequently obscured by
growths of bryozoa and red corallines. The range is from Bering Sea
to San Diego, and the animals are ordinarily solitary and fairly uncommon; but Mrs. Test records the presence of thousands of speci-

mens south of the Point Arena lighthouse, occupying pits of the purple urchin.*

The flatter *A. fenestrata,* formerly considered to be a subspecies of *scutum* (§25), is now rated of specific rank. It occurs from Moss Beach north at least to Newport, Mendocino County, and at Jenner it is said to be the commonest limpet. The apex is lower than in *mitra,* the faces are convex, and the aperture is more nearly circular than in any other limpet. Individuals may be identified readily by the fairly consistent size—25 × 23 × 11 mm. for a modal shell—and by the ecological distribution recorded by Grant: "smooth bare rocks located in sand, and free of all visible vegetation and fauna. Prefers rocks which are usually submerged, and, when the tide recedes, shows a tendency to crawl down to sand, half or wholly to bury itself. One must dig around bases of rocks to find them, unless working below tide level." At Dillon Beach, however, *fenestrata* is known to occur fairly high in the intertidal.

As in the previous zones, limpets more characteristic of other levels may be found occasionally, and reference should be made to §§11 and 25.

§118. The last form to be mentioned as belonging strictly to the protected rock habitat is the tiny colonial chaetopterid worm, similar to *Phyllochaetopterus prolifica,* whose membranous tubes mat large areas of vertical or slightly overhanging rock faces, especially where the boulders rest on a sandy substratum. The tubes are light gray in color, about ½₂″ in diameter, and 2″ or 2½″ long. They are intertwined at the base, and are encrusted with sand. A cluster the size of one's fist will contain, at a guess, several hundred tubes. As is so often the case, this form is easily overlooked until the collector has it brought to his attention and identifies it. After that it is obvious and seems to occur everywhere.

§119. A variety of eelgrass (*Phyllospadix*) grows in this habitat on the protected outer coast, and on its delicate stalks occurs a limpet, ill-adapted as limpets would seem to be to such an attachment site. Even in the face of considerable surf, *Acmaea paleacea,* called the chaffy limpet, clings to its blade of eelgrass. Perhaps the feat is not as difficult as might be supposed, since the flexible grass streams out in the water, offering a minimum of resistance. Also the size and shape of the limpet adapt it to this environment. A large specimen is less than ½″ long, is higher than wide, and the width (about ⅙ of the length) is less than that of a blade of eelgrass. A modal specimen is 6 × 1 × 3 mm. The ground color is brown, ridged, with white at

* This form is fairly common in Puget Sound quiet waters, far down (§195).

the apex where the brown ridged covering has been worn away. This eelgrass limpet is fairly common in its recorded range (Test, 1945a) of Trinidad to Lower California. Specimens are abundant at Carmel.

Another common marine plant, *Egregia,* provides on the mid-rib of its elongated leathery stipe (sometimes 20 feet long) attachment sites for still another limpet, *Acmaea insessa,* apparently limited specifically to this habitat. Test (1945a) records a range which, with a few gaps, pretty well includes the whole coast of California. The shell is brown, translucent, and smooth, or nearly so, but no description or illustration should be needed to identify an animal so obvious and so limited in its habitat. A typical shell is $16 \times 14 \times 9$ mm.

§120. A good many small or obscure animals, listed elsewhere as referable to other environments, may turn up here occasionally. Common in the north, and rare to occasional at Monterey is the sessile jellyfish *Haliclystus,* thought to be more characteristic of quiet waters (§273). In the Sitka semi-protected areas (but never so far south as the Washington outer coast), in coves off the open coast, or on the lee shore of protecting islands, the hydroid jellyfish *Gonionemus* (§283) may be locally abundant. The wave-shock factor, although possibly to some extent regulating the distribution of both this and *Haliclystus,* is thought to be secondary to that of pure and clear oceanic water. Both of these may be successful competitors in semi-sheltered and entirely quiet waters, but especially in the case of *Haliclystus* there must be strong currents of oceanic water from neighboring channels. They apparently tolerate no stagnation and very little fresh water.

(c) Under-rock habitat.

The fixed clams, the great tubed worms, the brittle stars, and the crabs are the most noticeable under-rock animals. The newly ordained collector will perhaps be attracted first of all by the brilliant and active brittle stars. He is likely to find most of the brittle stars that occurred under the middle tide-pool rocks, and, especially in the south, he will surely find others.

§121. Two of the large and striking forms not found north of San Pedro stray with considerable frequency into the middle zone, but never occur there in the great numbers that characterize this low zone. One of them, *Ophioderma panamensis* (Pl. XVII), has a superficial resemblance to *Ophioplocus* (Pl. VII), but it is larger, richer brown in color, and smoother in texture, and has banded arms. We have specimens as large as an inch in disc diameter with an arm spread of 7" from the Laguna region, which is near the upper limit of its recorded range of San Pedro to Panama. This form rarely autotomizes, and should prove to be a fair aquarium inhabitant. As in *Ophioplocus, Ophioderma's* short spines extend outward at an acute angle to its arms.

The other, *Ophionereis annulata* (Pl. XVII), is the southern counterpart of *Amphiodia* (Pl. VII), although it does not autotomize so readily. This very snaky-armed echinoderm, having a disc ½″ or less in diameter and arms up to 4″ in spread, ranges from San Pedro to Central America.

§122. *Ophiopholis aculeata* (Pl. XVIII), a dainty, prettily and highly variably colored, and well-proportioned animal—according to human esthetic standards—is notable for an astonishing range, both geographically and bathymetrically. The same species not only extends throughout the world in North Temperate regions but occurs in various depths from the low intertidal zone to the sea bottom at 600 fathoms. The physical conditions in the tide pools at Pacific Grove may not differ markedly from those at Sitka or on the coasts of Maine, England, or Spitzenbergen, but there is certainly a great difference between conditions at the surface and those on the ocean bottom seven-tenths of a mile below the surface. In the intertidal zone there is wave shock, sudden temperature change, alternate exposure to air and water, and bright light at least some of the time. Under 3,600 feet of water there is absolute stillness, unchanging low temperature, light sufficient to affect a photographic plate only after long exposure, and pressure so great that only reinforced steel cylinders can resist it. Yet varieties of the delicate-looking *O. aculeata* bridge this gap and are equally at home in both environments.

The disc of this form has a granular appearance, and the predominant color is rusty red, although green may form a part of the mottled pattern. It is found on this coast in Alaska, British Columbia, and Puget Sound, and we have taken it as far south as Point Sur.

§123. The ultra-spiny brittle star, *Ophiothrix spiculata* (Pl. XVIII), has its disc so thickly beset with minute spicules that it appears fuzzy. The arm spines are longer, thinner, and more numerous than in *Ophiopholis,* with which it is sometimes found. The color is so highly variable as to furnish no clue to the animal's identity, but it is often greenish-brown, with orange bands on the arms and orange specks on the disc. The disc may be ⅔″ in diameter, and the arm spread one of several inches. The egg sacs of ovigerous specimens may be seen protruding from the disc between the arms. Although this is a southern form, ranging from Monterey Bay to Central America, specimens are not at all uncommon at the northern extremity of the range. Associated with *Ophiothrix,* but treated with the more open coast forms, may be found any of several "sea scorpions" (isopods), the large *Idothea stenops* at Monterey, and *I. schmitti* here and elsewhere (§172).

§124. *Ophiopteris papillosa* (Pl. XVIII) occurs with other brittle stars in the south, where it is not uncommon, but seldom reaches there the great size and spectacular appearance that characterize the rare Pacific Grove specimens—a strange situation, since Pacific Grove is its northern limit. In the south, too, it is a relatively hardy animal, while at Pacific Grove it is so fragile that only once have we succeeded in taking an unbroken specimen. The spines are large and blunt, almost square-cut, and relatively few, although the temperamental animal still has a distinctly bristly appearance. The arms reach a spread of 6″ to 7″ and are brown, banded with darker colors. This brittle star is nowhere to be found in great numbers, and is never accessible except on the lowest of low tides, for it requires water that is pure and well aerated.

§125. The avid turner-over-of-rocks will surely see many such fixed clams as *Chama* and the rock oyster *Hinnites giganteus* (Pl. XVIII). The latter, when young, is not to be distinguished from a scallop. It swims about in just the same way by flapping its two equal shells. But the ways of senile old age creep on it rapidly. The half-buried under surface of some great rock offers the appeal of a fireside nook to a sedentary scholar, and there it settles. One valve attaches to the rock and becomes distorted to fit it; the other valve adapts itself to the shape of the attached one, and there *Hinnites* lives to an alert old age, with the half-open shell ready to snap shut and send a spurt of water into the face of some imprudent collector. The largest specimens of this species, which ranges from Alaska to Lower California, may have a diameter of more than 6 inches.

§126. Whereas *Hinnites* is fairly flat, without any sudden thickness curves, *Chama pellucida* (Pl. XVIII) is often higher than it is long. Nearly hemispherical, and only an inch or so high, the translucent white shell of this form is quite distinctive—like nothing else to be found in the tide pools. Except that it also snaps its shell shut at times most inconvenient for the observer, we have nothing to record of its natural history; and we suspect that little or nothing is known directly of its breeding habits, what it feeds on, how rapidly it grows, or what its span of life may be. In the Lower California region it grows so thickly on the tops and sides of rocks as to be practically a reef-building form, whereas in the Pacific Grove region it is found only under rocks at the lowest of low tides. It ranges from Oregon to South America.

Most of the species of *Chama,* which share with the not-related *Pododesmus* the name "rock oyster," are tropical forms, growing attached to coral reefs. The few species in the world today are only a fraction of the number of extinct forms. Many are highly frilled and ornamented—an indication that the species is reaching its old age and is likely soon to become extinct.

The rock oyster or jingle, *Pododesmus,* is occasional here, but is more common on rocks in quiet bays and on wharf piling (§217).

§127. The other molluskan inhabitants of the under-rocks areas are chitons—sea cradles—several species of which have already been mentioned. (See Frontispiece for illustrations in color of various specimens.) A majority of the 110–125 species of chitons that inhabit the West coast are light-sensitive and will be found underneath the rocks in this zone, carefully protected from daylight and especially from the sun.

Probably all chitons are vegetable feeders, and in most cases the sexes are separate. According to observations made by Dr. Heath, the females will never release their eggs until the males have liberated their sperm into the water. Spawning takes place on May and June days when low tides occur in the early morning—not, apparently, because of the influence of the moon or merely because the tide is low, but because the water in the pools is then undisturbed. Egg-laying may continue over a period of several hours, but it ceases the moment the returning tide sends the first wave breaking into the pool. Another investigator, however, Grave (1922) finds that moonlight is the chief factor influencing the sexual activity of an East-coast form similar to *Nuttallina* that he has studied.

Along a considerable stretch of coast all the *Stenoplax heathiana* (Pl. XIX) will spawn on the same day and almost at the same hour. Usually each female lays two long, jelly-like, spiral strings of eggs averaging 31″ long and containing, together, from 100,000 to nearly 200,000 eggs. The larvae are rotating within twenty-four hours, and in six days the young break through to swim freely for from fifteen minutes to two hours before they settle down. After settling they remain inactive for about two days, but within ten to twelve days they have undergone several metamorphoses and become miniature chitons. The same sequence of events appears to apply to the other species of *Stenoplax,* to *Mopalia muscosa,* and to *Katharina.*

Stenoplax heathiana (up to 3″ long) is a rather beautifully marbled, elongated, light gray to white chiton, ranging from Oregon to Magdalena Bay in Lower California and particularly common in Monterey Bay.

In the La Jolla tide pools the most abundant large animal to be found at present is the larger and relatively wider *Stenoplax conspicua* (Pl. XIX), its girdle covered with fine velvety bristles. Four-inch specimens are common there, in the San Diego area, and in northern Lower California, the extreme range being Monterey to the Gulf. Both of these large and noticeable chitons occur under fairly smooth and round rocks buried in types of substratum in which sand is the important constituent.

§128. Other common chitons (Pl. XIX) are distinguished readily by their shape or color. *Ischnochiton regularis,* reported from Mendocino to Monterey only, is a uniform and beautiful slaty blue, and up to 2" long. Another *Ischnochiton,* of unknown species, is also small and resembles *regularis* except that it is colored a brilliant turquoise. Specimens of *Callistochiton crassicostatus* (not illustrated), green or brown, have a noticeable median keel to the plates, are less than an inch long, and range from Alaska to San Diego. *Placiphorella velata* may be recognized by its almost circular outline. It is 2" or less in length. *Lepidozona mertensii,* up to 1½" long, with angular ridges and straight sides, is usually a mottled red, and ranges from Alaska to San Pedro. The similar but dull-brown *L. cooperi* occurs also. All of these are exceedingly shy animals, presumably because they find sunlight highly toxic; but the several species of *Mopalia*—broad, chunky chitons that have the mantle haired to the point of furriness—are more tolerant of daylight. We have found fine healthy specimens living on the walls and ceilings of caves, and during foggy weather they may often be found on rocks. Ordinarily, however, they are under-rock animals like their relatives.

Through a method recently devised at the University of California (for which we have to thank Mrs. Test), the common species of *Mopalia* may be differentiated in the field. *Muscosa* of §221 is unquestioned; the stiff and stout hair is diagnostic. Of the other two, the more common *ciliata* has a definite split notch at the posterior end of the girdle, and the sculpturing is very evident; *lignosa* lacks both, but has the color lines even more prominent, and the posterior valve has a decided central beak. This information has not so far been correlated with habitat; probably the various species are ecologically restricted. *Ciliata* and *lignosa,* especially the former, occur between tides on open shores, both ranging from Alaska to Lower California.

§129. The large tubed worms are of two sorts: serpulids, in which the tube is white, hard, and calcareous; and sabellids, which are larger, plumed worms with membranous tubes. The sabellid *Eudistylia polymorpha* (Pl. XX) is one of the vivid sights of the North Pacific tide pools. The dull yellow or gray, parchment-like tube is very tough and may be 18" long, extending far down into the crevices of rocks, so that nothing short of prolonged labor with a pick will serve to dislodge the complete animal. When the worm is undisturbed its lovely gills are protruded out of the tube into the waters of the tide pool, where they look like a delicate flower, or like the tentacles of an anemone. Touch them and they snap back into the tube with such rapidity as to leave the observer rubbing his eyes and wondering if there really could have been such a thing. So sensitive are the light-perceiving spots on the tentacles that the mere shadow of one's hand passing over them is enough to cause the tentacles to be snapped back. This worm ranges from Alaska to San Pedro but is not common south of Pacific Grove.

A serpulid worm, *Serpula vermicularis* (§213), having a sinuous to nearly straight stony tube several inches in length, which is stoppered up with a red operculum when the tentacles are withdrawn, may be locally common. This is the Pacific Grove large solitary serpulid which, removed from its tube, obligingly extrudes red eggs or yellowish-white sperm. The sexes are separate, but there is no apparent external difference between the male and the female, although probably, as with Roland Young's fleas, "she can tell, and so can he." Sexual maturity has been observed here during the spring.

A smaller tubed worm, *Marphysa stylobranchiata,* occurs in underrock chitinized tubes much like those of *Eudistylia* but considerably smaller, and with two big head palps projecting from the tube in place of the great sabellid's tentacle crown. *Marphysa* is a eunicid, a very near relative of the palolo worm of lunar spawning habits (§151), but apparently lacking on this coast that spectacular trait.

§130. The worm *Glycera americana* should be mentioned in passing, for although commoner in sloughs, particularly in eelgrass (§280), it will sometimes be found under rocks on the protected outer coast. These slender worms may be mistaken for *Nereis* (*Neanthes virens,* §311, is occasional here also), but differ in that the head tapers to a point and that the animal can shoot out a startling introvert. The long, slim, and fragile *Lumbrinereis zonata* will be taken here occasionally, also the ubiquitous scale worm, *Halosydna* (§49), and a good many smaller forms. Other worms frequently found are mentioned in the root-and-holdfast habitat (§153), but of the enumerating of worms there is no end: certainly twenty species could be taken in this environment at Monterey alone. Their differentiation offers a task even to the specialist; field determinations are rarely conclusive.

§131. Of the masking crabs, *Loxorhynchus crispatus* (Pl. XX) is easily the champion. Although it occurs so far down in the intertidal as to be more justly considered a subtidal form, it will be found often enough along shore between Point Reyes and San Diego to justify mention, and it is certain to occasion interested comment whenever found. It is perhaps the most inactive of all the crabs, moving seldom, and then sluggishly. Until it does move one never suspects that it is a crab.

To some animals the accidental growth of algae or sessile animals on their shells seems to be a source of danger, presumably because the weight and water resistance of such growth would hamper their movements. Such animals keep their shells scrupulously clean. Others tolerate foreign growths, and still others, notably some of the spider crabs, go to the extreme of augmenting the natural growths by planting algae, hydroids, sponges, etc., on their backs. This masking may serve a double purpose: first, to make the animal inconspicuous to its enemies; and, second, to enable it to stalk its prey without detection. It has been observed that masking crabs placed in a new environment will head for areas containing the same kind of growth that they carry on their backs if such an area is available. If placed in a totally different environment they will often remove the existing growths from their backs and replace them with such forms as are common in the new locality.

Experimenting with a European masking crab (*Dromia*), Dembowska found that if the animal were deprived of its sponge covering and placed in an aquarium with a piece of writing paper, it would tear the paper into a pattern roughly corresponding to the shape of its back and put it on. This was an emergency measure, however, for when a sponge attached by a wire hook was hung within reach the crab went toward it at once, dropping the paper case on the way. It pulled itself up to the sponge, cut the sponge loose from the hook, and rolled with it to the bottom of the aquarium. Immediately afterward the crab placed the sponge on its back, holding it there with the upcurved fourth and fifth pairs of legs which are modified for that purpose.

The crab showed considerable adaptability to circumstances and some capacity for learning, for when the sponge covering was removed time and again and buried in gravel, deeper each time, the crab learned to uncover it and finally to dig at the right spot even when the sponge was entirely out of sight. Such experiments confirm the very complex nature of crab reactions, a matter that is further discussed in connection with the fiddler crab (§284). Observing such behavior, one is tempted to credit the animals with something akin to intelligence, but there is reason for believing that their actions are almost entirely automatic.

A more common and more truly intertidal masking crab is *Scyra acutifrons.* It is not more than half the size of *Loxorhynchus,* and is not so efficient a masker. Although reported from Kodiak to San Diego, it is uncommon below Pacific Grove.

§132. Under-rock collecting will turn up a number of other crabs which may be differentiated by reference to the illustrations. *Pachycheles* (§318), a common wharf-piling inhabitant, will occasionally be routed out of an unaccustomed home here.

Lophopanopeus frontalis is a common southern California form, its place being taken at Monterey Bay by *L. heathii* (Fig. 50).

Mimulus foliatus (Pl. XX), of which we have seen ovigerous females during June in central California, may have a carapace of bright red or yellow, caused, in some cases at least, by growths of sponges. An extreme range of Unalaska to Mazatlan is recorded.

The queer-looking *Cryptolithodes sitchensis* (Pl. XX) has so large a carapace that none of its appendages are visible from the upper surface, and resembles nothing so much as a time-worn fossil. This species ranges from Alaska to Monterey, and full-sized specimens are not uncommon even in the southern part of the range.

The furriest and fuzziest of the crabs is *Hapalogaster cavicauda* (Pl. XX), ranging from Cape Mendocino to the Channel Islands off Santa Barbara. In life the animal presents an interesting sight, especially when, as during the winter months, the already swollen tail is distended with eggs. The male also shows the characteristic redundance of tail.

§133. Conditions of semi-tropical heat and aridity being what they are, it is quite in the order of things for the intertidal animals of the south to be restricted to the under-rock habitat. From Santa Barbara as far down into Lower California as we have collected there is a prolific and interesting fauna, but only the upturning of rocks will reveal it. Such rock-beach inhabitants as *Ischnochiton*, octopi, brittle stars, ghost shrimps, and blind gobies, the two last restricted to the substratum, form an association in which a common top shell and several crabs figure also.

The crab, *Cycloxanthops novemdentatus* (Pl. XXI), a dull reddish brown, will be taken for a small *Cancer*. The obvious bumps on its big claws will serve to identify the dark red *Paraxanthias taylori* (Pl. XXI). Both of these extend down into Mexico from Monterey, but neither is common in the northern part of the range, while they form a feature of the intertidal at La Jolla, for instance.

Pilumnus spinohirsutus (Pl. XXI), recognizable immediately by its hairiness, is another of the retiring, probably light-avoiding crabs of the southern coast, ranging from Venice to Ecuador. Any of these three crabs may be found under rocks at Laguna, La Jolla, or Ensenada—sometimes all of them under a single large rock, possibly with *Lophopanopeus* and a small octopus thrown in for good measure.

§134. *Hippolysmata californica* (Pl. XXI) is a large transparent shrimp, up to $1\frac{1}{2}''$ long, with broken red stripes running fore and aft. A dozen may occur on a single under surface, but the collector who can capture more than one from a given rock is doing well, for when the rock is moved they hop around at a great rate and disappear very quickly. *Hippolysmata* has not been recorded north of Santa Barbara. We have taken specimens at Ensenada, and no doubt it ranges farther on down the coast.

§135. The much-maligned octopus—which, in the vernacular, shares the name of devilfish with the giant ray of tropical waters—is not often found in the intertidal regions of the north, but from Santa Barbara south a small species, *Octopus* (formerly *Polypus*) *bimaculatus* (Pl. XXI), is a common under-rock inhabitant of the outer tidelands. The octopus has eyes as highly developed as ours, and a larger and better-functioning brain than any other invertebrate animal. Its relatively high degree of intelligence is quite likely a factor in making possible its survival in the face of persistent collecting for food. Italians and Chinese justly relish the animals as food, and so does an occasional American. Delicious as their flesh is, however, it is decidedly tough and rubbery, and the meat-grinder treatment is recommended.

In the metropolitan areas about Los Angeles and San Diego, octopi are no longer to be had in their former abundance, for, in addition to the many people who hunt them specifically, hunters of abalones and spiny lobsters capture them incidentally. Nevertheless a good many are still to be had, even in the areas mentioned, where it is probably safe to say that several thousand are taken for food every year. This observation is based on personal experience. For several years we have collected, observed, and photographed along the Corona del Mar shore at Newport Bay and in the region north of Laguna. On one such visit to Corona del Mar we questioned one of several crews who we had supposed were collecting bait. It developed that they were capturing octopi, and their rather pernicious method, which we afterward watched, was as follows: Two men, armed with gaff hooks and carrying gunny sacks, station themselves quietly by a large isolated rock in a pool. Finding a hollow that indicates the probable entrance to an octopus's under-rock lair, one of the men pours into the water a bit of what he calls "lye" solution, probably chloride of lime. Usually within a minute the mollusk is forced to come out and seek less irritating water, whereupon he is promptly hooked and deposited in the gunny sack. These two men had captured thirteen octopi, totaling possibly thirty pounds, and several other crews appeared to have had equally good "luck." The whole situation has been approximately duplicated on each of the dozen or more times we have visited the

spot. So devastating a method of collecting as poisoning pools would
be regrettable anywhere, unless the collectors were in genuine need
of food. Along the coast of Lower California the octopi are more
fortunate, for the Mexicans we have talked with along the shore are
interested in abalones and spiny lobsters only and regard the eating
of octopi with the same horror that most Americans do.

At various points between Tia Juana and Ensenada we have found
octopi very numerous in April, May, and December of several years.
In December 1930 they were so abundant that one could count on
finding a specimen under at least every fourth rock overturned. Their
clever hiding and escaping strategies make them difficult to see, difficult to capture after they are seen, and difficult to hold after they are
captured. Two may occur under the same rock, but to take them both
with bare hands is almost an impossibility. A captured specimen will
sometimes cling to one's hand, and, if the animal is large enough, to
one's forearm; but unless the collector has acquired some skill in
handling the wily animals the specimen will at once let go, shoot out
of one's hand like a bar of wet soap, and disappear. A little observation will convince the collector that in a given area probably half of
the specimens will escape notice despite the most careful searching—
a highly desirable situation from the permanent collector's point of
view as well as from the octopus's.

This mud-flat octopus is known as *Octopus bimaculoides,* for the
two large, round, eye-like spots. These are wider apart than the real
eyes, which are raised above the body surface in knobs reminiscent
of the light towers on sailing ships. Each of the eight arms has
two rows of suction disks, so powerful that when even a small specimen decides to fight it out by main strength it is very difficult to detach him from his rock. In an aquarium very small specimens live
well, withstanding inclemencies of temperature and stale water most
amazingly for animals so delicate; but large specimens—an arm spread
of two feet is large for this species — live but a short time, usually dying before they can be transferred from the shore to an aquarium.

This octopus is inferior to the rest of his tribe in the ability to
change color, but even so he can produce startling and often beautiful
effects and harmonize his color so perfectly with his surroundings as
to be almost invisible until he moves. The usually larger *Octopus* sp.,
which is occasionally found in Monterey Bay, is a more versatile artist
at color changes, as is the *O. apollyon* of Alaskan waters.

Like all of the octopods and the related decapods, such as the
squid, the octopus has an ink-sac, opening near the anus, from which
he can discharge a dense, sepia-colored fluid, creating a "smoke

screen" that should be the envy of the navy. The junior writer once spent hours changing water in a five-gallon jar so that he might better observe the half-dozen octopi therein, but his arms were exhausted before the animals' ink-sacs.

The octopus, together with the squid and *Nautilus*, belongs to the molluscan class Cephalopoda. While the octopus has no shell, an internal vestige is to be found in most squids—in some forming the "cuttlebone"—and *Nautilus* has a well-developed external shell. The beautiful "shell" of the paper nautilus or *Argonauta* is actually the egg case, secreted not by the mantle, but by a specialized pair of arms of the female. The male argonaut has no shell.

The octopus can move rapidly over sand or rocks by the use of its arms and suckers, but in water its arms trail away from the direction of motion with an efficient-looking, streamline effect, while it propels itself swiftly backward with powerful jets of water from its siphon tube. The animal's usual method of hunting is to lie quietly under rocks, darting out to capture passing fish or crustaceans (crabs seem to be a favorite food), and then killing them, presumably, with the strong beak jaws that are normally concealed inside the mouth opening.

The method of reproduction is decidedly unique. At breeding time one arm of the male becomes enlarged and modified (hectocotylized) as a copulatory organ. From the generative orifice he charges this arm with a packet of spermatozoa which he deposits under the mantle-skirt of the female. In some squids a portion of the arm is detached and carried in the mantle cavity of the female until fertilization takes place—often a matter of several days. This detached arm was formerly thought to be a separate animal that was parasitic in the female cephalopod. In dissecting male squid, the senior writer has seen the packet of spermatozoa explode when the air reached it, shooting out a long arrow-like streamer which was attached with a cord to the spermatophore.

The act of fertilization accomplished, the male octopus has but to retire to repair his damaged arm. The female, however, has before her a long vigil, for a description of which we quote from a paper by Dr. Fisher. A small octopus had been captured, late in June 1922, near the Hopkins Marine Station at Pacific Grove. It was kept alive in an aquarium for three and one-half months, where it fed irregularly and usually at night on pieces of fish and abalone.

Dr. Fisher writes:

"For reference in conversation, the octopus was named 'Mephisto,' later changed for obvious reasons to 'Mephista.' She had a little shelter of stones in a front corner of the aquarium. A movable board was so arranged as to exclude all but dim light, since in the language of animal behaviorists an octopus is negatively phototactic (unless, perchance, it is too hungry to care).

"During the night of July 4 two or three festoons of eggs were deposited on the sloping underside of the granite roof of Mephista's retreat. These eggs were nearly transparent, and resembled a long bunch of sultana grapes in miniature. The central axis, consisting of the twisted peduncles of the eggs, was brown. During the following week about forty other clusters were deposited, always at night. The process was never observed.

"In the meantime she had assumed a brooding position. The masses of eggs rested against the dorsal surface of the body and the arms were curled backwards to form a sort of basket or receptacle." During one period of observation ". . . . the ends of the arms were in frequent gentle movement over the clusters and among them—almost a combing motion."

"Mephista was never observed away from the eggs during the day, unless badly irritated. If a morsel of fish or abalone was dropped close to her she endeavored to blow it away with water from the funnel. If this were not sufficient she caught the food in one or two arms and dropped it as far as she could reach. If then the fish was returned she flushed reddish brown, seized the offending morsel, crawled irritably out of her little cell, and, with a curious straightening movement of all the tentacles, fairly hurled the food from her. She then quickly returned to the eggs. In the morning the rejected food would be found partly eaten.

"Although the eggs were laid in early July they showed no signs of development for nearly a month. By August 20 the embryos were well advanced and their chromatophores were contracting and expanding. From time to time bunches of eggs had been removed for preservation, without causing unusual reactions on Mephista's part. About ten bunches were left. They hatched during my absence from the laboratory near the middle of September. On my return, October 1, Mephista was still covering the remains of her brood—the dilapidated clusters of empty egg-capsules. She refused to eat either fish or abalone, and had become noticeably smaller. On October 11 she was found dead at her post. . . . . Possibly during the post-brooding period the food reaction is specialized—that is, limited to relatively few things. I find it hard to believe that in Polypus death is a normal sequel to egg-laying."

Two years later another specimen, named Mephista II, repeated the performance, with some variation in details, and provided further opportunities for observing the embryos and newly hatched young. The latter, a shade less than $\frac{1}{16}$" long, are so translucent that some of

I. PROTECTED OUTER COAST

§§ 1–156, Figures 3–56, Plates I–XXIV

View of Cabrillo Point and Hopkins Marine Station, Pacific Grove. Cannery Row is the first street on the left in the background. U.S. Navy Photo.

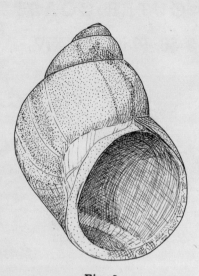

Fig. 3
Periwinkle shell, *Littorina
planaxis*; enlarged about five
times (§ 1).

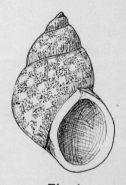

Fig. 4
Periwinkle shell, *Littorina
scutulata*; enlarged about five
times (§ 10).

PLATE I. (Opposite page)

ANIMALS OF THE UPPERMOST ROCKY BEACH

Upper: A characteristic assemblage of periwinkles, acorn barnacles, and
limpets on a vertical rock face. *Littorina planaxis, Balanus glandula*
and *Acmaea digitalis*. Same scale as lower (§§ 1, 4, and 6).

Lower: An owl limpet and scar, *Lottia gigantea* (§ 7).

100

Fig. 5
The pill bug, *Ligyda occidentalis;* natural size (§ 2).

Fig. 6
The flatworm, *Planocera californica* (§ 3).

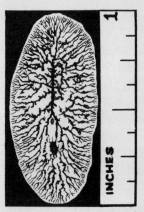

PLATE II (Opposite page)
ANIMALS OF THE UPPER TIDE-POOL REGION

1. A hermit crab, **Pagurus samuelis** (§ 12).
2. A cluster of the black turban snails, **Tegula funebralis**, reduced; photo copyrighted by George Stone (§ 13).
3. The volcano shell limpet, **Fissurella volcano** (§ 15).
4. The hairy-gilled worm, **Cirriformia luxuriosa**, which lives in the foul mud of rock crevices but leaves its "lungs" at the surface (§ 16).

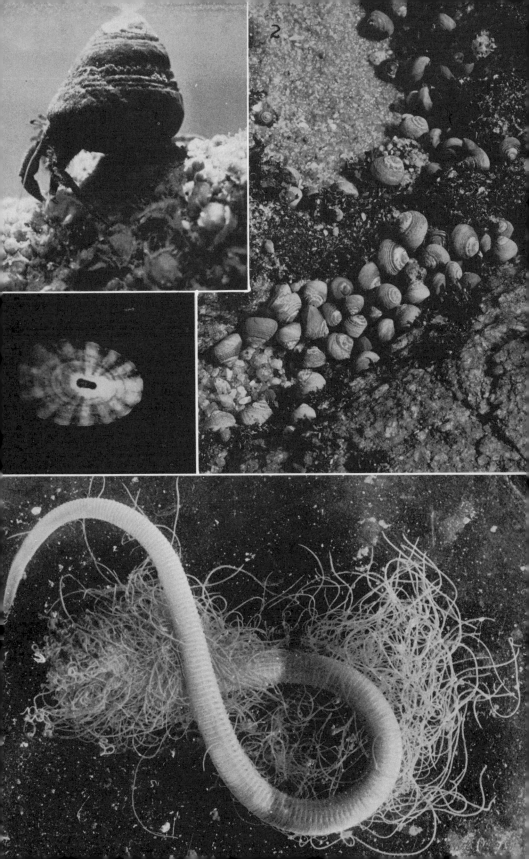

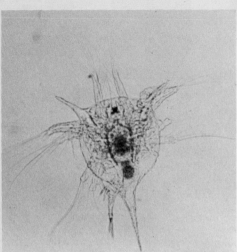

Fig. 7
Larval stage of barnacle, a
nauplius; greatly enlarged
(§ 4); photo by Woody
Williams

Fig. 8
Larval stage of barnacle, a
cypris, greatly enlarged
(§ 4); photo by Woody
Williams

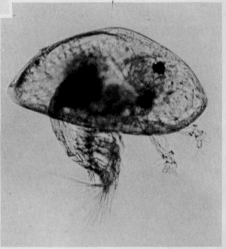

PLATE III (Opposite page)

ANIMALS OF THE UPPER TIDE-POOL REGION

1. The porcelain crab, *Petrolisthes cinctipes,* the most abundant under-rock crab of the upper and middle zones (§ 18).
2. The smallest brittle star of the Pacific coast, *Amphipholis pugetana;* Photo by Pacific Biological Laboratories (§ 19).
3. Tubes of the tiny serpulid worm, the sinistral *Spirorbis* (§ 22).
4. A portion of a bed of the aggregated *Cribrina;* all specimens contracted.
5. The sea bat, *Patiria miniata,* which provides eggs and sperm for experimental purposes; actual diameter, 5″ (§ 26).

104

Fig. 9
Acmaea digitalis (§ 6).

Fig. 10
The ribbed limpet, *Acmaea scabra;* natural size (§ 11)

Fig. 11
The shield limpet, *Acmaea cassis*; natural size (§ 11).

PLATE IV (Opposite page)

ANIMALS OF THE UPPER TIDE-POOL REGION

Upper: The purple shore crab, *Hemigrapsus nudus* (§ 27).

Lower: A rich area of protected outer coast at Carmel. E. F. Ricketts collecting at low tide; *Laminaria* and *Phyllospadix* exposed.

Fig. 12
The flatworm, *Leptoplana acticola* (§ 17).

Fig. 13.
The beach hopper, *Melita palmata* (§ 20).

Fig. 14
The pill bug, *Cirolana harfordi* (§ 21).

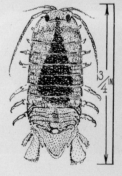

PLATE V (Opposite page)

ANIMALS OF THE UPPER TIDE-POOL REGION

1. The hermit crab, *Pagurus hemphilli,* an egg-bearing specimen removed from its shell; photo copyrighted by Pacific Biological Laboratories (§ 28).
2. The brown turban, *Tegula brunnea,* carrying the slipper shell, *Crepidula adunca* (§ 29).
3. The starfish *Leptasterias pusilla* (§ 30).
4. A purple encrusting sponge, *Haliclona permollis* (§ 31).
5. A red encrusting sponge, *Plocamia karykina,* or similar (§ 32).
6. A red encrusting sponge, *Ophlitaspongia pennata,* with two specimens of the red nudibranch, *Rostanga pulchra* (§ 33).

108

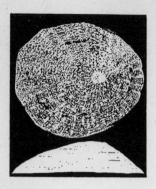

Fig. 15
The plate limpet, *Acmaea scutum;* natural size (§ 25).

Fig. 16
The file limpet, *Acmaea limatula;* natural size (§ 25).

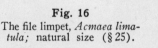

PLATE VI (Opposite page)
ANIMALS OF THE UPPER TIDE-POOL REGION

1. The nudibranch or shell-less snail, *Triopha carpenteri* (§ 34).
2. The nudibranch *Diaulula sandiegensis* (§ 35).
3. The lined chiton, *Tonicella lineata* (§ 36).
4. Left: an expanded specimen of the anemone, *Epiactis prolifera;* right: the same specimen contracted, showing young budding off (§ 37).
5. Unexpanded specimens of the solitary coral, *Balanophyllia elegans* (§ 39).
6. Small red anemones, *Corynactis;* note the clubbed tentacles (§ 40).

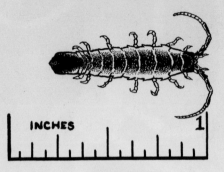

Fig. 17

The isopod, *Idothea urotoma* (§ 46).

Fig. 18

The long-fingered shrimp, *Betaeus longidactylus* (§ 46).

PLATE VII (Opposite page)

BRITTLE STARS OF THE MIDDLE ZONE

Upper: *Amphiodia occidentalis* (§ 44).

Lower: *Ophioplocus esmarki* (§ 45).

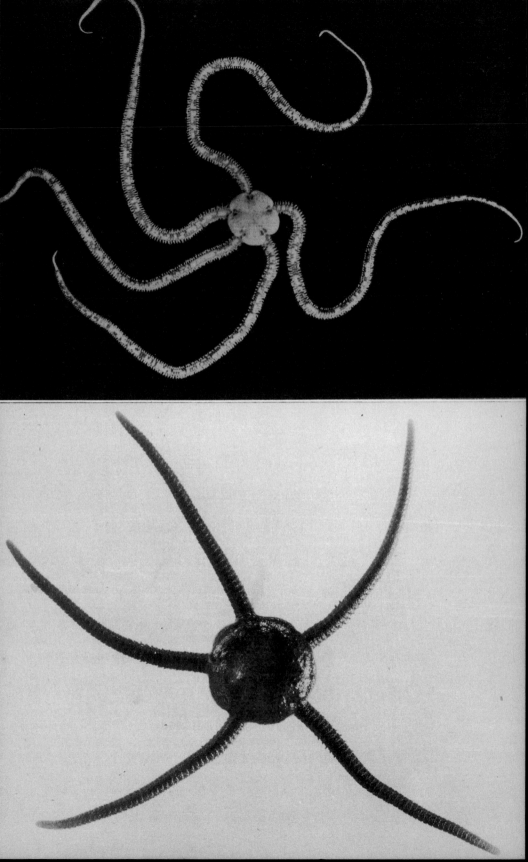

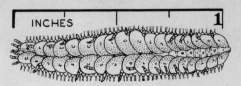

Fig. 19
The common scale worm, *Halosydna brevisetosa* (§ 49).

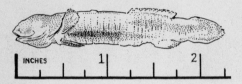

Fig. 20
The blind goby, *Typhlogobius californiensis* (§ 58).

Fig. 21
A plume hydroid, *Plumularia setacea* (§ 78).

½ in.

PLATE VIII (Opposite page)

ANIMALS OF THE UNDER-ROCK HABITAT; MIDDLE TIDE POOLS

1. Cluster of the fixed snails, *Aletes squamigerus;* reduced (§ 47). The encrusting substance growing on *Aletes* is a yellow sponge (§ 98).
2. The peanut worm, *Phascolosoma agassizii*, partially expanded (§ 52).
3. The tube-building worm, *Thelepus crispus* (§ 53).

114

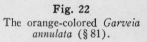

Fig. 22
The orange-colored *Garveia annulata* (§ 81).

Fig. 23
Hydractinia milleri (§ 82).

PLATE IX (Opposite page)

BURROWING ANIMALS OF THE UNDER ROCKS, AND FREE-
SWIMMING FORMS; MIDDLE TIDE-POOL REGION

1. The skin-breathing cucumber, *Leptosynapta albicans* (§ 55).
2. The ghost shrimp, *Callianassa affinis* (§ 57).
3. The clingfish, *Sicyogaster meandrica* (§ 51).
4. The transparent shrimp, *Spirontocaris paludicola;* life size and enlarged (§ 62).
5. The opossum shrimp, *Acanthomysis costata* (§ 61).
6. A blenny, probably *Epigeichthys atro-purpureus;* reduced (§ 51).

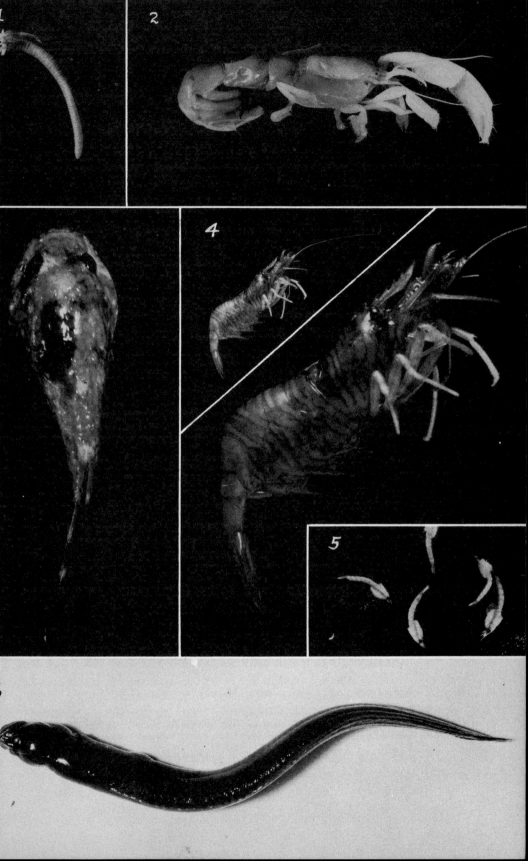

Fig. 24
The hydroid, *Abietinaria an-guina* (§ 83).

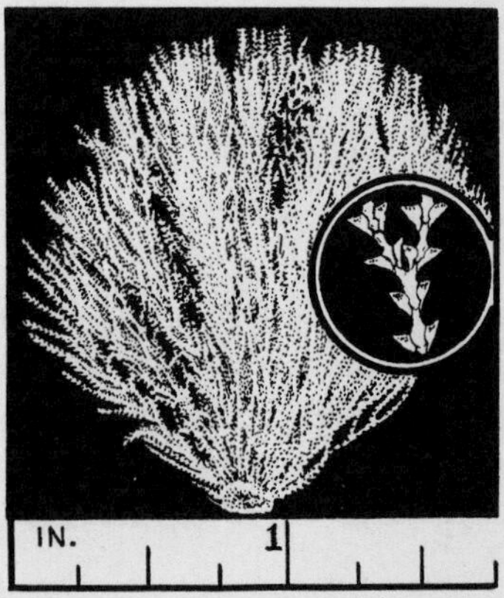

Fig. 25
The hydroid, *Abietinaria greenei* (§ 83).

PLATE X (Opposite page)

ANIMALS OF THE LOWER TIDE-POOL REGION

Upper: Under side of a sunflower star, *Pycnopodia helianthoides*, photographed in an aquarium; greatly reduced (§ 66).

Lower: Giant green anemones in a tide pool, the solitary *Anthopleura xanthogrammica*, greatly reduced; these usually occur more widely separated (§ 64).

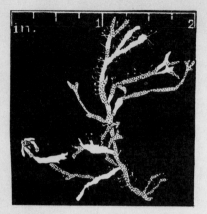

Fig. 26
The hydroid, *Eucopella caliculata* (§ 85).

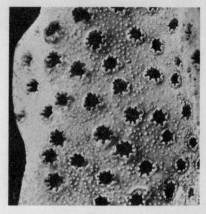

Fig. 27
The hydrocoral *Allopora por-
phyra* (§87). (From Walter
K. Fisher, *Proc. U.S. Nat.
Mus.*, Vol. 84, No. 3024.)

Fig. 28
The skeleton shrimp, *Caprella kennerlyi* (§ 89).

Fig. 29
A sea spider, *Lecythorhynchus marginatus* (§ 90).

PLATE XI (Opposite page)

STARFISH OF THE LOWER TIDE-POOL REGION

Upper: Three specimens of the highly variable *Linckia columbiae*, somewhat reduced; the specimen on the left is unusually symmetrical
(§ 71).

Lower: The sun star, *Solaster dawsoni;* the specimen shown is 9½″ in
diameter (§ 67).

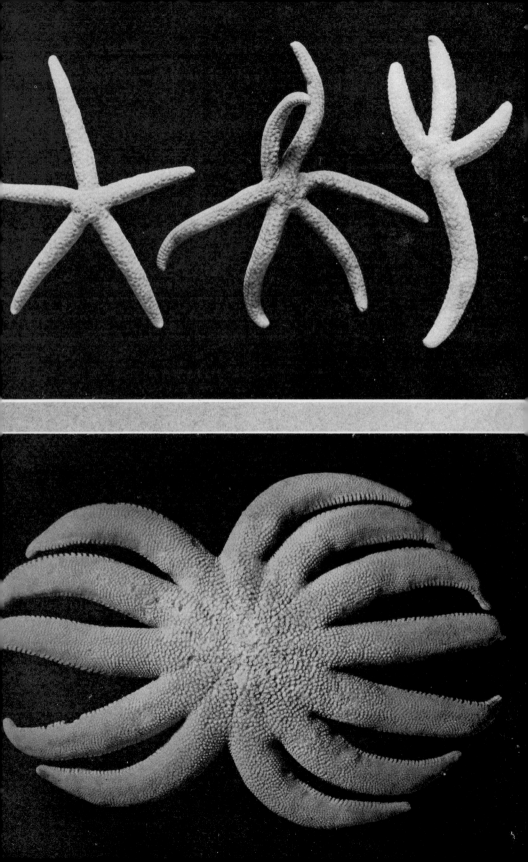

Fig. 30
Tylodina fungina crawling on a sponge. Photo by Woody Williams.

PLATE XII (Opposite page)
ANIMALS OF THE LOWER TIDE-POOL REGION
(All animals less than life size)

1. A red starfish, *Henricia leviuscula* (§§ 69, 211).
2. *Astrometis sertulifera* (§ 72).
3. The giant red urchin, *Strongylocentrotus franciscanus;* specimen was 6″ in diameter (§ 73).
4. Shell of the green abalone, *Haliotis fulgens* (§ 75).
5. The red abalone, *Haliotis rufescens,* which has been turned on its back and is extending its great foot preparatory to righting itself; the shell of the individual photographed was about 7″ in diameter (§ 74).

122

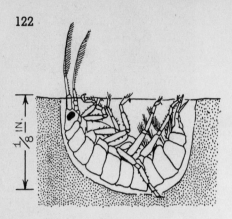

Fig. 31
The amphipod, *Polycheria osborni*, which lives in a
tunicate; from Skogsberg and Vansell (§ 100).

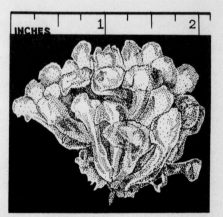

Fig. 32
The tunicate, *Clavelina huntsmani* (§ 101).

PLATE XIII (Opposite page)

ANIMALS OF THE LOWER TIDE-POOL REGION

1. The gum boot, *Cryptochiton stelleri,* a giant sea cradle, greatly reduced;
photo copyrighted by Pacific Biological Laboratories. (§ 76).
2. The California cucumber, *Stichopus californicus;* the white object on
the specimen's back is a 6-inch rule (§ 77). Inset shows the pea crab,
Opisthopus transversus (§ 76).
3. The hydroid, *Eudendrium californicum,* slightly enlarged (§ 79).

Fig. 33

Tunicate, *Euherdmania claviformis* (§ 102).

Fig. 34

The tunicate, *Polyclinum planum* (§ 103).

PLATE XIV (Opposite page)

HYDROIDS AND SPONGES OF THE LOWER TIDE-POOL REGION

1. An ostrich-plume hydroid, *Aglaophenia latirostris* (§ 84).
2. The hydroid, *Sertularia furcata* (§ 86).
3. The sponge, *Rhabdodermella nuttingi* (§ 94).
4. The sponge, *Leucosolenia eleanor* (§ 93).
5. The sponge, *Leuconia heathi* (§ 95).

Fig. 35
The sea hare, *Tethys californica*; three-fourths natural size (§ 104).

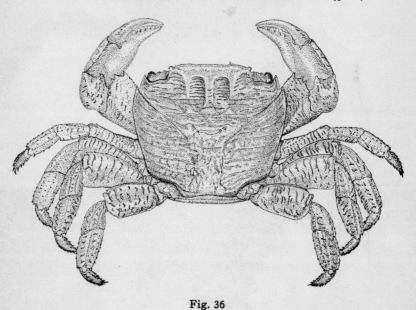

Fig. 36
The lined shore crab, *Pachygrapsus crassipes*, about one-half size (§ 14).
(From Robert W. Hiatt, *Pacific Science*, Vol. II, No. 3.)

PLATE XV (Opposite page)

CRABS OF THE LOWER TIDE-POOL REGION

Upper: The kelp crab, *Pugettia producta* (§ 107).

Lower: *Cancer antennarius* (§ 105).

128

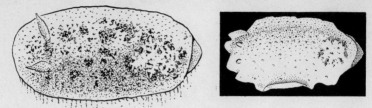

Fig. 37

Fig. 38

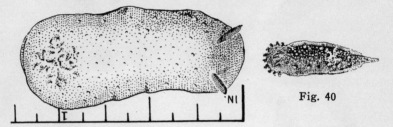

Fig. 40

Fig. 39

Fig. 41

Fig. 42

Fig. 37. Nudibranch, *Archidoris montereyensis;* dusty light yellow
(§ 109). Fig. 38. Nudibranch, *Cadlina marginata;* yellowish white;
tubercles tipped with lemon yellow; margin same color (§ 109). Fig.
39. Nudibranch, *Dendrodoris fulva;* rich yellow (§ 109). Fig. 40.
Nudibranch, *Triopha maculata;* background color yellowish brown,
usually a deep shade; bluish-white spots bounded by orange-yellow
lines (§ 109). Fig. 41. *Hopkinsia rosacea,* uniform bright rosy pink.
Fig. 42. Nudibranch, *Glossodoris californiensis;* deep blue with orange
stripes (§109).

PLATE XVI (Opposite page)

ANIMALS OF THE LOWER TIDE-POOL REGION

1. The brick-red Cancer, *C. productus.* A small adult (§ 106).
2. A young *C. productus* (§ 106).
3. A "moss animal," or bryozoan, encrusting on kelp. Inset shows an enlarged portion (§ 110).
4. The active and carnivorous snail, *Ceratostoma foliatum* (§ 117).

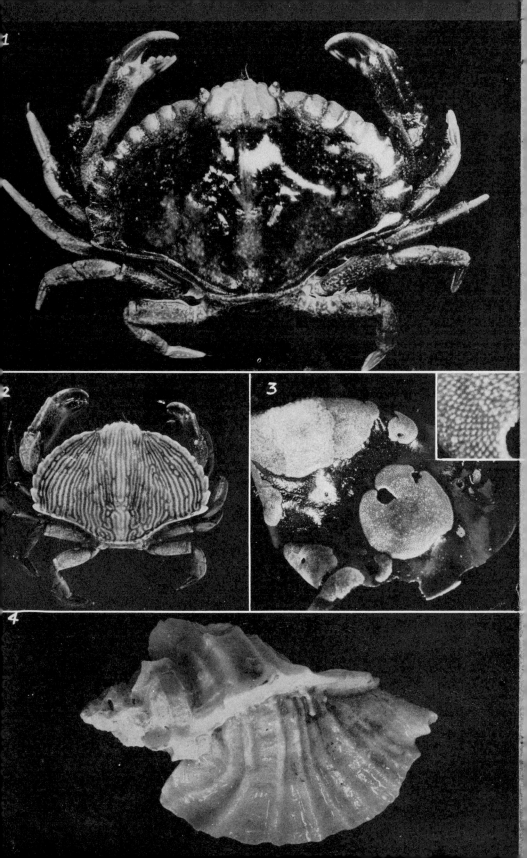

Fig. 43
The bryozoan, *Flustrella cervicornis*, growing on seaweed; natural size (§ 111).

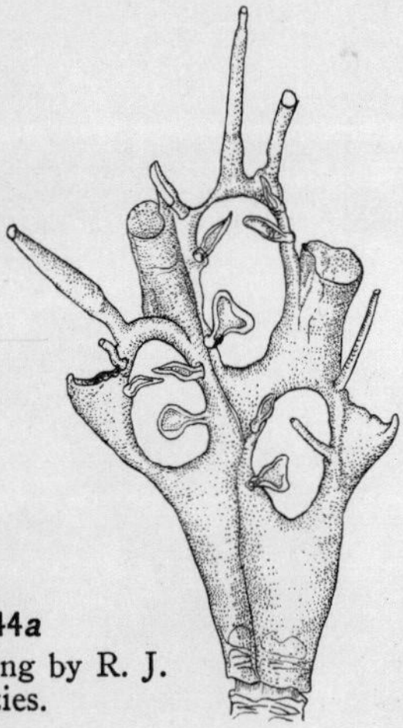

Fig. 44a
Detail; drawing by R. J. Menzies.

Fig. 44
The bryozoan, *Tricellaria occidentalis*; growing about the bases of eelgrass; natural size (§ 112).

PLATE XVII (Opposite page)
SOUTHERN BRITTLE STARS
Upper: *Ophioderma panamensis* (§ 121).
Lower: *Ophionereis annulata* (§ 121).

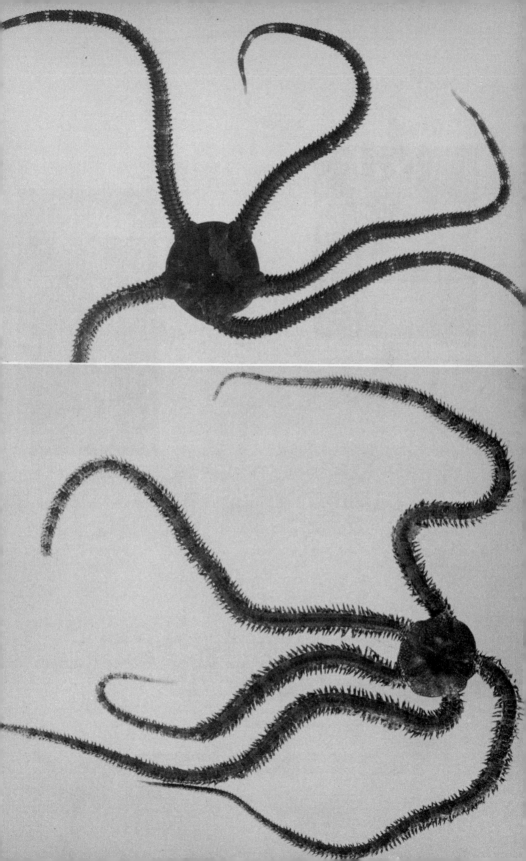

Fig. 45a
Detail.

Fig. 45
A bryozoan, *Bugula califor-nica* (§ 113).

Fig. 46a
Detail.

Fig. 46
Bugula pacifica, growing on a cluster of the hydroid, *Aglaophenia,* natural size; the inset, greatly enlarged, shows a "bird beak" gaping open (§ 114).

PLATE XVIII (Opposite page)

UNDER-ROCK ANIMALS OF THE LOWER TIDE-POOL REGION

Upper: Brittle stars.
  1. *Ophiopholis aculeata* (§ 122).
  2. *Ophiothrix spiculata* (§ 123).
  3. *Ophiopteris papillosa* (§ 124).

Lower:
  4. The fixed clam, *Chama pellucida;* slightly reduced (§ 126).
  5. The rock oyster, *Hinnites giganteus;* slightly reduced (§ 125).

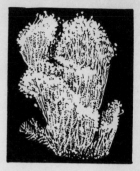

Fig. 47
One of the bryozoa, *Barentsia ramosa;* natural size (§ 115).

Fig. 48
The wavy top shell, *Astraea undosa;* natural size (§ 117). Drawing by Sam Hinton.

PLATE XIX (Opposite page)
UNDER-ROCK CHITONS (§§ 127, 128) OF THE LOWER TIDE-POOL REGION

Upper: *Stenoplax conspicua.*

Lower (in same scale):

1. *Stenoplax heathiana.*
2. *Ischnochiton regularis.*
3. *Lepidozona mertensii.*
4. *L. cooperi.*

5. *Placiphorella velata.*
6. *Mopalia ciliata.*
7. *M. mucosa.*
8. *M. ciliata,* eroded specimen.

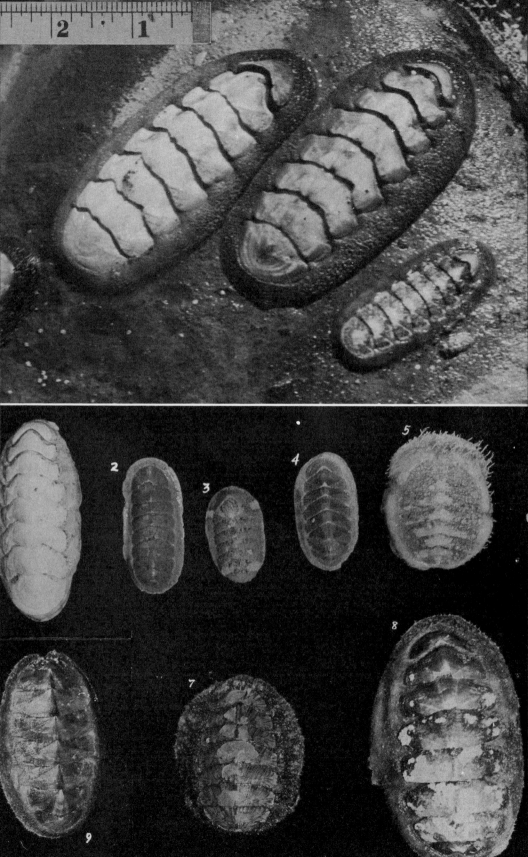

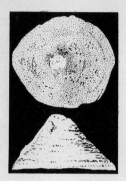

Fig. 49
The dunce-cap limpet, *Acmaea mitra;* natural size
(§ 117).

Fig. 50
Lophopanopeus heathii; natural size (§ 132).

PLATE XX (Opposite page)

UNDER-ROCK ANIMALS OF THE LOWER TIDE-POOL REGION

1. The plumed sabellid worm, *Eudistylia polymorpha*; actual length, 11½″
   (§ 129).
2. A masking crab, *Loxorhynchus crispatus* (§ 131).
3. *Mimulus foliatus* (§ 132).
4. Under side of the umbrella-backed crab, *Cryptolithodes* (§ 132).
5. The furry crab, *Hapalogaster cavicauda* (§ 132).

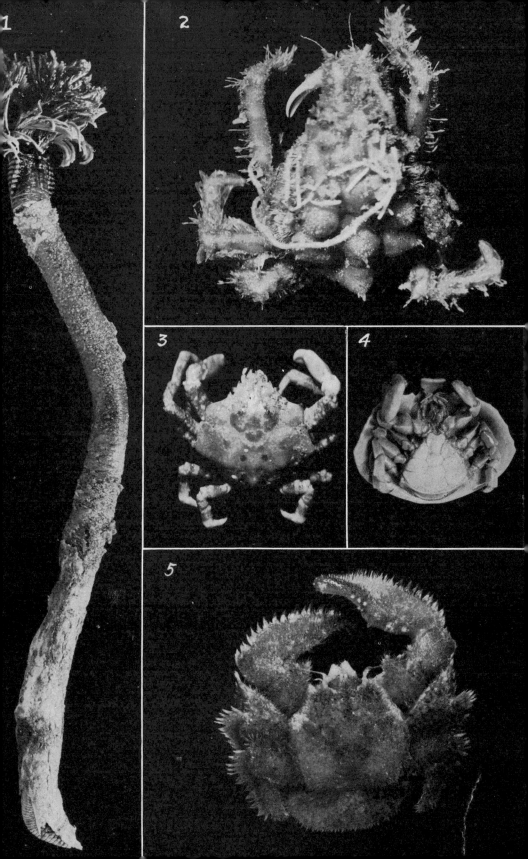

Fig. 51

An active snail, *Amphissa versicolor* (§ 137).

Fig. 52a

Bryozoa, *Hippodiplosia insculpta* (§ 140).

Fig. 52b

Bryozoa, *Phidolopora pacifica* (§ 140).

PLATE XXI (Opposite page)

SOUTHERN UNDER-ROCK ANIMALS OF THE LOWER TIDE-POOL REGION

1. *Cycloxanthops novemdentatus* (§ 133).
2. *Paraxanthias taylori* (§ 133).
3. The retiring southerner, *Pilumnus spinohirsutus* (§ 133).
4. The southern transparent shrimp, *Hippolysmata californica* (§ 134).
5. A young octopus, *Octopus* sp., in an aquarium. Photo by Woody Williams.

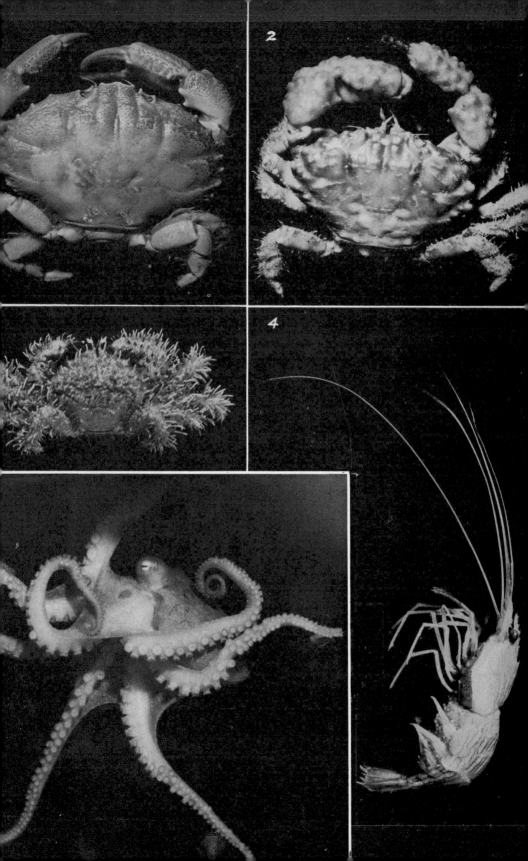

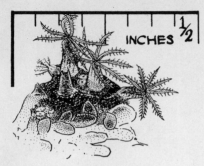

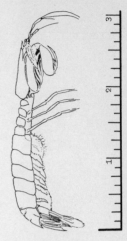

Fig. 53
A "soft coral," *Clavularia
sp.* (§ 144).

Fig. 54
The mantis shrimp, *Pseudosquilla* (§ 146).

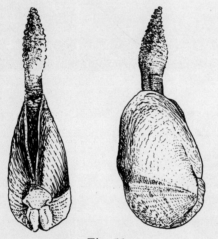

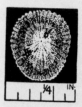

Fig. 55
A boring clam, *Pholadidea
ovoidea;* natural size (§ 147).

Fig. 56
The button-shell snail. *Trimusculus reticulatum* (§ 147).

PLATE XXII (Opposite page)

SOUTHERN CALIFORNIA MOLLUSKS AND A NORTHERN NEMERTEAN

1. The smooth brown cowry, *Cypraea spadicea* (§ 136).
2. A cone shell, *Conus californicus* (§ 136).
3. The small mussel, *Septifer bifurcatus* (§ 136).
4. *Cardita carpenteri* (§ 136).).
5. The smooth turban snail, *Norrisia norrisii* (§ 136).
6. A rusty-brown turban, *Tegula ligulata* (§ 137).
7. The nemertean worm, *Micrura verrilli* (§ 139).

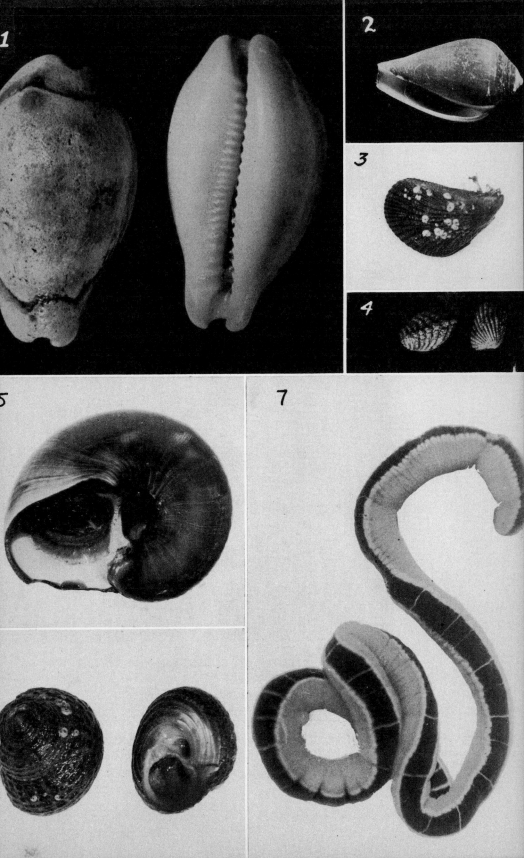

142

PLATE XXIII

UNDER-ROCK ANIMALS OF THE LOWER TIDE POOLS

1. An encrusting bryozoa, *Eurystomella bilabiata;* enlarged portion inset (§ 140).
2. The leaflike bryozoa, *Hippodiplosia insculpta* (§ 140).
3. The pistol shrimp, *Crangon californiensis* (§ 278). Photo by Martin W. Johnson.
4. The boring clam, *Saxicava pholadis* (§ 147).
5. *Pisaster giganteus capitatus,* a small colorful relative of the common starfish (§ 142).
6. The boring clam, *Platyodon cancellatus* (§ 147).

PLATE XXIV

ANIMALS FREE-SWIMMING IN POOLS AND OF THE UNDER-
ROCK SUBSTRATUM HABITAT, LOWER TIDE POOLS

1. The spiny lobster, *Panulirus interruptus;* reduced (§ 148).
2, 3, and 4. The "broken back" shrimps, *Spirontocaris prionota, S. palpator,* and *S. cristata;* photos copyrighted by Pacific Biological Laboratories (§§ 150, 278).
5. A flowering peanut worm, *Dendrostoma;* small specimen (§ 145).

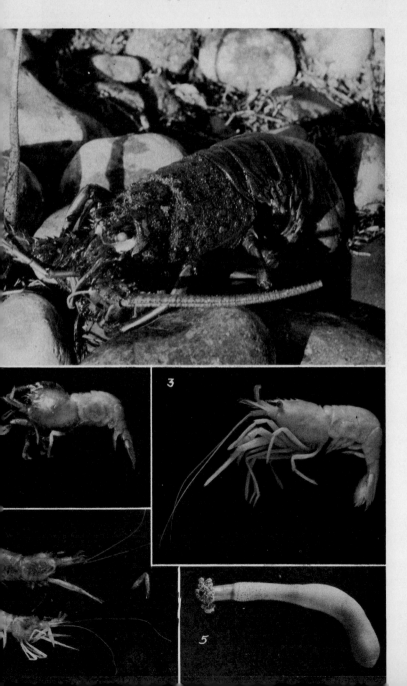

Hermissenda crassicornis, on *Eudendrium*. Photo by Woody Williams.

the internal organs are visible and "the beating of the systemic and branchial hearts may be observed." The body form is more like that of a squid than of an adult octopus. The young of Mephista II swam as soon as they were hatched, but they would not eat any food that was offered, even bits of yolk from their own eggs, and none lived more than three or four days.

The process of hatching usually involves a violent struggle. First the embryo squirms until it succeeds in splitting the capsule at one end; then "by vigorous expansions and contractions the body is forced out through the opening. . . . . The escape from the shell proceeds rather rapidly until the visceral sac and funnel are free. The somewhat elastic egg-shell seems to close around the head, behind the eyes, and the animal has to struggle violently to extricate itself. This final stage may occupy from ten to forty minutes." Once, in what might be interpreted as a flurry of temper at the difficulty of being born, one of the tiny animals discharged ink into its capsule.

§136. Conchologists have celebrated the richness of the southern California shores, and even the collector interested in animals rather than empty shells cannot fail to be impressed by it. Small representatives of the smooth brown cowries, *Cypraea spadicea* (Pl. XXII), and of the cone shells, *Conus californicus* (Pl. XXII), are likely to be found, both representative of families well developed in the tropics and featured in shell-collectors' cabinets. The top shells and purple snails are amply represented. The smooth turban, *Norrisia norrisii* (Pl. XXII), will be noticed for its size and numbers and enjoyed because of the pleasing contrast that the vivid red flesh of the living animal forms with the lustrous brown of the shell. It is a satisfying experience to find crawling about in tide pools living specimens of a type that one has known from empty shells only, especially since, for some of these mollusks, there are no known methods of anaesthetization that will permit preservation of the relaxed animal.

Septifer bifurcatus, a ribbed and slightly hairy mussel not unlike *Mytilus,* is found in these parts, but only under rocks and stones, often well up in the intertidal zone. Specimens may be more than $1\frac{1}{2}''$ long, but the average is smaller. Another common bivalve is *Cardita carpenteri,* a very small cockle-like form. For both see Plate XXII.

§137. *Tegula ligulata* (Pl. XXII), a rusty-brown turban with raised beaded bands, is gaily colored by comparison with its drab relative, *T. funebralis,* of the more shoreward rocks, and is more retiring, hiding under rocks during the day. South of the Los Angeles area the two may occur on the same beach, but north of that region *ligulata* is rarely found. It is recorded, however, as far north as Monterey.

No northern snail fills the place held by *T. ligulata* at, for instance, La Jolla. *Amphissa versicolor* (Fig. 51) possibly comes nearest. Restricted to the under side of rocks loosely buried in a gravelly substratum, this excessively active form sports a proboscis longer than the average. Most snails retract into and extend from their shells very deliberately. *Amphissa* emulates his enemy, the hermit crab. No sudden danger finds him napping, for he can retreat and advance a dozen times while *Tegula* is doing so once. This animal and expanded specimens of the giant moon snails (§252) are good for exhibition to whoever still believes that snails are mostly shell.

§138. A polyclad flatworm, *Leptoplana acticola,* has already been mentioned (§17) as an inhabitant of the upper tide pools. Along the central California coast, the polyclads are not abundant in the lower tide pools, but in the south it is under rocks in this lowest zone that they will be found—two of them, both probably unidentified, very commonly, and others occasionally. One of them we think of, for lack of any other name, as the "pepper and salt" flatworm. The other is an orange-red form. Two others, somewhat less common but more striking, have papillated furry backs and affix themselves to the rocks by means of suckers on their undersides. The one, likewise probably unidentified, is a soft brown form, up to 1½″ long. The second of them, probably a new species of *Thysanozoon,* the "scarf dancer," is not an impressive sight when found attached by its sucker and huddled up on the under side of a rock, but when it stretches itself to get under way in the clear water of a tide pool it presents a different picture. It is brilliantly colored and swims gracefully, undulating the margins delicately but effectively, and justifying its name. The people about Naples, Dr. Heath says, call the *Thysanozoon* there the "skirt dancer." Collectors who procure any of these undetermined forms will do well to preserve them carefully in six per cent formalin for forwarding to a specialist at present working with Pacific-coast polyclads.

§139. The most common habitat of nemerteans, or ribbon worms, is in the mud of bays and estuaries, so they are considered in some detail in that section (§312). However, a good many forms, some of them large and common, will be found at home under rocks on fairly open coast, and therefore require mention here. The most conspicuous of these, and indeed one of the most striking of all intertidal animals, is *Micrura verrilli* (Pl. XXII), whose body is vividly banded with sparkling lavender and white. It may be up to 12″ long, and ranges from Alaska to Monterey Bay, but unfortunately occurs not very frequently. *Paranemertes peregrina,* purple or brown with white under side, is commoner, ranging from the Commander Islands

(Alaska) to southern California, in length up to 6 inches. Near the Big Sur, and at Laguna, La Jolla, and Ensenada, we have found a long, stringy, pinkish nemertean we take to be *Cephalothrix major.* Its slightly flattened body is only about $\frac{1}{16}''$ wide, but it reaches a length of 4' and is comparatively strong. The mouth is set back some 2'' from the tip of the head, and this two-inch portion is cylindrical. Still another rocky-shore form is *Lineus vegetus,* known from Pacific Grove and La Jolla, a slender animal up to 6'' long, brown in color, with numerous encircling lighter lines. In contraction the body coils in a close spiral. This nemertean has been the subject of some interesting regeneration experiments reported in §312. A good many other forms may occur, most of which will be found treated in Coe's papers, but some unfortunately seem to be still undescribed. The brilliant *Carinella rubra* (§239) of quiet waters will be turned up here occasionally.

§140. Some of the bryozoa have been treated previously, so that the collector who has come with us this far will recognize several common encrustations under the rocks as belonging to this group. *Eurystomella bilabiata* (Pl. XXIII) is characteristically old-rose colored and always encrusts flatly on stones and discarded shells. A close examination even with the naked eye reveals much loveliness, but the esthetic appeal is much enhanced, as with other bryozoa, by the use of a binocular microscope or even a ten-power hand lens. *Hippodiplosia insculpta* (Pl. XXIII and Fig. 52a) is deep buff, and sometimes mildly erect in a leaf-like formation on sticks. When encrusting under rocks it may have an apparent thickness of several layers, rolled over at the margin. The living zooids of both these bryozoa can be seen, in fresh live colonies taken during the winter or spring, with the lowest power of a compound microscope. One of the so-called corallines, *Phidolopora pacifica* (Fig. 52b), is a bryozoan colony. Small lacy clusters of this latticed calcareous form are not uncommon under rocks in the south. The large colonies, up to a size that would make a double handful, can be got by dredging only. *Bilabiata* ranges from the Queen Charlotte Islands to Pacific Grove, *insculpta* from Sitka to Pacific Grove (and on to southern California as a subtidal form), and *pacifica* from Puget Sound to southern California. Attached forms include also the encrusting red sponges mentioned in §32, some of which are more at home in this deep littoral than further up. One, *Esperiopsis originalis,* brownish red, not even remotely resembling the magnificent erect *Esperiopsis* of central British Columbia inner waters, rarely occurs higher up. It encrusts the under sides of stones, but occurs also in crevices. A hard and pearly white encrusting form, thin and smooth, *Xesto-*

spongia vanilla, characteristic of the entire Pacific coast, looks like
cake frosting. The very lumpy, hemispherical, bright orange, woody-
fibered *Tethya aurantia* may be taken at Carmel, far down in rocky
crevices or on the under sides of rocks. If detached, the base with
its radiating core structure should be noted; this is diagnostic; there
is nothing else even slightly like it in the tide pools. This is a cosmopolitan form, almost worldwide in distribution, and more abundant
than might be supposed at first glance, since many specimens are
overgrown with green algae.

§141. Although the southern California cucumber, *Stichopus parvimensis,* has been treated (§77) as a protected rock animal, it often
occurs, especially when a low tide comes in the heat of the day, in
the under-rock habitat. North of central California the white *Cucumaria quinquesemita* occurs in this habitat, too, but is much more
common in sheltered waters such as Puget Sound (§235).

Thyonepsolus nutriens, a small, red, flattened cucumber that is
remarkable for carrying its young on its back, is occasionally found
in the Monterey region. Strangely, however, central California, a
region otherwise very fecund, has no shore cucumbers comparable
in abundance with *Stichopus* in the south or *Cucumaria miniata* in
the north. Presumably more efficient animals just happen to have
crowded them out. Another viviparous holothurian (cucumber), red
with white under side, is the small *Thyone rubra.* Either of these
may come to light in the examination of kelp roots.

§142. A definite form of the starfish *Pisaster giganteus,* called
capitatus (Pl. XXIII), is a not uncommon under-rock member of
the southern California fauna. It is by no means gigantic, despite
its name, being usually smaller than the common *Pisaster ochraceus,*
and is certain to be taken for a different species even by collectors
familiar with the typical *P. giganteus* of Monterey Bay and north
(Pl. XXVI), for it differs in habitat, shape, and color, as well as
in size. The few spines are large, stumpy, and vividly colored a
slaty purple on a background of ocher. The northern recorded
range is about San Luis Obispo, and we have taken it as far south
as Ensenada. With it may be taken an occasional *Astrometis* (§72)
or small *Patiria* (§26), most of the southern representatives of the
latter species being stunted and limited to the under-rock habitat.

§143. The noisy pistol shrimp, *Crangon dentipes,* may be taken
from under rocks in the lower extremity of the rocky intertidal zone
and from the sponges and bryozoa growing in kelp holdfasts. Unlike the good children of a past generation, it is more often heard
than seen. Very often the collector will hear the metallic clicking of
these shrimps all around him without being able to see a single speci-

men and, unless he is quick and industrious, without being able to take one. Captured and transferred to a jar, the animal is certain to cause excitement if his captor is inexperienced. It is hard to believe, on hearing the inevitable sound for the first few times, that the jar has not been violently cracked. This startling sound is made by the animal's snapping a thumb against the palm of the big claw, the suddenness of the force applied being made possible by a trigger-like device at the joint. Any attempt at a close investigation of the operation is likely to result in the investigator being left in possession of the detached claw, the denuded shrimp retiring to grow himself a new snapper. What purpose this snapping accomplishes, unless it frightens enemies, it is difficult to guess. *Crangon* is a rather cosmopolitan species in northern tropic regions, and occurs also, for some unknown reason, as far north as San Francisco, extending southward on this coast to Cape San Lucas.

In similar environments the colorful shrimp *Spirontocaris* (§150) of several species may be seen. Amphipods and isopods of several types occur, but none seems to be specifically characteristic here or of particular interest to anyone but a specialist.*

§144. Two "soft corals" (*Alcyonaria*) occur, most amazingly for deep-water forms, along Pacific-coast rocky shores even where there is some surf. From La Jolla south, one of them, probably a species of *Clavularia* (Fig. 53), is present in the very low-tide zone along the sides of rocks just where they are buried in the substratum, or on the bottoms of rocks. Typically there is a brown, ribbon-like stolon, which is not easy to detach, networked on the under surface of the stone, with cartridge-like polyps 1/8″ or so high in contraction beaded up from the stolon. Expanded (and they expand readily in aquaria), the polyps may be 3/8″ high, spreading eight feathery tentacles. Because this typically alcyonarian polyp is abundant, easy to get, and hardy, it should be useful for experimental work. We have found it most abundantly in Todos Santos Bay, north of Ensenada. This is the animal which has been considered, at Laguna Beach, to be *Telesto ambigua,* a form that is known from several hundred fathoms in Monterey Bay and that is related to a West Indian *Telesto* which may grow more than a foot tall, occurring on shallow bottoms like eelgrass. Miss Deichmann, however, refers it probably to *Clavularia,* in spite of the resemblance of the polyps to those of our deep-water *Telesto.*

In Monterey Bay there is a form similar to the *Clavularia* which

* Sea spiders (pycnogonids) are seen occasionally. One, *Ammothella bi-unguiculata* var. *californica,* is common and fairly characteristic under stones at Laguna Beach and elsewhere in southern California, specimens being taken on the hydroids also. There is a good illustration in Hall (1912), Fig. 50.

Dr. Hickson has very kindly identified for us as another and new species of *Clavularia*. It is white, clustered like a tunicate, and certainly different from the first-mentioned form. Both of these are related to the tropical pipe-organ corals seen in museums, but resemble them in neither appearance nor habitat.

(d) Fauna of the substratum under rocks.

Limited observation has failed to indicate any outstanding difference between the substratum faunae of the middle and lower tide pools. The ghost shrimps and blind gobies treated as substratum animals in the middle tide-pool zone belong more properly here, but are considered in the higher association because the collector will find them there first.

§145. A larger and handsomer sipunculid, or peanut worm, than *Phascolosoma* (§52) is *Dendrostoma pyroides* (Pl. XXIV), rich brown in color and having long plumed tentacles. It is this or a related species which is illustrated in Plate XXIV. The fully contracted specimens, as taken from their under-rock burrows, will usually flower out very beautifully if allowed to remain undisturbed in a dish of fresh sea water placed in subdued light. *Dendrostoma* may be taken as far north as Monterey Bay, where it occurs in the lowest reaches of the intertidal zone, but a related species, *D. zostericolum* (described as *zostericola*), occurs in some abundance at La Jolla and in northern Lower California under rocks and eelgrass. At the present writing, however, the animal is unaccountably scarce. Our last three collecting trips into Mexico (during the winter and spring of 1930) netted only a few specimens, although we specifically hunted the animal. Quite possibly the deep substratum under-rock *Dendrostoma,* of southern California and below, also belongs to *pyroides,* although it is ecologically different, while *zostericolum* occurs in the matted roots of the surf-swept eelgrass, *Phyllospadix.*

Records in our files bewail the fact that the usual narcotization methods fail for some of the sipunculids: "the retractor muscles retaining their viability even after decay has set into parts of the softer tissue." New light has recently been shed on this extraordinary vitality by Peebles and Fox, who report that experimentally treated *D. zostericolum* lived in evacuated Nujol connected to a 15–28" vacuum line for three days, and for more than a week in similarly conditioned sea water. It was determined that they could lose 43 per cent of their moisture content through desiccation, or 40 per cent of their total weight, without dying. One of the conclusions was to the effect that the worms possess an oxidizing (metabolic) system with a higher reducing potential than the methylene blue which was used as the most delicate chemical indicator available, since living animals stained with this dye decolorized it after all the free oxygen had been used up, the color returning as soon as fresh oxygen was introduced. Specimens of this type live in the sometimes putrefying matter at the roots of eelgrass in the La Jolla region, passing sand through their intestines for the sake of the contained nutriment.

§146. The mantis shrimp, *Pseudosquilla lessonii* (Fig. 54), is a shrimp-like crustacean up to 3″ long, related to the mantis shrimp (*Squilla*) of Europe and the southeastern coast of the United States. It is a strictly southern form, not occurring north of Point Conception, and living so deep in the substratum beneath the lowest intertidal rocks that probably none but the most ardent collector will find it. When he does find it he is likely to be rewarded for his labor by so severe a nip that he will be glad to let it go immediately. The nip will have been delivered by a unique instrument quite different from the plier-like claw of a crab. The last segment of the great claw has a row of sharp curved hooks which are forced, by muscular contraction, into sockets in the next segment. Thus if the animal lacks the sheer strength of a crab it compensates with greater mechanical efficiency.

Other mantis shrimps are reported from the southern region. We have failed to find them, but it is safe to assume that their habitat does not differ greatly from that of *Pseudosquilla*. The similar *Squilla polita* is known to occur even as far north as Monterey Bay (from one dredging record), but although the National Museum reports no occurrence in less than twenty-nine fathoms, this is probably one of the forms dug occasionally by enthusiastic shore collectors in the Laguna–La Jolla region.

In such environments also, along the San Mateo County shore, occasional gigantic annelids (up to several feet long) will be dug out, *Neanthes brandti* (§164), probably the largest polychaet on the coast, in appearance similar to the mussel worm illustrated in Plate XXVI.

§147. Where the substratum is formed of stiff clay, packed hard enough to provide attachment for sessile animals, any of several pholids, or boring clams, may occur, their sometimes highly colored siphons protruding from their burrows. The smallest of the lot is *Pholadidea ovoidea* (Fig. 55), with a cleancut, almost oval, shell and a creamy-lemon-colored siphon covered with tubercles. It ranges from the Bering Sea to the Gulf of California. *Pholadidea penita* (§242), the form that bores in concrete also, is a bit larger—a little larger than a man's thumb—and has a longer shell with leathery flaps or lips at the siphon end. *Saxicava pholadis* (Pl. XXIII), a nestler, with red-tipped siphons, is chunky, often distorted, and ranges from the Arctic to Panama. The same plate shows *Platyodon cancellatus,* a relative of the soft-shelled clam *Mya,* which may honeycomb whole banks of stiff blue clay and is undoubtedly a factor in the disintegration of certain shores. On a recent trip to Santa Cruz we found a tremendous chunk of clay, weighing many tons, that had been broken off and up-ended by the waves which were slowly pounding it to pieces. Hundreds of these boring clams were being exposed and killed by this process of disintegration—a process that they themselves had undoubtedly started. A few specimens of this species, whose recorded range is from Bolinas Bay to San Diego, have been found in low-grade concrete piles in Los Angeles Harbor. Another species, a giant red-siphoned form (probably *Parapholas californica*), is abundant at Santa Cruz, but we have never succeeded in taking a specimen because of its occurrence on outer reefs where the continual surf makes the prolonged labor of digging out so large an animal impossible. A smaller species occurring with *Parapholas* in stiff blue clay is apparently *Barnea pacifica,* although it is reputedly a mud-borer.

After these forms have completed their burrows their muscle feet degenerate and the shell closes over them, in contrast with *Zirfaea* (§305), which remains active throughout its life. The boring methods of the pholids are considered in §242.

The discarded burrows of dead borers furnish safe and comfortable homes for various smaller animals. Among them are likely to be the crab, *Pachycheles* (§318), and others—the flatworm, *Stylochoplana* (§243), and the button shell, *Trimusculus reticulatum* (formerly *Gadinia*). The latter (Fig. 56) looks like a small limpet, but has lungs, is hermaphroditic, and is related to the common garden snail.

(e) Pool habitat. Free-swimming or actively crawling animals not often found outside pools.

§148. In the pools at the lowest tide level there is a wealth of life. Most of the individuals occur in other situations as well and are treated elsewhere, but some of the larger animals are entirely free-swimming and essentially pool inhabitants. Only by the rarest accidents are they stranded high and dry. The famous spiny lobster, *Panulirus interruptus* (Pl. XXIV), which so often meets the fate of the innocent oysters that accompanied the Walrus and the Carpenter, belongs in this group. It is chiefly a subtidal form, but it so often allows itself to be trapped in pools that it may at least be said to have shore-loving tendencies.

Our spiny lobster lacks the pinching claw of its Atlantic relative, but is nevertheless perfectly capable of making its own way in a world that is hostile, cruel, and unco-operative. Unless captured with a spear or trap it has a good chance to evade the path that leads to mayonnaise and seasoning. If taken with bare hands it snaps its broad tail back so powerfully and in such a formidable manner as to intimidate its captor, possibly driving home some of its spines.

To prevent the extermination of the species by continual commercial fishing, the females under 10½" in length and over 16" are protected by law, the reason for the maximum being that the largest females lay the most eggs—possibly as many as half a million at one time. The "leaf-body" larvae are delicate feathery creatures which seem to consist mainly of two large eyes, the rest of the body being highly transparent. After the larval and intermediate stages the lobster continues to grow, like the crabs, by a series of moults. The moulted shell is left in such perfect condition that it may easily be mistaken for a live animal. Spiny lobsters are omnivorous feeders —almost anything will do, plant or animal, fresh or decayed—and are themselves preyed upon by octopi and large fish, particularly the jewfish. They move by walking—forward, sideways, or backward— or propel themselves stern first through the water by rapid flips of their powerful tails.

Panulirus is an entirely southern form not authentically known north of Point Conception but occurring far down into Mexico. A similar lobster occurs off the Florida coast, where it is known as the Florida crayfish.

§149. Another enlivener of southern tide pools is the vividly gold Garibaldi, a fish known to science as *Hypsypops rubicunda*. Vertebrates have scant place in this account, as an adequate treatment of fish alone would require a separate book, but the Garibaldi is too common and too obvious to omit entirely. Another fish that merits passing mention is variously known as the tide-pool sculpin, the Rockpool Johnny, and *Oligocottus maculosus*. It is a small fish with a sharply tapering body, a large ugly head, and large pectoral fins. It is red-brown and prettily marked.

§150. A number of shrimps may sometimes be common in the lower pools. They are members of the common genus *Spirontocaris,* "broken back" shrimps, having the characteristic of bending their tails suddenly under and forward and thus swimming backwards. The *Spirontocaris* to be found in the higher tide pools are small and transparent; those centering here (Pl. XXIV) are opaque and relatively massive. *S. prionota* ranges from Bering Sea to Monterey. *S. palpator* ranges from San Francisco to Magdalena Bay and *S. cristata* (§278) from Sitka to San Diego, but almost invariably subtidally or in eelgrass in quiet water. Less commonly, any of half a dozen others may be found, *S. taylori* in the south and notably *S. brevirostris* (not illustrated). This large and beautiful white shrimp has been reported from Alaska, and it ranges at least as far south as the area between Carmel and the Big Sur, for we have found it there in some quantity, under rocks in pools where the water is very pure. The typical littoral specimens, however, are smaller than the large and robust "bastard" shrimps of the Alaska shrimp dredgers.

These shrimps show a great variety of brilliant coloring which makes them conspicuous in a white tray but very difficult to see against the colorful background of a tide pool. There is no ready way of distinguishing the various species, reference to exact anatomical descriptions being the only method.

To the northward very much larger shrimps of the edible species of *Crago* and *Pandalus* (§283) may be trapped occasionally in the pools, but these must be regarded as rare visitors from another habitat.

§151. Some of the rhythms in nature are today as completely baffling as they have been since first they were observed. The palolo worm of the tropical seas near Samoa, living the year round in coral burrows at the sea bottom, for instance, is an entirely reliable calendar. To quote from an excellent English work, *The Seas*, by Russell and Yonge:

"But true to the very day, each year the worms come to the surface of the sea in vast swarms for their wedding dance. This occurs at dawn just for two days in each of the months, October and November, the day before, and the day on which the moon is in its last quarter; the worms are most numerous on the second day, when the surface of the ocean appears covered with them. Actually it is not the whole worm that joins in the spawning swarm. The hinder portion of the worm becomes specially modified to carry the sexual products. On the morning of the great day each worm creeps backwards out of its burrow, and when the modified half is fully protruded it breaks off and wriggles to the surface, while the head end of the worm shrinks back into its hole. The worms are several inches in length, the males being light brown and ochre in colour and the females greyish indigo and green. At the time of spawning the sea becomes discoloured all around by the countless floating eggs.

"The natives are always ready for the spawning swarms as they relish the worms as food. . . . . The worms are eaten either cooked and wrapt up in bread-fruit leaves, or quite un-dressed. When cooked they are said to resemble spinach, and taste and smell not unlike fresh fish's roe."

All of which is far from home but not entirely disconnected, for we have at least two similar annelid worms on the Pacific coast. One is *Odontosyllis phosphorea,* whose swarming periods have been plotted at Departure Bay. Only a very persistent or a very lucky collector will see them, for except in their brief periods of sexual maturity, when they appear at night in countless hordes, not a single specimen is to be found.

In the tide pools of the California coast a smaller form, only a fraction of an inch in length, is more common than the above. At dusk they may be seen swimming actively at the surface of pools, appearing as vivid pinpoints of phosphorescence.

The inevitable question with regard to such animals is: How do they know when the moon has reached a certain stage in a certain one of the thirteen lunar months? The obvious answer would seem to be that they do not, but govern their swarming time according to tides, which, in turn, are governed by the moon. Unfortunately this answer will not hold. The tides are governed not by the moon alone but by the sun and more than half a hundred additional factors. To suppose that the worms can take all of these factors into consideration passes the bounds of credulity. Furthermore, worms placed experimentally in floating tanks have spawned naturally at the usual times, although they had no means of sensing what the state of the tide might be. We are driven, then, back to the moon as the undoubted stimulus for their spawning, and confronted with a mystery beside which any of Sherlock Holmes' problems seem pale and insipid.

Nor are such worms as these the only sea animals that follow amazing cycles. The grunion (§192) is, if possible, an even more startling example.

§152. The occasional sandy pools found rarely between rock outcroppings a few feet apart, as at Carmel, more frequently along the outer coast of Washington, as at Queets and Mora, may be characterized by a colonial spionid worm, *Boccardia proboscidea,* extending from Washington to southern California or beyond, penetrating clay or shale rocks with vertical, U-shaped burrows, its two minute tentacles protruding from one end of the burrow. Here in these pools also will be found a few young edible crabs, *Cancer magister,* which stray up into the intertidal from deeper sandy bottoms. At Queets, specimens of this sort are relatively common, so that sportsmen vary their capture of razor clams on open sandy beaches with profitable excursions into these rockbound, sandy pools. As a commercial product, the life history of *magister* is known. The average life span is about eight years, the maximum ten; specimens do not become sexually mature probably until the fourth or fifth year.

(f) Root and holdfast habitat.

§153. A collector having sufficient strength and enthusiasm will find much of interest in pulling up, at extreme low tide, the holdfasts of various algae, or large clumps of eelgrass, roots and all. In a typical large holdfast or root he will find hundreds of individuals of dozens of different species. Nemerteans and occasional nestling clams live in the inner parts, while bryozoa, hydroids, sponges, tunicates, small anemones, holothurians (§141), and chitons cover the outside.* Crawling over and through this living mass are hordes of snails, hermits, crabs, brittle stars, starfish, amphipods, and isopods.† Here is a perfect little self-sufficient universe, all within a volume of less than a cubic foot. A census of the holdfast inhabitants of various regions has been suggested as an index of richness for comparing different areas. Most of the forms occurring thus in the Pacific have been considered in connection with other habitats. The few that do not occur elsewhere are forms so small as to fall outside the scope of this work, but if only for the sake of renewing a large number of old acquaintances the collector will find holdfasts and roots worth investigating.

* There are many small worms, particularly in the interstices. A *Lumbrineris*, possibly *L. erecta* (= *heteropoda*), green, and stouter than the attenuated *L. zonata* of §130, occurs in *Phyllospadix* roots from Monterey well into Lower California. A similar *Lumbrineris*-like form, very slim and breakable, green and highly iridescent, is the cosmopolitan *Arabella iricolor.* *Anaitides medipapillata,* one of the "paddle-worms" (phyllodocids), so called because of its broad, leaf-shaped appendages, will be turned up in this assemblage, not frequently, but with admiration and enthusiasm on the part of the fortunate observer who will admire its rich dark greens and brown or cream trimmings, with iridescent glints. Specimens of this sort may be several inches long. A similar form is illustrated on page 314, Volume 2 (1910), of the *Cambridge Natural History.* Also in *Phyllospadix,* sometimes in quantity sufficient to bind their roots together, will be found tubes of the small *Platynereis agassizi,* in appearance similar to the *Nereis* of Plate XXVI but lacking the broadness of the posterior appendages. Specimens experimentally deprived of their white tubes will construct others very quickly in aquaria, utilizing and cementing together with mucus any bits of plant tissue available.

† Sea spiders (pycnogonids) have been taken. One is characteristic of *Phyllospadix* roots, but has been taken also on hydroids, or even walking about on the pitted rocks: *Ammothella tuberculata,* extending from northern California to Laguna Beach. Figure 7, Plate 12 of Cole (1904), illustrates this form, which has a spread of under ½ inch. The amphipods occur in profusion, and among the more than seventy different species that we alone have turned up in Monterey Bay, many of them undescribed, the following might be considered characteristic of kelp holdfasts and similar habitats: *Eurystheus tenuicornis,* from Puget Sound to San Diego, especially common in the south; *Aoroides columbiae,* known also from Puget Sound, and from many habitats, including coralline algae, clusters of *Leucosolenia,* etc., even from *Pelvetia,* higher up; *Hyale,* probably of several species, possibly the commonest low-tide hoppers of the Monterey Bay region, and reported also by Dr. Light's students of invertebrate zoölogy at the University of California from the coast lines of Marin and San Mateo counties.

B. Sandy Beaches

PRESUMABLY because of their usually limited extent, the sandy beaches of the protected outer coast are the most barren of all intertidal areas. They occupy a strange position, biologically speaking. They are distinct, on the one hand, from the typical Pacific sandy beach, which is completely exposed and subjected to violent surf but nevertheless supports a highly specialized fauna, although it is neither abundant nor greatly varied. In closed bays, sounds, and sloughs, on the other hand, we find the completely protected sandy beaches supporting a fauna both rich and varied. No doubt the total area available for colonization is the chief factor in both the latter cases, for characteristic animals will not develop for a type of region that is represented by small and widely separated areas only, like the sandy beaches in question. Such beaches ordinarily occur in short stretches of a few hundred yards or a few miles, between outcroppings of rock, and are almost destitute of life. It might reasonably be asked why such areas are not colonized by the animals from surf-swept beaches; the answer is, apparently, that the animals of surf-swept beaches will not tolerate the more sheltered conditions. The same answer, reversed, would apply to completely protected bay animals, for whom these areas would be too exposed. At any rate, barrenness is the rule, and we have but three animals to record from the semi-sheltered sandy beaches, ignoring those forms which may occasionally be washed up from other habitats.

§154. A giant beach hopper, *Orchestoidea corniculata,* is successful in this barren environment, possibly because it lives high up, avoiding the "old devil sea" to which it belongs. During the day it hides in burrows in the sand, coming out at night to feed on decaying seaweed and storm wrack. Occasionally, however, it may be found during the day under piles of seaweed. This beach flea is probably the chief scavenger of the semi-protected beaches. When the waves bring it nothing it must find the food supply rather scanty unless, as is suspected, it turns with equal gusto to detritus originating on land. In appearance it is very similar to a still larger related hopper of surf-swept beaches (§185), but its antennae are not so long.

Smallwood, who has worked with an East-coast beach flea that is similar in form and habitat to our *Orchestoidea,* believes that the animals' reactions to light do not account for their nocturnal habits, but that keeping out of sight in the daytime is simply a protection against birds.

§155. A second and much smaller beach hopper, *Orchestoidea benedicti,* is the only animal from the surf-swept beaches that is at home here as well. Unlike the larger hoppers, it can be found at will during the day, which seems to upset the bird theory unless its size or flavor are protective factors.

§156. So deep down as to be chiefly a subtidal form, especially where the sand is firm, with an admixture of detritus, but sometimes to be seen from the shore, is a lugworm that belongs more properly in the mud flats of protected bays (*Arenicola,* §310). It is a burrowing animal that breathes by keeping two entrances open to the surface. About one of them characteristic castings of sand will be noticed. On these barren beaches it occurs, so far as we have observed, only where rocky outcrops divert the surf in such a way as to induce the deposition of some silt—the situation to be expected, since the worm feeds by eating the substratum and extracting therefrom the contained organic matter.

II. OPEN COAST

A. Rocky Shores

ALONG the surf-swept open coast, the rocky cliffs of the ineptly named Pacific have developed associations of animals with phenomenal staying powers and endurance of wave shock. It is not the fact that these animals will not live elsewhere that makes them characteristic but the fact that no other animals than these can tolerate the rigorous conditions of heavy surf. Obviously the prime requisites here are the ability to hold on in the face of breaking waves and the possession of structures fit to resist the sudden impact of tons of water. Hence the development of the tough skins and heavy shells generally present, the strong tube feet of starfish, and the horny hairs by which mussels are attached.

At first blush it seems amazing that in this surf-swept environment the same animals should occur almost unchanged all the way from Sitka to Point Conception (a few miles west and north of Santa Barbara), for the long intervening stretch of coast works an irregular traverse across twenty-two and a half degrees of latitude—across most of the North Temperate Zone. This range seems less remarkable when we consider that conditions are actually very uniform. Along the California coast there is an upwelling of relatively cold water such that the resulting water temperature is lower than would be expected considering the latitude, and in the north the Kuroshio, the warm Japan Current, sweeps inshore in direct proportion to the increase in latitude, with the result that the waters along the outside coast of British Columbia and southeastern Alaska are very nearly as warm as those along the California coast as far south as Point Conception. Also the summer-winter variation in the temperature of the water is one of only a few degrees. The water is almost constantly agitated, and throughout the Sitka to Point Conception range there are great depths close offshore and correspondingly uniform oceanic conditions. Finally, even the weather is relatively uniform along this immense coast line, fogs and cool weather being the rule, with no great peaks of heat or cold.

159

Perhaps a word of warning is in order here. Especially from central California northward such completely exposed rocky points as
are considered in the first part of this division are very dangerous
places. It has been stated that in some regions any person within
twenty feet of the water, vertically, is in constant danger of losing
his life, and every year the newspapers report, with monotonous regu-
larity, the deaths of people who have been swept from the rocks by
unexpected waves of great size. Such loss of life is usually as un-
necessary as it is regrettable. To lie down and cling to the rocks like
a starfish and let a great wave pour over one takes nerve and a cool
head, but more often than not it is the only sane course of action. To
run, unless the distance be very short, is likely to be fatal. As is likely
to be the case with mundane hazards, the danger from surf largely
disappears when its force is recognized and respected; hence no one
need be deterred by it from examining the animals on exposed points,
always bearing in mind that a brief wetting is better than a permanent
one. When collecting at the base of cliffs, we always keep handy a
rope made fast at the top of the cliff.

The force of the waves on stretches of completely open coast is
so great that animals up near the high-tide line are wetted by spray
on all but the lowest tides. Consequently there is not the relatively
sharp zonation that we find elsewhere, and some of the most obvious
animals are fairly well distributed throughout the intertidal zone.
Accordingly we shall depart somewhat from our usual method and
shall treat these wide-ranging animals first, taking up the more definitely zoned animals later.

§157. The most conspicuous of the open-coast animals is *Pisaster
ochraceus* (Pl. XXV), sometimes popularly called the purple starfish
but more properly the common starfish—an animal distinctly different
from the common starfish of the Atlantic. Specimens varying from
6″ to 14″ in diameter and having three color phases—brown, purple,
and yellow—are commonly seen on exposed rocks from Sitka to Point
Sal (near Point Conception). In the warmer waters below that point
a subspecies, *segnis,* extends at least to Ensenada.

Up to one per cent of the pisasters seen between northern California and Monterey Bay will be the more delicate and symmetrical
P. giganteus (Pl. XXVI), with beautifully contrasting colors (which
are lacking in *ochraceus*) on and surrounding the spines. This starfish is improperly named, as the average specimen is smaller than the
average *ochraceus.* The explanation is that the species was originally
named from a particularly large specimen which was assumed to
be typical.

Pisaster neither has nor seems to need protective coloration. Anything that can damage this thoroughly tough animal, short of the "Acts of God" referred to in insurance policies, deserves respectful mention. To detach a specimen from the rocks one heaves more or less mightily on a small pinch-bar, necessarily sacrificing a good many of the animal's tube feet but doing it no permanent injury thereby, as it will soon grow others to replace the loss. The detached tube feet continue to cling to the rock for an indefinite period. An Eastern investigator finds that the tube feet of the common starfish of the Atlantic will live for several days in clean sea water and will respond to stimuli for two days or more. Histological examination shows deep sense cells and a net of material that is probably nerves.

The action of the pedicellariae—minute, pincher-like appendages that keep the skin of starfish and urchins free of parasitic growths— can be demonstrated particularly easily with *Pisaster:* Allow the upper surface of a husky specimen to rest against the skin of your forearm for a few seconds; then jerk it away. The almost microscopic pincers will have attached themselves to the epidermis in such a way that you will feel a distinct series of sharp nips. A classic experiment to demonstrate the function of pedicellariae is to drop crushed chalk on the exposed surface of a living starfish. The chalk is immediately ground to a powder so fine that it can be washed away by the action of the microscopic waving cilia in the skin. Considering that sessile animals must struggle for even sufficient space for a foothold, and that starfish live in a region where the water may be filled with the minute larvae of barnacles seeking an attachment site, the value of these cleansing pedicellariae is very apparent. It is even possible that they have some value in the obtaining of food, for despite their small size they have been observed to catch and hold very small crabs, which may eventually be transferred to within reach of the tube feet.

Just how breathing is effected is not definitely known, but it is assumed that the tube feet may play a part. There are, in addition, delicate, finger-like extensions of the body wall scattered over its upper surface. These extensions are lined, both inside and out, with cilia, and probably assist in respiration. Many small shore animals have not even this degree of specialization of breathing apparatus— sponges, for example, getting what oxygen they need through their skins. In connection with the general subject of respiration, it is interesting to note the great number of marine animals, including some fishes even, that are able to get oxygen from the air as well as from the water. This is necessarily the case with a large proportion of the animals herein considered. Some, in fact, like the periwinkles, some of the pill bugs, and a fish that lives on the Great Barrier Reef, will drown if they cannot get to the air. Among the shore crabs the gill structure shows considerable progress toward air-breathing—a process that reaches its climax in some of the tropical land crabs which have developed a true lung and return to the sea only to breed.

We have found *Pisaster* feeding on mussels predominantly, less frequently on barnacles and snails, and rarely on goose barnacles and limpets. Its feeding habits, and the feeding habits of starfish in general, are noteworthy. The stomach is actually everted and thrust into the shell of the animal to be eaten, so that digestion takes place outside the body of the diner. This is an interesting adaptation to the method of food getting and the type of food utilized. On the Atlantic coast the starfish are very destructive to oyster beds, thereby achieving such economic importance that their natural history has been studied carefully. It was found that they open shellfish by attaching their tube feet to the two shells and pulling. Anyone who has tried to pry open the shell of a bivalve without cutting the muscles would be justified in believing that no starfish could have the requisite strength. A bivalve is, in fact, stronger than a starfish on a sudden pull, but it has not the staying powers of the starfish. Humped up over its prospective meal, the starfish exerts a slow steady pull that will eventually tire the muscles of even the largest bivalve and compel them to relax. The shell gapes open and the fight is over.

The starfish's humping-up process enables it to exert the necessary pull in opposite directions. It has been demonstrated that if a specimen is lightly compressed between two glass plates so that it cannot assume the humped-up position it cannot avail itself of food. Here on the Pacific coast at least one out of every fifty starfish will be found humped up over a mussel, either in process of opening it or with its stomach thrust in between the gaping shells.

Nothing is known about the life history or rate of growth of this Pacific form. Atlantic starfish become adult in one season, but there is reason to suspect that *Pisaster* grows very slowly. There is no season of the year, so far as is known, when the representative specimens are larger or smaller than at any other season, and we have found only one or two regions where there was a high percentage of small specimens. If growth were rapid, one would expect to find a high proportion of young specimens in the community, whereas if growth were slow the expectation would be just what we find—only a few small specimens in a representative area.

The sexual products are extruded from pores between the rays and on the upper surface, as with *Patiria* (§26), but probably not so frequently. Observations extending over five years, on several thousand *Pisaster* which were spread out prior to preservation, showed only five cases of extrusion—one in March, one in June, two in October, and one in December. Then in the warm summer of 1931 we found sexual products extruding from more than a score of specimens in one lot of four or five hundred.

At present *Pisaster's* chief claim to fame lies in its abundance and vivid colors. If we would know more of its natural history we must hope that it will become economically important enough to require investigating.

§158. The common starfish is the most obvious member of the triumvirate characteristic of this long stretch of surf-swept rocky coast. The others are the California mussel and the Pacific goose barnacle. The mussel, *Mytilus californianus* (Pl. XXV), ranging from Alaska to Mexico, forms great beds that extend, in favorable localities, from above the half-tide line to well below extreme low water. Here is another animal that is distinctly at home in crashing waves. Indeed it occurs only where there is surf, whereas some *Pisaster* may be found elsewhere. Each animal is anchored to the rock by byssal hairs, tough threads extruded by a gland in the foot. Contrary to the natural expectation, however, *Mytilus* is actually capable of limited locomotion, provided it is not too tightly wedged into position by other mussels. It can achieve a slight downward motion by relaxing the muscle which controls the byssal hairs, but it can go still farther than this by bringing its foot into play. By extending its foot and gripping the rock with it, it can exert a pull sufficient to break its byssal hairs a few at a time, or even pull the byssus out by the roots. Once the hairs are all broken, it can move ahead the length of its foot, attach new hairs, and repeat the process.

The mussel's chief enemies are man and *Pisaster,* but we have caught the snail *Thais* in the act of drilling neat holes through the shells of small specimens preparatory to extracting the body bit by bit. It is possible that some fish feed on them also. The mussels themselves feed, like other bivalves, on minute organisms in the water.

The California mussel is fine fare for humans as well as for starfish, but cases of paralytic poisoning following their consumption have been so frequent that it seems wise to refrain altogether or to eat them during the winter only. The situation has been investigated recently by the Hooper Foundation of the University of California, and an incidental report with some references will be found in *Science* for December 16, 1932, p. 574 (**76**, No. 1981). Only the open-coast bivalves seriously develop the poison, which results from the ingestion of certain planktonic organisms present during the summer only. The toxin is water-soluble and is destroyed by alkalis, such as boiling with soda. It has been suggested that the sand crab, *Emerita* (§186) may serve as an index for the guidance of public-health officials in estab-

lishing quarantine areas and periods, since these small burrowing
crustaceans of the open coast feed in a manner similar to *Mytilus*
and are similarly afflicted with the poison, which can be experimentally
demonstrated by injection in white mice. Unfortunately this toxicity
is not restricted to mussels; any open-coast bivalves may be dangerous when the particular type of floating organisms are running during
the summer. The razor clam (§189) may be dangerously poisonous,
and even such specimens of the Washington and horse-neck clams
(§§300, 301) as occur in inlets adjacent to ocean shores had best be
shunned during the summer months. Oysters, *Protothaca* (rock
cockles), *Mya,* and most of the Washington and horse-neck clams are
perfectly safe, being restricted to quiet waters.

One of us (Calvin), working up Alaska historical data at Sitka,
found frequent references to mussel-poisoning in translating the accounts of Father Veniaminoff and other early Russian explorers.
Baranoff lost a hundred or more Aleuts all at once in Peril Strait;
the stench arising from the stricken made even the others ill. One of
Vancouver's men is said to have died thus, and others nearly lost their
lives similarly.

The breeding season of *Mytilus californianus* has been investigated by Stohler (1930), who found July and December peaks in
the proliferation of eggs and sperm. The sexes are separate.

§159. Accounts of the starfish-oyster association of the East
coast are never complete without reference to the oyster crab. The
corresponding starfish-mussel assemblage on the Pacific is completed
by the commensal mussel crab or pea crab, *Fabia subquadrata*
(Fig. 57), which is found in about three per cent of the full-grown
California mussels. Curiously enough, only the female lives in the
mantle cavity of *Mytilus*. It has been presumed to be the case, as
with other pea crabs, that the male is smaller than the female and
free-living, but until recently it was supposed that the male had never
been seen. The situation became more and more curious when Wells
discovered (in 1928) that the male had been known for years but had
been considered not only a different species but a member of a different genus. He is, as was expected, smaller and free-living, and it
goes without saying that he bears almost no resemblance to the female.
Pinnotheres concharum was his former name, which he must now
relinquish in favor of his wife's.

It has been deduced that the male visits the female after she has
established herself in a mussel, for the males of other species than
our Pacific *Fabia* have been found trapped between the shell valves.
The male's visit is not as hazardous as it might seem, for he has a
carapace tough enough to resist crushing by the mussel's valves. The

sheltered females, however, are soft and weak, and show none of the
pugnacity that characterizes most free-living crabs.

In order to find out how the female conducted the affairs of daily
living, one investigator, working with a similar species, cut a window
in the shell of a mussel. He found that a large crab usually sat in the
middle of the bivalve, where she could most conveniently scrape food
from her host's gills—food which was intended for the host's own
consumption. Small crabs were likely to be anywhere, but most commonly on the gills. The pea crab is not a parasite, since it does not live
directly on the substance of its host, but is a commensal or "messmate."
The pea crab of the eastern oyster, however, may sometimes injure the
tissues of the oyster, demonstrating that the border line between "commensal" and "parasite" may sometimes be very narrow.

§160. The Pacific goose barnacle, *Mitella polymerus* (Pl. XXV),
the third member of an assemblage so common that we call it the
Pisaster-Mytilus-Mitella association, is fairly well restricted to the
upper two-thirds of the intertidal zone. These three animals, "horizon
markers" in marine ecology if ever there were any, are almost certain
to be associated wherever there is a stretch of rocky cliff exposed to
the open Pacific. The goose barnacle extends the general range of
the association, being recorded from Bering Strait to the middle of
Lower California, specimens on the open coast of Alaska, however,
being comparatively few and scattered.

Mitella is commonly chalky colored when dry, but there is a vividly
colored subspecies which is restricted to caves or rocks sheltered
from direct sunlight, identified for us by Dr. Pilsbry as *M. polymerus
echinata*. In the Santa Cruz region clusters of this subspecies increase
in brilliancy of markings as they range deeper into the darkness of
the cave. Although the adult goose barnacles resemble but vaguely
the squat and heavy-shelled acorn barnacles, they are closely related,
and both have substantially the same life history featuring free-
swimming nauplius larvae outlined in §4.

The *California Fish and Game Commission Publication* for 1916
gives a recipe for preparing goose barnacles, the "neck" or fleshy stalk
of which the Spanish and Italians consider a choice food.

The name, "goose barnacle," comes to us from the middle-seven-
teenth-century writings of that amiable liar, Gerard, who ended his
large volume on plants "with this woonder of England," "the Goose-
tree, Barnakle tree, or the tree bearing Geese." After declining to
vouch for the authenticity of another man's report of a similar marvel,
Gerard continued: "Moreover, it should seem that there is another
sort heerof; the Historie of which is true, and of mine owne knowledge: for travelling upon the shores of our English coast between

Dover and Rummey, I founde the trunke of an olde rotten tree, which (with some helpe that I procured by fishermens wives that were there attending on their husbandes returne from the sea) we drewe out of the water upon dry lande: on this rotten tree I founde growing many thousands of long crimson bladders, in shape like unto puddings newly filled before they be sodden, which were verie cleere and shining, at the neather end whereof did grow a shell fish, fashioned somewhat like a small Muskle, but much whiter, resembling a shell fish that groweth upon the rocks about Garnsey and Garsey, called a Lympit: many of these shels I brought with me to London, which after I had opened, I founde in them living things without forme or shape; in others which were neerer come to ripeness, I found living things that were very naked, in shape like a Birde; in others, the Birds covered with soft downe, the shell halfe open, and the Birde readie to fall out, which no doubt were the foules called Barnakles. I dare not absolutely avouch every circumstance of the first part of this Historie concerning the tree that beareth those buds aforesaide, but will leave it to a further consideration: howbeit that which I have seen with mine eies, and handled with mine handes, I dare confidently avouch, and boldly put downe for veritie."

Britannica Conchæ anatifera.
The breede of Barnakles.

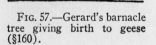

FIG. 57.—Gerard's barnacle tree giving birth to geese (§160).

Gerard was quite in accord with the modern tendency to popularize science. However, he perceived that pure scientists would desire certain definite information, so he added: "They spawne as it were in March and April; the Geese are formed in Maie and Iune, and come to fulnesse of feathers in the moneth after." Also he catered to the likewise modern feeling that pictures cannot lie: his graphic representation of the birth of barnacle-geese is reproduced in Figure 57.

The remainder of the wave-swept rocky-shore animals lend themselves better than the foregoing to treatment according to tidal zones corresponding to the upper, middle, and lower tide-pool regions of the protected outer coast.

Zone 1. *Animals of the uppermost shore, from the spray line to plus 5′ at Pacific Grove.*

§161. As in other regions, the first animals to be encountered will be the dingy little snails, *Littorina,* but whereas they occur a little above the high-tide line on protected outer shores, they will be found here twenty or twenty-five feet above the water. *Littorina* is famous for its independence of the ocean. Tropical species have taken to grass and herbage at the top of low oceanic cliffs, and even to trees bordering the water.

Next in the downward progression, but still many feet above the water, come very small specimens of the barnacle, *Balanus glandula* (§4), whose sharp encrusting shells are likely to exact a toll of flesh and blood from the careless visitor. In regions of excessively high surf, however, they may be absent, not because they lack the ability to hold on once they have colonized the region but because the delicate, free-swimming larvae may never be able to get a foothold if there is high surf during the season when they should attach. A tremendous and epic struggle for existence comprises the daily life of the animals of this region where the only unfought-for advantage is an abundance of oxygen. Barnacles and mussels begin to feed within sixty seconds after immersion, and their great haste is understandable when one considers that they are covered, in this highest zone, only when a wave dashes up over them, and that there is competition for every passing food particle. They must fight for a foothold, fight to keep it, and fight for their food.

Limpets occur here also, but not in the great numbers that characterize the highest zone of more protected shores. The commonest form is *Acmaea digitalis* (Pl. I and Fig. 9), but others will be found, including *A. cassis* and the giant *Lottia,* which, on these open shores, ranges high up.

§162. From Alaska southward to Santa Cruz, a semi-land-living pill bug or isopod, *Ligyda pallasii* (Fig. 59), haunts the rocky cliffs, being found invariably above the reach of water, whatever the state of the tide. Specimens taken during July at Mora, on the open coast of Washington, had the brood pouch turgid with developing young and when handled roughly deposited hosts of newly born children in one's hand. Another species of this landward-extending crustacean occurs on the protected outer coast south of Santa Cruz (§2).

Zones 2 and 3. *Upper and middle shore, high- and mid-tide regions.*

§163. Here mussels and goose barnacles begin to occur in large beds which afford shelter to a number of animals not themselves adapted to withstanding surf. Probably the most obvious of these is the predaceous worm *Nereis vexillosa* (Pl. XXVI), known variously as the mussel worm, the clam worm, and the pile worm. Certainly it is the most important from the standpoint of sportsmen, who seek it along thousands of miles of coast line to use for bait. Possibly because of its proclivity for letting other animals provide its shelter from surf, *Nereis* is one of the few animals that may be found in nearly all types of regions, from violently surf-swept shores to the shores of bays and completely protected inlets, and in such varying types of environment as rocky shores, gravel beaches, and wharf piling. Not only does it occur from Alaska to San Diego,* but it seems to be abundant throughout its range, whereas other animals occupying so great a stretch of coast usually have optimum areas, dwindling away toward the north or south. Thus *Nereis* might be considered in almost any section of this handbook. It is treated in this particular place because the largest specimens are commonly found in the mussel beds of the open coast, where they vary from 2″ to 12″ in length. They are usually colored an iridescent green-brown.

The animals are very active and squirm violently when captured, protruding and withdrawing their chitinous jaws which terminate a wicked-looking, protrusible pharynx and make carnivorous *Nereis* a formidable antagonist. These powerful jaws are capable of delivering a business-like bite to tender wrists and arms, but in collecting many hundreds of them bare-handed we have rarely been bitten, always taking the precaution of not holding them too long.

In its breeding habits *Nereis* is one of the most spectacular of all shore animals. In common with other segmented worms, its sexual maturity is accompanied by such changes in appearance that early naturalists considered *Nereis* in this condition to be a distinct animal, *Heteronereis*—a name which has been retained to denote this phase of the animal's life cycle. The posterior segments (red in the female) containing the gonads, swell up with eggs or sperm, and the appendages normally used for creeping become modified into paddles for

---

* Chamberlin regards the southern California specimens as *N. mediator.* It takes microscopic work on the part of the specialist to distinguish these and related *Nereis.*

swimming. When moon and tide are favorable, the male heteronereis, smaller than the female, leaves his protective shelter, seemingly flinging caution to the wind, and swims rapidly and violently through the water, shedding sperm as he goes. Probably a large proportion of the males become food for fishes during the process, and no doubt a similar fate awaits many of the females, who follow the males within a short time, releasing their eggs.

It has been determined experimentally in connection with related species that females liberate their eggs only in the presence of the male, or in water in which sperm has been introduced. If a specimen of each sex can be obtained before the ripe sexual products have been shed, the experiment can be performed easily. The female, in a glass dish of clean sea water, will writhe and contort herself for hours with frenzied and seemingly inexhaustible energy. Introduce the male, or some of the water from his dish if he has shed his sperm in the meantime, and almost immediately the female will shed her eggs. When the process is over the worms, in their natural environment, become completely collapsed, empty hulls and die or are devoured by fishes, birds, or other predaceous animals.

We have many times found the large heteronereis of *N. vexillosa* in the mussel clusters on surf-swept points—abundantly in late January, less frequently in February or early March. Dr. Martin W. Johnson (1943, *Biol. Bull.* **84**) found spawning heteronereid adults at Friday Harbor in the summer of 1941 and identified gelatinous egg masses of the species. According to Dr. Johnson, *N. vexillosa* spawns only at night, usually an hour or two before midnight. Shedding specimens of a smaller wharf *Nereis* (*N. mediator*) are common in Monterey Harbor (*see* §320).

§164. A second nereid, not as common as *vexillosa* but sufficiently startling to put the observer of its heteronereis stage in a pledge-signing state of mind, is the very large *Neanthes brandti*, differing from the similar *N. virens* in having many, instead of few, paragnaths on the proboscis. Specimens may be nearly three feet long, and are broad in proportion—a likely source for sea-serpent yarns. To the night collector, already rendered a bit jumpy by weird noises, phosphorescent animals, and the ominous swish of surf, the appearance of one of these heteronereis, threshing madly about at the surface of the water, must seem like the final attack of delirium tremens. We have found this great worm, not in the free-swimming stage, under the mussel beds at Moss Beach, San Mateo County. It has been reported from Puget Sound to San Pedro, and we have a specimen from southeastern Alaska.

§165. Associated with *Nereis* in the mussel beds are the scale worm, *Halosydna brevisetosa* (§49), the porcelain crab, *Petrolisthes* (§18), and, at times, the pill bug, *Cirolana harfordi* (§21). In some regions the nemertean worm, *Emplectonema gracile,* is so common as to form tangled skeins under the mussels. This rubber-band-like animal is tinted a pale yellow-green on its upper surface, white on its lower. It is slightly flattened, but is rounder than most ribbon worms, and is from 1″ to 4″ long when contracted. We have found great masses of these at Mora, on the outer coast of Washington, and at Santa Cruz, California. Other nemerteans have the unpleasant habit of breaking up into bits when disturbed; but this one—a highly respectable animal from the collector's point of view—has that trait poorly developed and may be taken therefore with comparative ease. A fuller account of nemerteans is given in §312.

Another haunter of the mussel beds is a snail which in the past we have mistakenly supposed to be a young *Thais* (§182). This form, *Acanthina spirata* (Fig. 60), occurs higher up than *Thais,* however, occupying on surf-swept shores about the relative position taken by *Tegula* on the protected outer shores. It is recorded from Puget Sound to Socorro Island.

Two small crustaceans will be found at this level. The minute amphipod, *Elasmopus rapax* (Fig. 61), is exceedingly abundant in the middle-zone beds of mussels. The much larger isopod, *Idothea wosnesenskii* (Fig. 62), up to 1½″ long, ranges from Alaska to central California. We have found it only on rocky shores, but it is said to occur also in sand. This is the commonest small crustacean at Santa Cruz, in numbers more than equivalent to the mussels which make up the clusters in which it most characteristically occurs.

§166. Great honeycombed colonies, often dome-shaped, of the tube worm, *Phragmatopoma californica* (Pl. XXVI), may share available areas with the mussel beds. They are very likely to be found taking advantage of the slightest bits of shelter in the way of overhanging ledges and concave shorelines. The thin-walled tubes which make up the colonies are made, apparently, of sand cemented together. The worms themselves, rarely seen unless one chops into a colony, are firm, chunky, and dark, with a black operculum that stoppers up the tubes when the animals are retracted. The similar, more northern, *Sabellaria cementarium* has a rough, amber-colored dome. Like other tube worms, these are dependent for food on what chance brings their way, although they can assist the process by setting up currents with the cilia on the protruded gill-filaments. The previously recorded range was from San Francisco to San Diego, but we have seen large colonies near Half Way House, between Tia Juana and Ensenada. The colony shown was photographed west of Santa Cruz.

§167. In situations similar to the above, but where the shore formation is tipped more horizontally, beds of the small aggregated anemone often occur. They are not so characteristic here, however, as in the protected outer coast environment (§24).

§168. A fairly large barnacle, dull brick-red in color, conical in shape, and with the semi-porous consistency of volcanic slag, is *Tetraclita squamosa rubescens*. Average specimens are easily twice the size of the *Balanus* (§4) found in the same association, and they are more solitary, rarely growing bunched together or one on top of another as is the case with the white barnacle.

§169. *Nuttallina californica* (Pl. XXVI) is a small sea cradle or chiton, rarely more than 1½″ long, that is pretty well restricted to the middle intertidal of fairly exposed shores. It can be distinguished by its rough uncouth appearance, spiny girdle, and color—dull brown streaked with white. It may be found occasionally well up toward the high-tide line, but never much below the middle zone. At Laguna Beach and other places in the south this chiton lives in sculptured furrows in the rock. If these furrows are of the chiton's own making, as they appear to be, they are comparable with the excavations made in rock by the owl limpet and the purple urchin. In all three cases the object is apparently to gain security of footing against the surf. The recorded range is Puget Sound to the Coronado Islands.

Below the middle zone, *Nuttallina's* place is taken by the larger *Katharina* (§ 177). Both of these chitons are perfectly well able to take care of themselves at times of high surf, for they are very tough and attach to the rocks so tightly that a flat, sharp instrument must be used to pry them away. Detached from their supports, chitons promptly curl up like pill bugs.

§170. Where there are rock pools at this level, congregations of purple urchins may be found, with occasional hermit crabs (*Pagurus samuelis*) and rock crabs (§14) and purple shore crabs (§27), but these are all treated elsewhere, in the zones and habitats where they find optimum conditions. Theoretically, any animals common in the middle tide-pool region of protected outer shores may be found also in these more or less protected rock pools, but they are scarce or local, not characteristic of the region in general as is the *Pisaster-Mitella-Mytilus* association, which finds its climax in this level.

§171. Plants are out of the province of this book, but in connection with methods of resisting wave shock it is worth while to mention the brown alga called the sea palm, *Postelsia palmaeformis*. It is restricted to the temperate Pacific coast of North America, and occurs only where the surf is continuous and high. Along the central California coast great forests of these beautiful plants are found on

rocky benches and flats. Instead of sustaining the shock of the tower-
ing breakers by rigid strength, as do most of the animals in the
region, the sea palms give to it. Under the force of a powerful
breaker a row of them will bend over until all fairly touch the rock,
only to right themselves immediately and uniformly as the wave
passes. This particular form of resistance is made possible by the sea
palm's tremendously tough and flexible stalk, which is attached to
the rock by a bunchy holdfast of the same material. It will be noted
that specialized individuals of a limpet considered previously, *Acmaea
cassis* (§11), may be found on the swaying stalks of *Postelsia,* thus
extending their range into an environment otherwise too rigorous
on account of surf, were it not for the protection and amelioration
offered by this plant's flexibility.

ZONE 4. *Lowest intertidal. Low-tide region.*

§172. On violently surf-swept cliffs and tablelands where even
the sea palm cannot gain a foothold, bare rock constitutes the typical
tidal landscape. A few scrawny laminarians may occur, but never on
the boldest headlands, and not until the collector descends (the surf
permitting) to the extreme low-tide level will he find any common
plant. Even then he is likely to overlook it unless he accidentally
knocks a bit of inconspicuous red crust from a rock. This very flat
encrusting material is the alga *Lithophyton,* under the surface of
which most of the small animals of the region are to be found. The
animals so occurring, however, are on the completely exposed shore
only by virtue of the protection which this encrusting plant gives
them, for all are protected coast forms (and hence treated elsewhere).
Many of them occur again in kelp holdfasts.

The great green anemone is very much at home here, growing luxuriantly to a size that makes it a close second to the anemones of the
Australian Barrier Reef. This giant beauty will always be found,
however, in situations where it is reasonably sheltered from the full
force of the surf. For this reason, and because it is quite likely to
have been first seen in the tide-pool regions, it has been treated as
a member of the protected outer coast fauna (§64).

A more characteristic animal, occurring also under flat rocks and
imbedded boulders, is *Idothea stenops* (Fig. 63), one of the largest
of the isopods, recorded only from the Monterey Bay region. The
smaller *I. schmitti* will be found under similar circumstances, and at
San Remo, below Carmel, we have taken both at the same place.

§173. A great ostrich-plume hydroid, *Aglaophenia struthionides,*

occurs in rock crevices, especially in large vertical crevices in the
line of surf. This form is considerably larger than members of the
genus found on relatively protected shores, and the largest clusters
are so dark as to be nearly black. Otherwise there is little difference
and the reader is referred to Plate XIV.

This is one of the few hydroids that occur in bona fide surf-swept
environments, except on the open coast at Sitka. There tufted colonies of two great and coarse sertularians will be found. The ranker
of the two, *Abietinaria turgida* (reported as common in the Bering
Sea–Aleutian region), occurs in great coarse growths up to 6″ or 8″
high, with short branches (which may be branched again) almost as
coarse as the main stem, and with the cup-like hydrothecae crowded
close on stem and branch. The more delicate and elongate *Thuiaria
dalli,* ranging from Bering Sea to Puget Sound, has a straight heavy
main stem; but the branches, which take off at right angles, are slender and without secondary branches, and the cup-like receptacles into
which the tentacles are withdrawn are small and comparatively few.

However, where the crevices are deep enough, even along the
California coast, or where overhanging ledges simulate the semi-
sheltered conditions of reef and tide pool, such other hydroids as
Eudendrium (§79), *Abietinaria anguina* (§83), and even *Tubularia
marina* (§80) may occur, with the sponge, *Rhabdodermella* (§94), the
hydro-coral, *Allopora porphyra* (§87), and the bryozoan, *Bugula
californica* (§113), all of which are treated in Division I.

In fairly barren rock formation off the coast of Alaska near
Sitka, we recently turned up a magnificent red-encrusting soft coral,
Eunephthya rubiformis, at first taken for a compound tunicate, but—
once we had set out a mass in a tray of fresh sea water—allocated
correctly as an alcyonarian by its high-expanding and white, 8-ten-
tacled polyps. This "sea-strawberry" is characteristic of high Arctic
waters, and it was a surprise to find it so far south.

§174. Here the purple urchin, *Strongylocentrotus purpuratus* (Pl.
XXVII), is distinctly at home, having made one of the most interesting adaptations of all to the pounding surf. The animal will commonly be found with at least half of its bristling bulk sunk into an
excavation in the rock. For more than a hundred years the method
of producing these excavations has been a subject of controversy, but
it is generally agreed now that Fewkes stated the situation correctly
in 1890. He believed that the teeth and spines of the animals, aided
by motions produced by waves and tides, were sufficient to account
for the pits, however hard the rock and however frayable the urchins'
spines, for the latter would, of course, be continually renewed by
growth. Sometimes an urchin will be found that has imprisoned

itself for life, having, as it grew, gouged out a cavity larger than the entrance hole made when it was young.*

This purple urchin ranges from Alaska to Cedros Island, probably entirely on the outer coast, as opposed to the green urchin of Puget Sound and northern inside waters. The reproductive season at Monterey is during March and April at least. The food-getting, reproductive, and fighting habits of urchins have been discussed in connection with the giant red urchin (§73). A good many of the latter occur here at a level below the pits of the purple urchins. In fact, they are possibly as common here as in the outer tide pools of the more protected areas.

All three of these urchins, red, purple, and green, have a number of hangers-on, both inside and out. An intestinal flatworm has already been mentioned in connection with the giant red form. In addition to the flatworm, Lynch finds practically one hundred per cent infestation of the intestine with one or more of twelve distinct species of protozoans, some of them comparatively large (¼ mm.). For zoölogy classes near the seashore these would provide easy demonstrations of living marine protozoa. There are also isopods, *Colidotea rostrata*, that occur nowhere except clinging to the spines of urchins. Mrs. Grant (MS.) notes that on the reef at Point Arena pits formerly occupied by purple urchins now contain dunce-cap limpets (§117) by the hundred.

§175. The gigantic horse mussel, *Volsella modiolus*, formerly *Modiolus*, up to 9″ in length, is no longer common, its depletion being the result, probably, of too many chowders, too many conchologists, and the animal's presumably slow rate of growth. Although it occurs a bit below the low-tide line, the horse mussel's brown shell, naked except for a fine beard, is very noticeable, especially by contrast with the California mussels alongside it. Such of the California mussels (§158) as occur this far down are giants of the tribe but are never clean-shelled as are the colonies higher up in the intertidal. Many plants, from coralline algae to small laminarians, grow on their shells, providing almost perfect concealment. Some common starfish (§157) range down this far also, undeceived by the mussels' disguise; but their apparent base of distribution is higher up. The smaller and more southern *V. recta* may also be seen, particularly along less strongly exposed shores, as at La Jolla.

* G. W. Otter ("Rock-burrowing echinoids," *Biological Reviews*, 7: 89–107, 1932), reopening this question, confirms Fewkes' findings except to observe that tide and current have nothing to do with burrowing activities, which are entirely voluntary through the agency of just such organs as would prevent the animal from being whirled about. The start is almost invariably at a natural depression, and sudden storms undoubtedly dislodge many young specimens before they have adequately bored in.

§176. In the Monterey Bay region, beds of the foliose coralline *Cheilosporum* (the coralline being stiffened by the same encrusting red alga that grows on rocks in this zone) are certain to harbor very tiny cucumbers, *Cucumaria curata,* that look like bits of tar. The animals are so small that they can be mounted whole on micro slides, with the internal anatomy diagrammatically visible under the microscope. We do not know of their occurrence anywhere except in the region mentioned, where, in addition to their coralline habitat, they are occasionally found under mussels in this lowest zone. We have found ovigerous specimens in December, the eggs being brooded on the under side as in *Thyonepsolus* (§141).

On the same coralline there occurs also a very similar but much larger species, *Cucumaria lubrica* (Fig. 64), which is often more than an inch long. Size alone will distinguish the two, but an additional difference is that *lubrica* has ten large tentacles, while *curata* has eight large and two small ones. We have specimens of *lubrica* from the vicinity of Juneau and from Puget Sound (the northern specimens being larger and lighter in color), as well as from Monterey Bay; hence it will probably turn up at various places along the intervening coast line.

§177. *Katharina tunicata* (Pl. XXVII), whose dead black tunic has almost overgrown the plates of its shell, is one of the few chitons that does not retreat before daylight, or even sunlight, and next to the "gum boot" (*Cryptochiton*) it is the largest of the family. In the low-tide area *Katharina* assumes the position held in the middle zone of the same surf-swept regions by *Nuttallina,* but *Katharina* shows more definite zonation, occurring, in suitable locations, in well-defined belts a little above the zero of the tide tables. In Alaska *Katharina* is the most abundant intertidal chiton, and it ranges plentifully as far south as Point Conception, where there is a great colony, and less commonly below there to the Coronado Islands.

On the most exposed parts of the open coast *Katharina's* eggs are shed in July, at least in the central California region, but in Puget Sound sexual maturity comes a month or two earlier. Strangely enough, on at least one occasion *Katherina* was found to be not only the commonest chiton but one of the most prevalent of all littoral forms, in a British Columbia locality almost completely protected from wave shock (but directly fronting a channel to the open coast), an anomalous situation recalling the remarks of the ecologist Allee (1923) to the effect that if the search is long enough one can turn out very nearly any animal in any environment, however far-fetched.

§178. Where laminarians or other algae provide the least bit of shelter, the sea lemon, *Anisodoris nobilis,* one of the largest of all nudibranchs, may be found. The average length is around 4 inches, but 8-inch specimens have been taken. Their usual vivid yellow color sometimes tends toward orange. All have background splotches of dark brown or black, while the knob-like tubercles that cover the back are yellow. In common with other dorid nudibranchs, especially the yellow ones, *Anisodoris* has a fruity, penetrating, and persistent odor. This species ranges from Vancouver Island to Laguna Beach. Mac-Farland wrote, in 1906, that it occurred on piling in Monterey Harbor; but it disappeared from there, along with many other animals, with the oil fire of 1925. We have seen these hermaphroditic animals depositing strings of eggs in November.

§179. The black abalone, *Haliotis cracherodii* (Pl. XXVII), prefers more surf than its red cousin or, more likely, tolerates more surf because it finds food-getting conditions more to its liking on surf-swept shores. Some abalones, this black form in particular, seem to derive much of their nourishment from plankton—a fact which explains why the black abalone is so often found in the crevices of barren rocks where there is no visible food in the way of fixed vegetation. Again unlike the red form, which invariably carries a small forest on its back, the black abalone keeps its shell clean and shining. The latter is definitely smaller and with 5 to 8 perforations; the legal size is 5½ inches. It makes quite as good steaks or chowder as the red abalone provided that it is pounded a little more energetically. Ranging from Oregon to Lower California, the animal is always most at home in vertical fissures in the rock, where tide and surf provide heavy currents for respiration.

On the outer coast of British Columbia and Alaska is another abalone, whose thin, pink, and wavy shell is the prettiest of the lot; this is *H. kamtschatkana* (§74), commoner in semi-protected waters.

§180. The largest of the keyhole limpets, which are related to the abalones and no more than a family or so removed from them in the phylogenetic scale, is *Megathura crenulata* (Fig. 65), known also as *Lucapina*. A good-sized specimen is 7″ long and massive in proportion. The flesh of the under side of the foot is yellow, and the oval shell, which has many fine radiating ridges, is nearly covered by the black mantle. Many animals lose their color after death, but this giant keyhole limpet is unique in that its black will come off in life if the mantle is rubbed. The range is from Monterey to Lower California, and we have found specimens particularly common in Todos Santos Bay.

§181. *Diodora aspera* (Pl. XXVIII), another of the keyhole limpets, is small by comparison with the above, but still large for a limpet. Large specimens will measure 2″ to 3″ long, and the recorded

II. OPEN COAST

§§ 157–193, Figures 58–69, Plates XXV–XXIX

Point Lobos from the air. U.S. Navy Photo.

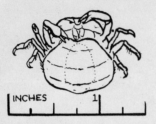

Fig. 58
The mussel crab, *Fabia sub-quadrata* (§ 159).

Fig. 59
The isopod, *Ligyda pallasii;* actual size (§ 162).

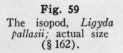

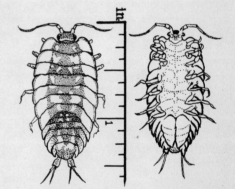

PLATE XXV (Opposite page)

THE "BIG THREE" OF SURF-SWEPT ROCKY SHORES

1. Bed of California mussels, *Mytilus californianus;* in same scale as lower (§ 158).
2. Cluster of goose barnacles, *Mitella polymerus;* in same scale as lower (§ 160).
3. Group of common starfish on vertical rock face, *Pisaster ochraceus* (§ 157).

Fig. 60
A mussel-bed snail, *Acanthina spirata*; about twice natural size (§ 165).

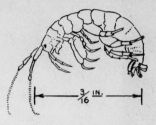

Fig. 61
A tiny amphipod of the mussel beds, *Elasmopus rapax* (§ 165).

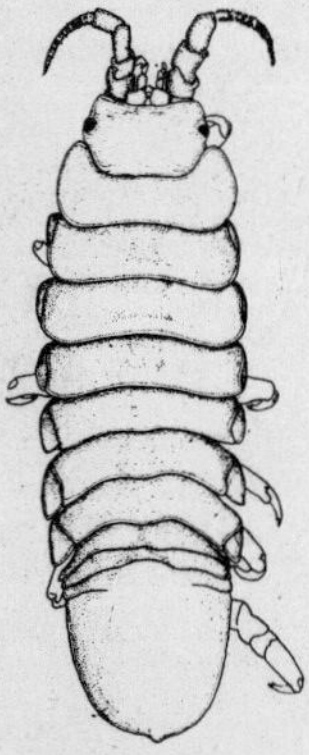

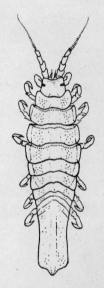

Fig. 62
The isopod, *Idothea wosnesenskii* (§ 165). Drawing courtesy R. J. Menzies.

Fig. 63
One of the largest of the isopods, *Idothea stenops*; life size (§ 172).

PLATE XXVI (Opposite page)

OTHER SURF-SWEPT ANIMALS

1. The predaceous mussel worm, *Nereis vexillosa;* the specimen shown was 11½" long (§ 163).
2. *Pisaster giganteus,* usually smaller and always less numerous than its relative, the common starfish; reduced (§ 157).
3. The chiton, *Nuttallina californica* (§ 169).
4. The red barnacle, *Tetraclita rubescens* (§ 168).
5. A colony of the tubed worms, *Phragmatopoma californica* (§ 166).

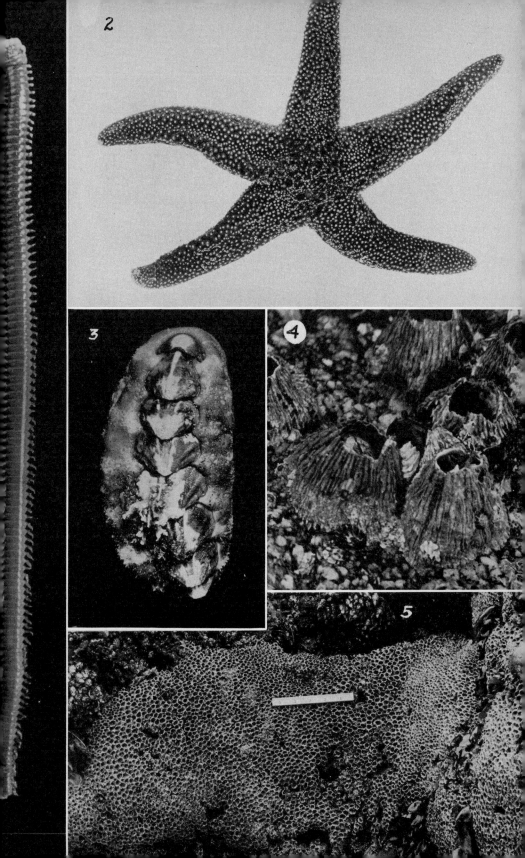

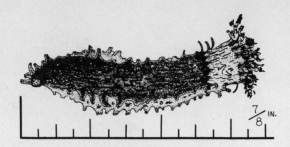

Fig. 64

A black cucumber, *Cucumaria lubrica* (§ 176).

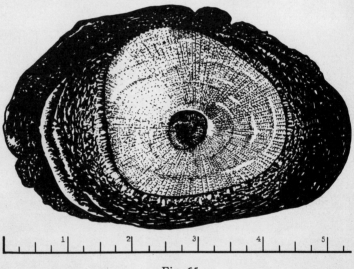

Fig. 65

The giant keyhole limpet, *Megathura crenulata* (§ 180).

PLATE XXVII (Opposite page)

LOW-TIDE ANIMALS OF SURF-SWEPT SHORES

1. *Katherina tunicata*, the second largest of the chitons; actual length of specimen, 3¾″ (§ 177).
2. The black abalone, *Haliotis cracherodii;* actual length 4″ (§ 179).
3. Bed of purple urchins, *Strongylocentrotus purpuratus;* specimens were about 2″ in diameter. Note that all are at least half buried in the rock (§ 174).

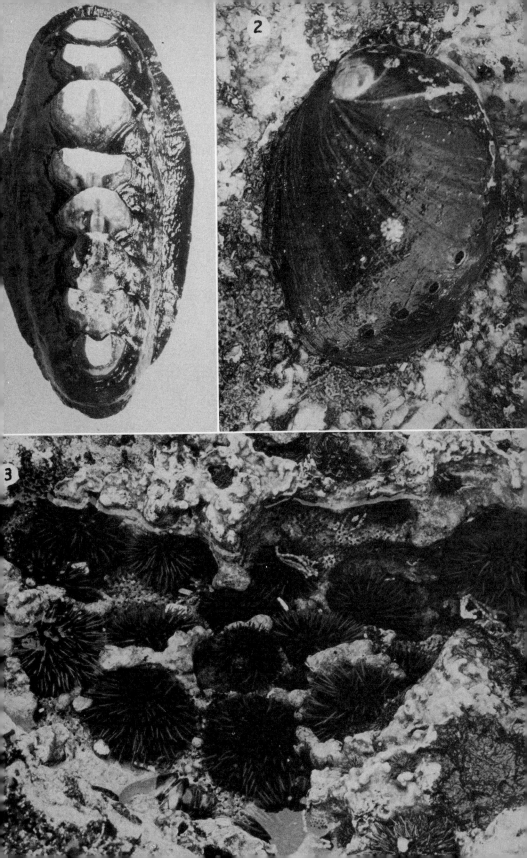

184

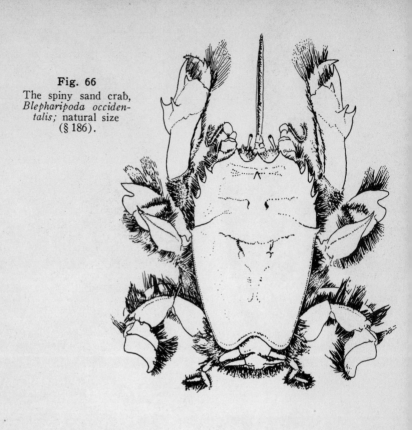

Fig. 66

The spiny sand crab,
*Blepharipoda occiden-
talis;* natural size
(§ 186).

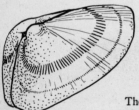

Fig. 67

The bean clam, *Donax Gouldii;*
one and one-half times natural
size (§ 188). Drawings by Sam
Hinton.

PLATE XXVIII (Opposite page)

LOW-TIDE ANIMALS OF SURF-SWEPT SHORES

1. A keynote limpet, *Diodora aspera,* slightly reduced (§ 181).
1a. View of under side shows commensal scale worm, *Arctonoë vittata*
(§ 76).
2. The short-spired purple snail, *Thais emarginata* (§ 182).
3. The snail, *Calliostoma ligatum* (§§ 182, 215).
4. An expanded cluster of the tubed worms, *Salmacina,* natural size (§ 183).
5. *Salmacina,* enlarged (§ 183).

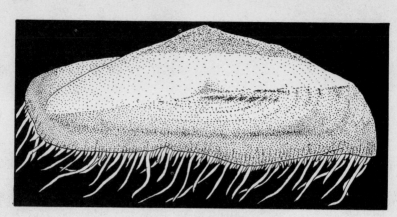

Fig. 68

A purple jellyfish that "sails," *Velella lata;* natural size (§ 193).

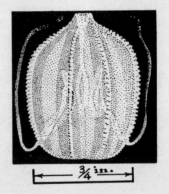

Fig. 69

The comb jelly, *Pleurobrachia* (§ 193).

PLATE XXIX (Opposite page)

ANIMALS OF OPEN COAST SANDY BEACHES

1. The great beach hopper, *Orchestoidea californiana* (§ 185).
2. The mole crab, *Emerita analoga* (§ 186).
3. A razor clam, *Siliqua patula;* photo courtesy of Mrs. Oldroyd (§ 189).
4. Shell of the Pismo clam, *Tivela stultorum* (§ 190).

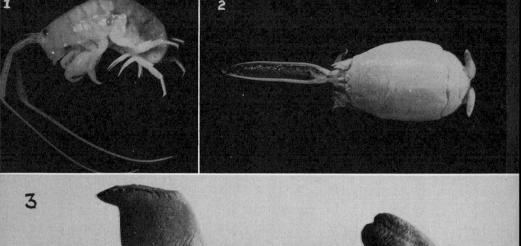

A view of the exposed outer coastline on Tomales Point, Marin County, California.
Photo by Wm. L. Wells.

range is Alaska to Lower California. Any specimens found should be examined for the commensal scale worm *Arctonoë vittata,* formerly *Halosydna lordi,* which has been mentioned as occurring with *Cryptochiton* (§76). In 1866, Lord, in British Columbia, wrote interestingly of this commensal. He remarked that the position of the worm—like a ribbon on edge—prevents its being crushed when the host clamps down to the rock. The length of the worm, considering the size of the host, is remarkable, and the worm often has to curl around the mantle so completely that its ends almost touch.

A third member of the group, the volcano-shell limpet, is the smallest of the lot, but is handsome nevertheless. It has been treated (§15) as a protected–outer-coast form, but it is practically as common in this environment.

§182. The leafy horn-mouth snail, *Ceratostoma foliatum* (§117), is occasionally found in surf-swept areas where there is a bit of shelter just at the low-tide line. Occasional also, but sufficiently spectacular to cause comment, is the prettily marked ring top shell, *Calliostoma annulatum,* up to an inch in diameter and ranging from Alaska to San Diego. The body is salmon pink, and the yellow shell has a purple band following the beaded spiral. The larger *C. canaliculatum* will be found similarly, but on bare rock, and far down in this zone and well into the sublittoral. Occasional *C. ligatum* (§215, Pl. XXVIII) will also be taken in this environment, but this is most characteristically a Puget Sound quiet-water form. These rather similar species of *Calliostoma* can be differentiated most readily by means of Figures 2, 5, 6, and 7 of Plate 36 of Packard (1918, cited on our p. 448), but illustrations on page 548 of Johnson and Snook (1927 ed.) are fairly diagnostic.

Most characteristic of all is the short-spired purple, *Thais emarginata* (Pl. XXVIII), which is not only abundant on rocky shores where the surf is fairly heavy but is almost entirely restricted to such regions. Writing in 1871, Verrill and Smith said that a whelk similar to our *Thais* (*Purpura lapillus*) "is seldom found living much below the low water mark, and prefers the exposed rocky headlands on the ocean shores, where it flourishes in defiance to the breakers. It lays its eggs in smooth, vase-shaped capsules, attached to the sides or under surfaces of stones by a short stalk, and usually arranged in groups." If they had been describing our purple, they could not have hit it more closely. We would only add that the egg cases, called "sea oats," are yellow, and are likely to be mistaken at first sight for purse sponges.

Purple snails are so named not for the color of their shells (usually black and white) but because they are reputed to be the snails from which the Tyrian dye of ancient times was made. Irreverent modern investigators find the dye to be a rather dull purple that fades badly. It is suspected that the color sense of ancient peoples was based on standards that would seem strange to us. No doubt the colors that thrilled the ancient Romans would arouse contempt in a schoolboy artist of today, since the civilization of Tiberius knew nothing of our lacquers and brilliant coal-tar dyes. Our *Thais* is usually a uniform white, gray, or brown in color, and ranges from Alaska to Mexico. It is a voracious animal and will sometimes be caught in the act of drilling, with its radula, through the shell of a mussel.

In connection with *Thais,* a mild dissertation on birth control, prenatal care, and race suicide seems to be almost mandatory, for the tribe of *Thais* persists in spite of the most arrant cannibalism. The adults eat snail eggs indiscriminately, including their own, and the larval *Thais* eat each other while still in the egg capsule. Instead of there being a single egg, with a sufficient supply of nutritive yolk, there are many eggs in each capsule, with not enough yolk to carry the embryos through to hatching time. Consequently they eat each other until only one—and that one presumably cock of the walk—is left to emerge from the capsule into a world where its chances of survival are still poor.

§183. Two encrusting forms which have puzzled us until recently may puzzle the amateur collector also. A roughly circular growth that looks like a tightly adherent mass of corallines is composed of tiny-tubed annelid worms, the serpulid *Salmacina* (Pl. XXVIII). They are not unlike intertwining tubes of *Serpula* or *Sabellaria,* but on a pin-point scale. At first sight the mass may appear dingy, but on closer examination it will be seen to have an encrusted, dainty, filigree pattern. En masse the gills are a rusty red, individually a brighter red and rather attractive.

The other form, occurring in similar situations on vertical cliff faces almost at the lowest-water mark, is the sponge *Hymeniacidon sinapium,* which may thinly encrust areas of several square feet. This is the yellow-green, slightly slimy form, with nipple-like papillae, recognizable by the European observer as similar to *Axinella,* and originally so called in this area. De Laubenfels notes that the open-coast habitat is rare, specimens occurring more characteristically in quiet water (§225), on oyster shells, etc.

B. Sandy Beaches

WHEREAS the animals living on surf-swept rocky shores have solved the problem of wave shock by developing powerful attachment devices, the inhabitants of surf-swept sandy beaches achieve the same end by burying themselves in the sand. Some, like the mole crab and the razor clam, are able to burrow with extraordinary rapidity. Others (Pismo clam) burrow more slowly, depending on the pressure-distributing strength of their hard, rounded shell. These have achieved the necessary great strength and resistance to crushing, not through the development of such obvious structural reinforcements as ribbing, with the consequent economy of material, but by means of shells which are thick and heavy throughout. Ribbing would provide footholds for the surf-created currents which could whisk the animal out of its securely buried position in a hurry. Natural selection presumably has "bred out" a race of thick- and smooth-shelled clams over which the streaming and crushing surf can pour without effect. In addition the actively burrowing forms particularly, such as *Emerita* (§186), must be provided with a sense of orientation not dependent on sight.

That the problems faced by sand dwellers on an exposed coast are reasonably baffling is indicated by the fact that few animals are able to hold their own under such conditions. While these beaches are not the barren wastes we found the smaller sandy beaches of the protected outer coast to be, they are still sparsely populated in comparison with similar rocky shores. Actually we know of only six or seven common forms that occur in any abundance on heavily surf-swept sand beaches, and two of them are already well along toward extinction as a result of human activities. This reflects a situation quite different from that assumed by most amateur collectors, who would have one but turn over a spadeful of beach sand to reveal a wealth of hidden life.

§184. We have already cited several examples, notably the periwinkles, of animals with marked landward tendencies. On the sand beaches of the open coast there is another, the little pill bug, *Alloniscus perconvexus,* about ⅝″ long. This isopod is an air-breathing form which will drown in sea water. It will be found, therefore, in the highest zone, above the high-tide line, and because of the obvious nature of its burrows it is often one of the first animals to be noticed in this environment. The mole-like burrows are just beneath the surface, and in making them the animal humps up the surface sand into ridges. Another air-breather, the isopod *Tylos punctatus*, a ¼" to ½" oval form resembling *Exosphaeroma* (§198), is restricted to the southern California beaches.

§185. During the night, or most noticeably at dusk or at dawn, the foreshore seems to become alive with jumping hordes of the great beach hopper, *Orchestoidea californiana* (Pl. XXIX). They are pleasant and handsome animals, with white- or old-ivory–colored bodies, while the head region and long antennae are bright orange. The bodies of large specimens are considerably more than an inch long, so that, adding the antennae, an over-all length of 2½" is not uncommon. Like the other beach hoppers, this form avoids being wetted by the waves, always retreating up the beach a little ahead of the tide. These hoppers seem always to keep their bodies damp, however, and to that end spend their daylight hours buried deep in the moist sand, where they are very difficult to find. Night is the time to see them. Observers with a trace of sympathy for bohemian life should walk with a flashlight along a familiar surfy beach at half-tide on a quiet evening. These huge hoppers will be holding high carnival —leaping about with vast enthusiasm, pausing to wiggle their antennae over likely looking bits of flotsam seaweed. They will rise up before the intruder in great windrows, for all the world like grasshoppers in a summer meadow. Too closely pursued, they dig rapidly into the sand, head first, and disappear very quickly. Ovigerous females have been taken in March in Monterey Bay.

§186. *Emerita analoga* (Pl. XXIX) is the mole crab or sand crab, the "sand bug" of the beach-frequenting small boy. The shell is almost egg-shaped—a contour that is efficient for dwellers in shifting sands where the surf is high, since the pressure is distributed too evenly to throw the animal out of balance. Most of the crabs characteristically move in any direction—forward, backward, or sideways—but whether the mole crab is swimming, crawling, or burrowing, it always moves backward. Crawling is apparently its least efficient mode of locomotion, but while its swift burrowing is its chief accomplishment in that respect, it is also a fairly good swimmer— an action achieved by beating its hindmost, paddle-like appendages above the after margin of the shell. The same appendages assist in burrowing, but most of the work of burrowing is done by the other legs.

When in the sand, the mole crab always stands on end, head end up. Characteristically the entire body is buried, while the eyes—tiny knobs on the ends of long stalks—and the feathery antennae project above the surface of the sand. The film of water receding after each

wave provides the animal with minute food particles which it scrapes
from its antennae before another wave brings the next course. The
projecting antennae, which are withdrawn after the water has re-
ceded, serve a double purpose, for they also direct a stream of water
to the gill chambers. The same film of water that brings food and
oxygen, however, betrays the mole crab's presence by forming a V-
shaped ripple in the sand where the water's straight course has
been deflected by the projecting eyes and antennae—a fact that is
taken advantage of by hungry birds as well as by curious collectors
and bait-gatherers. The latter use the animals in their soft-shelled
stage, that is, just after they have moulted.

Emerita lives at about the half-tide line, but shifts its base of
operations somewhat according to changes in the tidal level. Often it
occurs in great beds, so that turning up a single spadeful of sand may
reveal a large number. The females average a little less than an inch
in length, and the males are at least a third smaller. This form ranges
from Oregon to South America, and allied forms occur on the East
coast and elsewhere.

One investigator (Mead)* has thrown some light on *Emerita's*
methods of orienting itself. He found that its strongest direction instinct is to move down a slope—an action that would normally take it
to the sea. On a level plot of ground a group of specimens still moved
toward the sea, even though some distance removed from it and unable to see it; but on a steep slope slanting away from the sea they
headed inland. On a landward-slanting slope of about 7 per cent
their oceanward tendency and their downhill tendency just balanced,
so that they moved in all directions in complete confusion.

When first captured, the mole crab "plays 'possum," lying perfectly still on its back. Ordinarily it comes to very suddenly, rights
itself, and attempts to burrow. Frequently, however, according to
the same experimenter, one never comes out of its death feint but
continues to play dead until it is killed by the sun's heat. It is a
weird defense mechanism that goes as far as to kill the animal possessing it.

The spiny sand crab, *Blepharipoda occidentalis* (Fig. 66), may
occur with *Emerita*. It is larger, with a carapace up to 2″ long, and
is by no means as common. It has a recorded range of Monterey
southward, and reports say that it is abundant outside Morro Bay.
Occasionally it is found as far north as Stinson Beach, Marin County.

§187. At about the mole-crab's level are minute, shrimp-like crustaceans, *Archaeomysis maculata,* called opossum shrimps because,
like the other mysids, they retain the young in a marsupial pouch

---

* MacGinitie's work, however, casts doubt on Mead's findings.

under the thorax. *Archeomysis* is without gills, although some mysids have rudimentary gills. There is a trick to finding these animals, for they are so transparent that they cannot be seen directly with the naked eye. On a sunshiny day, however, they cast shadows on the sand below the smooth runoff of waves dammed back momentarily by a shovel, and so can be located and captured. This form is related to the more visible mysids of the tide pools (§60).

§188. The bean clam, *Donax gouldii* (Fig. 67), is common from the San Luis Obispo region to Mexico. This small wedge-shaped clam, averaging an inch in length, is said to have been so common at one time that it was canned commercially at Long Beach. For many years it has not been available in commercial quantities, but the individual collector can still find enough for a delicious chowder by combing the sand just beneath the surface. The bean clam's hiding place is commonly revealed by tufts of a hydroid that grows on the shell and protrudes above the surface of the sand. This elongate hydroid, *Clytia bakeri,* related to *Obelia,* and occurring also on the Pismo clam, is the only hydroid found on exposed sandy shores.

§189. A razor clam, *Siliqua patula* (Pl. XXIX), corresponds ecologically, on the open sand beaches of Washington, to the different-looking Pismo clam of similar stretches in California and Mexico. *Siliqua* is long (shell up to 6″) and thin, with fragile shiny valves— just the opposite of what one would expect in a surf-loving animal. Apparently it depends on speed of digging for protection from wave shock. A clam that was displaced by a particularly vicious wave could certainly be reburied under several inches of sand before the next comber struck, for specimens laid on top of the sand have buried themselves completely in less than seven seconds. The foot, projected half the length of the shell and pointed, is pushed into the sand. Below the surface the tip expands greatly to form an anchor and the muscle, contracting, pulls the clam downwards. The movement is repeated several times in rapid succession before the clam disappears. A digger must work quickly to capture the animal before it attains depths impossible to reach.

Along the Washington coast, from the mouth of the Columbia northward, there is a stretch of thirty-eight miles of beach that is worked by commercial diggers for local canneries, and the average annual pack, from 1915 to 1927, was 37,000 cases. In Alaska, too, the canning of razor clams is an industry of some importance, the fisheries and canneries being at Cordova, Chisik Island, Cook Inlet, and Kukak Bay. It is estimated that tourists take from the Washington coast at least a third as many clams per year as the canneries use. Many are taken also for crab bait and for consumption by local residents. All together the drain on the beds is too great for an animal that takes (in Washington) three and one-half years to attain its legal size of 4½ inches, and the supply is decreasing steadily. At Cordova the clams require six years or more to reach the same size. A *Bureau of Fisheries Bulletin (Doc. 984)* records some further interesting differences between the northern and southern clams:

In the south (Washington, etc.) the time of spawning is simultaneous, all the clams along several miles of beach spawning on the same day when there is a sudden rise in water temperature. This usually occurs at the end of May or early in June. Sometimes the set of young is enormous, but in other years the animals almost fail to spawn at all. In Alaska they are likely to spawn without fail but not suddenly and not simultaneously, and the set of young is more uniform. Spawning is usually in July and early August. The larval stage for both regions lasts for eight weeks. The average maximum age in Washington is twelve years; in Alaska specimens up to seventeen and eighteen years old are known.

Fraser (1930) examined nine year-classes on Queen Charlotte Island beaches. Eighty-six per cent of the three-year specimens were mature or maturing. Spawning took place from late July on, depending on the minimum temperature of 13° C. The following is from Weymouth and McMillan's (1930–31) summary of a statistical study of fourteen thousand individuals of the four species of razor clams recognized: "Over the wide range of the species a high correlation is found between the relative growth rate, age, length, and geographic position. . . . . Under the conditions of the southern beds there is initially a more rapid relative growth rate which, declining more rapidly, reaches a low final level, and the clams show a smaller final size and a shorter life span than in the northern beds." This situation was found by the same authors in another paper to apply to Washington and Alaska cockles (*Clinocardium nuttalii,* §259).

The species illustrated, ranging from the Bering Sea in the north, is said to extend as far south as San Luis Obispo, but it is rarely seen along the central California coast. In this connection it should be noted that specimens may be lethal for food at times during the summer, owing to mussel poisoning (§158).

Up to 80 per cent of these clams, according to canners, carry an internal commensal, the nemertean worm, *Malacobdella grossa.* The percentage of clams so accompanied increases toward the north. MacGinitie, in a verbal communication, reported this or a related form from clams at Humboldt Bay. We have taken it also, but sparsely (only one was found in a lot of several dozen *Siliqua),* along the open sand beaches near Queets, central Washington. These flat nemerteans, up to 1½″ in length, attach themselves to the clams' gills by a sucker and feed on minute plankton in the water passing through the gills. Seemingly they have no harmful effect on the host.

§190. The Pismo clam, *Tivela stultorum* (Pl. XXIX), does not merely tolerate surf; it requires it. Clams removed from their surf-swept habitat to lagoons and sheltered bays to await shipment live but a few days, even though tidal exposure, temperature, and salinity are the same. Apparently *Tivela* has accustomed itself, through generations of living in an environment so rigorous that it would be fatal to most animals, to the high oxygen content of constantly agitated water, and has carried the adaptation to such an extreme that it can no longer survive under less violent conditions. An interesting feature of the clam's adaptation is its inhalant siphon. Most clams live in relatively clear and undisturbed waters, but the Pismo clam, living in waters that are commonly filled with swirling sand, must provide against taking too much sand into its body with the water that it must inhale in order to get food and oxygen. It makes such provision by having a very fine net of delicately branched papillae across the opening, forming a screen that will exclude grains of sand and yet permit the passage of water and the microscopic food that it contains.

Many years ago, when the Pismo clam was as common on exposed beaches in southern California as are sand dollars on bay and estuary beaches, teams of horses drew plows through the sand, turning up the clams by the wagon load. Now adults of the species are almost unobtainable in the intertidal zone. Experienced diggers with rakes or forks work at low tide, wading out waist deep or even shoulder deep, where the surf frequently breaks over them. It is hazardous work, for the diggers must feel their way along bars that are separated from the shore by deeper channels, and now and then the surf claims a victim.

Because of this clam's commercial importance, a good deal is known of its natural history, particularly through the work of Weymouth and Herrington. During stormy weather the clams go down to considerable depths to avoid being washed out, but normally they lie at a depth about equal to the length of their shells. They show a strikingly constant orientation in the direction of wave action, being found always with the hinged side toward the ocean. While they are not as active diggers as the razor clams, they can, especially when young, move rather rapidly, and given a reasonable chance can dig themselves back in from the surface. Weymouth observed that "the ordinary action of the foot in burrowing appears to be supplemented in the Pismo clam by the ejection of the water within the mantle cavity . . . . recalling the method of 'jetting' a pile, ... an important factor in moving such a bulky shell though the sand."

It is a very slow-growing form, requiring from four to seven years to reach its present legal size of 5 inches, and continuing to grow, but not so rapidly, until it is at least fifteen years old. The rate of growth varies according to a definite seasonal rhythm—rapid in summer and slow in winter. The winter growth of the shell is darker and is deposited in narrow bands. The animal is hermaphroditic, spawns in late summer, and produces eggs, after it becomes sexually mature at the end of its second or third year, in direct proportion to its size, a large clam producing an estimated seventy-five million in one spawning season.

The Fish and Game Commission takes an annual census of the animals, based on test counts in strips of beach running from the upper limit of the intertidal zone out to the water line at extreme low water. The results indicate that, despite the present restrictions (fifteen 5-inch clams per person per day, certain areas closed, and all shipments prohibited), the species is in danger of becoming extinct unless still more stringent restrictions are applied and enforced.

With the exception of man, the Pismo clam's natural enemies are few. Starfish do not frequent sandy beaches, and boring snails are unable to penetrate the hard thick shells of adults. Gulls will devour small specimens that are turned up by diggers and left lying on the surface, but they cannot get at the clams in their normal buried habitat. The nearest relatives of this clam are tropical forms, and it can be considered subtropical. It ranges from Half Moon Bay to Socorro Island, off Mexico, but is not common in the northern part of its range. In Monterey Bay it is well known, but still not abundant by comparison with its occurrence on the southern beaches. The most famous region for Pismos at present is south of San Luis Obispo, where several towns depend chiefly for their support on tourists lured by the possibility of capturing this large delicacy. There is reason for believing that when our own beaches are depleted the coast of Lower California can be called upon to supply large quantities of Pismos. It is to be hoped that the Mexican government, which has shown itself to be wide awake in the matter of conserving wild life, will enact and properly enforce legislation that will help *Tivela* to hold its own. Like the bean clam, *Tivela* will be found occasionally harboring a cluster, several inches long, of the hydroid *Clytia bakeri* (§188), which, protruding above the surface, reveals the hidden presence of the clam.

§191. Although we ourselves have never taken them, E. and C. Berkeley report (1932) from Long Bay, an exposed beach on the

west coast of Vancouver Island (in addition to abundant specimens
of a nephtys, *N. caeca,* similar to those treated in §265), an annelid
worm which merits consideration. It is *Thoracophelia mucronata,* previously known only from southern California, and is said to occur
"in vast numbers . . . . , whole stretches of sand being tunnelled by
countless millions. Judging by the complex system of furrows on the
sand beds they inhabit, they seem to emerge from their burrows and
crawl on the surface of the sand, but none were found exposed.
Large flocks of sandpipers are frequently seen at low tide, extracting
these worms and feeding on them." This was decribed as a slender
ophellid, 35 × 1 to 25 × 2 mm., with triangular head, and bearing
gills on the lower middle two-thirds of the body.

In certain exposed sand beaches at and below the lowest-tide level,
bait-gatherers frequently dig out the nereis-like *Naineris dendritica,*
which may be had sometimes by the shovelful. Except for its smaller
size, this so nearly resembles *Nereis vexillosa* (§163) that bait collectors confuse them, swearing up and down that it is the height of
folly to dig under mussels when the desired worms occur so availably
in easily dug sand.

§192. A good many favorably known food fish, notably striped
bass, are found along sandy shores just outside, or even within, the
line of breakers. The live-bearing surf perch occurs similarly, but
is usually too small for food. Athough these can scarcely be considered intertidal forms, one interesting southern fish (which has
been reported in Monterey Bay also) actually comes high into the
intertidal zone for egg deposition. This is the famous grunion, *Leuresthes tenuis,* a smeltlike fish about 6″ long.

The egg-laying time of the grunion is holiday time for tremendous
numbers of southern Californians. Along the coast highways cars
are parked bumper to bumper for many miles, and the moon and
thousands of beach fires light up the scene. The fish are caught with
anything available, from hats to bare hands, and are roasted over the
fires, making fine fare indeed.

The grunion's extraordinary spawning habits are as perfectly
timed as those of the palolo worm of the South Seas, and the timing
force is as mysterious. On the second, third, and fourth nights after
the full moon—in other words on the highest spring tides—in the
months of March, April, May, and June, and just after the tide has
turned, the fish swim up the beach with the breaking waves to the
highest point they can reach. They come in pairs, male and female.
The female digs into the sand, tail foremost, and deposits her eggs
some three inches below the surface. During the brief process the
male lies arched around her and fertilizes the eggs. With the wash

of the next wave the fish slip back into the sea. Normally the eggs remain there, high and dry, until the next high spring tides, some ten days later, come to wash them out of the sand. Immediately on being immersed the eggs hatch, and the larvae swim down to the sea.

It is an astounding performance. If the eggs were laid on any other tide, or even an hour earlier on the same tide, they would probably be washed out and so destroyed. If they were laid at the dark of the moon they would have to wait a month to be hatched, for the full-moon tides are never as high as those of the dark of the moon. But the interval between two sets of spring tides is the proper period for the gestation of the eggs and the period that the grunion contrives to utilize. Incidentally, the succeeding lower high tides actually bury the eggs deeper by piling up sand.

The fish mature and spawn at the end of the first year, and they spawn on each set of tides during the season. During the spawning season their growth ceases, to be resumed afterward at a slower rate. Only 25 per cent of the fish spawn the second year, however, 7 per cent the third, and none the fourth.

§193. The storm wrack and flotsam cast up on sandy beaches is sure to contain the usually incomplete remains of animals from other kingdoms—representatives of floating and drifting life and of bottom life below the range of the tides. Both of these great life zones lie outside the scope of this book, and the stray specimens thrown inshore can be given but scant mention.

Shells of deep-water scallops, snails, piddocks, and other clams are very commonly washed up. While perfect specimens of this sort are adequate for the conchologist, to the biologist they are merely evidence that the living animals probably occur offshore.

In the spring of 1927 the junior writer, aboard a sailing ship a few hundred miles off the coast of central California, sailed for several days through incalculable numbers of purple-sailed "floats"— siphonophores, that are locally but incorrectly called Portuguese man-of-war. Often the beautifully iridescent animals were so thickly distributed that there was, by extremely rough estimate, one to every square foot of the surface of the sea as far as the eye could reach in every direction. A little later, storms drove tremendous numbers of the creatures, *Velella lata* (Fig. 68), ashore along the California coast —a performance that is repeated once in every few years. Specimens picked up on the beach are usually dismal objects compared with the undamaged living animals, but occasionally a perfect one may be found, with purple zooids trailing below the disc and even with a purple goose barnacle attached. A transparent triangular sail surmounts the relatively firm body, which averages 3″ to 4″ in diameter, so that a very light breeze will keep the animal (really a colony of specialized animals) moving through the water.

"Gooseberries," the "cat's eyes" of the fishermen, are occasionally cast up on the beach, where succeeding waves roll them around until they are broken. These are comb jellies or ctenophores, usually *Pleurobrachia bachei* (Fig. 69). The nearly transparent spheres, usually ½" to ¾" in diameter, carry two long tentacles. Of these also we have picked up fresh and living specimens so perfect that the iridescent paddles of the plate rows started to vibrate the moment the animals were placed in sea water.

Great blubber-like masses of the jellyfish *Aurelia* (§330) are often cast up in the fall, but usually so wave-torn as to be scarcely recognizable. A smaller dome-shaped jellyfish, *Polyorchis* (§330), with tentacles along the open margin of the bell, may sometimes be found in great numbers. Perfect specimens of this form will often revive in fresh sea water, swimming around vigorously by kicking the knee-like manubrium inside the bell.*

---

* Any number of other animals may be stranded at times, but those mentioned can be expected fairly regularly. Flotsam timbers, if they have been in the water any length of time, will almost surely have adherent goose barnacles, *Lepas anatifera*, etc., relatively similar to the *Mitella* of §160.

III. BAY AND ESTUARY

Environmental Factors

THE chief environmental factor that marks off the animals of bays, sounds, sloughs, and estuaries from all the others so far considered is the complete, or almost complete, protection from surf. This single factor, it is true, will segregate only a few animals, for of the many already mentioned a scant half dozen actually require surf, however many may tolerate it. The absence of surf, however, will alter the habits of many animals, and from several incidental standpoints a coherent treatment of the animals living on completely sheltered shores is desirable. For one thing the tides in such locations are invariably later, often, as in parts of Puget Sound and the inside waters of British Columbia and southeastern Alaska, many hours later. The result is that the intertidal areas are bared during the heat of the day or the chill of the night, necessitating the ability on the part of the shore animals to withstand temperature changes far greater than animals in corresponding positions on the outer coast ever have to meet. The "completely protected" shore animals must also tolerate more variable salinity, which is decreased by fresh-water streams and sometimes increased to a considerable degree by evaporation from quiet shallow areas. All together, the animal communities in this environment are characteristic and very different, however much of a potpourri they may be from a geographical and ecological standpoint.

Such previously encountered environments as rocky shores and sandy beaches will be found in these sheltered waters and, in addition, gravel beaches and mud flats. Each type of shore has an assemblage of specific forms not found elsewhere, mingled with animals that occur almost anywhere and a few strays from neighboring environments.

A. Rocky Shores

HERE we shall find many animals that will be recognized as having occurred outside, plus many that, finding no rigorous wave shock, creep up from deeper water. The fauna of such environments is particularly well developed on the reefs and cliffs at the south end of Newport Bay, along the railway embankment in Elkhorn Slough, in the San Juan Islands and other parts of the Puget Sound region, and in hundreds of places in British Columbia and southeastern Alaska.

ZONES 1 and 2. *Uppermost shore and high-tide horizon.*

Although, as on the outer coast, the highest fixed and lethargic animals are barnacles, limpets, and littorines, it necessarily follows from the lack of surf that their absolute level (allowing for tidal differences) is lower. That is, since spray and waves will not ordinarily come up to them, they must go down to the water, and instead of ranging several feet above high-tide line they will be found at or a little below it.

§194. An extremely common small barnacle of fully protected waters throughout the entire coast line herein considered is *Balanus glandula,* which has already been discussed (§4) as the dominant acorn barnacle of the protected outer coast. As was pointed out in the previous account, this great variability of habitat bespeaks a tolerance and generalization that is uncommon among marine invertebrates. In the outer-coast environment there are wave shock, low temperature, high salinity, and plenty of oxygen. In bays and estuaries the animals must put up with variable and often high temperatures, variable and often low salinities (because of the influx of fresh water), and relatively low oxygen content in the water, gaining no apparent advantage except escape from wave shock. To make the situation even more puzzling, *glandula* actually thrives best, according to Shelford *et al.* (1930), in such regions as Puget Sound, in enclosed bays where these apparent disadvantages are intensified, avoiding the more "oceanic" conditions of rocky channels that have swift currents and more direct communication with the sea. And the term "thrive" translated into figures means that, although *glandula* is never compressed by crowding in Puget Sound, there may be as many as 70,000 individuals per square meter.

Another barnacle, the much larger *Balanus cariosus,* comes very near to reversing *glandula's* strange predilections. In Puget Sound this form prefers steep shores, with strong currents and considerable wave action, that is, the nearest approach to oceanic conditions that these waters afford. When this same barnacle moves to the protected outer coast, however (and it is fairly common as far south as Monterey Bay), it avoids oceanic conditions most assiduously, occurring only in deep crevices and under overhanging ledges in the low zone where it finds the maximum protection available. The net result, of course, is that whether it occurs in Puget Sound or in Monterey Bay it maintains itself under the nearest possible approximation to identical conditions—a much more logical procedure than that of *glandula.*

The young of *cariosus* have strong radiating ridges in a starry pattern and are beautifully symmetrical. An adult specimen that has not been distorted by crowding is conical, sometimes has shingle-like thatches of downward-pointing spines, and is up to 2″ in basal diameter and slightly less in height. The largest specimens are found to the northward of Puget Sound, but under ideal Sound conditions the animals sometimes grow in such profusion and are so closely packed together that "lead-pencil" specimens develop which reach a height of 4″ with a diameter of less than half an inch. Test counts have shown 15,000 of these per square meter. *Cariosus* occurs, as a rule, at a lower level than *glandula,* and where the two are intermingled *glandula* will often be found attached to the larger form rather than to the rock.

Still a third barnacle, *Chthamalus dalli,* occurs abundantly from Alaska to Puget Sound, filling in that region the position held by *Chthamalus fissus* in the south, and even extending, though not in great numbers, as far south as Monterey. It is the smallest of the lot, being about ¼″ in basal diameter and half as high. It is a definite and cleancut form, never crowded and piled together like *cariosus,* although one test count in the San Juan Islands showed 72,000 to the square meter. In the Puget Sound region it will be found chiefly interspersed with *B. glandula,* rarely or never competing with the lower *cariosus.* It is very hardy, however, for it can tolerate, at one extremity, high salinity, and at the other small enclosed bays where there is so much fresh water or decaying vegetation that no other barnacles can survive. Only in the latter environment will it ever be found in pure stands. This small form shows particularly well the six equal plates or compartments of which the shell is composed. The various species of *Balanus* have six also, but they are unequal in size and overlap irregularly, so that it is often difficult to make them out.

Many species of barnacles resemble each other so closely that it is usually hopeless for the beginner to try to identify them surely. However, the collector who is sufficiently interested to dry the specimens and separate the valves can probably determine their species through the use of Pilsbry (1916), listed in the bibliography.

§195. Several familiar limpets occur in these quiet waters. *Acmaea cassis olympica* is foremost, a variety of the shield limpet mentioned in §11, by far the commonest limpet in southern Puget Sound and often the only one, on rocks, on gravel, and on piling. Great colonies of small specimens occur high up with the small barnacles, on smooth rocks and on the shells of mussels. Farther down—and these animals occur at least to the zero of tide tables—they are solitary and larger. The dingy little *A. digitalis* (§6) occurs also, but only in the more exposed parts of the Sound, and both the plate limpet (§25) and the low-tide dunce-cap limpet (§117) exceed it in abundance according to the published lists.

A common Puget Sound periwinkle, especially in the quiet waters where the barnacle *B. glandula* and the quiet-water mussel thrive, is *Littorina sitkana* (Fig. 70), usually under ½″ in diameter and having a gaping aperture. In the less protected parts of the Sound, with the *Balanus cariosus*-California mussel association, the small, cross-stitched snail, *L. scutulata* (§10), is the most common form. Farther north a few of the variety of *L. sitkana*, formerly called *L. rudis*, will be seen. Recent tagging experiments indicate that the littorines are great stay-at-homes, never migrating from the immediate neighborhood of the pool in which they happen to have been born.

The purple shore crabs, *Hemigrapsus nudus* (§27), cavort around rocky beaches in Puget Sound, and on gravel shores mix with their pale and hairy brothers, *H. oregonensis* (§285). The latter, however, distinctly prefer regions where there is some mud, while the former are equally partial to rocks. In San Francisco Bay *oregonensis* is the common form.

§196. Small hermit crabs with granulated hands, *Pagurus granosimanus*, appropriate the shells of the northern periwinkles. These hermits, which we have previously noted as occurring in the minority among the dominant *P. samuelis* (§12) in Monterey Bay, differ from their very similar relatives in a few slight anatomical characters. Their external characteristics, however, may serve to identify them in a reasonable percentage of cases. In the first place, *granosimanus* lacks the more southern form's slight hairiness, and in the second it is typically the smallest intertidal hermit to be found in Puget Sound. Beyond that lies color—and confusion. Not only is there likely to be great color variation in a large number of the animals herein listed, but it is apparently impossible to find any two persons who will use the same color terms in describing an animal even if they are looking at the same specimen. As an experiment we submitted one specimen to three people and got three sets of color terms with almost no overlapping. One writer describes this particular hermit as "buffy olive to olive" with "porcelain blue" granules on the claws. Our own description, boldly set forth in the first-draft manuscript of this book and now offered dubiously, is "dull red to bright red in all-over color." The harassed amateur collector can do no better than find an undoubted specimen and make his own color chart—a chart that will very likely have to be altered to fit the next specimen he finds.

P. granosimanus ranges from Unalaska to Todos Santos Bay, but is relatively uncommon below Puget Sound.

§197. The animals mentioned so far differ only in species from comparable forms familiar to the reader. The same thing is true of the mussel, *Mytilus edulis,* but it is an exclusively quiet-water animal and notable for its wide distribution—literally around the world in North Temperate regions. The rich beds along the coasts of England and France provide great quantities for food and bait for commercial fisheries, and on the west coast of France they are cultivated very much as oysters are cultivated in other places. When "farmed" they grow larger than in the typically overcrowded natural beds.

M. edulis is wedge-shaped and rarely more than 2″ long, and the shell is smooth, whereas that of *californianus* (§158) is ridged. Sometimes the battle for living space drives it to establish itself on gravel beaches. We found a particularly fine example of this in Hood Canal, a long arm of Puget Sound, where the mussel beds formed a continuous belt along the beach. The byssal threads were so closely intertwined that one could tear the bed away from the gravel in a solid blanket-like mass, exposing the hosts of small animals that lived beneath it.

In Puget Sound and northward to Alaska this mussel occurs in tremendous quantities. It may be expected also in nearly every quiet-water bay southward of Puget Sound as far as Lower California, but never as commonly as in the north. A few anemic-looking specimens can be found on gravel banks and rocky points in San Francisco Bay, but most of those that have survived the Bay's contamination occur on wharf piling. A parasitic copepod, *Modiolicola gracilis,* has recently been reported from the gill region of Elkhorn Slough specimens.

§198. Under the crust formed by mussels on gravelly shores there is an important and characteristic assemblage of animals. There are few species, but tremendous numbers of individuals; and of the larger forms the commonest, to the eternal joy of bait-gatherers, is a small and quiet-water phase of the segmented worm *Nereis vexillosa* (§163), rarely exceeding 4 or 5 inches.

The little pill bug, *Exosphaeroma oregonensis* (Fig. 71), less than ¼" long, flaunts its belief in large and frequent families. The average under-crust population of this squat isopod with its widely separated eyes will run many dozen to the square foot in Puget Sound, and it is the commonest pill bug in San Francisco Bay. Heretofore it has been recorded from Alaska to Pacific Grove only, but we have found specimens in the shelly substratum as far south as Lower California.

There are several ribbon worms, notably our acquaintance, *Emplectonema gracile,* the pale yellow-green rubber-band nemertean (§165) from under open-coast mussel clusters, and the purple or brown form (*Paranemertes peregrina,* §139) that occurs under rocks. Small individuals of the northern blenny (*Anoplarchus purpurescens,* §240) will be seen.

The infrequent bare spaces on the sides of mussel-covered stones, but chiefly the crevices, may be occupied by an encrusting sponge, *Haliclona rufescens* (similar to the outside form treated in §31), described originally as a *Reneira.*

Zone 3. *Middle intertidal; the mid-tide region.*

§199. The quiet-water form, *confertus,* of the starfish, *Pisaster ochraceus* (§157), haunts the mussel beds in completely sheltered waters as does its rough-water relative the beds of larger mussels on the open coast. *Confertus* may be found in the lower zone as well as in the middle zone, but we have never seen it below the low-tide line— a fact entirely consistent with its unfriendly relationship with mussels. On certain quiet-water gravelly and rocky shores in Puget Sound and British Columbia, to which region the animal is restricted, most of the specimens are colored a vivid violet.

§200. The common quiet-water snails are the purples—various species of *Thais,* especially *Thais canaliculata* (Pl. XXX), the channeled purple, and *Thais lamellosa* (Pl. XXX), the highly variable wrinkled purple. These two replace here the *Tegula* of protected outer-coast rocky beaches. Both range from Alaska to Monterey Bay and are common in the Sound and in San Francisco Bay. *Thais* is the snail whose progeny practice cannibalism while still in the egg capsule, as described in §182.

The wrinkled purple is famous for its great variation in shell structure. Specimens living on rough rock surfaces where there are currents or where there is some wave action have their projecting plates coarse, rugged, and relatively abbreviated, while specimens from rocks in quiet backwaters develop exquisite ornamentations. This is an interesting correlation between habitat and structure. Animals living in swift currents would be at a disadvantage in the possession of projecting flat surfaces; thus utilitarianism appears to be, in this case, the determining factor in limiting what is presumably the animal's natural tendency toward ornamentation.

Locally, *Searlesia dira,* the elongate "dire whelk," may be abundant, especially to the north, where in the quiet pools and channels of northern British Columbia it becomes the commonest littoral snail. A murex, *C. foliata* of § 117, also occurs in these northern waters— surprisingly for a relative of these tropical shells—as one of the three very common snails in certain locally rich pockets, as at Fisherman's Cove, south of Prince Rupert.

§201. The shells of the snails *Thais* provide portable homes for the hairy hermits, *Pagurus hirsutiusculus* (Pl. XXX), which, in quiet northern waters, attain great size. At Friday Harbor specimens have been taken with 2-inch bodies and an over-all length of more than 3 inches. The animal's extreme range is Alaska to Lower California, but south of Puget Sound the specimens are smaller and less hairy. They are fairly plentiful at Elkhorn Slough, however, and are the common hermits of San Francisco Bay.

To one whose acquaintance with hermits has begun with outer-coast forms, those found in Puget Sound and northern inside waters will exhibit a strange trait—a trait which we deduce to be a direct result of the great difference in environment. The outer-coast hermits will never desert their shells except when changing to another or when dying. Usually they cannot be removed by force unless they are caught unawares (a difficult thing to do) or are literally pulled apart. In Puget Sound, however, the animals will abandon their shells very readily—so readily, indeed, that on more than one occasion a collector has found himself holding an empty shell, the hermit having deserted in mid-air. Our unproved inference is that the presence or absence of surf is the factor determining how stubbornly a soft-bodied hermit will cling to its protecting shell.

§202. The ubiquitous warty anemone, *Cribrina* (aggregated phase,

§24), is found in the quiet waters of Puget Sound as an attractive red
and green form. This anemone, with its many variants, is certainly
an efficient animal, for it is universally characteristic of the north
Pacific. A recent visitor from Japan reports it to be common there,
where they know it as *Anthopleura* (still another title for this already
over-burdened form!), but he considers the center of distribution to
be on the American coast, since it is more variable and more highly
developed here.

On erect rocks of the inner waters at Sitka, an anemone that we
have been provisionally considering to be *Charisea saxicola* is very
abundant. It grows fairly high up, colonizing rock crevices and vertical and sharply sloping surfaces, the average specimen longer (to 2″)
than it is thick, and generally dingy white to buff in color. We found
it nowhere else, and Torrey (1902) records it only from "the shore
rocks at Sitka," where it was taken abundantly by the Harriman
expedition.

§203. Everywhere on the Puget Sound rocky shores the purple
shore crab, *Hemigrapsus nudus* (§27), replaces the rock crab, *Pachygrapsus,* of the California coast. Conditions in Puget Sound would
lead one to expect *Pachygrapsus* there also, but for some reason, possibly the somewhat lower winter temperatures, it does not extend that
far north. The purple crab modifies its habitat somewhat with the
change in regions, occurring on the California coast chiefly in the
middle zone and below *Pachygrapsus,* but reaching considerably
higher in Puget Sound. Northern specimens, however, at their best
are smaller than those on the California coast, and the highest specimens are very small. Hart (1935) records females in "berry" (ovigerous) in April and May at Departure Bay, and has studied the development, finding five zoeal stages and one megalops.

Numerous other species already treated are frequent in Puget
Sound, such as the lined chiton (§36) and the keyhole limpet
Diodora (§181). Small and undetermined polyclad worms similar
to *Leptoplana* (§17) are very common. The estuary fauna in the
south derives largely from open-coast constituents. In Newport Bay
great twisted masses of the tubed snails *Aletes* (§47) may almost
cover the rocks, and the rock oyster *Chama* (§126) grows so thickly
that it appears to form reefs.

§204. Along the shores of Hood Canal and generally in the Puget
Sound region we have found great hordes of the small crustacean *Epinebalia pugettensis* occurring mostly in pockets of silt among the rocks
and in the organic mud under half-decayed masses of seaweed (*Fucus*
and *Enteromorpha*). It also occurs in abundance among the beds of
green algae and eel grass in upper Tomales Bay, and has been recog-

nized from Pacific Grove. This, or a closely related species, occurs in similar sheltered situations in Morro Bay, Los Angeles Harbor, San Diego, and southward to San Quintín. While it thrives on organic detritus, it seems to require situations where the tidal action is enough to prevent completely foul conditions. Cannon, who studied the feeding habits of the North Atlantic *Nebalia bipes,* a closely related species (Fig. 72), describes the manner in which this animal feeds. Like many other small "filter feeding" arthropods, the nebaliid sets up a food current by oscillating its abdominal appendages. The food is then strained by the armature of bristles or setae on the anterior appendages, which function much as a sieve. It can also feed on larger particles.

These curious little crustaceans are of particular interest to students of classification because they are the representatives of the subclass Leptostraca, which possesses characters transitional between the smaller, less specialized crustacea (the Entomostraca of the older textbooks), and the more specialized crustacea (the Malacostraca). They bear a small bivalve shell, somewhat like that of the ostracods, but their loss of the nauplius larva characteristic of the entomostracans and their arrangement of appendages and sex openings have earned them a place as the lowest division of the Malacostraca.

§205. Under the rocks there are the usual pill bugs and worms, occurring in such variety and such abundance as to distract the specialist. As in other environments, the algae provide homes for numerous isopods, the predominant species being *Idothea resecata* (Fig. 73) (common also on eelgrass) and *Idothea urotoma.* The former is a yellow-brown form, just the color of the kelp to which it often may be found clinging with great tenacity. Forcibly removed from its kelp, it seems lost until it can regain a similar position. The body is long (nearly 2″) and narrow, and terminates in two jawlike points. We found a particularly rich culture near Port Townsend, and it occurs from British Columbia to southern California. The second species mentioned is usually less than an inch long and is relatively wider.

§206. Occasional geyser-like spurtings that will be noticed wherever a bit of substratum has no covering rock can usually be traced to clams, often to the chalky-shelled *Protothaca* (formerly *Paphia*) *staminea,* the rock cockle (Pl. XXXI). This well-rounded clam (called a cockle because its strong radiating ridges suggest the true cockle) is also known popularly as the little-neck clam, the hard-shell clam, the Tomales Bay cockle, and the rock clam. As the number of popular names would suggest, it is well known and is widely used for food. In suitable localities it occurs so thickly that the valves often touch, and on the level gravel beaches of Hood Canal and such southern Puget Sound places as Whollochet Bay we have found it in such superabundance that two or three shovelfuls of substratum would contain enough clams to provide a meal for several hungry people. In October 1931, however, we found the clams of all market species considerably depleted in the Sound country, partly, at least, because the prevalent unemployment had driven many more people than usual to digging clams for a living. In 1935 the depletion had become very marked; it was then difficult to find any large specimens.

The rock cockle is a poor digger, and for that reason never lives in shifting sand where rapid digging is essential. It will be found in packed mud or in gravel mixed with sand, but seems to prefer clayey gravel, where it usually lies less than eight inches below the surface. Where these favorable conditions exist it grows almost equally well in isolated bits of the protected outer coast. At several points, especially Tomales Bay, the clam assumes some commercial importance, and at many other places it is an attraction to tourists. Open-coast specimens should be used warily during the summer, on account of "mussel poisoning" (§158). Typical specimens seldom exceed 3" in length, although larger ones may be taken from below the low-tide level.

In the vicinity of Sydney, British Columbia, at least, according to work done by Fraser and Smith, spawning takes place in February and March, with no evidence of summer spawning. They found also that the rate of growth, being determined by the extent and constancy of the food supply, seems to depend on the animal's position in relation to tidal currents and on the degree of protection from storms, rather than on the character of the beach. Growth is relatively slow; at the end of the second year, when about half of the animals spawn, the average length is only 25 mm., and, when the balance spawn, a year later, only 35 mm.

Psephidia lordi (Fig. 75) is a small secondary clam of some importance in Puget Sound and to the northward, having a total range of Unalaska to Lower California. It has a polished and gleaming white or light olive shell that is somewhat triangular in shape, flatter than that of the rock cockle, and usually only a fraction of its size.

ZONE 4. *Low-tide* area.

(a) Rock and rockweed habitat.

In the Puget Sound area the most obvious and abundant animals of the low-tide rocky channels are a large starfish, a green urchin, a tubed serpulid worm of previous acquaintance, a great snail, and a vividly red tunicate.

§207. The starfish *Evasterias troschelii* (Plate XXXI) can, it is suspected, be considered as a mainly subtidal animal, but in quiet waters, too stagnant even for *Pisaster*, it is very much a feature of the low intertidal zone and therefore deserves consideration here even though its proper habitat is below our scope. Elsewhere, it takes up the starfish burden where, in the matter of vertical zoning, the common *Pisaster* drops it. Except that in a large number of specimens the average *Evasterias* has a smaller disc, more tapering arms, and a slimmer and more symmetrical appearance than the common starfish, the two are much alike and are sure to be confused by the amateur collector. Since both occur so frequently in the same region, the interested observer will want to differentiate them. This can be done readily with a pocket lens, or even with a keen naked eye. On the under side of the rays, and among the spines just bordering the groove through which the tube feet are protruded, *Evasterias* has clusters of pedicellariae (§157). These are lacking in the common *Pisaster*.

At Departure Bay, and elsewhere on the inside coast of Vancouver Island, this starfish occurs in great numbers, but although it is recorded from Unalaska to Carmel Bay the shore collector will seldom see it south of Puget Sound. Dr. Fisher, the final authority on starfish, distinguishes several forms, but considers the animal to be one of the most variable of starfish. Specimens with a diameter of 2′ or more are not rare. Sexual maturity comes in June, July, and August.

A good many *Evasterias* have polynoid worms living commensally in the grooves under the rays. Johnson noted, more than thirty years ago, that several of these, *Arctonoë* (formerly *Halosydna*) *fragilis,* might be found in a single specimen.

§208. The very fragile starfish *Orthasterias koehleri,* also chiefly subtidal and occurring probably less than one per cent as frequently as *Evasterias,* may occasionally be found in the lowest intertidal zone at Departure Bay and Friday Harbor. It is a striking and brilliant form. The noticeable spines, often surrounded by wreaths of pedicellariae, are white or light purple and are set against a background of red marked with yellow. Strangely, this apparently quiet-water animal is fairly common in the subtidal zone in Monterey Bay, straying, on rare occasions, just above the lowest of low tides. Even more strangely, it has been found there in surf-swept regions, but probably creeps up into the influence of waves only when the surf is light. Dr. Fisher records the range as Yakutat Bay, Alaska, to Santa Rosa Island, off southern California, and remarks: "Northern specimens shed their rays readily and are difficult to preserve well. The Monterey form is not at all difficult to preserve and does not detach its rays readily. I have handled both sorts, alive, and have kept the Monterey form in aquaria where it is fairly active and eats a variety of food including dead squid, crabs, and fish."

§209. In Puget Sound, *Pisaster brevispinus* (Pl. XXXI), a pink-skinned short-spined edition of the common starfish, attains gigantic proportions. We have seen many specimens, notably in Hood Canal, that were more than 2′ in diameter and massive in proportion. They occurred there on soft bottoms below rocky or gravelly foreshores, usually just below the line of low spring tides. *P. brevispinus* is normally a deep-water form (drag-boat hauls from sixty-fathoms mud bottom in Monterey Bay bring them up by the thousand), ranging into the intertidal on sand, mud, or wharf pilings only in the most quiet waters. Its softness and collapsibility mark it as an animal that is obviously not built for long exposure to the air. The specimen photographed had been out of water less than ten minutes, but the collapsing of the tissues below the skeletal framework is already apparent. This pink form ranges as far south as Monterey Bay and at least as far north as British Columbia.

§210. Types of the small six-rayed starfish *Leptasterias* occur in these quiet waters, the common form in Puget Sound being *L. hexactis* (Pl. XXXI), an Alaska species that ranges as far south as Cape Flattery. *L. hexactis* is rarely more than 3″ in diameter, usually less. As with the more southern species (§68), the females incubate their eggs, carrying the young until they are fully formed miniature starfish. In Alaska ovigerous females have been taken in April, and in Puget Sound the breeding season is known to be finished before summer.

§211. A number of other starfish may be seen. The slim-armed red starfish, *Henricia leviuscula* (Pl. XII), is common in these quiet waters of the north as well as on the protected outer coast. We have taken one specimen that harbored a commensal scale worm, *Arctonoë vittata,* much as *Evasterias* entertains its similar guest.

Dermasterias imbricata, the leather star (Pl. XXXI), is a "web-footed" form resembling *Patiria.* This is another of the very beautiful animals for which the tide pools are justly famous. The sleek smooth covering of skin is commonly delicately purple with red markings, and the tips of the rays are often turned up. Ranging from Sitka to Monterey, the leather star, nowhere very common, is most numerous in the northern half of its range, and the specimens found in Puget Sound are gigantic (having a diameter up to 10″) by comparison with those in the tide pools of the protected outer coast.

The seventeen- to twenty-one–rayed sunflower star, *Pycnopodia* (§66), occurs also, and the fewer-rayed sun star, *Solaster* (§67).

§212. The common urchin in the Sound and northward into southeastern Alaska is the mildly green *Strongylocentrotus dröbachiensis,* of circumpolar range. Except for its color, its pointed spines, and its usually smaller size it resembles the south-ranging purple urchin (Pl. XXVII). Many specimens occur in the rocky San Juan Islands, and it is interesting to note that they appear to be crowding out the purple urchins that were once common there. The latter still retain unquestioned dominance on surf-swept shores along this coast, although on the East coast and in Europe the green urchin populates the open shore as well as protected regions. This cosmopolitan green urchin, in common with others, passes through several free-swimming stages not even remotely resembling the adult. It is an omnivorous feeder, but lives mainly on fixed algae.

The giant red urchin (§73), so common along the California coast, occurs also in northern inside waters but mainly below the low-tide line. It does range into the intertidal, however, at least as far north as the Juneau vicinity.

§213. Great twisted masses of the limy-tubed worm, *Serpula vermicularis* (Fig. 76), formerly called *S. columbiana,* cover the rocky reefs in the Puget Sound–Strait of Georgia region. Except that these worms have red "stoppers" to their tubes and exhibit vividly red gills which snap back into shelter on slight provocation, they occur just as do the tubed snails on the rocks in Newport Bay. Even as far south as Elkhorn Slough near Monterey this serpulid may be found on the sides of rocks in quiet regions. There is a good drawing of expanded living specimens on page 340, Vol. 2 (1910) of the *Cambridge Natural History.*

Serpula, like other tube worms, is dependent for its food on such diatoms and other microscopic organic matter as chance may bring it. It assists the process, however, by setting up currents with the hairlike cilia on its delicate gill filaments. Puget Sound specimens are sexually mature in July and early August, and if the removed animals there extrude as readily as do the related Pacific Grove forms (§129), they should provide very accessible embryological material.

§214. The hairy Oregon triton, *Fusitriton oregonensis* (Pl. XXXII), is the largest of the rocky-intertidal snails in the entire territory herein considered, for large specimens reach a length of almost 6 inches. The animal, with its handsome coiled shell, brown and hairy, is a feature of the extreme low-tide rocks and reefs near Friday Harbor, and has a recorded range of Alaska to La Jolla. During the summer, egg capsules are found on the same rocks. A murex,

Ceratostoma foliatum (§117), may be found this far down also, associated with the Oregon triton, but its center of distribution is thought to be higher in the intertidal.

Only the correspondingly largest intertidal hermit crab on the coast would have any use for so huge a shell as the Oregon triton's, and we find such a hermit in *Pagurus beringanus*. The only other large hermit common on shore in the Puget Sound region and lower British Columbia is the smaller, slimmer, hairy-handed hermit, *P. hirsutiusculus* (§201). The former has granules and short scarlet spines on the hands, but no true hair. The general color is brown with scarlet and light green markings.

§215. Two other common shelled snails, *Trichotropis cancellata,* the checkered hairy snail, and *Crepidula nummaria,* the northern slipper shell, are illustrated in Figures 77 and 78. The blue top shell, *Calliostoma ligatum,* with contrasty yellow shell, ranging from Alaska to San Diego on the protected outer coast, occurs in these quiet waters also, and is particularly abundant in Puget Sound, under overhangs and in rocky crevices fairly well up, and thence clear into the subtidal (Pl. XXVIII).

§216. The tunicate *Cnemidocarpa finmarkiensis* (Fig. 79), formerly *Styela stimpsoni,* has an extraordinarily bright red test (shell) that makes it one of the most conspicuous animals in the Puget Sound region. The crater-like projections — the excurrent and incurrent siphons that provide the animal with water for respiration and for the contained food particles—are rather prominent. In collecting and preserving specimens we have noted that these orifices have considerable power of contraction, closing almost completely under unfavorable conditions. We have found eggs in August.

The stalked *Styela gibbsii,* as found under rocks at Pysht (near the entrance to the Strait of Juan de Fuca) and probably in many other places, is a small and short-stalked edition of the tunicate so well developed on wharf piling (Fig. 107). The former is interesting in that it plays host to several other animals: a commensal pea crab; the parasitic and degenerate cirripede *Peltogaster,* one species of which is sometimes found on hermit crabs; and a vermiform copepod, *Scolecimorpha huntsmani,* which more nearly resembles a degenerate isopod.

Pyura haustor (Pl. XXXII), another large Puget Sound tunicate (often several inches long), has a bumpy test covered with all sorts of foreign material—a veritable decorator crab among tunicates. A subspecies, *P. haustor johnsoni,* is common under and alongside rocks in Newport Bay, and more rarely in Elkhorn Slough.

Several other tunicates occur, some obviously and many commonly, but for their sometimes difficult determination the reader must be referred to the scattered literature.

§217. The rock oyster or jingle shell, *Pododesmus macroschisma* (Fig. 80), occurs fastened to Puget Sound reefs just as a similar but smaller jingle, *Anomia peruviana*, occurs in the quiet bays of southern California. Curiously, both of these are associated with similar-looking but widely differing tube masses, *Serpula* in Puget Sound and *Aletes* in southern California. *Pododesmus* is one of various animals that are called jingles presumably because of the sounds made by dead shells on shingly beaches. The valves are thin, and the adherent valve has a notched foramen or opening through which passes the byssus that attaches the animal to its support. Large specimens may be more than 3″ in diameter. The range is from Bering Sea to Lower California. Below Puget Sound specimens will be found on wharf piling almost exclusively. The flesh of *Pododesmus* is bright orange, but despite its livid color it has an excellent flavor.

Old shells of this and other mollusks, north of Puget Sound and clear into Alaska, are likely to be honeycombed to the point of disintegration by small, yellow-lined pores, evidences of the work of *Cliona celata,* the boring sponge. Break apart one of the shells so eaten—they are fragile and crumbly if the process is well advanced—and note how the interior is composed almost entirely of the yellow spongy mass. In the Monterey Bay region *Cliona* attacks the shells of abalones, but usually only those growing in deep water, and the sponge is not in any case the important littoral feature that it becomes up north. Oyster shells in southern California estuary regions may be overgrown exteriorly with a sponge, *Hymeniacidon* (§183), encountered also in wave-swept crevices.

§218. Enclosed in Newport Bay is a stretch of fully protected reef that is the counterpart of Puget Sound reefs. In its unfortunately small area at least two Panamanian animals, neither of which is known to occur commonly elsewhere along the California coast, maintain an extreme northerly outpost. The first is a rather beautiful gorgonian, *Muricea californica,* that is related to the "sea fans" and "sea whips" and hangs in graceful, tree-shaped, brown clusters from the vertical cliff face. The minute zooids that extend from the branches when the animal is undisturbed are in pleasantly contrasting white. Clusters may be more than 6″ in length and as large around as one's fist.

The second is the pale urchin, *Lytechinus pictus,* about 1½″ in diameter, a light gray form that occurs abundantly in the Gulf of California. This Newport Bay region appears to be more plentifully supplied with urchins (as to number of species) than any other similar area on the United States Pacific coast. Both the purple urchin and the giant red urchin may be taken along with this pale-gray form on the same rocky reef, and on the neighboring sand flats the ubiquitous sand dollar occurs, and an occasional heart urchin or sea porcupine (§247).

§219. The small native oyster, with its irregular white shell, is familiar to most coast dwellers from Sitka to Cape San Lucas. *Ostrea lurida* (Fig. 82) occurs characteristically in masses that nearly hide the rock to which the animals are fastened. For many years it was scorned as food because of its small size, and even now this is prob-ably the chief factor in preventing the animal from being used for food as extensively as it deserves. People acquainted with its delec-table flavor, however, often pronounce it more delicious than the larger Eastern oyster, and probably its virtues will come to be more generally appreciated. Already the cultivating of *O. lurida* forms a considerable industry in Puget Sound, where it is known as the Olympia oyster. It is marketed up and down the Pacific coast and is shipped to the Eastern market under refrigeration, the value of the total pack amounting to about three-quarters of a million dollars a year.

In Oyster Bay, near Olympia, the method of cultivation is as follows: Low concrete dikes are built, partitioning off many acres of mud flats, which are carefully leveled, the object being to retain water when the tide goes out, so that the growing oysters are never exposed. Since oysters would smother in mud, quantities of broken shell are scattered over the surface, and to these bits of shell the "spat" or free-swimming young attach. Nelson studied the method of attach-ment of the Eastern oyster and found that a larva moves about over the selected area, testing it out with its foot. They will not settle on shells that are badly riddled. After choosing an attachment site one circles about, wiping its large and turgid foot over the area and ex-truding enough cement to affix the left valve. The cement, which hardens in ten minutes, is secreted by a gland similar to the one which in the mussels produces the byssal hairs.* After two years the "spat," as the young oysters are called, are transferred to more ex-tensive beds, and after five or six years they reach maturity and a diameter of about 2 inches. Then they are ready to market. It takes from 1,600 to 2,000 "shucked" oysters to make a gallon, solid pack.

The native oyster is cultivated in Tomales Bay also, and there

---

* The attachment of the Olympia oyster has also been investigated. Hopkins (1935) finds spat more commonly on the under surface of shells, and this condition is said to be due not to their greater survival there but to the fact that the normal swimming position of the larva, with foot upward, enables it more readily to affix under overhangs.

seems to be no good reason why oyster culture on this coast should not eventually rival the thriving East-coast industry. There are certain opposing factors, to be sure. Snails eat the young oysters, as elsewhere; starfish exact some toll, and stingrays prey on the adults where the beds are not protected by wand fences. In the Puget Sound beds the oysters have accidental enemies in "crawfish"—the mud shrimp, *Upogebia,* and the ghost shrimp, *Callianassa*—which bury many oysters with the mud carried out from their burrows and which so riddle the ground that at low tide much water drains out from the diked areas. Starfish, however, the chief liability of Eastern beds, find the combination of mud and shells not to their liking, and have never taken to raiding the West-coast beds in hordes.

The introduced Eastern oyster, *Crassostrea virginica* (Fig. 83), has never established itself on this coast, although considerable quantities are grown in San Francisco Bay, Tomales Bay, and Puget Sound from imported spat, usually in subtidal beds. A third oyster is being grown commercially from imported spat of the Japanese oyster, *C. gigas.* Both of these importations have interesting sidelights in the unwanted settlers that came with them. With the Japanese oyster came a cosmopolitan anemone (§224), which seems to thrive somewhat better than the oyster; and with the Eastern form came the oyster drill, a snail with a voracious appetite (§286).

The sexual vagaries of the oyster are worth detailed mention. It has been known for some time that a European oyster changed its sex, and recently it has been discovered that our Eastern oyster also is what is known as a protandrous hermaphrodite. Still more recently Coe, working at La Jolla, has shown that *Ostrea lurida* belongs in the same category. It is never completely male or completely female, but goes through alternate male and female phases. The gonads first appear, showing no sexual differentiation, when the animal is about eight weeks old. At twelve to sixteen weeks the gonads show primitive characteristics of both sexes, but thereafter the male aspect develops more rapidly until, at the age of about five months, the first spermatozoa are ready to be discharged. Before the clusters of sperm are discharged, however, the gonads have begun to change to female, and immediately after the release of the sperm the first female phase begins—a phase which reaches its climax when the animal is about six months old. Coe reports: "Ovulation then occurs, the eggs being retained in the mantle cavity of the parent during fertilization and cleavage and through development until the embryos have become provided with a bivalved, straight-hinged shell—a period of approximately ten to twelve days, perhaps. It is not improbable that ovulation takes place only when the animal is stimulated by the presence in the water of spermatozoa of other individuals. . . . ."* As before, the phases overlap, so that the second male phase has begun while the embryos are still developing within the mantle cavity. The second male phase produces vastly greater numbers of sperm than the first. When they are discharged (except a few clusters that are retained, as always) the body of the oyster is "soft, flabby and translucent, presenting a marked contrast to its plump whitish condition preceding the discharge of the gametes. A period of recuperation follows," before the assumption of the next female role. Apparently this cycle of female, male, and recuperative phases is continued throughout the animal's life. It is definitely affected by temperature, a lowered temperature causing a particular phase to be arrested or prolonged. Coe remarks: "It is not unlikely that in the colder portion of the range of the species a single annual rhythm or even a biennial rhythm may be found to occur, as is the case with the European oyster in some localities." In Puget Sound sexual maturity comes in early summer, but in southern California, where Coe worked, spawning takes place during seven or more months of the year.

The period from the fertilization of the egg to the time when the shelled larva leaves the parent is sixteen or seventeen days. The free-swimming period lasts for fourteen days, after which the larva settles down, as previously described.

In summing up this situation, Coe (1934, *American Naturalist,* 48: 236–51) rates the Pacific oyster as a true hermaphrodite (possessing both male and female gonads constantly, but with one or the other temporarily ascendant), of larviparous habits, and invariably passing through the male phase first. The oviparous Eastern oyster is stated to be dioecious, that is, with sexual alternation but ordinarily lacking the side-by-side development of the gonia of both sexes, and in 3 to 30 per cent of the cases passing directly to the female phase without having first become a male. But even within the species there is much variation, the sex-differentiating factors being in a condition so labile that even a small impetus, such as food or temperature differentials, may effect a drastic change. The fact that in *O. virginica* "most of the relatively small numbers of females are among the largest of the age group" indicates to Coe (1932*b*) "that the female is metabolically the more active sex or that she requires better nutritive conditions in order to mature, or that sex in this species is

* As a matter of fact, Galtsoff and Smith (1932, *Science,* 76: 3712) report that the spawning of either sex, other conditions being suitable, can be induced by the presence of sexual products of the opposite sex not only of the species in question (*O. virginica*), but by those of, for instance, the Japanese oyster, and the apparently normal larvae resulting from this union show no higher mortality rates than those of the controls.

so labile that the nutritive conditions of the individual at the critical period of sex differentiation determine which of the alternative types of cells in the primary bi-sexual gonad shall predominate."

§220. In the Puget Sound area another edible shellfish, the scallop, *Pecten hericius,* and other species, forms the basis of an important industry. Motor and steam trawlers sweep the bottom with nets, scooping up hundreds in a single haul. Although scallops in commercially valuable quantities occur in deep water only, the collector along rocky shores will be certain to see them in the intertidal zone and below the low-tide line. All scallops are characterized by projecting "ears" on either side of the hinge and by prominent radiating ridges on the handsome shells. The species mentioned, which ranges from Bering Sea to San Diego, is rather similar in outline to *P. circularis* (§255 and Pl. XXXVII), but has finer and more numerous radiating ridges. Also the left valve is a darker pink than the right. *P. hericius,* like most other species, remains symmetrical throughout its life. Scallops have but one large muscle for closing the shell, instead of a large one and a small one as in the mussels and clams. It is usually this single muscle that is marketed, the rest of the body being thrown away, although the entire animal, as with the oysters, is edible, indeed, delicious.

Next to the octopus, the scallop is the "cleverest" of all the mollusks. It is quick to take alarm, being warned of impending danger by a row of shining functional eyes along the mantle fringe, and darts away by clapping the two valves of its shell together. The motive power for this peculiar swimming is provided by two jets of water which the sudden closing of the shell drives out through openings in the mantle. Necessarily, then, the motion is hinge-first, or backwards, a reversal of the usual movement, which is slower and in the direction of the shell opening. This emergency reversing of the normal direction of movement is characteristic of several other animals also, including the octopus.

De Laubenfels remarks that very few *Pecten* in the Puget Sound area lack the symbiotic sponge, *Ectyodoryx parasitica* (formerly *Myxilla*), or the less frequent *Mycale adherens.* Both of these occur only on scallops, and no other sponges occur thus. The *Mycale* "may be distinguished by comparatively coarser structure, and best by this: when torn, it reveals prominent fibers thicker than thread, absent in *Myxilla*" (personal communication).

§221. Of chitons, the black *Katharina* (§177) can be expected on relatively exposed shores. The giant brick-red *Cryptochiton* (§76) occurs also, but the specimens are smaller than those found on the central California coast. One or more species of *Mopalia* will also be found, as differentiated in §128. *Mopalia hindsii* is known to occur in such sheltered localities as Elkhorn Slough and San Francisco Bay. The closely related *M. muscosa* ranges from the Shumagin Islands to Lower California. Puget Sound specimens are sexually mature in July and August.

§222. Not many crabs will be found walking about on top of the rocks in this low zone—a situation quite the opposite of that existing higher up, where the purple shore crabs scamper over every square foot of rock surface. The small Oregon *Cancer* may be taken occasionally on the rocks, but is commoner in the under-rock habitat (§231). A lanky "all legs" spider crab (*Oregonia gracilis,* §334), that occurs more characteristically on wharf piling, strays into this rocky-shore region also. Another small spider crab, *Pugettia gracilis,* the graceful kelp crab, seems to be characteristic here, but it occurs also in eelgrass and in kelp. It looks like a small and slim *P. producta* (Pl. XV). Like that larger kelp crab, which also is occasional in this association, the graceful one keeps its brown, yellow, or red carapace naked and smooth, not deigning to disguise itself with bits of sponge, bryozoa, or algae, as the more sluggish spider crabs do. These kelp crabs, being very active and having hooked and clawed legs which can reach almost backward, are amply able to defend themselves without recourse to such measures as masking. Most crabs can be grasped safely by the middle of the back, but the safe belt in the kelp crabs is narrow, and he who misses it on the first try will pay the penalty. *P. gracilis* ranges southward from Alaska as far, though rarely there, as southern California.

§223. The only other noticeable exposed crustaceans are barnacles. Except in Puget Sound and comparable waters to the northward, barnacles are rare in the very low intertidal zone, although they are everywhere tremendously common in the higher zones. It would be expected that these low-zone barnacles would be of species different from those previously treated, since the relative periods of exposure and immersion are so different. Until recently this has been assumed to be the case, but it seems to be well established now that the commonest barnacle of this low zone is *Balanus cariosus* (§194), the same form that occurs in such tremendous numbers in the upper zone of quiet-water regions, although field identifications of barnacles are so uncertain that some of these may turn out to be *Balanus nubilus* (§317), the second commonest form, which seems to achieve its greatest development on fairly exposed wharf pilings. On Puget Sound rocks, however, the largest examples reach the considerable size of 3″ in basal diameter by 2½″ tall.

§224. Anemones, abundant on all the quiet-water rocky shores

from Alaska south, are especially noticeable in Puget Sound. Elsewhere in the Pacific, the white-plumed *Metridium senile* (§321) occurs
only on piling and in deep water, but in the Sound it occurs not infrequently on the lowest intertidal rocks and ledges and in the pools, just
as it does on the coast of Maine. North of Nanaimo, British Columbia,
we have seen large numbers of them hanging pendent from the under
side of strongly overhanging ledges.

The large red tuberculated *Tealia* (§65) is occasional, and the
small semi-transparent *Epiactis prolifera* (§37), with its eggs and
young in brood pits around the base, certainly attains its maximum in
size, though probably not in abundance, in these quiet waters.

One of the common Japanese and cosmopolitan anemones, *Diadumene luciae,* has been introduced on this coast, it is safe to assume, along
with oysters, for it has appeared at or near places where Japanese
oysters are known to be grown. We have seen it above the Strait
of Georgia, on Puget Sound floats with *Metridium,* and it has appeared suddenly in Elkhorn Slough, in central California. It is a small
form, usually under ½″ in diameter, but it is attractively colored—
dark green, with 4 to 48 orange stripes. If the form in question is
identical with the Atlantic *luciae,* a good deal of information is available in Hausman (1919). A circumboreal form, it appeared suddenly at Woods Hole, Massachusetts, and owing to its competitive
ability and rapid asexual reproduction colonized very quickly in areas
where its colors and small size conceal it effectively. Hausman found
it to be a voracious feeder on small crustacea and annelids.

§225. Reaching its apparent southern limit at Pender Harbor,
British Columbia, a large erect sponge occurs (Pl. XXXII) that is
similar in appearance to the *Neosperiopsis rigida* reported by Lambe
from deep water north of Vancouver Island. Specimens from Refuge
Cove are up to 8″ long. They are brightly colored with reds or
lavenders that fade immediately in preservative. Forests of these
upright sponges, growing at or below the lowest tide line, add something of a coral-reef atmosphere to this northern fauna.

Although we have not been successful in finding it along the
shore, a most interesting sponge, *Choanites suberea* var. *lata,* the
home of the hermit crab, *Pagurus dalli,* is recorded from Puget Sound
and northward as occurring in the low-tide zone as well as in deep
water. Clusters of this yellow "cheesey" or carrot-like sponge may
be 3″ in diameter, and are said to be pierced almost invariably with
an opening that harbors the large hermit. The mutual advantages are
obvious: the crab gets a protective covering, and the sponge gets
plenty of food and oxygen by being so much on the move.

De Laubenfels remarks that the slimy, papillated sponge *Hymeni-*

acidon (§183) occurs abundantly in these quiet waters, as near the marine station at Newport Bay, and we have noted it also in connection with oyster shells.

§226. In this low zone of the quiet-water rocky environment sea cucumbers are common in the south, entirely absent in Elkhorn Slough, and occasional in Puget Sound. Under rocks, however, they are common in the northern regions (§235). One of the strange, slug-like, creeping cucumbers, *Psolus chitonoides* (Pl. XXXII), is a fairly frequent migrant into the intertidal zone from deep water. If seen below the surface, and unmolested, *Psolus* will be noted and recognized at once. There will be a crown of gorgeously expanded tentacles at the head end, often in rosy reds or purples contrasting with the yellow or white of the scales that cover the back, and on the soft belly are the tube feet that provide the not overly rapid locomotion.

§227. *Terebratalia transversa* (Fig. 81) represents a group of animals not previously mentioned and that will be met only once again in this account. The brachiopods, bivalved animals resembling clams but in no way related to them, comprise a line tremendously important in past geological ages but now restricted to a few hundred species, most of which occur in deep water. The hinged valves of clams are right and left; those of brachiopods (sometimes called "lamp shells") are upper and lower and unconnected except by muscles. Again unlike clams, brachiopod shells are dissimilar in size and shape. The upper is the larger, and through an opening in its overhanging margin protrudes the fleshy peduncle by which the animal is attached to the rock. Although brachiopods of this type are usually (and correctly) assumed to be sessile animals, we observed that specimens taken in British Columbia were able to rotate the shell considerably on the contractile peduncle. A cluster of the living animals will show all the shells slightly agape but ready to snap shut immediately at the least sign of danger. They feed on minute organic particles brought to them by the tidal currents or the slight currents created by waving the ciliated tentacles on the lophophore—a "coil spring" organ that transmits food into the mouth and stomach. Thus, like other plankton-feeding forms, they must keep constantly on the job, opening their shells the instant they are unmolested. *Terebratalia* is restricted to the lowest part of the low intertidal zone, where it is a feature of the rocky fauna of British Columbia. It is taken occasionally as far south as Friday Harbor, and in deep water it extends to southern California. In the summer of 1932 we found a great colony of these in a land-locked marine lake, Squirrel Cove, in south-central British Columbia. This unusual environmental condition was reflected in the great size of the individual brachiopods, in their large number, and in the dark color of their shells. Interestingly, the very abundant *Stichopus californicus* (§77) taken in this rocky lagoon were also more blackly purple than usual, higher in the littoral (this species is more common subtidally), and small, climbing all about the tops and sides of the rocks. *Dermasterias* (§211) taken in this assemblage were also darker than usual.

§228. At Elkhorn Slough (and probably elsewhere along the coast, although there are no other records) the observing amateur will sooner or later find a group of ivory-white polyps, each about half an inch long, attached to a rock on the side sheltered from the current. If disturbed, they immediately contract into stalked translucent lumps less than half of their normal length. These tiny unspectacular polyps are the parents of highly spectacular pelagic animals—the great jellyfish (the scypho-medusae) that are sometimes stranded on the beach. It will be remembered that there is an alternation of generation between the relatively large and plant-like hydroids and the small free-swimming jellyfish. The giant jellyfish also have an alternation of generation, but the attached polyp is small and rarely seen. It is this polyp, the scyphistoma of *Aurelia* or similar species, that will be found at or below the lowest tide line at Elkhorn Slough. We have transferred a good many examples to aquaria, where they live well, being extraordinarily tough and resistant, and have watched them with interest. They are accomplished contortionists. Fully relaxed specimens are pendulous, with dainty tentacles extending the equivalent of the length of the polyp. At such times the mouth forms a raised crater in the center of the tentacles. At other times the internal anatomy will, for no apparent reason, be everted through the enormously stretched mouth. When the animal contracts, the tentacles almost disappear, and the scyphistoma becomes merely a ball at the end of the stalk. In producing its "children" jellyfish, the polyp is modified into a "strobila" by constriction so that it is topped by a "saucer" or stack of saucers which, when budded off, become the free-swimming young, the "ephyrae," of the giant jellyfish. The jellyfish, normally to be seen only offshore (except in northern inside waters, §330), produce eggs which are liberated as ciliated larvae, the "planulae." These larvae, frequently drifting inshore, settle down to become polyps, and the cycle is complete. Several of the scypho-medusae are famous for the stinging powers of their long tentacles, and it was a member of this group, the "Lion's Mane," that provided a mystery which taxed the powers of Sherlock Holmes. There is evidence, however, that the Master bungled this case (Hedgpeth, *Scientific Monthly*, 60, March 1945, pp. 227–32).

§229. Along these sheltered rocky shores there are, finally, many hydroids and bryozoa and occasional sponges, mostly of types already mentioned. Some of the ostrich-plume hydroids (*Aglaophenia,* §84), but more frequently the "sea firs" (*Abietinaria,* §83) and the delicate, almost invisible *Plumularia* (§78) will be seen. Collectors from the south will recognize a sponge cluster, *Leucosolenia nautilia,* similar to the California species considered in §93.

In the Puget Sound area we have found the erect, tree-like bryozoan, *Bugula pacifica* (§114), with some of the exposed clusters colored a vivid salmon pink, but the more flabby European form, *Dendrobeania murrayana,* restricted, in the Pacific, to this region, may be seen more commonly. The white crinkly bryozoan *Tricellaria* (§112) occurs in these northern sounds on the roots and holdfasts of marine plants just as it does in less-sheltered areas along the California coast.

The "sea lichen," *Dendrobeania lichenoides,* occurs on shells, rocks, and worm tubes as a leafy encrustation. It ranges from Alaska to central California and is common in Puget Sound.

The white *Membranipora* (§110) encrusts on kelp, as do the small and dainty-tubed colonies of *Tubulipora flabellaris.* Colonies of the latter are $\frac{1}{4}''$ to $\frac{1}{2}''$ across, and the tubes are as hard as those of serpulid worms. This form ranges from the Sound to San Diego.

A southern form, known from San Diego Bay only, is the soft *Zoobotryon pellucidum,* which forms great, flexible, tree-like masses. The listing of bryozoa might go on indefinitely, for more than 150 species are known from Puget Sound alone. In the Strait of Georgia Dr. O'Donoghue took some 76 species in a single dredge haul, and almost half of the total may be taken inshore. Most of us can scarcely hope to recognize more than a few.

Exceedingly common in the Nanaimo region, but restricted apparently to such areas (unless this is the animal taken rarely on Pacific Grove rocks), will be found great gelatinous masses of a rare and curious, worm-like form, *Phoronis vancouverensis,* related to but not resembling the solitary phoronids (§297).

(b) Under-rock habitat.

It would be expected that bay and estuary regions in the south would have their rocky-shore fauna pretty well concentrated under rocks as protection from sun and desiccation, and that is what we find. In Puget Sound also, however, the under-rock habitat is well populated—a fact probably attributable to the late (diurnal) tides which bare the intertidal areas during the heat of summer days.

§230. The energetic upturner of rocks will find that in sheltered waters the most obvious under-rock animals are crabs, worms, and

sea cucumbers, and, in the north, nemerteans. Other previously encountered animals are the eye-shaded shrimp, *Betaeus* (§46), and the
small and active bent-in-the-middle shrimp, *Spirontocaris* (§§62, 150),
that occurs throughout our territory. Another shrimp, *Hippolyte californiensis* (Pl. XXXIII), is fairly well restricted to quiet waters and
will be found, in the daytime, hiding under rocks and in crevices. At
night it may be seen in great congregations swimming about among
the blades of eelgrass. Like the form mentioned above, this graceful,
green (quickly turning white after preservation), and excessively
slender shrimp has an absurd rostrum, or forward projection of the
carapace. It is known from Bodega Bay to the Gulf of California, but
is common only as far south as Elkhorn Slough. The sometimes bulging carapace is a pathological condition due to infection by a parasitic
isopod, *Bopyrina striata*.

§231. The Oregon cancer crab, *C. oregonensis* (Pl. XXXIII), the
roundest of the family, is the commonest *Cancer* of the Puget Sound
region and is almost entirely restricted to the under-rock habitat. Its
extreme range is from the Aleutians to Lower California, but it is
rare south of Washington.

The black-clawed *Lophopanopeus bellus* (similar to *L. heathii*,
Fig. 50, but with slimmer big claws) cannot be mistaken, as it is the
only member of its genus in the Puget Sound region and is uncommon below there, although ranging south to Monterey Bay. Eggs
are carried in April, hatching May to August, as determined for
British Columbia specimens by Hart (1935). Northern specimens
of both of these crabs are often parasitized with the obvious *Sacculina*
(§327), and at Sitka possibly 25 per cent of the tide-pool specimens
will be so afflicted.

A quiet-water anomuran crab, *Petrolisthes eriomerus,* may be
taken in Puget Sound and in Newport Bay. It differs only slightly in
appearance from the outer-coast form shown in Plate III. A reddish
or brown, hairy crab, *Hapalogaster mertensii* (resembling *H. cavicauda* of Pl. XX except that it has tufts of bristles instead of fine
hairs), also occurs in the under-rock environment to the north, ranging from the Aleutians to Puget Sound.

§232. Tube worms of several types will be found here, some with
pebble-encrusted, black tubes up to 10″ long. Dark-colored, almost
purple, specimens may be turgid with eggs, or, if light-colored, with
sperm. *Amphitrite robusta* (similar to *Thelepus,* Pl. VIII) is one of
the largest and commonest. Field directions for distinguishing the
several genera will be found in §53; but only a specialist, interested
also in ecology, could straighten out this situation. The varying environments have undoubtedly exerted a selective influence on the

various species. We ourselves have noted differences in tube construction and in appearance of the worms predominating in wave-swept, cold-water California habitats, and in quiet-water sounds, but have not been able so far clearly to correlate the data.

Any of the several scale worms may take to living in the tubes of these larger and more self-reliant worms. Our friend *Halosydna* (§49), of the profitable degeneracy, is frequent; *Hololepidella tuta* (§234) also occurs. Meticulous search will also reveal, in practically every tube, one or more of several pea crabs—*Pinnixa tubicola* (§53) or *P. franciscana* juveniles. *P. schmitti* juveniles, the echiurid commensal (§306), have also been taken, but *tubicola* is by far the commonest pea crab found thus, in both the north and the south, in quiet and in open-coast situations. The combination of tube builder, polynoid, and pea crab is, however, particularly characteristic of quiet waters. The smaller commensals apparently have adapted themselves to gathering the proverbial crumbs. There is a nice economy about the situation, for what one animal rejects as too large or too small exactly suits one of its partners.

§233. For a number of years we have been taking a gray, sluggish "bristle worm" from the muddy interstices of rocks dredged up from below forty fathoms in Monterey Bay. During the summer of 1930 we were surprised to find this *Stylarioides papillata,* apparently perfectly at home, at several points along the shore in Puget Sound. Here is another case of an animal quite competent to live in the intertidal zone once the menace of surf is done away with. It has often been said of Pacific-coast invertebrates that northern-shore forms may be found in the south, but in deep water; and it has been assumed that the determining factor is temperature. In Puget Sound, however, the summer mid-day temperature that these animals must tolerate at low tide is greater than the maximum along the Monterey shore at any time, and the northern winter temperatures are correspondingly lower. It is easy to believe, therefore, that the absence of wave shock permits a normally deep-water animal to migrate upward until it has established itself successfully in the lowest intertidal zone.

§234. Many worms will be turned up here. *Neanthes virens* (§311) makes semipermanent burrows where the substratum is readily penetrable. *Phascolosoma* (§52) occurs, and, under Puget Sound mussel beds on a gravel substratum, *Nereis vexillosa* (§163), a variety of the glycerid worm (§280, Pl. XXXIX), and the slaty blue *Hemipodus borealis.*

But of the enumerating of worms also there could be almost no end. Certainly more than a hundred could be taken, and the unfortunate aspect of the worm situation is that any of them might prove to be common at some of the good collecting places that we have necessarily missed.

In any event, just one more dainty little polynoid must be mentioned, although until recently we had not known its name: this is called *Hololepidella tuta*. It has a serpentine gait, and will literally wiggle itself to pieces when disturbed too persistently. When first molested it will protestingly shed a few of its beautifully colored scales; lifted from its favorite under-rock surface it immediately breaks in two, and before the transfer to jar of water or vial of alcohol can be completed the disappointed collector is left with a number of short fragments that continue the characteristic wiggle. We have never been able to keep a specimen intact long enough to photograph it. It occurs frequently also as a commensal with various tube worms (terebellids, §§53, 232).

§235. The large reddish cucumber seen so abundantly under rocks in Puget Sound, or between the layers of friable shale ledges, is *Cucumaria miniata* (Pl. XXXIII), a form that reaches a length of 10 inches. The tube feet, which are arranged in rows paralleling the long axis of the body, hold fast to the rock very efficiently, but seem to be used rarely for locomotion. Surrounding the mouth are long and much-branched tentacles that are drawn in when the animal is disturbed or when the ebbing tide leaves it high and dry. In an aquarium they will flower out beautifully. The animal's color varies, in different specimens, from yellow and red to deep purple. *C. miniata* has been variously considered as synonymous with an Oriental cucumber and with a cucumber occurring on both sides of the Atlantic, but in any case it is the North Pacific representative of a circumpolar and almost cosmopolitan form. The pentamerous symmetry that marks cucumbers as relatives of the starfish, brittle stars, and urchins is rather apparent in *miniata*. We were greatly surprised to find, in the spring of 1931, several specimens of this northern animal in rock crevices near Carmel.*

A smaller white cucumber, *Eupentacta quinquesemita* (see Pl. XXXIII), may be considered as living primarily under rocks, since it is rarely found elsewhere in the intertidal, although below the low-tide line it occurs in all sorts of situations. The two double rows of long tube feet give the animal a bristly appearance. This form and *C. miniata* differ from the *Stichopus* we have considered earlier in

---

* It occurs commonly at least as far north as Sitka. In British Columbian channels such as Canoe Pass it is one of the most spectacular of animals; great beds are zoned at from one to five feet below mean lower low water. The delicate beauty of these expanded colonies, their diagrammatically extended, translucent, coral-red tentacles literally paving the rocks, surprise the zoölogist who has known them only from preserved specimens or has seen them only as contracted animals exposed at low tide.

having the tentacles around the mouth fairly long, branched, and yellow- or orange-colored. *Eu. quinquesemita* is very temperamental about evisceration. Specimens we took in the summer of 1930 at Pysht, in Juan de Fuca Strait, achieved a record of one hundred per cent evisceration in a few hours and before we could get them into anesthetizing trays. This is the more surprising when it is realized that the temperatures in the seaweed-filled buckets could not have been appreciably higher than those customarily tolerated on the tide flats during the late midsummer lows, when the sun and wind dry the algae to the point of crispness. This white cucumber ranges from as far north as Sitka to Pacific Grove, but at the latter point it occurs infrequently and then so far down as to be practically a subtidal form. In Puget Sound it is often found associated with the reddish *Cucumaria miniata*. In southeastern Alaska a very similar form occurs, described by Deichmann as *Eupentacta pseudoquinquesemita*, which has heretofore been known from subtidal depths only. It is scarcely distinguishable from the more southerly-ranging white cucumber except that it is thinner-skinned, so that in preservation it partially constricts itself, producing many ringed wrinkles in the body wall.

C. miniata has recently provided laboratory material for some preliminary study of invertebrate muscle tissue. The powerful retractor muscles that pull the tentacles back into safety at the least disturbance have been histologically examined, and it has been shown that, as one has always suspected, invertebrate muscle tissue differs radically in minute structure and in physico-chemical nature from comparable muscle tissue in the vertebrates. This is a field that we believe should be more thoroughly investigated. Mammalian and lower-vertebrate muscle tissue has been studied microscopically and experimentally; chemical relaxants and contractors are known. Even crustacean muscles have received some attention. But the fascinating, unbelievably resistant, and apparently highly specialized muscles of such forms as *Cribrina,* scyphistomae, *Glycera,* sipunculids (cf. *Phascolosoma),* many of which hold after the surrounding tissue has started to disintegrate, are wholly unknown. In many cases it is not known whether the muscle is smooth or striped, or whether the type of innervation is automatic or voluntary.*

Cucumaria vegae is a small black holothurian taken from low tide rock crevices at Auk Bay, north of Juneau. Another occasionally intertidal form in the Puget Sound area (but pulled up at Pacific Grove in subtidal holdfasts of kelp only) is the white "pepper and

---

* See also Wyman and Lutz (1930), "The Action of Adrenaline and Certain Drugs on the Isolated Holothurian Cloaca," *Journal of Experimental Zoölogy,* 57: 441–54.

salt" *Cucumaria piperata.* Large and light-colored *C. lubrica* (§176) may also occur here.

With the northern cucumbers and elsewhere under rocks, a really gigantic flatworm, tough and firm, will sometimes be turned out, large enough to be the paternal ancestor of all the polyclads the southern collector will have seen. This *Cryptophallus magnus,* which we have taken at Sitka, in British Columbia at several points, and on the rocks near Port Orchard, is reported to be common in the San Juan region by Freeman, its describer (1933). Individuals are reported up to 10 × 7 cm. Most of the polyclads are photo-negative—light-shunning—and *C. magnus,* taken on the under sides of rocks or in deep crevices, is no exception, although a diver working in these rocks at high tide or at night no doubt would find them crawling about on the upper surfaces actively enough. A specimen taken during the summer of 1935 seems to have attempted to engulf the soft parts of a limpet when, en route from tide pool to laboratory, it and others were placed in a jar of miscellaneous animals. A colored illustration of this form appears as Figure 4, Plate IV, in Johnson and Snook (1927).

Another smaller (to 4 × 1 cm.), thinner, and more delicate polyclad, often secured with the above, is probably the *Notoplana segnis* reported by Freeman as abundant around Friday Harbor.

The brittle star, *Ophiopholis aculeata* (§122), occurs frequently enough in beds of *Cucumaria miniata,* especially north of Puget Sound, so that the presence of one can almost be considered an index of the other. South of Prince Rupert and at Sitka we have turned up colonies of large examples, up to 5″ in diameter, literally by the hundreds, and associated with *Cucumaria* so that several individuals would be found clinging to each cucumber. Mixed up into the assemblage characteristically are dozens of the "peanut worms," *Phascolosoma* (§52), larger and darker in color than the possibly more numerous individuals available at Monterey.

§236. Along the California coast south of Los Angeles, octopi (§135) have moved into estuaries where there are suitable pools containing rocks arched over the mud. Living in such mud-rock caverns in quiet waters they attain, when unmolested (which they rarely can be in this heavily populated country), sizes that are large for their usually small species. Wherever numerous enough, they might be considered dominant animals, for their size, strength, and cunning put them pretty well in control of their surroundings.

§237. In the northern waters there are several under-rock chitons that we have met before, noticeably the small, red-marked *Lepidozona mertensii* (§128). In Puget Sound there is a still smaller, greenish to tawny chiton, *Cyanoplax dentiens.* This species occurs as far south as Monterey, and in waters south of Monterey will be found the very similar but slightly larger *Lepidochitona keepiana.*

§238. Under rocks in such varied quiet waters as those of Departure Bay and Pender Harbor, British Columbia, and Elkhorn Slough and Newport Bay, California, we have found a flat encrusting sponge described originally from the central California estuary as *Mycale macginitiei,* yellow, smooth, and slightly slippery to the touch, although it has stiffening spicules and is marked by furrows. An additional characteristic is that it adheres closely to the rock, probably by slightly penetrating the pores. Also, just by way of passing interest to zoölogists who have seen the true slime sponge elsewhere, a species of *Halisarca, H. sacra,* is known to occur at Elkhorn Slough, along with *Mycale,* but always below low water. Since there are various additional species not mentioned, which, on the basis of field characters alone, could be confused with the above and with previously treated species, the value of careful laboratory work should be kept in mind. For the necessary technic, see de Laubenfels (1932), page 4.

§239. The rubbery nemertean worms will often be seen under rocks in the north. Two fairly common forms especially are sure to be seen sooner or later and will occasion excited comment. Both are brilliantly scarlet, brighter than most reds even in the brilliant tide pools, large (to 3 meters, although the average will be no more than a couple of feet), and both occur under loosely imbedded stones, especially on gravel substratum, from Dutch Harbor clear into Puget Sound. But they may easily be differentiated. *Carinella rubra* is soft and rounded, very distensible, sluggish, and apt to be coiled in angular folds. The head is wide and rounded, pinched off from the rest of the body. We have found this to be one of the very common and characteristic under-rock inhabitants of quiet waters. In lower Saanich Inlet, about Deep Cove, for instance, in the summer of 1935, almost every suitable stone upturned revealed one of these brilliant worms in an apparently fabricated mild depression. *Cerebratulus montgomeryi,* however, is ribbon-like and flattened, with longitudinal slits on the sides of the head, which is tipped with white, and with lateral thickenings extending to thin edges (probably correlated with its swimming ability) running the entire length of the body. *Cerebratulus* is famous for fragmenting at even the slightest provocation; but this species, Coe remarks, lacks that trait to the extent that specimens may be killed whole by immersion in hot formalin.

§240. At least one vertebrate belongs with the under-rock fauna from Puget Sound clear into Elkhorn Slough—the grunting fish, *Porichthys notatus,* possibly better known as the midshipman, for its pattern of round sense organs is reminiscent of the buttons of a naval uniform. At night these "buttons" are luminescent. The eggs, each the size of a small pea, are deposited in handful clusters which may be seen under and around rocks during the summer. On one Puget Sound beach, in the summer of 1929, we found a small boy capturing the fish for food, using a method that must have seemed, to the fish, to violate Queensbury rules. He poked a slender stick under each likely rock and listened. If a midshipman grunted, he reached under with a heavier stick made into a gaff by the attachment of a large fish-hook. A quick jerk, and another betrayed grunter was added to his string. One of them came off the string, however, after certain negotiations, and was added to our chowder, with satisfactory but not phenomenal results. Blennies will also be found commonly in this zone under rocks in Puget Sound—*Anoplarchus purpurescens* and similar forms (see *Epigeichthys,* Pl. IX), such as will have been seen higher up (§198).

(c) Substratum (burrowing) habitat.

§241. In a few features the animals of the under-rock substratum, and also the animals living on the rocks, differ in quiet waters from those outside. For instance, the rocks in Newport Bay are often completely honeycombed by the burrowing date mussel, *Lithophaga plumula* (Pl. XXXIV), which we have never seen on the exposed coast. Quite possibly the answer in this case is temperature. The date mussel is a tropical form and might reasonably be expected to find the warm, sun-steeped climate of Newport Bay more to its liking than the climate of the colder, wave-swept shore outside.

The date mussel is a close relative of the common mussel, but has two important differences directly connected with its mode of life. One is that it produces an acid which attacks calcareous rocks, such as limestone. By means of this acid, secreted by a special gland, the animal excavates a home having a high degree of protection. It maintains communication with the outside world through its siphons, obtaining its oxygen and microscopic food, like all of its relatives, from the stream of water that flows in and out of the double siphon.

Obviously this chemical boring involves another problem, which might be stated in the form of a syllogism. Major premise: The date mussel's acid secretion attacks calcareous matter. Minor premise: The date mussel's own shell is calcareous. Conclusion: The date mussel's acid secretion attacks its own shell. The factor so fatuously overlooked is the animal's second difference from related forms. Covering the date mussel's shell is a thick brown layer of horny material which is resistant to the acid. It is the color of this protective layer, as well as the shape of the shell, that has given the animal its popular name.

§242. Another bivalve, *Pholadidea penita,* the common piddock or rock clam (Pl. XXXIV), drills into rock so hard that nothing short of a sledge hammer powerfully swung will break into the burrows, and it apparently drills without the aid of chemicals, using mechanical means only. The animal twists and rocks itself on its round muscle foot (which takes the form of a suction disc that grips the rock), pressing its rough valves outward at the same time so as to bring them into contact with the walls of the burrow. Such a method of drilling is necessarily slow in direct ratio to the hardness of the rock, partly because the continual wearing away of the shell by the grinding process must be compensated for by growth. In their recent book, *The Seas,* Russell and Yonge express the opinion that although no acid-forming gland can be found in the piddocks there must nevertheless be some chemical action, for while the head of the burrow is unquestionably excavated by mechanical action the outer part of the burrow, too, through which the soft siphons protrude, is enlarged. They sometimes bore, however, in rock, such as sandstone, that is immune to chemical action.

This rock clam or piddock occurs, in deep water at least, throughout its range from Alaska to Ecuador, but it seems to colonize in the intertidal zone in quiet water only. It has caused considerable damage to concrete harbor works on this coast. One investigation revealed the fact that more than half of the concrete-jacketed piles at four different places in Los Angeles Harbor were being attacked, sometimes with seven or eight borers to the square foot. In some cases the animals had turned aside after penetrating the concrete jacket, in order to avoid entering the wood.

The rock-boring clams are sometimes used for food, but he who gets a meal of them will have earned it.

§243. The burrows of dead rock-borers are likely to be appropriated by any of several homeseekers. The most numerous of these is the porcelain crab of wharf pilings (§318), but it has not adapted itself as completely to the borrowed home as has a large suckered flatworm (probably *Stylochoplana heathi*) which resembles *Planocera* (Fig. 6) in outline. This worm has the gray-brown color so common to retiring animals, and is very sluggish. It is firm in texture and outline, but when routed out of its quiet nest it curls itself up ever so slowly. Most polyclad worms crawl about and eat detritus that works into rock crevices. It would be interesting to determine if this one depends for its food on what the slight currents may bring it, or if it actually leaves the burrow and goes out hustling for something to eat.

§244. In the substratum between rocks, and ranging in its circumpolar distribution at least as far south as Puget Sound, is the burrowing anemone, *Edwardsiella sipunculoides,* which is similar to the *Edwardsiella* of Figure 95. It is a dull-brown form, with long transparent tentacles, and shows but faintly the eight longitudinal bands that are reputed to distinguish it from other anemones. A more readily apparent difference is that it has no attachment disc, living simply loosely buried in the soil.

§245. Nearly any of the animals that occur in the low-zone substratum in protected outer-coast areas may be taken here also—a state of affairs that would be expected from the obvious fact that in the substratum the degree of protection does not vary greatly between the two regions. Because of their abundance, mention should be made of the transparent, worm-like cucumber, *Leptosynapta* (§55), the soft blue burrowing shrimp, *Upogebia* (§313), and the clam *Protothaca* (*Paphia*) (§206), that spouts from between tide-pool rocks in Puget Sound. In the south the mantis shrimp, *Pseudosquilla* (§146), is taken infrequently far under loosely imbedded rocks. There are in the fully protected waters of Alaska (as at Jamestown Bay, Sitka, and Auk Bay, Juneau) such characteristic forms as the echiurid, *E. pallasii* (treated in §306 with mud-flat forms), the ubiquitous peanut worm (§52), and a slimy, apodous cucumber, *Chiridota albatrossi.* This last slim and slug-like form, covered with peppery black dots, may be 5″ or 6″ long, the otherwise smooth skin bearing the calcareous white particles—"anchors," mentioned already in connection with *Leptosynapta* (§55).

B. Sand Flats

IN quiet-water beaches of fairly pure sand, where there is no eel-grass, we find a type of region that, from the point of view of many animals, must seem Utopian. The usual environmental problems are almost entirely lacking—a fact which undoubtedly accounts, in part, for the extraordinary richness of the sand bars in Newport Bay and parts of Puget Sound. There is no wave shock to be withstood; the substratum is soft enough so that feeble burrowing powers will suffice and yet not so soft as to require special adaptations to avoid suffocation; there is no attachment problem, for a very little burrow-ing is enough to secure the animals against being washed out by the innocuous currents; and a little more burrowing protects them from sunlight and drying winds. These pure sands are likely to contain little organic food, by comparison with the rich stores of mud flats and eelgrass beds, but every tide brings in quantities of plankton, and such predaceous animals as require firmer food can prey on each other.

There is usually, however, something wrong with apparent Utopias. In this case the elimination of the struggle against natural conditions results in proportionately keener competition among the animals, and overcrowding is the rule. There is no obvious zonation in areas of pure sand, but the region corresponding to the lowest zone of other shores is, for most of the animals, the only one that is habit-able. The crowding is therefore accentuated, and since the upper beach is so sparsely inhabited it is scarcely worth while to explore sand flats except on tides below the zero of the tide tables.

§246. The sand dollars definitely belong in this environment, and occur in tremendous numbers. Their round shells are 3″ to 4″ in diameter, very flat, and colored so deep a purple as to be almost black. At first glance they seem to have little resemblance to other urchins, but urchins they are. The spines, instead of being 3″ or 4″ long as in the giant red urchin of the outer coast, are about $\frac{1}{16}$″ long and so closely packed as to make the animal look and feel as though it were covered with velvet. The tube feet are there, too, visible to the naked eye if one looks closely enough. In motion the spines and tube feet give an impression of changing light rather than actual motion. The five-pointed design on the back, another urchin characteristic, is visible in the living animal, but is more obvious in the familiar white skeletons that are so commonly cast up on exposed beaches as to lead many people to believe that the living animals must occur near by. They do—in deep water. The sand dollar avoids surf at all times, and will seldom be found alive by the shore collector except on these completely sheltered flats.

When a low tide leaves the animals exposed, they will ordinarily be found lying flat, partly or completely buried. When still water covers them, they stand vertically, with two-thirds of the disc buried in the sand; but when there is a current, they lean away from it at an angle that is uniform throughout the entire bed and apparently in direct proportion to the strength of the current.

Sand dollars scour the sand for minute edible particles, selecting particularly tasty grains covered with diatoms and using the tube feet to pass them into the mouth—a food-getting process in contrast with that of many other sand-living forms, which pass great quantities of sand through their intestines in order to extract from it whatever nourishment it may contain. Reproduction is similar to that of other urchins, eggs and sperm being extruded from different individuals for chance union and the development of free-swimming larvae that bear no resemblance to the adults. In Puget Sound sexual maturity comes in late spring, and in Elkhorn Slough specimens with ripe eggs and sperm have been taken in August.

Two species occur on this coast. The common form from Alaska to Lower California is *Dendraster excentricus* (Pl. XXXV), with the star design off center and consequently a bit lopsided. We have seen great beds of them in southern Puget Sound, Elkhorn Slough, Newport Bay, San Diego Bay, and in El Estero de Punta Banda, just south of Ensenada. The other species, *Echinarachnius parma,* is even flatter and is more symmetrical, the pentamerous design centering at the apex of the shell. It is a circumpolar form, known on this coast from Alaska to Puget Sound. Working with the latter, Parker and Van Alstyne (1932) found that burrowing and most locomotion is a function, not of the tube feet as in the case of starfish, but of "waves of co-ordinated spine movements," the cilia being "concerned only in feeding, cleansing and respiration."

§247. A red to rose-lavender heart urchin or sea porcupine will be found occasionally on the southern sand flats, where it lies half buried near the extreme low-tide line. This *Lovenia cordiformis* (Pl. XXXV), while by no means common in the intertidal, still occurs often enough to provide an excellent argument against barefooted collecting, and unless handled carefully it can inflict painful wounds on bare hands. Ordinarily the long sharp spines point backward, their thrusting effect aiding the animal to walk through the sand; but they bristle up in a formidable manner when their owner is disturbed. We have seen specimens during the winter at Newport Bay, which probably represents the northern limit of their range.

§248. *Renilla köllikeri* (formerly called *R. amethystina*), the sea pansy, is one of the most obvious animals of the southern mud flats. When seen in their natural habitat, sea pansies seem misnamed, for they lie with their heart-shaped discs almost covered with sand, their stalks buried. A specimen should be transferred to a porcelain or glass tray containing clean sea water and left undisturbed for a time. The disc will there enlarge to three times its size when taken from the sand, and scores of tiny hand-shaped polyps, beautifully transparent, will expand over the purple disc. Not the least of the sea pansy's charms is the blue phosphorescent light which it will almost invariably exhibit if mildly stimulated with a blunt instrument after being kept in the dark for an hour or so.

In Newport Bay sea pansies occur by the hundred, in El Estero de Punta Banda by the thousand. They are said to have been plentiful in San Diego and Mission Bays also before the days of commerce and industry. Southern California is the northernmost part of the range. The similar broad, kidney-shaped, true *R. amethystina* extends at least to Panama.

The eight-tentacled polyps of *Renilla* are nearly always infested with minute parasitic copepods, *Lamippe* sp. The same genus is said to infest all alcyonarians all over the world, and the members of a similar species, living parasitically on fish, are known as fish lice.

§249. The three true crabs that occur on sand flats (Pl. XXXV) are found nowhere else in the intertidal zone. *Heterocrypta occidentalis* might, lacking any other name, be called the elbow crab, for its large forelegs, which terminate in absurdly small claws, suggest an energetic customer at a bargain counter. This very weird creature is the only northern representative of a group of crabs well represented in tropical and equatorial regions. We have taken it, with the other two, at Newport Bay, and it is known from deep water elsewhere along the coast.

Randallia ornata has the round, bulbous body and gangly legs of a spider, but it is not closely related to the "spider" crabs. The carapace is mottled purple, brown, or dull orange, and the legs are usually curled underneath it as the animal lies half buried in the sand.

The third, *Portunus xantusii*, is a swimming crab and one of the liveliest of its kind. Its last pair of legs are paddle-shaped, and with them the crab swims sideways rather rapidly, keeping its big claws folded. Two long spines, one at each side of the shell, are effective weapons of defense, and in addition the crab is unduly hasty about using its sharp and powerful pincers, so that a collector who captures one without shedding any of his blood is either very lucky or very skillful—probably both. *Portunus* is a small relative of the much-prized blue crab of the Atlantic. It occurs as far north as Santa Barbara, but the other two crabs are not likely to be found in the intertidal above Balboa.

§250. One of the starfish, *Astropecten armatus* (Pl. XXXVI), occurs on sand flats from Newport Bay to Panama, usually below the water line but occasionally exposed. Now and then a specimen will be found having an arm spread of more than ten inches. They are beautifully symmetrical animals, sandy gray in color, and with a beaded margin and a fringe of bristling spines. Normally they lie half buried in the sand.

§251. Several snails and at least one nudibranch are members of the sand-flat assemblages. In El Estero de Punta Banda we once saw tremendous hosts of the nudibranch *Pleurophyllidia californica* (Pl. XXXVI), which were living, peculiarly for nudibranchs, half buried in the sand—another of the interesting adaptations to this fruitful environment. Thin, white, longitudinal stripes alternating with broader stripes of dark brown or black make *Pleurophyllidia* a conspicuous animal. In aquaria it has been observed to feed on sea pansies, and it undoubtedly does the same thing in its natural habitat, for the two always occur together.

§252. The moon snails or sand-collar snails are common inhabitants of sand flats throughout the whole stretch of coast from Alaska to Mexico. The form illustrated (Pl. XXXVI) is *Polinices draconis*, which ranges from Alaska to Catalina Island. The average shell length is between 3 and 4 inches, and a fully expanded animal is several times larger than its shell, almost completely covering it. When alive and expanded this species is scarcely to be distinguished from *P. lewisii*, which has a shell somewhat longer in proportion to its diameter and occupies about the same range, except that the latter is possibly more common in regions where there is a good admixture of mud. The average shell length of *lewisii* is more than 4 inches.

The strictly southern moon snail, *P. recluzianus*, is much smaller—usually less than 2″ in shell length—and, like *lewisii*, shows a preference for muddy sand. It can be distinguished from the other moon snails by its occluded umbilicus; that is, the "navel" is grown over so that that part of the shell is smooth. Frequently the shells of *recluzianus*, which ranges from Crescent City to Chile, are occupied by a giant hermit crab (§262).

Any of the three will commonly be found partially buried in the substratum, through which they plow with apparent ease. All are capable, also, of so contracting the immense fleshy foot as to stow it away completely within the shell, which is then closed with the horny door common to other snails. This process involves the ejection of considerable quantities of water from perforations around the edge of the foot, and the animal cannot live long when so contracted, since it cannot breathe.

The moon snail's method of food-getting is varied, but generally consists in clamping the foot around a clam, mussel, or other mollusk and drilling a neat counter-sunk hole through the shell with its radula. It is suspected that the moon snail often takes the easy way by smothering its victim with its large muscular foot. Shells perforated, by the moon snail or some of its relatives, are often found along the beach. A less spectacular method consists in suffocating the victim by holding it inside the foot until dead, or by sucking the foot over the siphon of a clam. In this case the proboscis is merely inserted between the shells of the dead animal and the contents are cut out. Apparently the great snail will feed also on any dead flesh that comes its way.

Cannibalistic members of its own tribe and the multi-rayed sunflower star (*Pycnopodia*) seem to be the moon snail's only natural enemies. In an aquarium a sunflower star has devoured two moon snails within three days.

The egg cases of these giant snails are, to most laymen, one of the puzzles of the intertidal world, for they look like nothing so much as discarded rubber plungers of the type plumbers use to open clogged drains. Many years ago the junior writer of this book squandered a great deal of nervous energy in a fruitless search through unfamiliar literature in an attempt to find out what manner of animal they might be. It was some consolation to him to learn eventually that for a long while naturalists had made the same mistake. Certainly there is no obvious reason for connecting the rubbery, collar-shaped egg cases with the snails that make them. The eggs are extruded from the mantle cavity in a continuous gelatinous sheet, which, as fast as it emerges, is covered with sand cemented together with a mucous secretion. The growing case travels around the snail, taking its shape from the snail's foot as it is formed. In time the egg case crumbles, releasing a half million or so free-swimming larvae. There is some poetic justice in the assumption that many of the minute larvae will provide food for the mussels, which later on will be eaten by adult moon snails.

§253. The beautifully marked and polished *Olivella biplicata* (Pl. XXXVI), the purple olive snail, leaves a betraying trail on the sand, although it is itself out of sight, by plowing along just under the surface. Sometimes the shell is above the surface, the foot below. This form ranges from Vancouver to Lower California, and *O. baetica,* a smaller, slimmer species, will be found most commonly south of Point Conception, although its total range is about the same as the plumper olives.

The fragile bubble shell may be first noticed in pools on bare sand flats, but it is much more at home in beds of eelgrass (§287).

§254. Two edible animals are found—a shrimp and a scallop— usually in pools in the sand or buried in the sand, but occasionally exposed. *Crago nigricauda* (Fig. 84), the black-tailed shrimp, is a literally flippant little fellow that positively cannot be captured without a dip net unless it is accidentally stranded on the sand. It has, even on its legs and antennae, "pepper and salt" markings that make it extremely difficult to see against a sand background. This is one of the common market shrimps in California, along with several others got from deep water only. Shrimp-dredging boats net these animals from depths of from a few fathoms in San Francisco Bay to more than a hundred in Puget Sound, and it is in such depths that *Crago* presumably finds its optimum conditions, since only occasional specimens are found in the intertidal. The black-tailed shrimp ranges from Alaska to Lower California. Market specimens will be found occasionally with the carapace swollen out on one side into a blister, the result of infection with an asymmetrical isopod (bopyrid), *Argeia pugettensis,* especially common on commercially netted *Crago communis* in Puget Sound, where one out of possibly every twenty or thirty specimens will be noticeably afflicted.

§255. The thick scallop, *Pecten circularis* (Pl. XXXVII), frequently found buried in the sand, is fairly common. The peculiar swimming habits of the relatively "intelligent" scallops have been mentioned before, as have their toothsome qualities. In addition to this sand-flat form, which ranges from Monterey to Peru, and the rocky-shore form (*P. hindsii*), another scallop will be found in eelgrass (§276). There is nothing new or different about this diversity of habitat in closely related animals, but it is nevertheless interesting to note another example.

§256. Although all the sand-flat animals so far considered burrow somewhat, or at times, the remainder are strictly burrowing forms. Perhaps the most obvious of these, when it occurs at all (it does not occur intertidally north of Southern California), is a great burrowing anemone similar to *Cerianthus aestuari,* which lives in a black, parchment-like tube that is covered with muck and lined with slime. More energetic diggers than the writers have taken specimens with tubes six feet long. The very muscular lower end of the animal is pointed and adapted to digging, and at the upper end there are two concentric sets of tentacles—a short stubby series about the mouth, and a long waving series around the border of the lividly chocolate-colored disc.

We have found a much smaller *Cerianthus,* probably a different species, in the sand flats at Ensenada.

§257. Another burrowing anemone, common in southern California, is *Harenactis attenuata* (Pl. XXXVII).* It is a tubeless form, sandy gray in color. The long, wrinkled, worm-like body is largest in diameter at the disc, tapering downward until it swells into an anchoring bulb. When annoyed, *Harenactis* pulls in its tentacles in short order, retracts into the sand, and apparently sends all its reserve body fluids into this bulb, thus swelling it so that it is impossible for a hungry bird or an avid human collector to pull the animal out. The bulb of a large specimen may be eighteen inches below the surface, so that digging out a specimen with a spade is very difficult, as the shifting sand fills up the hole almost as rapidly as it is made. While the excavation is in progress the anemone retracts still more and makes its bulb even more turgid. Having done that it can do nothing but sit tight and rely on Providence—a fatalistic philosophy that in this case is usually justified. Only if the sand can be shoveled away from the side of the bulb can a specimen be secured uninjured.

§258. To the extreme north of our range is a third anemone, the substratum *Evactis,* possibly *Evactis artemisia* (Pl. XXXVII), that is related to, and by some thought to be identical with, the great green anemone of the lower rocky tide pools. This form occurs in flats of rather pure sand, but only where small cobblestones or cockleshells are available underneath the surface for basal attachment. At low tide they retract completely beneath the surface and are to be found only by raking or shoveling as for cockles. The contracted specimens are white or gray-green, and may easily be mistaken for *Metridium* (§321). Placed in a jar of sea water they soon flower out beautifully, their long wavy tentacles colored with lovely greens and pinks, and their discs semi-transparent. We took the specimens shown in the photograph in British Columbia near Comox, not far from Discovery Bay, from which the animals were originally described in 1846 in the report of the United States Exploring Expedition.

§259. According to Weymouth there are nearly 500 species of bivalves on this coast. Many, of course, are too small or too rare to be considered in this account, and in order that the volume may

---

* Now reported, MacGinitie (1935c), from Elkhorn Slough and Humboldt Bay.

not grow out of all proportion we must further limit ourselves to the large, the obvious, or the interesting forms. After the scallop, with its peculiar flapping-swimming proclivities, the basket cockle, *Clinocardium nuttalii* (Pl. XXXVII), is the bivalve most likely to be noticed in this environment by the casual collector. Reaching its maximum development in British Columbia and Puget Sound, the basket cockle extends southward in decreasing numbers as far as Lower California and northward to Bering Sea. In the north, specimens are found very frequently in flats of "corn meal" sand that would be very shifty if surf could ever get to it. Basket cockles are occasionally found entirely exposed, but they are active animals and can dig in quickly with the large foot. They burrow shallowly, however, for they have no siphon tubes, the siphon holes being merely openings in the margin of the mantle. This cockle makes excellent food, although rather tough, but is too scarce to be used extensively. Specimens will frequently be captured with tiny commensal crabs, *Pinnixa littoralis* (§300), in the mantle cavity.

Dr. Fraser (1931) has reported on the natural history of this form in British Columbia. Most of the 760 specimens examined were three or four years old, and none were more than seven years. This genus is hermaphroditic, with ova and sperm shed usually simultaneously, sometimes the ova first, during a long spawning period in the spring which affects all animals two years old or more. Fraser suspects that the free-swimming larvae may settle only in the sublittoral, moving inshore with age, which possibly explains why so few small individuals are found alongshore. The §189 data on the growth rates of northern and southern razor clams is known to apply also to the races of *Clinocardium*.

§260. One would scarcely expect to find a clam throwing off a part of itself as a crab throws off a leg, but *Solen rosaceus* (Pl. XXXVIII), one of the jackknife clams, actually autotomizes rather readily. *Solen's* siphon, too large to be entirely retracted within its pink-tinged, nearly cylindrical shell, has prominent annulations. If the animal is roughly handled, or if its water gets somewhat stale, it drops off its siphon bit by bit, the divisions taking place along the lines of annulation. Presumably this autotomy was developed as a defense against the early bird in search of a worm and not averse to substituting a juicy clam siphon. This clam, which averages around 2″ in shell length, ranges from Santa Barbara to the Gulf of California, and a similar but somewhat larger species, *Solen sicarius* (§279), occurs occasionally in mud flats and commonly in eelgrass roots as far north as Vancouver Island. The two may be distinguished by the fact that the latter has a slightly bent shell, colored a glossy yellow. Both species dig rapidly and well, but not as efficiently as their cousin *Tagelus* of the mud flats.

Other common sand-flat clams, which may be identified with the aid of the photographs in Plate XXXVIII, are *Chione,* of three species, all known as the hard-shell cockle and all ranging from San Pedro into Mexico; the purple clam, *Sanguinolaria nuttallii,* another southerner; and any of several small tellens, *Tellina bodegensis,* etc., most of which extend throughout the range considered in this book. The similar *T. tenuis* is one of the characteristic components of the Scottish fjord faunae, hence its natural history is well known. Stephen (1928, 1929), investigating the distribution, found small individuals (but in great numbers, up to 1000 per quarter square meter) at the low level of spring tides. The optimum zone for larger specimens, however, was higher up, toward high-water mark, where there were fewer individuals—an interesting zonation that reverses the usual situation. He found also that growth is more rapid higher up (probably a function of the lessened intra-racial competition), that it decreases in regular progression with the age of the animal, and that it almost stops in winter. There were four age groups, representing four annual spawnings, the males becoming sexually mature in May, the females in June. Specimens were found to feed on plant detritus, in the spring exclusively on diatoms. These data on growth rates coincide with what is known of razor clams (§189).

Still another sand-flat clam (not illustrated) is the white sand clam, *Macoma secta,* which reaches a length of 4 inches. It rather closely resembles its mud-flat relative, the bent-nosed clam (§303 and Pl. XLIII), but is typically larger and lacks the "bent-nose" twist in the shell at the siphon end. The shell is thin and the left valve is flatter than the right. This species makes very good eating, but as the intestine is invariably full of sand the clams should be kept in a pan of clean sea water for a day or so before eating. The range is British Columbia to the Gulf of California.

§261. A mole crab occurs in this environment—*Lepidopa myops* (Pl. XXXVIII)—that never under any circumstances subjects itself to the pounding waves that delight its surf-loving cousin, *Emerita.* Visitors to the sheltered sand beaches at Newport Bay and southward will find it well submerged in the soft substratum but with its long hairy antennae extending to the surface to form a breathing tube. This form burrows rapidly in the shifting sand, but not with the skill of *Emerita,* whose very life depends on its ability to dig in quickly enough to escape an oncoming breaker.

§262. One December afternoon we found, in the unpacked sand

along the channel in El Estero de Punta Banda, thousands of hermit
crabs, *Holopagurus pilosus* (Pl. XXXIX), all living in the shells of
moon snails. The largest were giants of their tribe—larger than any
intertidal hermits we have seen south of Puget Sound—but the
really remarkable thing about them was their habitat. Many of
them, probably most of them, were completely buried in the sand.
Above the water line they could be detected only by their breathing
holes, below the water by occasional bubbles. These very hairy and
rather beautifully colored hermits have been known heretofore as an
offshore form only, in water up to thirty fathoms deep between San
Francisco and San Diego. Here hosts of them could be turned out
by merely raking one's fingers through the sand.

§263. At the same time and place, and in the same manner, a considerable number of brittle stars were taken. Occasionally a waving arm showed above the surface, but the vast majority were completely buried. These were *Amphiodia barbarae,* also formerly
thought to be exclusively deep-water animals, having been reported
as ranging from San Pedro to San Diego in depths up to one hundred twenty fathoms. Except that their disc is thicker, these animals resemble *A. occidentalis* (Pl. VII).

§264. A large cucumber with a most un-holothurian appearance,
Molpadia arenicola (Pl. XXXIX), is taken now and then at Newport Bay, in El Estero de Punta Banda, and probably other places.
Habitués of the Newport intertidal regions call it the "sweet potato,"
and the name is rather appropriate. A sweet potato as large and well-
polished as one of these animals, however, would be a sure prize
winner at a county fair. The first specimens we saw were dug near
Balboa and put in an aquarium for the edification of a collecting
party. We took them to be giant echiurid worms, and certainly
there is little about them to suggest their actual identity. The mottled,
yellowish-brown skin is tough, smooth, and slippery. There are no
tube feet and no obvious tentacles. *Molpadia* feeds by passing continuous masses of sand through its digestive tract for the sake of
the contained detritus. As it lives in sand that appears to be fairly
clean and free from organic matter, it must be compelled to eat enormous quantities of inert matter to get a little food. We have no
notes on the speed with which the sand mass moves through the
animal, but the better part of the weight of a living specimen and
much of its bulk is in the contained sand. Remove the sand, and
the rotund "sweet potato" collapses.

Molpadia has one cucumber trait, however, in that it always has
guests in its cloaca, the pea crab, *Pinnixa barnharti,* occurring so commonly as to be considered almost diagnostic. When specimens are being

narcotized with epsom salts for relaxed preservation, the pea crabs are likely to come out just as the pea crabs *Opisthopus* escape from *Stichopus* (§77) under the same circumstances.

§265. Sand flats support the usual host of segmented worms. The tubed *Mesochaetopterus taylori* is a striking and usually solitary form which, unfortunately, breaks so readily that it can rarely be taken whole, the hindmost segments being the parts first shed and the least often seen. For so delicate a creature this worm has an unusual range, occurring intertidally at Departure Bay, British Columbia, and a similar or identical form at Elkhorn Slough, Morro Bay, Newport Bay, California, and El Estero de Punta Banda, Lower California—points representing a considerable range of temperature, humidity, and sunlight conditions. In some localities around Puget Sound it occurs in colonies. It is somewhat similar in appearance to *Chaetopterus* (Fig. 102).

The tubed and sociable "jointworm," *Axiothella,* occurs in this environment, but it is more characteristic of areas of hard-packed muddy sand (§293).

Every shovelful of sand turned up in search of lancelets (next paragraph) will rout out one or two specimens of a third segmented worm, a small and nereis-like species of *Nephtys.* The collector intent on snatching the swift lancelets the instant they are exposed will often grab a specimen of this smaller and slower form before he can check the motion of his hand. A similar shorter form taken in similar environments of loose-packed sand is *Armandia bioculata.*

MacGinitie (1935c) says (p. 693): "it can burrow very rapidly, and in its activities reminds one somewhat of *Amphioxus* . . . . can swim through loose sand as rapidly as some worms are able to swim in the water."

§266. The lancelet, *Amphioxus,* a famous animal that is seldom seen, comes into its own on this coast in southern California and (at least) northern Lower California.* Where there is a low-tide sand bar opposite the mouth of a sheltered but pure-water bay, and far enough in to be protected from wave shock, these primitive vertebrates are likely to be found. Our form, *Branchiostoma californiense* (Fig. 85), is reputed to be the largest lancelet in the world, adult or sexually mature individuals being up to 3″ long. Specimens of that size will very rarely be taken, however, and the average size is less than half of the maximum. Violent stamping on the packed sand in just the right area will cause some of the animals to pop out. They will writhe about for a moment and, un-

---

* Hubbs (1922) reports it from Monterey Bay, California, to San Luis Gonzales Bay, Gulf of California. It certainly never occurs littorally in the north, however, and we have never been successful even in dredging it at Monterey.

less captured quickly, dive back into the sand. The usual method of capture is to turn up a spadeful of sand, trusting to one's quickness and skill to snatch some of the animals before all of them disappear. Until one has actually seen them in the act, it is hard to believe that any animal can burrow as rapidly as does *Amphioxus,* for the tiny eel-like creatures are as quick as the proverbial greased lightning. They hurl themselves head first into the sand—veritable living projectiles. Seemingly they can burrow through packed sand as rapidly as most fish can swim. They will lie quietly on the bottom of a dish of sea water, but if disturbed will swim rapidly with a spiral motion.

While the drawing shows the shape of the animal, it is utterly impossible for any illustration, with the possible exception of a motion picture, to convey a clear notion of the appearance of a living lancelet in its natural habitat.

Amphioxus has achieved unique fame in the last half century through being interpreted as a form ancestral to the other vertebrates. An important theory of craniate development makes this lancelet a vital step in the evolution of all the higher animals. We have taken it at Newport Bay, at San Diego Bay, and in El Estero de Punta Banda. It is known from the Gulf of California also, and is no doubt common in deeper water below the effect of waves, as it has been dredged off San Diego and in the Gulf. Off the coast of China a similar species is dredged by the ton for food, and the Chinese, with their epicurean palates, consider it a great delicacy. Probably *Amphioxus* is not as rare as has been supposed, even on our warmer shores, for its small size, retiring habits, and great speed in escape make it a form easily overlooked.

Living submerged in the sand with *Amphioxus* is a small fish, *Gillichthys mirabilis,* the sand goby. We have no data concerning its habits.

§267. The worm-like and degenerate acorn-tongue worm, *Dolichoglossus pusillus,* shares with *Amphioxus* the honor of being an ancestral vertebrate, or at least of coming from the same primitive stock. Thirty years ago it was abundant in San Diego Bay and what is now Los Angeles harbor, but suction dredging and industrial wastes have very materially changed the shore lines where it was once found. Ritter, when working up the embryology of the animal, wrote of taking more than a hundred on one tide; but now even the most proficient collector must be locally familiar in order to procure any in the southern region. It is reported to occur in Puget Sound, but we have never found any there.

The males are pale orange, the females brighter. Various observers differ as to whether the animals do or do not have castings at the mouths of their burrows and whether they do or do not protrude their orange or red probosces at low tide so that they lie flaccid on the surface. Probably the conflicting statements arise from the fact that there are several species, all of them undescribed, which have different habits and habitats. We have never taken a whole specimen, but we have seen fragments of a size to indicate an animal at least 24″ long—much larger than has been reported for *D. pusillus*. The excessively soft bodies are long, round, and very likely to be broken, and the animals secrete more than their share of slime. The various species of acorn-tongue worm have a not unpleasant but extremely pervading and persistent "estuary" odor that will scent the hands of the successful digger for several days.

§268. In their upper reaches, estuarine sand flats offer an added obstacle to prolific colonization by marine animals—the matter of fresh water. Where this occurs abundantly or sporadically the faunal aspect is correspondingly changed. But a good many of the crabs and some of the shellfish tolerate greatly lowered salinities, and Reid (1932) has shown that fresh water, even if actively flowing over the flats, has little effect on the sea water contained in sand below the surface, so that even minimal burrowing ability would protect a sessile form so situated until the return of the tide.

C. Eelgrass

Since the eelgrass, *Zostera,* occurs on flats of many types, from almost pure sand to almost pure muck, it seems desirable to list the animals associated with this seed plant before going on to the mud-flat forms. The start of a bed of eelgrass is an important step in the conversion of a former ocean region into wet meadow land and, ultimately, into dry land. The matted roots prevent the sand from being readily carried away by wind and tide, provide permanent homes for a less nomadic tribe of animals than inhabit the flats of shifty sand, and enrich the substratum with decaying organic matter until it can be classed as mud. The grass supports a rather characteristic group of animals that live on the blades, about the bases, and among its roots in the substratum.

§269. In El Estero de Punta Banda we have found small and delicate sea urchins crawling about on the blades of eelgrass, possibly scraping off a precarious sustenance of minute encrusting animals but more likely feeding upon the grass itself. They are so pale as to be almost white, but with a faint coloring of brown or pink. This urchin, *Lytechinus anamesus,* is known from shallow water in the Gulf of California and from the west coast of the peninsula. The largest recorded specimens are just over an inch in diameter. Ours are less than half an inch. They resemble bleached, miniature, purple urchins.

§270. In an adjoining eelgrass pond in the same region were many thousands of small snails, the high-spired *Nassarius tegula* (Pl. XXXIX), also known as *Nassa* and *Alectrion.* Apparently these dainty little snails lead a precarious life, for about half of their shells were no longer the property of the original tenant, having been preempted by a small hermit crab, probably a new species of *Pagurus.*

These snails and hermits, and the urchins mentioned in the previous paragraph, were all seen in the winter. The summer sunlight and temperature conditions in this region being decidedly unfavorable, it is likely that every animal able to do so would move downward beyond the chance of exposure. It is quite possible that El Estero, which we have not visited in hot weather, might then be a relatively barren place.

Many of the little *Nassarius* shells, whatever their tenants, are covered with white, lacy encrustations of the coralline bryozoan,

Idmonea californica. On a superficial examination the erect, calcareous branches of this form cannot be distinguished from tiny staghorn coral. It is fairly common in southern California, and it will be quickly noted wherever found and almost certainly mistaken for a coral. When it encrusts on *Nassarius* it makes the shells at least half again as heavy.

§271. Any of several hydroids will be found attached to eelgrass —*Aglaophenia, Plumularia,* or *Sertularia,* as previously mentioned, or in forms specific to this environment. The cosmopolitan *Obelia dichotoma* is common in situations of this sort all up and down the coast, and, in fact, in temperate regions throughout the world. Compared with other delicate and temperamental species of *Obelia, dichotoma* is very hardy and obliging. It stands transportation well even when its water becomes somewhat stale, lives for several days under adverse conditions, and expands beautifully when its proper conditions are approximated. The delicate white clusters of this and of *O. longissima* (§ 316) are conspicuous on the tips of eelgrass in such places as Elkhorn Slough. Judging from specimens determined by Dr. Fraser, it is this form and *dubia* (§332) which have frequently been called *gracilis* locally; the differences in any case are slight. *O. dichotoma* ranges on this coast from Alaska to San Diego; there is a good description, with an illustration of a living colony, in Johnson and Snook, pages 59–60, which we need not repeat here. We have not so far taken this form on the outer coast, but it occurs on Puget Sound wharf pilings with *longissima,* etc. At least some of the eelgrass hydroids taken at Jamestown Bay, Sitka, turn out to be the ubiquitous *longissima,* and it may be that the two are mingled there in the same habitat as they seem to be at Elkhorn Slough.

A minute nudibranch, *Galvina olivacea,* lives among these hydroids, presumably feeds on them, and tangles them up at certain times of the year with its white, jelly-covered egg strings. Some of the *Obelia* nudibranchs are among the smallest occurring within our geographical range—a small fraction of an inch in length and identifiable only with a binocular microscope. It is an interesting fact that by a peculiar symbiosis, or by partial digestion, nudibranchs fed on hydroids soon get to bear living and functioning nematocysts (the poisonous, barbed defenses borne by hydroids, jellyfish, sea anemones, etc.) in their gills. These transplanted barbs work so well that nudibranchs so protected cannot be eaten by larger animals.

§272. Associated with the eelgrass of Elkhorn Slough, and similar places where the bottom is compact, sandy mud, there is a skeleton shrimp, *Caprella scaura.* It is large, even by comparison with *C. kennerlyi* (§89) of the rock-pool hydroid colonies. Sometimes great numbers of them may be seen at night in the beam of a flashlight, under the surface of the water. Occasionally they will be found even on shores of pure mud. The animal may be bright green, or red, or dull-colored, depending upon whether it occurs on eelgrass, red algae, or muddy bottoms.

§273. Of the many eelgrass beds of Puget Sound we know of one west of Port Townsend (and there are undoubtedly others) that supports a tremendous population of the fixed jellyfish *Haliclystus* (probably *stejnegeri*) (Fig. 86). This form is actually one of the large (scyphozoan) jellyfish such as are seen offshore in summer, pulsating lazily at the surface of the sea, and yet it is small and has lost almost all power of motion. The small, stalked attachment disc has some power of contraction, and the tentacle-studded mouth disc is able to fold somewhat, but the animal swims not at all. We have never seen any of them so much as change their position on the grass blades, but it is presumed that they can glide about slowly on a smooth surface, like an anemone. Specimens detached from their grass will get a new hold with their tentacles and bend the stalk down until it can be reattached. An interesting feature of the digestive system is the presence of filaments which mix with the food in the body cavity, thus greatly increasing the area that the enzymes can act upon. The animal's colors are subtle rather than striking, but it is large enough (up to an inch in diameter) to be seen without difficulty.

Originally described from the Commander Islands, Alaska, *Haliclystus* is known to occur in the Friday Harbor region and may be expected in many other places in Puget Sound and to the northward. Some years ago Dr. Fisher took a single specimen at Point Joe, near Monterey, but its occurrence there was presumed to be accidental. No others were reported until, in May, 1931, we discovered to our amazement that the animals had suddenly colonized at Monterey almost as abundantly as we found them in Puget Sound. They have continued to appear at Monterey each spring, have already been seen in Carmel Bay, and very likely have established themselves in other unpolluted spots where it is to be hoped they will become a permanent part of the fauna. Recent experience with this form, and the fact that it is not reported from the Nanaimo region, indicates that, although abundant in quiet spots, it requires fairly oceanic water.

§274. Necessarily small snails of several kinds frequent the slender leaves of eelgrass. *Lacuna porrecta,* shaped like *Littorina* but only one-fourth to one-half its size and having an aperture that takes up most of the front of the shell, may be found either on the grass or by screening the soil about the roots. MacGinitie remarks that this form waddles like a duck. It ranges from Bering Sea to San Diego. The related *L. variegata,* of zigzag markings, may be found similarly on *Zostera* in the Puget Sound–Georgia Strait region.

Haminoea vesicula is a small, white, bubble-shell snail, up to almost an inch in shell length but usually about half of that, ranging from Vancouver Island to the Gulf of California. Like the great *Bulla* (§287) with which it sometimes occurs, it can scarcely stow away its comparatively large body in its fragile shell. In some speci-mens the beating heart can be seen through the shell. The eggs of this form are laid in deep yellow ribbons about $\frac{3}{8}''$ wide and up to nearly 8″ long.

These two snails, with a minute black *Philine,* found at Elkhorn Slough, are tectibranchs, related to the large and shell-less sea hares. *Philine* always moves through a slime envelope of its own secreting. The larger *Navanax* (§294) is a feature of the southern eelgrass beds, as well as of the adjacent mud flats, feeding on *Haminaea.*

Another tectibranch, which looks much more like a nudibranch than like its relatives already mentioned, is a pretty green form with India-ink lines of stippling. It is probably *Phyllaplysia taylori,* reported from Nanaimo to Elkhorn Slough, and very common in To-males Bay. Ovipositing individuals of *Nassarius fossatus* (§286) will be found among blades of eelgrass during the late summer, depositing encapsulated eggs. Even an annelid worm, the small *Nereis procera,* known more commonly from dredging in Monterey Bay, will be found at home here on the *Zostera* (and on *Enteromorpha*), where it con-structs permanent membranous tubes on the blades and about the roots.

A highly modified limpet is specifically restricted to this habitat —*Acmaea depicta,* the painted limpet, not at all obvious, but readily discoverable if one runs a quantity of eelgrass through one's hands. In the extensive and rich Estero de Punta Banda, below Ensenada, Lower California, we have taken this animal very abundantly during the winter. Possibly every tenth blade of grass is inhabited by it. Also at Sitka in the summer of 1932 we found a similar limpet (un-fortunately not determined) equally abundant on the quiet-water *Zostera* of Jamestown Bay. Mrs. Grant describes it as having "Ex-ternal surface smooth and highly lustrous, marked only by concentric growth lines, and color pattern of fine brown lines upon a white surface," and records a common distribution of from Santa Barbara to Lower California, with one doubtful Monterey record. A large specimen is $9 \times 4 \times 3$ mm.

§275. *Chioraera* (known also as *Melibe*) *leonina,* a large nudi-

branch of eelgrass areas, seems to be in the process of becoming a
pelagic animal—that is, a drifting or mildly swimming animal.
When the water is smooth, and especially during cloudy weather,
this queer creature puffs out its hood with air, thus floating to the
surface where its tentacles rake in small crustacea for food. It is
common in some years in the Friday Harbor region, particularly on
Brown Island. In 1928 approximately 1000 appeared at one time,
and of these an estimated 150 pair were in coitu, mostly mutual
coitus. Guberlet wrote: "During the act of copulation the animals
lie side by side, or with the bottom of the foot of each together,
with their heads in opposite directions, and the penis of each inserted in the vaginal pore of the other . . . . and the animals so
firmly attached that they can be handled rather roughly without
being separated." After they have spawned the animals take on a
shrunken appearance, and many, if not all of them, die, the indications being that they live only one season and spawn but once. The
eggs are laid during the summer in broad spiral ribbons 3" or 4"
long.

The recorded range is from Nanaimo to San Diego, but south of
Puget Sound it must be rare or sporadic.* In southern Puget Sound
we have found occasional solitary forms only, but in central British
Columbia we once came upon a great host of them about one of
the rare eelgrass beds in this ordinarily precipitous region.

§276. The southern scallop, *Pecten latiuratus,* is commonly seen
at Newport Bay and southward, attached to eelgrass clusters or swimming about their bases after the peculiar manner of the scallop tribe.
It differs from *P. circularis* (Pl. XXXVII) in being flatter and in
having wider "ears" at the hinge line.

§277. A massive and most amazing sponge, *Tetilla* (§298), is
sometimes attached to eelgrass clusters, but it is more common on the
mud flats, where it leads an apparently normal life under abnormal
conditions.

§278. In and about the roots of eelgrass lives a pistol (snapping)
shrimp, *Crangon californiensis,* that differs from its relative of the
outside pools (Pl. XXIII) only in minor characters, such as having
a slightly smaller snapping claw of somewhat different shape.

Another quite different shrimp to be found here, and also in mud-
flat pools, is the lovely transparent *Spirontocaris paludicola* (Pl. IX).
The specimen photographed was taken in a rock pool on the pro-

* Fosberg, however (*Journal of Entomology and Zoölogy,* 21: 133–35, 1929), lists
minute specimens as among the commonest constituents of an assemblage occurring
on the blades of *Macrocystis* in the open ocean off Laguna Beach.

tected outer coast, but the species is far more common in this environment. It is scarcely distinguishable from the *S. picta* described in §62. In Puget Sound a grass-shrimp, *Hippolyte clarki*, occurs commonly in this association even in the daytime, its green color matching so well that of the eelgrass to which it clings that the observer may be working in a colony of them without realizing it until one of the graceful animals swims away. *Idothea resecata* also (§205) will be found clinging lengthwise to the blades, often abundantly, without its presence being suspected. Farther north other crustacea may be found; at Sitka, in addition to the forms above mentioned, *Spirontocaris cristata* (Pl. XXIV) and *S. camtschatica* have been taken, among others.

§279. The jackknife clam, *Solen sicarius,* is, for its kind, an extremely active animal. It digs so rapidly that it can bury itself in thirty seconds with only four or five thrusts and draws of its foot. But it has even more striking accomplishments, for, according to Mac-Ginitie, it can jump a few inches vertically and can swim by either of two methods. Both involve the familiar "rocket" principle. By the first method water is forcibly expelled from the siphons, thus propelling the clam forward. By the second, water is expelled from the mantle cavity through an opening around the foot, and the resulting darting motion is accelerated by a flip of the extended foot, the combined forces sending the animal some two feet through the water in a reverse direction.

S. sicarius has a glossy yellow, bent shell, reaches a length of a little more than 3 inches, and ranges from Vancouver Island to Lower California. Like its somewhat smaller, straight-shelled relative of the sand flats, *S. rosaceus* (§260), it autotomizes its siphons at the annular constrictions. The two may at times be found together in the sand flats, but *S. sicarius,* although it is occasional in mud flats also, is far more common among the roots of eelgrass.

§280. Of many of the worms that writhe about in the roots we freely confess our ignorance. Of others, which we can recognize, so little is known that a full list would "little profite the Reader" and of them all only three will be named. The first of these is the slender and iridescent *Glycera americana* (Pl. XXXIX), which looks not unlike a *Nereis* with a pointed head. The difference becomes obvious when *Glycera* unrolls a fearful and wonderful introvert almost a third as long as itself—an instrument armed with four black terminal jaws which obviously are made for biting. It will be noticed in the illustration that when the introvert is extended the head loses its characteristic pointedness. Specimens occur singly and may be 8″ or even more in length.

§281. The second worm to be mentioned is *Pectinaria brevicoma* or *auricoma* (Fig. 87), whose body is tapered to fit the slender, cone-shaped tube which it builds of sand grains cemented together. This worm digs by shoveling with its mouth bristles, which may, as in the case of one specimen that we dredged from the mud bottom of Pender Harbor, British Columbia, be of brilliant gold. A model woven of cloth of gold could not be more striking. We have specimens from the vicinity of Juneau also, and they occur in Elkhorn Slough. The minute and highly specialized pea crab, *Pinnixa longipes* (§293), widest of the lot, is a common commensal.

Watson worked with Fabre-like patience on these animals, and his observations, hidden away from popular reach in an English biological periodical, seem to us as popularly fascinating as those of that French entomologist. "Each tube is the life work of the tenant," he writes, "and is most beautifully built with grains of sand, each grain placed in position with all the skill and accuracy of a human builder." Each grain is fitted, as a mason fits stones, so that projecting angles will fill hollows, and one appreciates the nicety of the work when one perceives that the finished wall is only one grain thick. Furthermore, no superfluous cement is used. Suitable grains for building are selected by the mouth and applied to the "two papillated lobes of the cement organ, ... after which the worm applies its ventral shields to the newly formed wallings, and rubs them up and down four or five times, apparently to make all smooth inside the tube. . . . . The moment when an exact fit has been obtained is evidently ascertained by an exquisite sense of touch. On one occasion I saw the worm slightly alter (before cementing) the position of a sand grain which it had just deposited." Only very fine grains are used, from 1/1000″ to 1/500″ in diameter, but one specimen in captivity built ¾″ of tube in two months.

Pectinaria lives head downward, usually with the tube buried vertically in the substratum, although sometimes, and especially at night, an inch or so of the small end of the tube may project above the surface. Digging is accomplished in a vigorous manner by means of the golden bristle-combs which project from the head, "tossing up the sand by left and right strokes alternately." The worm eats selected parts of the sand which it digs: that is, passes sand through its body for the contained food. The digging therefore creates a hollow about the head, and frequent cave-ins result. Thus the worm is not only able to dig its way to new feeding grounds, but is able to remain in the same place for a time and make its food fall to within reach of its mouth. There are strong hooks at the hind end of the body which enable the animal to keep a firm grip on its tube while digging. For respiration and the elimination of waste matter, two currents of water are pumped through the tube in opposite directions. *Pectinaria* is able to repair breaks in its tube, appears to be light-sensitive, and probably has a tasting organ.

§282. The third worm, perhaps the most striking of all but the least common, is a magnificent species, *D. perimeces,* of the tropical *Dendrostoma.* Large specimens of this slim sipunculid are almost 10″ long when expanded. Except for its slimmer body and usually larger size it does not differ greatly from *D. pyroides* (the species illustrated in Pl. XXIV). Closer examination will reveal the fact that the tentacles of *D. perimeces* branch clear to the base, whereas the lower part of the smaller form's tentacles is bare. The delicately branched and beautifully flowering tendrils presumably gather food particles and transfer them to the intestine by rolling in the introvert. This form has been taken at Elkhorn Slough only.

§283. In a good many of the quiet-water channels of Puget Sound, the subtidal gravel shores support a variety of eelgrass that is always at least partially submerged on even the lowest tides. The characteristic fauna that belongs to these deep plants can scarcely be considered intertidal, but the shore collector will fringe this zone and will surely see, among other things, the hydroid jellyfish, *Gonionemus vertens* (Fig. 88). This graceful little bell-shaped medusa (½″ to ¾″ in diameter), almost invisible except for an apparent cross inside the bell formed by its reddish-brown gonads, has some sixty to seventy long, slender tentacles with which it stings and captures small fish and crustaceans. It seems to be restricted to these particular growths of deep eelgrass, but every such location that we have examined in summer has, without exception, turned out a few specimens. When they are not at first visible, thrusting an oar into the eelgrass, or merely wading slowly through it, will send some of them pulsing toward the surface. On overcast days, however, they will be found near the surface, often in considerable numbers. In the winter, judging by one collecting trip in 1931, there is not a single specimen to be found.

Watching and timing the life cycle of this form through the hydroid stage is one of the many tasks that await some enthusiast who has the requisite time and patience. In this case the knowledge would be particularly welcome, for *Gonionemus* has for many years been the classic type of its group for teaching purposes. Some work has been done in this connection. It is known, for instance, that the fertilized egg develops into a ciliated, free-swimming larva that is oval in shape and somewhat drawn out at one end. The larva settles down on its broad end, and develops at its drawn-out upper end first a mouth and, a few days later, four tentacles, two at a time. In this hydra-like, hydroid stage the animal is scarcely more than 1/16″ high with its tentacles expanded. Additional hydranths are budded off, but how the medusae are produced is not known.

Rugh has shown, after extensive experimentation with an East-coast species, that under normal conditions *Gonionemus* never lays its eggs in the light, although light is probably necessary for the maturation of the egg cells. During the breeding season the animals prepare to discharge their eggs within one minute after being placed in artificial darkness. Apparently the eggs are laid in installments, certain numbers each night during the breeding season, the dates and duration of which the experimenter does not mention. He thinks there are many eggs, and that the individual egg is large for so small an animal.

Also in this environment, occasional visitants from deep water may sometimes be seen. *Stichopus californicus* (§77) is common underfoot. Shrimps occur, especially at night, including such commercially important forms as the "coon stripe," *Pandalus danae,* but rarely, and solitarily. While considerations of this nature are beyond the scope of this work, it may be interesting to note the answer, worked out by Berkeley (1930), to a question frequently asked by shrimp fishermen. They have wondered why it is that the only males taken of a given species are small, while all the females are large. The rather spectacular answer is that the five species investigated by Berkeley invariably undergo a sexual metamorphosis. Young specimens are always male. At the age of from 18 to 40 months, depending on the species, they become females and spend presumably the rest of their lives as functioning members of that sex.

D. Mud Flats

THE problems of respiration and food-getting in mud flats and the lack of attachment sites make for a rather specialized fauna. The skin breathing of starfish and urchins makes them unsuited to this environment, and, with the exception of an occasional *Pisaster brevispinus,* none occur. There are only one sponge and one hydroid, and there are no chitons or bryozoa, but the many worms, clams, and snails make up for the scarcity of other animals.

Even in the south the animals extend farther up into the intertidal on the mud flats proper than they do on the sand flats anywhere on the coast. Some of them, like the fiddler crab, seem to be changing into land dwellers—a tendency that reaches an extreme in Japan, where one of the land crabs has worked up to a point almost two thousand feet above sea level.

ZONES 1 and 2. *Uppermost beach and high-tide horizon from highest tide mark to the mean of the lower of the two highs.*

§284. The little fiddler crabs, *Uca* (Pl. XL), are characterized, in the males, by the possession of one relatively enormous claw which is normally carried close to the body. It is a formidable-looking weapon, but seems never to be used except in combat with other males of the same species and as a secondary aid to digging. In battle the two contestants lock claws, each apparently endeavoring to tear the other's claw from its body. Sometimes, according to one capable observer, a crab loses its hold on the substratum and is "thrown back over his opponent for a distance of a foot or more"—a performance that suggests a jujitsu wrestling match. At breeding time, and particularly when a female is near by, the males make a peculiar gesture, extending the big claw to its full length and then whipping it suddenly back toward the body. One might conclude, with some logic, that the big claw is a distinctly sexual attribute comparable to the horns of a stag.

The Japanese call the fiddler crab *siho maneki,* which is translated as "beckoning for the return of the tide." It is too picturesque a name to quibble over, but one might reasonably ask why Mahomet does not go to the mountain, for the presumably free-willed fiddler digs its burrow as far away from the tide as it can get without abandoning the sea entirely. There it feeds, like so many other animals occurring on this type of shore, on whatever minute plants and animals are contained in the substratum. Instead of passing quantities of inert matter through its body, however, the fiddler crab selects daintily such morsels as appeal to it. The selecting process begins with the little claws (the female using both claws and the male his one small one) and is completed at the mouth, the rejected mud collecting below the mouth in little balls which either drop off of their own weight or are removed by the crab.

Dembowski, working with the sand fiddler of the East coast, made careful observations of the animal's behavior and came to the interesting conclusion that its behavior is no more stereotyped than that of man. He found that in their natural habitat the fiddlers construct oblique burrows up to three feet long that never branch and usually end in a horizontal chamber. In sand-filled glass jars in the laboratory they actually sought the light, digging their burrows along the sides of the jars. Apparently it was an advantage to be able to see what they were doing, and although such a condition had never existed in nature they made use of the opportunity when it did occur. They dig by packing the wet sand between legs and carapace and pressing it into pellets which they then carefully remove from the burrow. The smallest leg prevents loose grains from falling back while the pellet is being carried. Sometimes hours are spent in the very careful work of making the end chamber, the depth of which Dembowski thinks is determined by how far down the fiddler must go to reach sand that is very moist but not wet. In pure sand water would filter into the burrow at high tide, but the fiddler crab always takes care to locate in substratum that has so high a mud content as to be practically impervious to water. Furthermore it lines its burrow —a process that probably adds to its airtightness—and plugs the entrance before each high tide. Thus at high tide or during heavy rains the animal lives in an airtight compartment.

Under experimentally unchanging conditions the crabs showed no signs of periodicity such as might be expected in an animal that stoppers up its burrow against each high tide. Evidently the door-closing process is due not to memory of the tidal rhythm but to the stimulus of an actually rising tide which would moisten the air chamber before the surface of the ground was covered. If a little water was poured into the jars the crabs became active as soon as the moisture reached them, carrying pellets to build a door. If the water was poured in rapidly the crabs rushed to the entrance and pulled pellets in with great haste, not pausing to construct a door. If the jar was then filled up carefully, so as not to damage the burrows, the crabs would stay in their air chambers and not stir for a week. Dumping water in, however, filled the burrows and caved them in, burying the animals. Their response this time was to dig out and wait on the surface of the sandy mud for the "tide" to ebb.

Each "high" high tide destroys part of the burrow, and the animal must dig itself out by somewhat reversing its former operations. It "causes the chamber to rise slowly in an oblique direction, still keeping its volume unaltered, as the sand is always carried from the roof of it to the bottom," again by means of pellets. The procedure varies widely with the "individuality" of the animal. Dembowski insists that this and other reactions are plastic, very little being automatic. Thus the fiddler crab has to adjust not merely a pellet of sand but "always *this single pellet* with all its individual particularities." The animal's nervous system (including its nearest approach to a brain) is too simple to account for such a variety of reactions. To further quote the investigator: "We are compelled to admit a plasticity of the nervous centers; they must possess a certain creative power that enables them to become adapted to entirely new situations. The number of possible nervous connections is limited, but the number of possible reactions is infinite. This discrepancy may be avoided only by admitting that each nervous center may perform an infinity of functions."

Under natural conditions the fiddlers are probably never out of air longer than is necessary to moisten their gills, and they can live in air for several weeks without changing the water in their gill chambers. Nevertheless several animals lived for six weeks in sea water with no apparent ill effects. Dembowski concludes that they are true water-breathers, not air-breathers, but have interesting land-living adaptations, the gills probably being filled with sea water rather than with nearly fresh water as has been assumed.

Uca crenulata, if not the only fiddler crab on the coast, is at least the only common one north of southern Lower California, and it is known only as far north as Anaheim Bay. A second species of *Uca* is reported from Vancouver Island! One learns to be cautious in making definite statements about intertidal animals, but this is something too much. It is most certainly either an outright error, the record of an exceedingly rare animal, or the result of a single specimen's happening to live in the vegetation on a boat bottom until it dropped off, half dead, at this point. High on the shore south of the highway along Mission Bay we used to find colonies of *crenulata,* but lately we have failed to find a single specimen. The shore line has been artificially built up there, and the animals probably have been buried. There are plenty, however, at Anaheim Slough.

It has been remarked that specimens are common only in summer. We got an inkling of why that should be, in January several years back, when we persistently dug out a burrow in the estuary south of Ensenada. The living animal was at the 40″ level in a tunnel that extended to a measured 48″ from the surface. The water in the pool at the bottom was bitterly salt.

§285. Pretty well throughout Newport Bay, extending almost as far as the slough reaches and ranging from the high-tide zone well down into the zone of low tides, is a small burrowing crab, *Speocarcinus californiensis* (Pl. XL). This crab (with a carapace about an inch wide) will often be mistaken at first glance for a fiddler. Both bristle up at the mouths of their burrows to intimidate an intruder, and both scurry down into the security of their burrows before danger comes near. The lively fiddler crab never goes much below the high-tide line, however, while the less active *Speocarcinus* roams through the whole intertidal region. The latter has fringes of hair on its legs and carapace edges, and short eye stalks, while the fiddler is hairless and has long and prominent eye stalks.

North of *Speocarcinus'* range, which is Los Angeles to San Diego, the common mud-flat crab of the higher tidal reaches is *Hemigrapsus oregonensis* (Fig. 89). This form looks like a small edition of the purple crab of rocky shores (*H. nudus*) that has been bleached to a uniform light gray or muddy yellow on top and white underneath, deprived of its under-side spots, and given, in compensation, a slight hairiness about the walking legs. Night, half tide, and an estuary such as Elkhorn Slough furnish the ideal combination for seeing an impressive panoply of crab armor. Hordes of these aggressive yellow shore crabs rear up in formidable attitudes, seeming to invite combat. The gesture is largely bluff, for if hard pressed they resort to that comforting philosophy which says that he who runs away will live to fight some other time when he is more in the mood. *H. oregonensis* ranges southward from Alaska, and is the common shore crab of San Francisco Bay. In Puget Sound and British Columbia it is extraordinarily abundant. Hart (1935), investigating the development, found that the young are hatched from May until August at Departure Bay.

The purple shore crab occurs to a limited extent along the clay banks in the upper parts of sloughs, but will generally be found pretty closely associated with rocks.

ZONE 3. *Middle intertidal.*

(a) At the surface.

§286. The channeled basket shell, *Nassarius fossatus* (Pl. XL), also known as *Nassa* and as *Alectrion,* is the commonest of the large predaceous snails on suitable mud flats between British Columbia and Lower California, although it is predominantly a northern species. Incidentally it is one of the largest nassas known, large specimens being nearly 2″ long, and the cleancut beauty of its brown shell makes it a very noticeable animal. Ordinarily it will be seen plowing its way through flats of mud or muddy sand, probably in search of food. MacGinitie found that the animals are attracted by either fresh or decaying meat and will reach up for meat held in the air above them. When feeding, one wraps its foot completely around the food, hiding it until it is consumed.

In August, at least, many individuals may be found depositing eggs in "shingled" capsules on the blades of eelgrass. The same investigator watched this process. The snail first explores with its sensory siphon the surface to be utilized, and then cleans a spot with its radula. Next it forms a fold in its foot to connect the genital pore with the pedal gland, and through this fold the naked egg mass is passed. The lip of the pedal gland is pressed against the cleaned surface for nine and one-half minutes during the process. When the eggs have entered the pedal gland, the infolded tube disappears, and the foot is used to form a water chamber, presumably for aerating the egg capsules already laid. During this nine and one-half minutes both the body and the shell oscillate, for some unknown reason, and after this period "the anterior part of the foot is lifted upward and backward, and, as the capsule is now cemented to the object to which it is being attached, it pulls out of the pedal gland as a completed egg capsule." The entire process has occupied twelve and one-half minutes, and the animal is ready to move on and repeat the operation on a newly cleaned area just ahead. One typical string a little more than two and one-half inches long contained forty-five capsules and was nine hours in the making. The flattened capsules, averaging just over ⅛″ long, are laid with the base of one overlapping the base of the next, producing the "shingled" effect mentioned.

Another considerably smaller predaceous snail is the oyster drill, *Urosalpinx cinereus* (Fig. 90), a snail which was accidentally introduced from the East coast along with the Eastern oyster. It is an inoffensive-looking animal, like a small dingy gray *Thais,* but once it gets established it can work considerable havoc with the oyster

beds. Its method of attack—the same as that employed by *Thais* and
the great moon snail—is to drill a hole through the bivalve's shell and
hack out the soft body.*

Southern mud flats have several characteristic snails. The tall-
spired horn shell *Cerithidea californica* (Fig. 92) extends to the
upper reaches of such sloughs as Newport Bay even where there is
some admixture of fresh water, and *Acanthina paucilirata* (Fig. 93)
occurs in the stretches more frequently washed by ocean water. The
shell of the former is dark brown or black; that of the latter is *Thais*-
like, with 4 to 6 whorls which are crossed by broad black longitudinal stripes and narrower white stripes, giving a somewhat checkered
appearance.

§287. In the south a large tectibranch, the bubble-shell snail,
Bulla gouldiana (Pl. XL), with a shell some 2″ long, is the commonest
of all gastropods in the Newport Bay and Mission Bay region—so
common that whoever has been there must surely have seen it. The
paper-thin shell is mottled brown, and the body, which is too large
for the shell, is yellow. When the animal is completely extended and
crawling about in the mud, the mantle covers most of the shell. One
observer says that the bubble-shell snails eat bivalves and smaller snails,
swallowing them whole. The long strings of eggs, lying about on the
mud or tangled in eelgrass, are familiar sights in summer.

A pea crab of the ubiquitous species known also from *Cryptochiton* and the cucumber *Stichopus* is sometimes found in the mantle
cavity of *Bulla*.

A much smaller snail that we believe to be the barrel shell, *Acteon
punctocaelatus* (Fig. 94), is sometimes common well up in the slough
at Newport Bay. The animal is less than ½″ long but is so striking
that it is sure to be picked out of its surroundings, for narrow black
bands follow the whorls around its white shell.

§288. Mud flats would seem to be the most unlikely localities of
all to harbor hydroids, but the tubularian *Corymorpha palma* (Fig.
95) is famous in the Newport–San Diego Bay area. Specimens at-
taining the (for a shore hydroid) very great size of 3″ have been
taken, and in some areas whole forests of these delicate fairy palms
grow on the flats. The solitary individuals fasten themselves to the
substratum by ramifying roots that come away as a chunk of mud.
The animals are watery and transparent, and therefore will often be
overlooked if the light is poor. When the ebbing tide leaves them

---

* Introduced presumably at the same time, and surely in the same way, was the
small (⅛″ to ¾″) dog whelk, *Ilyanassa obsoleta*, which according to Mrs. Grant has
become an important constituent of the San Francisco Bay mud-flat fauna. Through
the 1905 account of Dimon considerable information is available on this common
mud snail, frequently associated with oysters and oyster culture.

without support they collapse on the mud, there to lie exposed to sun and drying winds until the tide floods again. It is remarkable that so delicate an animal can survive such exposure, but it apparently suffers no harm therefrom.

Around the single flower-like "head" of the animal (the hydranth) the tiny jellyfish are developed, which, although they pulsate like free jellyfish in the act of swimming, apparently never succeed in freeing themselves from the parent hydroid. There they stay until they reach maturity, deposit their eggs, and wither away. The eggs may be transported some distance by currents, but wherever they touch they settle and begin to grow as hydroids, so that there is no free-swimming stage whatever.

Corymorpha is one of that minority of Pacific-coast intertidal animals that has been closely observed and studied. In aquaria it remains erect with spread tentacles so long as a current of water is maintained, but begins a slow and regular bowing movement as soon as the current is stopped. During each bow it sweeps the mud with its tentacles; then, as it straightens up again, it rolls up its long tentacles until its short tentacles can scrape the food from them and pass it to the mouth. The animal is well known for its remarkable powers of regeneration. If the entire hydranth is cut off, a new one will grow within a few days, and sections cut out of the "stem" will grow complete new individuals.

Like other hydroids, *Corymorpha* has its associated sea spiders. Near Balboa we once found, in August, a bank of muddy sand that supported a *Corymorpha* bed about which were strewn large numbers of straw-colored and quite visible gangly pycnogonids, *Anoplodactylus erectus,* occurring also with southern *Tubularia* (§333). Presumably it was a seasonal occurrence. The sea spiders had probably just grown to an independent stage and released themselves from their hydroid nurses—quite likely by eating their way out.

(b) Burrowing in the substratum.

§289. The most noticeable substratum animal in the Newport Bay flats of sandy mud is certainly the sea pen, *Stylatula elongata,* but whether or not it should be considered as a burrowing animal will depend on the observer's reaction, which, in turn, will depend on the state of the tide. The collector who appears on the scene between half tide and low tide will be willing to swear before all the courts in the land that he is digging out a thoroughly buried animal. But let him row over the spot at flood tide, and he will see in the shallow water beneath his boat a pleasant meadow of waving green sea pens, like a field of young wheat. The explanation comes when he reaches down with an oar in an attempt to unearth some of the "plants." They snap down into the ground instantly, leaving nothing of themselves visible but the short spiky tips of their stalks. Like the anemone *Harenactis,* they have a bulbous anchor that is permanently buried deep in the bottom. When molested, or when the tide leaves them exposed, they retract the polyps that cover the stalk and pull themselves completely beneath the surface. When cool water again flows over the region they expand slowly until each pennatulid looks like a narrow green feather waving in the current.

Pennatulids as a group are notably phosphorescent, and our local species are no exception. Both *Stylatula elongata* and *Acanthoptilum gracile* (Pl. XL), common in Tomales Bay, exhibit startling flashes of light when adapted for about half an hour in a dark room and touched with a needle or stimulated with an electric current.

Both in Newport and in Tomales bays the sea pens occur in extensive "fields." It would be interesting to obtain counts of the population per square yard. The next step would be to dig up such a proof square, remove all the individuals, dry them, and weigh the product. The per-acre production of fruit, grain, or live stock on various types of farm land is well known; but until recently almost nothing has been known of the productivity of the sea except in "farmed" beds of oysters and the like. The fact remains that the oceans are the great primal sources of food. Many food chains start or end in the sea, and others are indirectly tied up with this great motherland, which provides by far the oldest and greatest areas of production in the world.

Based on estimates made in the English Channel, the annual yield of primal foodstuffs (diatoms—primitive, one-celled organisms) has been calculated to be five and a half tons per acre of water surface. The account* from which we take this figure compares it with the annual potato yield of an acre of laboriously cultivated land—where the average is less than five tons. The mathematically inclined reader can easily, by determining the number of acres of ocean surface, compute an estimated total production. It is safe to predict, without indulging in the thankless labor of that multiplication, that the resulting figure would be so large as to be meaningless to those of us who are accustomed to thinking in terms of one nickel and two dimes.

§290. Even in this middle intertidal zone there are many burrowing animals besides the spectacular *Stylatula.* Another relative of the hydroids, jellyfish, and corals is the burrowing anemone,

* F. S. Russell and C. M. Yonge, *The Seas,* 1928, p. 248.

Edwardsiella californica (Fig. 96), which also occurs in great profusion. Early in March 1931 we found a sandy mudbank east of
Corona del Mar that must have averaged more than fifty of these
animals to the square foot. It goes without saying that they are not
large, a good-sized, extended specimen being possibly 2″ long. The
worm-like body, which normally protrudes slightly above the surface, is almost covered with a brown and wrinkled tube. When first
dug up, the animal looks very much like a small peanut worm
(sipunculid). In an aquarium the disc flowers out, during the
afternoon, with symmetrically arranged tentacles, and the attachment bulb expands and becomes transparent so that the partitions
are visible as eight longitudinal bands. This species of *Edwardsiella*
is known from southern California only, but a similar or identical
form occurs (or occurred) rarely at Elkhorn Slough.

§291. During some years the southern California muddy sand
contains a considerable population of the stalked brachiopod, *Glottidia albida* (Pl. XL)—the second and last of its group to be here
mentioned. This small bivalved animal, which, although it resembles
a stalked thin clam, is not even distantly related to the mollusks, is
almost a facsimile of the large tropical *Lingula,* the oldest living
genus in the world. Remains of *Lingula* date back to the Ordovician
period, the second oldest geological horizon in which undoubted fossils
occur. Millions of years after *Lingula* was established, myriads of
other animals developed, most of which perished a few more millions of years before the first man learned to stand on his hind legs.
It certainly speaks much for the tolerance and adaptability of an animal
that it has lived from such a remote geological age to the present time
and still persists in such numbers that races bordering the Indian Ocean
use it for food, selling it in public markets as we sell clams.

Our Pacific-coast specimens of *Glottidia* live in burrows, retracted at low tide so that only a slitted opening can be seen at the
surface. The white horny shells are rarely more than an inch long.
The fleshy peduncle with which the animal burrows and anchors itself may be two or three times the length of the shell. The animal
is not helpless when deprived of its peduncle, however. One specimen so handicapped was able to bury itself head first, presumably
with the aid of the bristles which protrude from the mantle edge.
When covered with water and undisturbed, the animal projects its
body halfway out of its burrow, and at such times the bristles are
used to direct the currents of water that carry food and oxygen
into the body.

§292. One of the burrowing ghost shrimps, the red *Callianassa
californiensis* (Pl. XLI), will be found in this zone. Next to the

fiddler crab and the somewhat similar *Speocarcinus,* this pink and white, soft-bodied, ghost shrimp seems to be the most shoreward of the burrowing forms with an optimum zone of 0 to +1.0′. It occurs, too, over a wide geographical range, reaching southeastern Alaska to the northward. We have seen it in the Strait of Georgia, Puget Sound, Elkhorn Slough, Newport Bay, and El Estero de Punta Banda. The ghost shrimps have adapted themselves to their narrow burrows so completely that if not allowed to feel the burrow walls around them they will die within a few hours, even when all other conditions are satisfactory. In other words, they are positively thigmotactic to an amazing degree. This fact has been demonstrated by MacGinitie (1934), who has made a further careful study of the animals' habits. The claws of the first and second legs dig, he found, and draw the sandy mud backward, collecting it in a receptacle formed by another pair of legs. When enough material has been collected to make a load, the shrimp backs out of its burrow and deposits the load outside. All of the legs are specialized, some being used for walking, others for bracing the animal against the sides of the burrow, and still others for personal cleansing operations.

The burrows are much branched and complicated, with many enlarged places for turning around, but the work of adding new tunnels, or extending the old ones, is unending. When they pause in their digging operations, the shrimps devote the time to cleaning themselves; seemingly they are obsessed with the Puritan philosophy of work. The feeding process consists in extracting detritus, of which bacteria are thought to form an important part, from the continuous stream of mud that passes through the digestive tract.* Judging from their age grouping, the animals are surprisingly long-lived, perhaps reaching an age of fifteen or sixteen years. In central California breeding is continuous throughout the year, with an optimum season during June and July.

As happens with many other animals that make permanent or semipermanent burrows, the ghost shrimp takes in boarders, which are likely in this case to be a scale worm, *Hesperonoe complanata,* and the same pea crab, *Scleroplax granulata,* that occurs with the remarkable innkeeper, *Urechis* (§306). Five other commensals are known to occur, including the copepod, *Hemicyclops callianassae,* on the gills, and, in Lower California, a new species of *Betaeus.* But the most prominent commensal is the red copepod, *Clausidium vancouverense,* according to Dr. Light.

* Thus they "subserve much the same function for the bottom soil of estuaries that the earthworm does for the field," turning the soil over to a depth of thirty inches once every two hundred and forty days.

§293. It is almost axiomatic to remark that there are the usual hosts of worms here. The slim and very long *Notomastus tenuis,* looking like a piece of frayed red wrapping twine, elastic, and up to 12″ long, may be present in nearly every spadeful of mud, sometimes occurring so thickly as to bind the soil together, but it is so common and so ready to break that one soon loses interest in it. In the south will be found a long, white, wrinkled sipunculid with a threadlike "neck." This form, *Golfingia hespera,* sometimes occurs with the burrowing anemone, *Edwardsiella,* or the brachiopod, *Glottidia.* The long and slim *Lumbrineris zonata* is exceedingly common at Elkhorn Slough. MacGinitie (1935c) records a specimen with 604 segments.

Sandy tubes projecting a little above the surface in areas of hard-packed muddy sand are likely to be occupied by the fragile "jointworms," *Axiothella rubrocincta* (Fig. 97), whose segmented bodies are banded in dull ruby red. Large specimens extend 6″ or 7″ below the surface. The anal end of the worm bears a funnel-shaped rosette, and the head end, which is slightly enlarged, embodies a plug for stopping up the tube when the animal is retracted. *Axiothella* has been taken in Puget Sound and Tomales Bay and at San Pedro.

Occurring in *Axiothella* tubes is the most specialized of all commensal crabs, the pea crab, *Pinnixa longipes,* which, in adapting itself to moving sideways in the narrow tube, has become several times as wide as it is long and has achieved tremendous development of the third pair of walking legs. Seeing a specimen outside a tube one can scarcely believe that it could possibly insinuate itself through the small opening. The passage takes some pains, but the tiny crab manages it, inserting one huge leg first and then carefully edging itself in sideways. Despite this high degree of specialization, *Pinnixa longipes* is an animal that could probably live almost anywhere. On the East coast this species occurs with the tubed worm, *Chaetopterus,* but no such commensal crabs have been found with that worm on the West coast.

Two other burrowing worms will be taken frequently in this habitat. The first, *Cirriformia spirabrancha* (see §16 for similar form), with its coiled tentacles writhing about on the mud of such estuaries as Elkhorn Slough, will at first be taken for a cluster of round worms, but a little serious work with the shovel will turn out the pale, yellowish or greenish cirratulid which lies hidden safely beneath the surface while its active tentacles keep contact with the outside world of aerated water. In San Francisco Bay, the muddy eastern shores, at Berkeley for instance, are characterized by great beds, acres in extent, of the cosmopolitan tubed worm *Capitella capitata,* several inches long, lying head up in vertical, dirt-encrusted, black membranous tubes.

Zone 4. *Low-tide horizon.*

(a) At the surface.

§294. Many snails crawl about on the mud flats in this low zone. The largest are slugs, not popularly recognized as true snails, but actually belonging with this group of animals. *Navanax inermis* (Pl. XLI), near to the sea hares, is large (up to 6" or 7") and strikingly colored with many yellow dots and a few blue ones on a brown background. It is common in southern California and northern Mexico and has been taken frequently at Morro Bay and occasionally at Elkhorn Slough. We find it commonly on bare mud but almost as often in association with eelgrass. Johnson and Snook find that it feeds, both in the aquarium and in its natural environment, on the white bubble-shell snails, *Haminoea,* and that attached to its gills there are almost invariably parasitic copepods (*Pseudomolgus navanacis*). Since these fish lice are less than $\frac{1}{10}$" in length, they are merely mentioned in passing. We have seen the egg masses of *Navanax* in December, and they are known to breed in summer also. The eggs are laid in light-yellow, stringy coils, woven together in pleasing designs.

The sea hare, *Tethys* (§104), is a frequent visitor to the mud flats. At Elkhorn Slough huge specimens, weighing ten pounds or more, may frequently be seen when none are to be found on the rocky shore outside.

§295. *Hermissenda crassicornis,* a yellow-green nudibranch up to an inch long and having its back covered with brown plumed gills, exhibits a seasonal abundance in Elkhorn Slough. During February, 1929, thousands were present, many ovipositing. They have been known to deposit eggs in August also. A very similar nudibranch, probably the same animal, has been seen in Puget Sound during the summer.

§296. Of the shelled snails there are many kinds. A tropical brown cowry (*Cypraea spadicea,* §136), that ranges as far north as Newport, and a cone shell (*Conus californicus,* §136) are fairly common. The latter packs about more than its allotment of the slipper shell, *Crepidula onyx* (Fig. 91)—a combination that extends into the upper reaches of the estuary at Newport. Ovipositing specimens of the olive snails (§253) have been noted in August at Elkhorn Slough. One of the "muricks," *Ceratostoma nuttalli,* is especially characteristic of southern mud flats. The ambitious collector at Newport may also run across the flared *Pterynotus trialatus* (both in Pl. XLI), prize of the conchologists in that region. The largest of the moon snails (*Polinices lewisii,* §252) is almost as characteristic an inhabitant of the mud as it is of the sand flats. Of the bivalves the heavy-shelled *Chione* (§260) may be taken on flats of sandy mud, often, strangely, at the surface.

§297. The most noticeable animal of all, but one that is by no means obtrusively common, is a magnificently orange-plumed *Phoronis* that has been seen at Newport, its gelatinous body protected by a tube that is buried in the mud. This anomalous "worm," which, according to MacGinitie, proves to be *Phoronopsis californica* Hilton, 1930, extends down into the substratum, retracts immediately at the least sign of trouble, and is difficult to dig. Although occurring solitarily, it is a near relative of the green-plumed *Phoronopsis viridis* that grows in great beds at Elkhorn Slough, and of the similar *Phoronopsis harmeri* of the Vancouver region, which sometimes carpets the mud with green fuzz for many square yards. These are not at all difficult to dig, and colonies of the stringy worms in their stiff and upright, sand-covered, parchment-like tubes are very much a feature of the estuary fauna.

The phoronids have been an enigmatic group to zoölogists, who have classed them with the bryozoa because both have a horseshoe-shaped circlet of tentacles (the lophophore) around the mouth. They have also been thought to be related to the degenerate *Dolichoglossus.* But the recent tendency is to regard them as constituting a separate phylum.

§298. *Tetilla mutabilis* (Fig. 99) is one of the most remarkable of sponges. It attaches loosely, now and then, to the roots of eelgrass, but for the most part it rolls aimlessly about in Newport Bay or lies around on the mud flats—an unheard-of line of conduct for a sponge. The light-weight clusters, sometimes as large as a clenched fist, are sometimes dirty yellow to purple but are usually red with green glints. This sponge has been likened to the egg case of a spider; to another observer it suggests the gizzard of a chicken.

(b) Burrowing in the substratum.

§299. The clams and worms are the obvious animals in the substratum of this low zone, and there is a varied assemblage of both. Largest of all our clams, if not one of the largest intertidal

III. BAY AND ESTUARY

§§ 194–314, Figures 70–102, Plates XXX–XLIV

Morro Bay and Morro Rock. U.S. Navy Photo.

Fig. 70
A Puget Sound periwinkle,
Littorina sitkana; about four
times natural size (§ 195).

Fig. 71
A pill bug, *Exosphaeroma
oregonensis* (§ 198).

Fig. 72
A crustacean, *Epinebalia* sp.; about four times
life size (§ 204).

PLATE XXX (Opposite page)
QUIET-WATER ANIMALS OF THE MIDDLE HORIZON

1. The hairy hermit, *Pagurus hirsutiusculus,* removed from shell (§ 201).
2. Two shells of the wrinkled purple snail, *Thais lamellosa,* both slightly reduced: the upper shell, which is light and fragile, was taken from very quiet waters; the much heavier lower shell was taken from a relatively exposed position (§ 200).
3. The channelled purple snail, *Thais canaliculata* (§ 200).

Lower: Collecting near the Port Townsend lighthouse in the Strait of Juan de Fuca; this region was particularly rich in the attached jellyfish, *Haliclystus.*

Fig. 73

The isopod *Idothea resecata*; drawing courtesy R. J. Menzies.

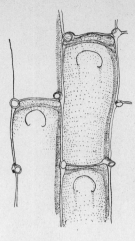

Membranipora membranacea

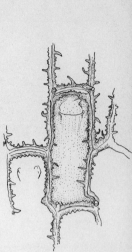

Membranipora serrilamella

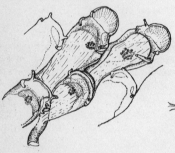

Dendrobenia lichnoides

Membranipora tuberculata

Fig. 74

Various types of encrusting bryozoa. Drawings by R. J. Menzies.

Fig. 75

The clam, *Psephidia lordi;* a young specimen several times life size (§ 206).

PLATE XXXI (Opposite page)

QUIET-WATER ANIMALS OF THE MID- AND LOW-TIDE REGIONS

1. The rock cockle, *Protothaca* (formerly *Paphia*) *staminea*, color variety; life size (§ 206).
2. The leather star *Dermasterias imbricata*; reduced (§ 211).
3. *Pisaster brevispinus*, a pink-skinned sea star; reduced (§209).
4. *Leptasterias hexactis*; life size (§ 210).
5. *Evasterias troschelii* (§ 207).

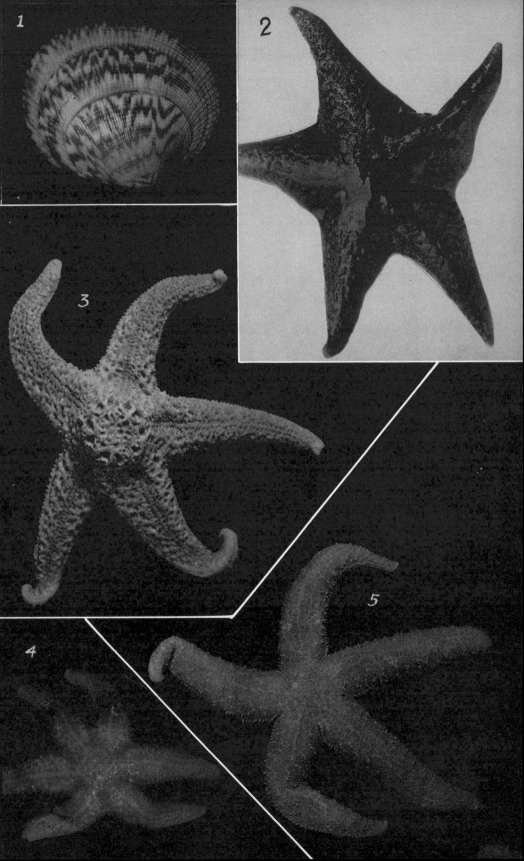

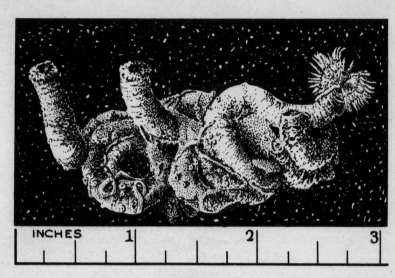

Fig. 76
Tube worms, *Serpula vermicularis* (§ 213).

PLATE XXXII (Opposite page)

QUIET-WATER ANIMALS OF THE NORTHERN LOW-TIDE
REGIONS

1. An erect sponge of northern waters, similar to *Neosperiopsis rigida*;
   actual height, 8″ (§ 225).
2. The hairy Oregon triton, *Fusitriton oregonensis*; reduced (§ 214).
3. The tunicate, *Pyura haustor* (§ 216).
4. The creeping cucumber, *Psolus chitonoides* (§ 226).

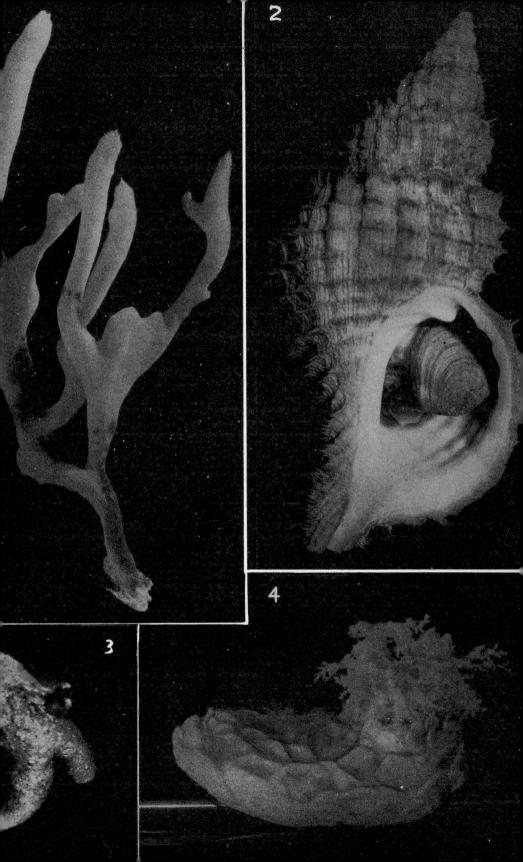

Fig. 77
The checkered hairy shell,
Trichotropis cancellata,
which ranges from the
Bering Sea to Oregon;
twice natural size
(§ 215).

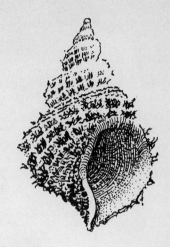

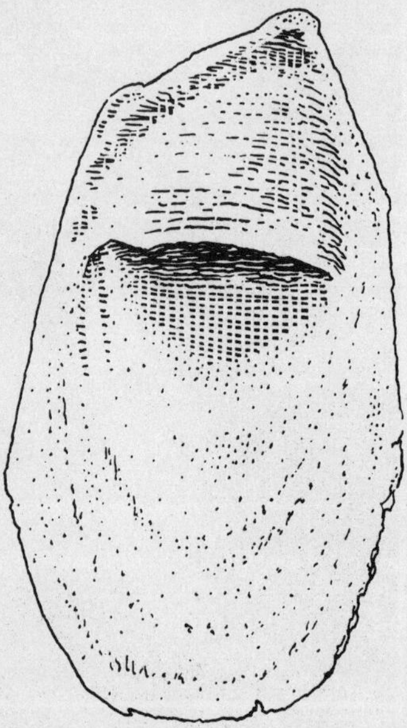

Fig. 78
The northern slipper shell,
Crepidula nummaria; twice
natural size (§ 215).

PLATE XXXIII (Opposite page)
UNDER-ROCK ANIMALS OF QUIET WATERS

1. *Cancer oregonensis;* a small specimen (§ 231).
2. A green shrimp, *Hippolyte californiensis* (§ 230).
3. The reddish cucumber, *Cucumaria miniata;* specimen measured about 6″ (§ 235).
4. The white cucumber, *Eupentacta quinquesemita* (§ 235).

Fig. 80
The rock oyster, *Pododesmus
macroschisma;* natural size
(§ 217).

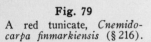

Fig. 79
A red tunicate, *Cnemido-
carpa finmarkiensis* (§ 216).

Fig. 81
The brachiopod, *Terebratalia
transversa;* natural size
(§ 227).

PLATE XXXIV (Opposite page)

ROCK-BORING BIVALVES OF QUIET WATERS

Upper: The common piddock or rock clam, *Pholadidea penita;* the rock
has been split open to show the animal in its burrow (§ 242).

Lower left: The date mussel of southern shores, *Lithophaga plumula;* this
form excavates its burrows by chemical action (§ 241).

Lower right: The commensal hydroid, *Proboscidactyla* sp., on fragment of
tube of the sabellid *Pseudopotamilla*. Greatly enlarged. Photo courtesy
of John R. Hendrickson.

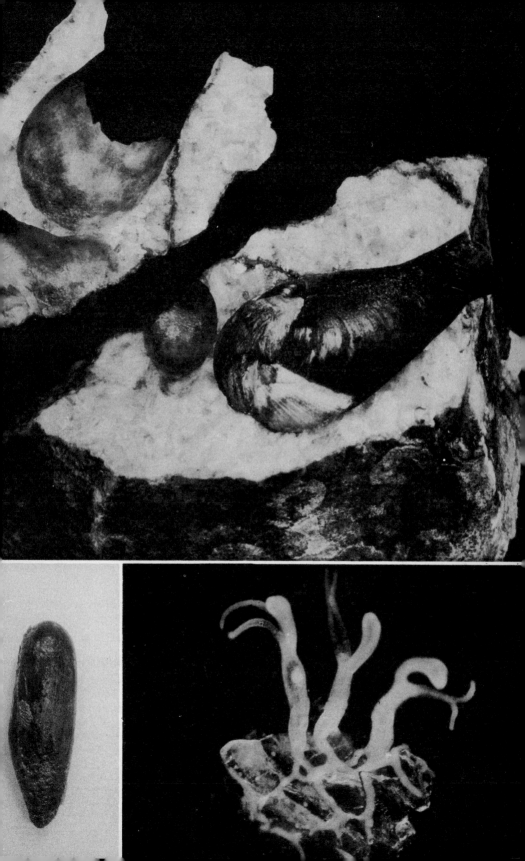

280

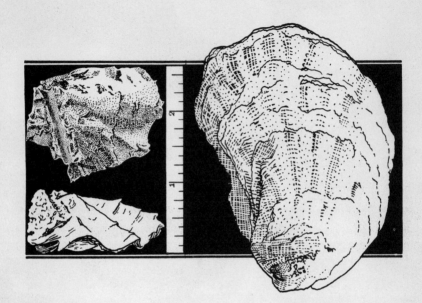

Fig. 82
The native oyster, *Ostrea
lurida* (§ 219).

Fig. 83
The Eastern oyster, *Crassostrea
virginica* (§ 219).

PLATE XXXV (Opposite page)

SAND-FLAT FORMS OF SOUTHERN CALIFORNIA

1. Skeleton of the sand dollar, *Dendraster excentricus*; actual diameter,
4" (§ 246).
2. The heart urchin or sea porcupine, *Lovenia cordiformis*; actual length,
about 3" (§ 247).
3. The elbow crab, *Heterocrypta occidentalis* (§ 249).
4. *Randallia ornata*; a small specimen (§ 249).
5. The swimming crab, *Portunus (P.) xantusii* (§ 249).

282

Fig. 84
The black-tailed shrimp, *Crago nigricauda*; natural size (§ 254). Photo
by Woody Williams.

PLATE XXXVI (Opposite page)
MORE SAND-FLAT DWELLERS

1. The sand star, *Astropecten armatus;* reduced (§ 250).
2. A moon snail, *Polinices draconis,* with its foot partially contracted; reduced (§ 252).
3. Egg case of the moon snail; reduced.
4. Shell of the olive snail, *Olivella biplicata* (§ 253).
5. The nudibranch, *Pleurophyllidia californica* (§ 251).

4

3

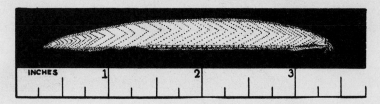

Fig. 85

The California Amphioxus, *Branchiostoma californiense* (§ 266).

Fig. 86

The fixed jellyfish, *Haliclystus stejnegeri* (§ 273).

Fig. 87

The tube-building worm, *Pectinaria* (§ 281).

PLATE XXXVII (Opposite page)

SAND-FLAT ANIMALS

1. The thick scallop, *Pecten circularis* (§ 255).
2. The burrowing anemone, *Harenactis attenuata*; note the anchoring bulb (§ 257).
3. The burrowing anemone, *Evactis artemisia* (§ 258).
4. The basket cockle, *Clinocardium nuttallii*, with foot extended; slightly reduced (§ 259).

2

3

286

Fig. 88
A hydroid jellyfish, *Gonionemus vertens;* natural size (§ 283).

Fig. 89
Hemigrapsus oregonensis; natural size (§ 285).

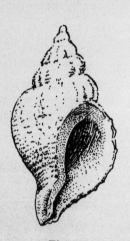

Fig. 90
The oyster drill, *Urosalpinx cinereus;* twice natural size (§ 286).

Fig. 91
The slipper shell, *Crepidula onyx;* natural size (§ 296).

PLATE XXXVIII (Opposite page)

ANIMALS BURROWING IN SAND FLATS

1. The jackknife clam, *Solen rosaceus* (§ 260).
2. The hard-shell cockle, *Chione undatella* (§ 260).
3. Probably *Spisula planulata*, a southern California clam.
4. The quiet-water mole crab, *Lepidopa myops* (§ 261).
5. Shell of the purple clam, *Sanguinolaria nuttallii;* somewhat reduced (§ 260).

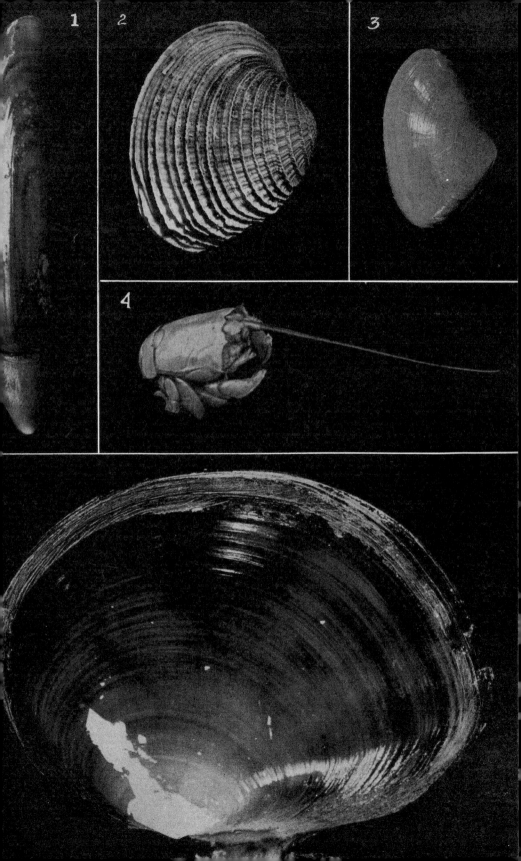

Fig. 92
The tall-spired horn shell, *Cerithidea californica*; twice natural size (§ 286).

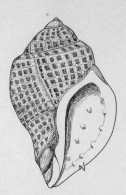

Fig. 93
Acanthina paucilirata, the southern California thorn shell; twice natural size.

Fig. 94
The barrel shell, *Acteon punctocaelatus* (§ 287).

Fig. 95
The mud-flat hydroid, *Corymorpha palma;* natural size (§ 288).

PLATE XXXIX (Opposite page)
SAND-FLAT ANIMALS

1. The "sweet potato," *Molpadia arenicola*, a cucumber; actual length, 8" (§ 264).
2. The hermit crab, *Holopagurus pilosus* (§ 262), in the shell of the moon snail, *Polinices recluzianus* (§ 252).
3. Snail shells covered with the coralline bryozoan, *Idmonea californica*, and occupied by the hermit crab, *Pagurus* sp. (§ 270).
4. The proboscis worm, *Glycera americana*, with proboscis extended (§ 280).

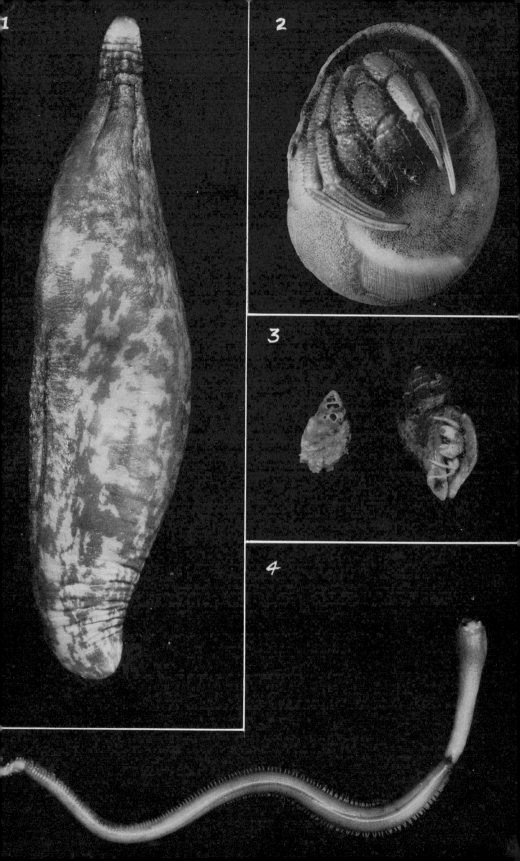

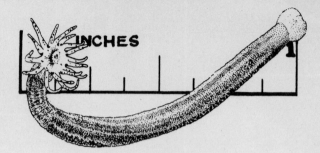

Fig. 96

A burrowing anemone, *Edwardsiella*
californica (§ 290).

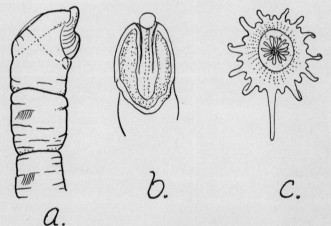

Fig. 97

The "jointworm," *Axiothella rubrocincta*: (*a*) lateral view of head
end; (*b*) dorsal view of cephalic plate; (*c*) anal rosette and
cirri. From Johnson, *Proc. Boston Soc. Nat. Hist.*, **24**.

PLATE XL (Opposite page)

MUD-FLAT ANIMALS

1. The fiddler crab, *Uca crenulata;* about twice life size (§ 284).
2. The burrowing crab, *Speocarcinus californiensis* (§ 285).
3. The channeled basket shell, *Nassarius fossatus* (§ 286).
4. The bubble shell, *Bulla gouldiana* (§ 287).
5. The brachiopod, *Glottidia albida* (§ 291).
6. The sea pen, *Acanthoptilum gracile*, from Tomales Bay (§ 289). Photo by Woody Williams.

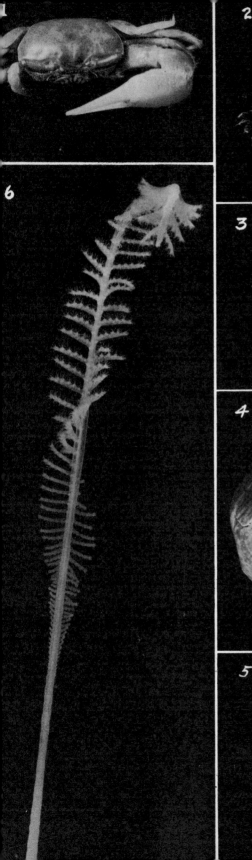

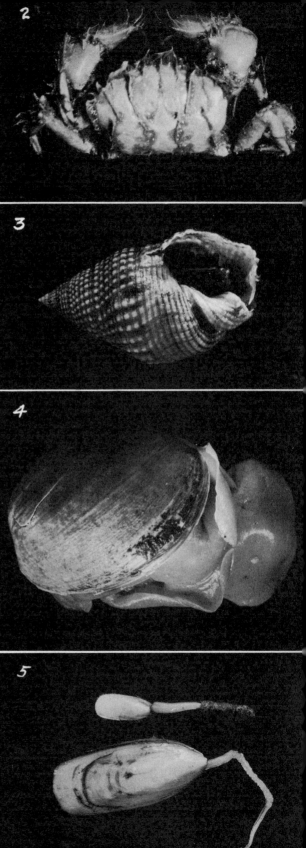

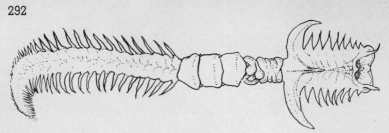

Fig. 98
A segmented worm, *Chaetopterus variopedatus;* natural size (§ 309).

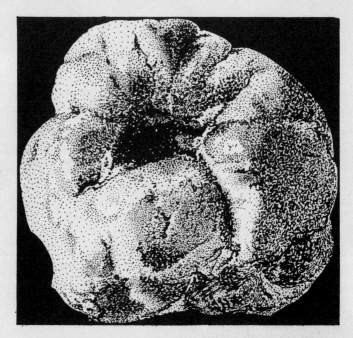

Fig. 99. The wandering sponge, *Tetilla mutabilis* (§ 298).

PLATE XLI (Opposite page)

MUD-FLAT ANIMALS

1. The red ghost shrimp, *Callianassa californiensis;* photo copyrighted by Pacific Biological Laboratories (§ 292).
2. The sea hare, *Navanax inermis;* slightly reduced (§ 294).
3. A murex, *Pterynotus trialatus* (§ 296).
4. Another murex, *Ceratostoma nuttalli* (§ 296).

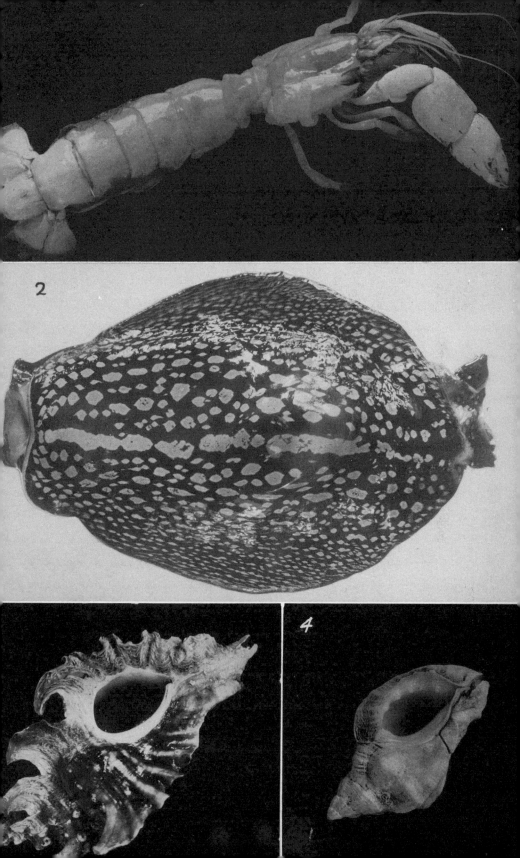

294

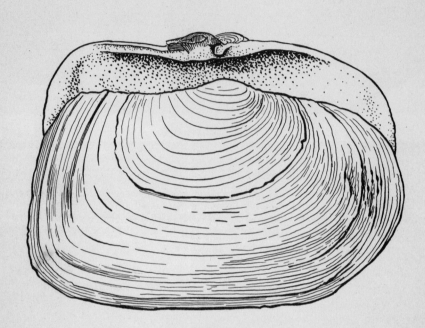

Fig. 100
Shell of the geoduck, *Panope generosa*; about two-thirds size (§ 299).
Drawing by Sam Hinton.

PLATE XLII (Opposite page)

CLAMS FOUND BURROWING IN THE MUD FLATS

(All reduced)

1. The gaper or horse clam, *Schizothaerus nuttallii* (§ 300).
2. The Washington clam, *Saxidomus nuttalli* (§ 301). .
3. Shell of the soft-shell clam, *Mya arenaria* (§ 302).

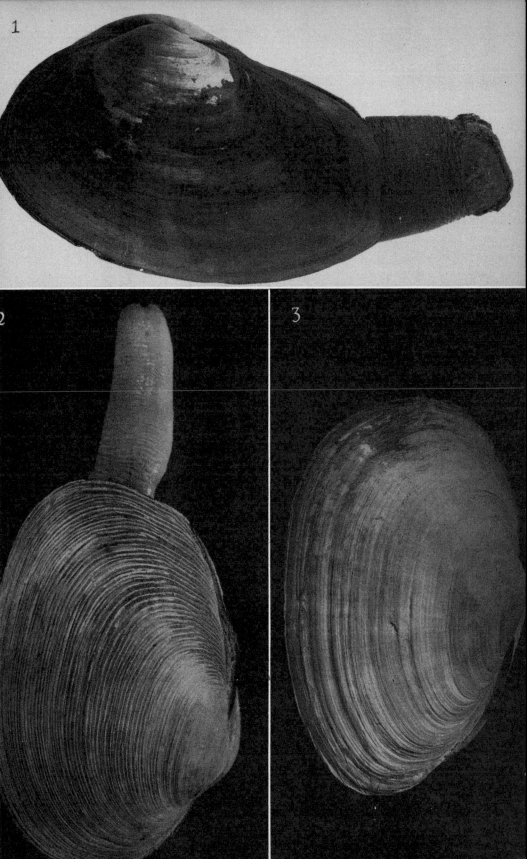

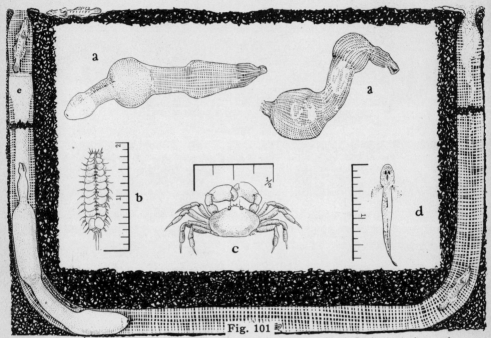

Fig. 101

The innkeeper, *Urechis caupo,* in its burrow with its guests. (*a–a*) Innkeepers drawn from a photograph of living animals in a dish. (*b*) A permanent guest, the scale worm *Hesperonoë adventor.* (*c*) The pea crab, *Scleroplax granulata,* another permanent guest. (*d*) A transient guest, the goby, *Clevelandia ios.* (*e*) Slime net made by the innkeeper in the burrow. Burrow and commensals after Fisher and MacGinitie (§ 306).

PLATE XLIII (Opposite page)

MUD-FLAT ANIMALS

1. The bent-nosed clam, *Macoma nasuta* (§ 303).
2. Shell of the jackknife clam, *Tagelus californianus* (§ 304).
3. The rough piddock, *Zirfaea pilsbryi,* the largest of the boring mollusks (§ 305).
4. The sipunculid worm, *Sipunculus nudus* (§ 308).

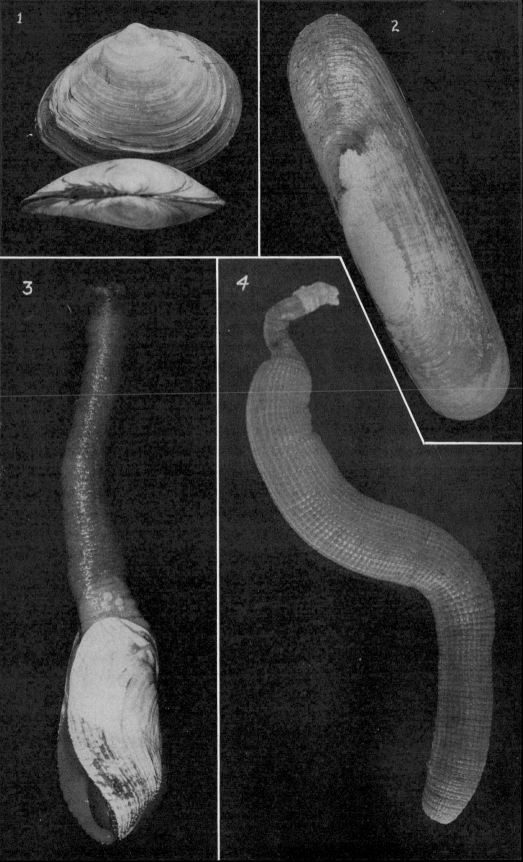

Fig. 102

View of eelgrass in the Tomales Bay flats. Note the burrowing
anemones, *Evactis artemisia*. Photo by Woody Williams.

PLATE XLIV (Opposite page)

INHABITANTS OF MUDDY SHORES

1. The blue mud shrimp, *Upogebia pugettensis* (§ 313).
2. Mud flat in Newport Bay. Many fixed clams or rock oysters cover the
rocks, and octopi live in mud caves under the rocks.

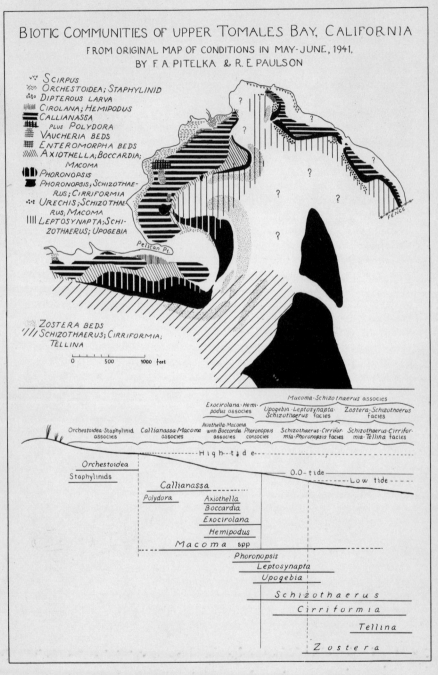

Map of communities of the Tomales Bay tidal flats near Dillon Beach.
(See pp. 315–16.) Courtesy of Dr. Frank A. Pitelka.

bivalves in the world, is the geoduck, *Panope generosa* (Fig. 100). (Weymouth, in his paper on the edible bivalves of California, says that the name was taken from the Indians of the north, which undoubtedly accounts for the pronunciation: the "eo" is pronounced like "oi" in "oil.") The geoduck lives in soft muck, or even in fairly loose sand; for, contrary to the popular belief, it is an extremely poor digger. Lest this statement should rouse the ire of many people who have exhausted themselves in the fruitless effort to reach one of the animals, we hasten to explain. The geoduck lives in a semipermanent burrow that is often three feet below the surface, sending his immense siphons upward to the surface. Any disturbance in his neighborhood causes him partially to retract his siphons, expelling contained water from them as he does so, and thus giving the impression that he is digging down to greater depths. Continued disturbance causes continued retraction, although the siphons are much too large ever to be withdrawn completely into the shell.

The geoduck has been credited, too, with a vast amount of will power which he probably does not possess, because of the fact that inexperienced diggers often try to pull him out by his siphons. The siphons break, and the obvious conclusion is that the animal is hanging on with grim determination. As a matter of fact he could not come out if he would, for his siphons are by no means strong enough to drag his bulging body through the substratum. Apropos of the difficulty of procuring the animal whole, Rogers remarks that a noted conchologist who, with the aid of two other men, had spent a long time in digging one out, referred to it feelingly as "a truly noble bivalve."

Individuals with shells more than 8″ long are not uncommon, and the maximum weight of the entire animal is about twelve pounds. Some of the specimens we have seen would probably have tipped the scales at ten pounds. The shells are relatively light weight and not only are not large enough to contain more than a small part of the siphons but are unable fully to contain the animal's portly body, so that even in living specimens the valves always gape open an inch or so.

Some time ago a movie newsreel showed the digging of geoducks in Puget Sound, while the "spieler" made the statement that the animals were known only from Puget Sound and from Africa. The statement is incorrect, for the geoduck is taken at Elkhorn Slough and Morro Bay, although not very plentifully, and is known from many quiet-water areas as far south as southern California. Anyone who has ever tried to dig it will understand why it is known so slightly and is used so infrequently for food.

§300. Another large clam that resembles the geoduck in appearance, habits, and size and is often mistaken for it is variously known as the gaper, the summer clam, the rubber-neck clam, the big-neck clam, the horse clam, the otter-shell clam, and the great Washington clam. After this appalling array of popular names it is almost restful to call the animal *Schizothaerus nuttallii* (Pl. XLII). The individual gaper-etcetera is readily located by its siphon hole in the mud—"squirt hole" in the vernacular—from which, at fairly regular intervals, it shoots jets of water two or three feet in the air. These jets are particularly powerful when the clam is disturbed, and are often aimed with deadly accuracy; but at any time a succession of the largest geysers produced by any clam betrays the presence of a bed. Digging them out, however, is no small job, for they lie from one and one-half to three feet below the surface. Their average size is smaller than the geoduck's, but the shell may be 6″ to 8″ long and the clam may weigh four pounds. As with the geoduck, the easily broken shell is incapable of closing tightly over the large body, and the huge siphon must shift for itself. The siphon is protected by a tough brown skin and by two horny valves at the tip—a device not found in any other of the common clams. Nevertheless the siphon, or part of it, must often be sacrificed, for the tips are commonly found in the stomachs of halibut.

Of the big clams this one is the least used for food (although it is popular locally), partly because its gaping shells cannot retain moisture and therefore make it unfit for shipment. Appearances are against it, too. The mud-flaked brown neck is unappetizing to look at. Weymouth says, however, that the Indians used to dry the siphons for winter use, and that at Morro Bay the siphons are skinned, quartered, and fried, although the bodies are discarded. As a matter of fact the bodies are perfectly edible and, after being run through a meat grinder, make a not unsatisfactory chowder. The clam under discussion is protected by California law, ten per person being the limit for one day. But it is possibly the poorest of the food clams and in little danger of extermination; *Saxidomus* should have been protected instead.

Schizothaerus nuttallii is interesting biologically (and this will probably further mitigate against its use as food, although it is perfectly safe) as the host of minute, fluke-like tapeworm larvae in which the living flame cells (excretory organs) can be seen under the microscope. MacGinitie has determined that the adult tapeworms (tetraphyllids) are to be found in the intestines of sting rays. The large pea crab, *Pinnixa faba,* is quite likely to be present in the mantle cavity in California, in Puget Sound, and in British Columbia, and numerous specimens of *Opisthopus* (§76) have been found. Occasionally the smaller *P. littoralis* will be taken in addition.

The clam ranges from Alaska to San Diego, and while it decidedly prefers quiet bays it may be found also on the outside coast; but such individuals are small and usually look rather battered. Specimens taken "outside" or even from the portion of inlets directly adjacent to oceanic waters ought never to be used for food during the summer because of the danger of mussel poisoning (§158).

§301. *Saxidomus nuttalli* (Pl. XLII), the Washington clam, butter clam, or money shell (this last because the California Indians used the shells for money), ranges from Bolinas Bay to San Diego. Clam diggers, however, do not distinguish between this clam and the very similar but smaller *S. giganteus,* which is the most abundant clam on suitable beaches in Alaska, British Columbia, and Puget Sound and occurs, but not commonly, as far south as Monterey. The same popular names are used for both. The shells of *S. nuttali* sometimes rival those of the geoduck in size, but are characteristically only 3" to 5" long, while *giganteus*—again proving that there is not much in even scientific names—averages about 3 inches. Both appear in the markets, but not commonly except in the Puget Sound region, where the smaller form is used rather extensively. A pea crab, the small *P. littoralis,* as in the gaper, may be found occasionally in the mantle cavity; but the Washington clam is on the whole remarkably free from parasites.

In a study of the distribution and breeding of *S. giganteus,* Fraser and Smith examined 2,600 British Columbia specimens. Tidal currents are an important factor in distribution because of the animals' pelagic larvae. With the exception of clams in their seventh year, the result of a particularly prolific season, the age distribution was fairly regular from the fourth year to the tenth. About half of the clams spawn at the end of the third year. At Departure Bay spawning took place in August, but at other beaches along the inner coast of Vancouver Island there was much variation. The larvae appeared as bivalved veligers in two weeks, and at the end of another four weeks, when still less than 3/16" long, they settled down on the gravel. It is reported also that mussel poisoning (§158) may be present during the summer to a dangerous degree in Washington clams occurring (as they do rarely) on the open coast or in inlets directly adjacent to oceanic waters.

§302. The soft-shell clam or mud clam, *Mya arenaria* (Pl. XLII), was accidentally imported more than fifty years ago along with spat of the Eastern oyster. It appeared a few years later (1880) in Willapa Bay, Washington, and may now be found established in firm-soiled flats from Georgia Strait to Monterey. In San Francisco Bay it is "farmed" by fencing off several acres of mud flats in order to keep out the skates or stingarees. It has thrived so well that in some years it has replaced all native clams in the markets except the Pismo clam, and, since the Pismo clam is becoming more and more scarce, will probably replace it also in the course of time. It is dug extensively in Humboldt Bay also.

Mya is egg-shaped in outline, averages less than 5″ in length, and is characterized by a large, spoon-shaped projection on the left valve at the hinge. Only one other species (*Platyodon,* §147) has this projection. The shell is light and brittle. The adults of the species are incapable of maintaining themselves in shifting substratum, having lost all power of digging, and hence require complete protection. They thrive in brackish water, however, if it does not become stagnant, and can stand temperatures below freezing. In the north *Mya* is likely to carry the same pea crab as the gaper.

In common with several other clams that can live in foul estuary mud, *Mya* exhibits, but to a striking degree, a facility for anaerobic respiration—the ability to live in a medium absolutely lacking in free oxygen. Experimentally they have been known to live in an oxygen-free atmosphere for eight days. They produced carbon dioxide continually but showed no subsequent effects beyond a decrease in stored glycogen (an animal "sugar") and a considerable increase in the metabolic rate after being replaced in a normal environment. Many bacteria are anaerobic, but such a revolutionary physiological process in an animal as specialized as a mollusk is somewhat startling. It has been suspected that one of its specialized organs called the crystalline style has a hand in the matter, for it is possible that it may be capable of oxidizing certain of the products of animal metabolism, thus enabling the life processes to go on temporarily just as well as though free oxygen were available.

§303. The bent-nosed clam, *Macoma nasuta* (Pl. XLIII), is a small, hardy species (seldom reaching 2½″ in length) that may be turned out of almost every possible mud flat between Kodiak and Lower California. At Elkhorn Slough it is the commonest clam. It can stand water so stale that all other species will be killed, hence it is often the only clam to be found in small lagoons that have only occasional communication with the sea. Also it can live in softer mud than any other species. At rest the clam lies on its left side at a depth of six or eight inches, with the bend in its shell turned upward following the upward curve of the separate yellow siphons. When burrowing it goes in at an angle, sawing back and forth like a coin sinking in water.

The California Indians, and possibly those to the northward, made extensive use of the bent-nosed clam for food, and many of their shell piles or kitchen middens contain more shells of this species than any other. Later on, San Francisco Chinese dug these clams, kept them in boxes for a day or two and furnished them with several changes of water by way of an internal bath (to void the contained sand and mud), and then marketed them. Now, however, this species seems to be very little used.

In a nearly related small clam of the Atlantic, *Cumingia*, similar in form and habitat, a lunar periodicity of the breeding seasons has been detected, the sexual products being extruded most plentifully at full moon during the summer.

§304. South of Santa Barbara the common jackknife clam of mud flats is the active *Tagelus californianus* (Pl. XLIII), a nearly cylindrical form reaching a length of 4 inches. It has a long, flexible, and powerful foot that cannot be completely withdrawn, and it can dig in rapidly, even from the surface. It lives in a permanent burrow about sixteen inches deep, within which it moves up and down at ease. If pursued it will dig down still farther. Seen from the surface, the burrow appears to be double, for there are two separate openings for the separate siphons, one and one-half or two inches apart.

§305. In some estuaries there are regions of stiff clay or hard mud where relatives of the rock-boring mollusks may be found. One of these, *Zirfaea pilsbryi* (formerly *gabbi*) (Pl. XLIII), the rough piddock, is the largest of the borers, reaching a shell length of 4½ inches. It occurs from Bering Sea to San Diego, and is found in outside rocky reefs as well as in protected mud and clay, but it is apparently more characteristic of the latter habitat. As with other borers, the valves gape at both ends and at the "head" end are roughened with grinding teeth. MacGinitie has watched the boring movements of this form in a glass tube. While the foot, which is modified to a sucking disc, holds on to the substratum, the shell is moved up and down and slightly rotated. Thirty-two turning movements make one complete revolution, requiring a minimum of seventy minutes. At approximately each revolution the direction of rotation is reversed. During the process the mantle is pulled back to allow the loosened material to be drawn up and shot out through the siphons. The shell is fragile, since the animal is amply protected in its burrow, and much too small to contain the long siphons even when fully contracted. Unlike most of the pholids, which quit work when their burrows are completed, *Zirfaea* remains active throughout its life of seven or eight years or more.

§306. Two perfectly gigantic true worms and one worm-like

echiurid are at home in the mud flats. The echiurid is *Urechis caupo* (Fig. 101), aptly named the fat innkeeper, for it is the portly chief of as motley a crew of guests as one could hope to find. At the low-tide water's edge, or below it, *Urechis* constructs a burrow in the shape of a broad U, with entrances from sixteen to thirty-eight inches apart. The entrances are constricted like the muzzle of a shotgun, and for the same reason, so that they are only about a third the diameter of the burrow, and around one of them is a pile of castings. Once completed the burrow is semipermanent, and needs only to be enlarged at infrequent intervals, for the animal is a slow-growing form. Our knowledge of the innkeeper's habits is attributable to Fisher and MacGinitie, who found that it would live and carry on its usual activities in a laboratory glass burrow placed in an aquarium. There the strange animal's housekeeping, feeding, digging methods, and social life were closely watched for months.

The innkeeper itself is roughly cigar-shaped when resting, and up to 19½″ long, although the average is perhaps nearer 8 inches. It is flesh-colored, with two golden bristles under the mouth, and a circlet of bristles around the anus. When the animal is active its shape is con-tinually changing owing to the peristaltic movements that pump water through the body and through the burrow. These movements also pro-vide locomotion, naturally, in either direction: To move forward, the animal swells the forward part of its body so that it presses firmly against the walls of the burrow. The remainder of the body is now contracted and drawn up, after which the swelling is transferred to the after part of the body. The contracted forward part is then pushed ahead, reanchored, and the cycle repeated.

Digging is begun with the short proboscis and the burrow is en-larged by scraping material from the walls with the bristles about the mouth end. The animal crawls over the loosened material and works it backward with the anal bristles. The material accumulates for a time, along with the castings, and is "finally blown out the 'back door' by a blast of accumulated respiration-water from the hind gut." This is where the constriction of the burrow entrance becomes useful, for it momentarily accelerates the velocity of the issuing water, thus enabling *Urechis* to expel rather large chunks of debris. Pieces too large to be so forced out are buried.

The animal's most remarkable trait is the spinning of a slime net with which it captures its microscopic food. The net permits the passage of water, and yet is so fine that particles one micron in diameter (one-millionth of a meter) are caught.* The openings are

* More recently MacGinitie (1932) reports (*Science*, 76: 490) that *Urechis* can live apparently indefinitely and increase in size with no food other than pure cul-tures of bacteria.

invisible even under a microscope. In preparing to feed, the inn-keeper moves up the vertical part of the burrow at its head end and attaches the beginning of the net to the burrow walls close to the entrance. It then moves downward, spinning a net that may be from 2″ to 8″ long. At first the net is transparent, but as it collects detritus it turns gray and becomes visible. For about an hour *Urechis* lies at the bend in its burrow, pumping water through the net, increasing the force of its pumping activities as the net becomes clogged. When sufficient food has been collected, the animal moves up its burrow, swallowing net and all as it goes. The net is now digested along with its contained detritus. The innkeeper, a fastidious eater, discards all large particles as the net is swallowed.

It is scarcely to be expected that so ready a food supply would go to waste, and it does not. The innkeeper's three guests stand ready to grab all particles the instant they are discarded. The most de-pendent of these is an annelid, the beautiful reddish scale worm *Hesperonoë* (formerly *Harmothoë*) *adventor,* from ½″ to 2″ long, which remains almost continually in contact with the body of its host. To quote Fisher and MacGinitie further: "It moves from place to place with its host, making little runs between peristaltic waves, and turns end for end when *Urechis* does. After *Urechis* spins its mucus-tube *Hesperonoë* may crawl forward and lie with its palps almost touching the proboscis. As soon as *Urechis* starts to devour the tube *Hesperonoë* also sets to, making absurd little attacks on the yielding material with its eversible pharynx."

The second guest, of which there are sometimes a pair, is the pea crab, *Scleroplax granulata,* usually not more than 5/16″ across the carapace.* The third guest is a goby, *Clevelandia ios,* and there may be from one to five specimens in a burrow. This little fish is a tran-sient guest, foraging outside much of the time and using the inn-keeper's burrow chiefly for shelter. *Urechis* derives no apparent benefit from any of these commensals. On the contrary, "both crab and annelid interfere with the regular activities of *Urechis,* especially its feeding and cleaning reactions. A particle of clam dropped into the slime-net is immediately sensed by both commensals. Their at-tempts to reach it cause *Urechis* prematurely to swallow the tube when the clam morsel is stripped out the open end. It is usually snapped up by *Hesperonoë* and swallowed if small enough; otherwise *Scleroplax* will snatch it away, when the annelid must be content with what re-mains after the crab's appetite is satisfied. . . . . Enmity exists be-tween crab and annelid in which the latter is the under-dog. This

---

* Another pea crab, *Pinnixa franciscana* (§232), occurs rarely, and *P. schmitti,* which is the commonest *Echiurus* commensal, has also been taken here.

feud may account for the close association of *Hesperonoë* with *Urechis.*" A more congenial relationship exists between the crab and the goby, for the goby has actually been observed to carry to the crab a piece of clam meat which was too large for it to swallow or tear apart and stand by to snatch bits as the crab tore the meat apart. Even the crab and the scale worm forget their differences, however, when danger threatens, for at such times both rush to their host and remain in contact with his body wall until the danger is past.

In *Urechis* the sexes are separate.* There must be the usual tremendous mortality among the larvae, but once the animals become established in burrows they are relatively safe except from sting rays. At Newport Bay *Urechis* breeds during the winter and is usually spawned out before the end of the summer, but at Elkhorn Slough specimens are normally ripe throughout the year. The difference is caused by the difference in temperature at the two places—a fact that was interestingly borne out when, during the exceptionally warm summer of 1931, many of the animals at Elkhorn Slough were spawned out before August.

Urechis is known chiefly from Elkhorn Slough, but has been found also in Newport, Morro, San Francisco, and Humboldt bays. A related, smaller form, *Echiurus echiurus alaskensis*, with its pea crab *Pinnixa schmitti*, is exceedingly abundant in southeastern Alaska, occurring embedded in gravelly substratum where there is a clay admixture, as well as in the mud flats proper. The Alaska form lacks the food net of *Urechis*, but the scoop-shovel proboscis achieves results just as effectively, if abundance of individuals is an index of successful food getting.

§307. Two species of echiurid worms, in addition to *Urechis,* occur in Newport Bay, the small green *Listriolabus pelodes* (found also in Tomales Bay), and the larger, also greenish, *Ochetostoma Octomyotum. Ochetostoma* is similar in habit to *Urechis* but has a longer proboscis, and feeds by sweeping detritus from the walls of its burrow onto

* MacGinitie (1935c) has shown recently that in its breeding habits (the sexes are separate and the eggs and sperm are discharged into the water) *Urechis* exhibits a specialization as remarkable as that evidenced by its feeding. The eggs and sperm mature while floating freely in the blood, where very young, immature, and fully ripe sexual products are mixed together indiscriminately. A remarkable set of spiral collecting organs—modified nephridia—pick up only the ripe cells and reject all other contents of the body cavity, and provide an instant means of disposal for sexual products as soon as ripe. After being removed from the body, these collecting organs function outside as autonomous organs. But even in cultures of blood or of sea water, the excised collectors refuse to pick up eggs other than those of *Urechis* (which have a characteristic indentation through which the organs operate), although the foreign eggs are identical in size. The same investigator has determined (1934b) that the eggs can be fertilized artificially while still in the body cavity, and that the resulting development is more rapid than that of controls under simulated normal conditions, quite the opposite of what usually occurs with most sea animals, owing to the self-inhibitory effect exercised by the animal's blood upon the fertilization process.

the mucus-covered surface of this appendage. A concise summary of
the domestic ways of the various echiurids will be found in the Mac-
Ginities' book.

§308. Of the sipunculid worms, at least two noticeable species
occur at the lowest intertidal level in mud flats where there is a considerable admixture of sand, one characteristically, the other occasionally. The striking *Sipunculus nudus* (Pl. XLIII), cosmopolitan
on warm shores, is common at Newport Bay and has been taken in
Mission Bay and at Ensenada. The white skin is shining and iridescent, and shows the muscles in small rectangular patches. Like the
"sweet potato" (*Molpadia,* §264), this form passes great quantities
of the substratum through its intestines for the contained nourishment. More than half the weight of a test *Sipunculus* at Naples
consisted of sand in the intestine. It has often been remarked that
such animals play a large part in turning over and enriching the
shallow bottoms of bays, just as earthworms function in the production of rich vegetable mould on land. *Sipunculus* finds its optimum
conditions, on our coast, in a downward extension of the flats
peopled by the burrowing anemone, *Edwardsiella,* the brachiopod,
Glottidia, and the sea pens.

The occasional sipunculid is a handsome species of *Dendrostoma*
which has been mentioned (§282) as occurring more frequently in
eelgrass.

§309. The true segmented worms have large and obvious representatives in the lugworm and the large tubed *Chaetopterus variopedatus* (Fig. 98), the latter known from Newport Bay, Vancouver, and
widely distributed elsewhere. It is found on the European coast, e.g.,
near Naples. In its U-shaped burrow it constructs a fairly thick and
woody brown tube which may be several feet long, while the curiously
shaped worm itself is from 6 to 15 inches. Many generations of tube-
dwelling have softened the worm's body to the point where it is helpless outside the tube, and it almost invariably registers its protest at
being removed therefrom by breaking in two just behind the head.

The animal secretes a great amount of slime, which covers its
body and lines the tube and seems to have some connection with its
brilliant phosphorescence; for when the worm is touched, some of the
slime will come off on one's fingers and continue to glow there.

§310. The low-tide mud flats in Puget Sound are the favored
environment of the black, rough-skinned lugworm, *Arenicola pusilla,*
which is popular with fishermen for bait. Specimens from other regions may be a foot long, but 6″ is about the average length for this
coast. The animal's presence is indicated by little piles of mud castings, for, like so many other inhabitants of the mud flats, its adjust-

ment to the food-getting problem consists in eating the substratum. It usually lies in a U-shaped burrow of a size that will permit both its greatly swollen head end and its tail end almost to reach the surface. Sometimes, however, the head is buried deep in the substratum. In either case it maintains a current of water through its body by dilating successive segments. This current, which can be made to flow in either direction, serves to aerate the animal and assist its delicate bushy gills in respiration. At low water the current is up, that is, from head to tail; but when the animal is covered, the current is reversed, thus being filtered through the sand in the body—a process which neutralizes any toxic alkalinity caused by the nearness of certain seaweeds.

The whole mud-burrowing situation, as typified by the lugworm, offers an interesting example of adaptation to environment; for by burrowing the animals conceal themselves from enemies, escape wave-action and drying, and place themselves in the midst of their food supply. The habitat requires, however, provision against suffocation, and in the case of the lugworm the protruded gills and the stream of water are the solution.

In the spring great transparent milky masses, containing possibly half a million eggs, can be seen extending up from the burrows below the tide line. Wells (1928) reports a new species of pea crab, *Pinnixa eburna,* from *Arenicola* tubes at Friday Harbor.

Arenicola is the only member of the bay and estuary fauna that can live also in the barren sand of the protected outer beaches, where very few animals seem able to exist. On such beaches the lugworm occurs, as has been previously noted, only where some silt is deposited around rocky outcrops.

§311. We have had biting worms and pinching crabs, stinging jellyfish and stinging sponges; in *Pareurythoë californica* we have a stinging worm. On such mud flats as those in Elkhorn Slough the digger of *Urechis* or nemertean worms will sometimes see a long, pink, flabby-looking worm somewhat resembling *Glycera* but with white and glistening spicules about the "legs." If he picks it up, as he undoubtedly will the first time he sees it, he will regret the action instantly unless his hands are extraordinarily calloused. Once a specimen is preserved it may be handled with impunity, but for some unknown reason the living spicules are capable of penetrating human skin with mildly painful consequences. Dr. Schmitt of the National Museum writes that the large specimens from semitropical coral reefs are even more painful to handle.

The proboscis worm, *Glycera,* is fairly common in mud flats, the relatively gigantic *G. robusta* (similar to the form illustrated in

our Pl. XXXIX) occurring in beds of black mud. Of other worms,
there are the forms mentioned in §293 as occurring higher up, and,
at Newport Bay, a plumed tube worm, *Terebella californica* (in appearance similar to the *Thelepus* of our Pl. VIII). This is interesting
because it very commonly harbors a commensal crab, *Parapinnixa
affinis,* formerly known from a single specimen only. Here is another
example of the fact that, once the ecological station of an animal is
known, it can be taken almost at will.

Neanthes virens occurs where there is an admixture of sand in the
firm mud, building semipermanent tubes just as it does on the Atlantic coast where this cosmopolitan form has been studied extensively.
Copeland and Weimar (1924) have considered the feeding reactions,
in a definitive manner confirming what has been suspected of its predacious habits. These aggressive worms actively search out clam
meat which is hidden experimentally, and are not to be deceived by
similar-appearing substances; there is apparently a delicate sense of
smell involved. The Copeland and Brown (1934) report seems to
prove also that *Nereis* can form conditioned responses ("learn"
through trial, error, and memory). The method was to touch the
head with a glass rod, which provoked a negative response, and then
immediately to present a clam fragment to the worm, which would
normally evoke a positive response. After repeated performances of
this sort, the investigators were able so to condition the worms that
they reversed their previous behavior, exhibiting a positive response
to a normally negative stimulus even in the absence of food. "After
forty trials . . . . the behavior of the worms following tactile stimulation alone could not be distinguished from that of worms which had
been chemically stimulated by clam juice and were searching for
food." The learning curve dropped off slightly after periods of discontinued training.

It appears that in *Neanthes virens* we have a generalized and well-
adjusted animal capable of meeting new situations as they arise, with
no particular fixed pattern which must first be overcome. Yet the
breeding habits are instinctive in a pattern which may date in its in-
ception to the probably great tides of the Cambrian or before. The
lunar rhythm in the breeding habits of polychaet worms, among them
Nereis, is famous (see §151) ; and those of the Atlantic species have
been investigated and plotted (Lillie and Just, 1913).

The giant *N. brandti* (§164) is frequently considered as a subspecies of *virens.* Specimens up to 5½′ long have been taken in the
sandy mud of Elkhorn Slough (MacGinitie, 1935c).

§312. As would be expected from the terrain, nemerteans (ribbon
worms) are abundant both as to species and as to number of indi-

viduals. Some of the larger species have extensible probosces that
can be shot out literally several feet and that are armed with a ven-
omed barb or stylet that serves for capturing prey, but is incapable
of penetrating human skin. The animal's armchair method of hunting is to lie quietly in safety while extending its proboscis in search
of food. Evidently the stylet is lost either regularly each time an
attack is made or by accident at fairly frequent intervals, for in little
pouches within the body the animal carries several spare stylets, much
as a goodly yeoman carried spare arrows in his quiver. These stylets
apparently make nemerteans much more formidable antagonists than
their appearance would lead one to believe. We once put a nemertean
and a mussel worm (*Nereis*) together in a dish of sea water, antici-
pating a speedy slaughter of the nemertean. Instead, the nemertean's
questing proboscis touched the mussel worm amidships and took hold,
evidently inflicting considerable pain. The mussel worm writhed for
several minutes before it succeeded in shaking itself free, and then
showed no disposition to return the attack. Dr. Coe remarks that
some species are known to be able to swallow living *Nereis* larger
than themselves.

The most conspicuous trait of nemertean worms is their habit of
breaking themselves into pieces when persistently disturbed. It has
long been known that in some forms the separate fragments would
grow into complete animals, and Coe has recently demonstrated that a
worm may be cut and the resulting portions recut until eventually
"miniature worms less than one one-hundred-thousandth the volume
of the original are obtained." The limiting factor is that the wound
will not heal nor will regeneration take place unless the fragment is
nearly half as long as the diameter of the body. In other words, a
worm an eighth of an inch in diameter could be cut into one-sixteenth-
inch slices, or a little less, and all the fragments, barring accident,
would become new worms. Decidedly this is an item for the "believe
it or not" addicts. Coe found further that the animals can survive
freezing, and that an adult worm, or a large regenerated fragment,
can live for a year or more without food. The deficiency is compensated for by a continual decrease in the body size—a trait that we
have noticed in captive and improperly fed nudibranchs as well,
although the nudibranchs cannot continue the process for more than
a few weeks. The species Coe used for his experiments was *Lineus
vegetus* (§139).*

* In a later paper Coe (1930) suggests that this extraordinary fragmentation
constitutes the normal method of reproduction during warm weather, since such
fragments (in an Eastern *Lineus*) develop into normal adults, and since fragmentation can be induced experimentally at any season of the year simply by raising the
temperature.

A wide white *Micrura* is very common in this habitat, as is a dirty-pink, band-like *Cerebratulus*. The latter has a firm consistency and may be 12' or more long, but when captured it immediately breaks into many fragments. It is an efficient digger and swims well. An Atlantic *Cerebratulus* takes first prize in rapidity of digestion; Wilson (1900) records that one of the creatures ingested the tentacle of a squid. The squid itself was too large to be swallowed, and the tentacle could not be broken off, so the nemertean was compelled to regurgitate what it had eaten. This it did, but the portion of the tentacle which was spewed out, after only five or six minutes, was almost completely digested! MacGinitie has found our Pacific species associated with large annelid worms which he believes constitute its food supply.

§313. Among the crustacea native to this lowest zone of the mud flats is the long-handed ghost shrimp, *Callianassa gigas,* which differs from the related *C. californiensis* (Pl. XLI) chiefly in being very much larger and in having a longer and more slender large claw. It is usually white or cream-colored, but is sometimes pink. Recorded from Vancouver Island to San Quintín Bay, it probably parallels the range of *californiensis* and reaches into Alaska.

Burrowing in the lowest areas of mud bared by the tide, between southeastern Alaska and San Quintín Bay at least, but with small individuals rather high up in the north, occurs the most striking shrimp in this zone—the blue mud shrimp, *Upogebia pugettensis* (Pl. XLIV), whose actual color is usually a dirty bluish-white. These animals are firmer, larger, and more vigorous than the ghost shrimps found higher up. They are harder to dig out, also, because the ground in which they live is not only continually inundated by the tide but is so honeycombed with burrows that the water pours in almost as fast as the mud can be spaded out. The blue mud shrimp's burrow is permanent and little branched, and has several enlarged places for turning around. It extends downward from the surface for about eighteen inches, horizontally for two to four feet, and then to the surface again. It is inhabited, almost always, by one male and one female, and they are probably moderately long-lived.

In burrowing, MacGinitie observed, the animal carries its load of excavated material in a "mud basket" formed by the first two pairs of legs. Four other pairs function as paddles to keep the water circulating through the burrow, while the mud basket, when it is not being used as such, serves as a strainer to catch the minute food particles in the water. For this latter purpose the mud-basket legs are provided with hairs. The fifth pair of legs terminate in brushes, and are used not only for walking but also for cleaning the body.

Their function is particularly important in an egg-bearing female, who spends a great deal of time in brushing her eggs to keep them clean of diatoms and fungus growths that would otherwise kill the larval shrimps. She also keeps the eggs aerated with her swimmerets. The shrimp's telson, or recurved tail, can be used to block a considerable head of water, or, on occasion, can be flipped powerfully so as to cleanse the burrow by blowing out a swift current of water. Like the related ghost shrimp, this mud shrimp will die if its body is not in contact on all sides with the walls of its burrow or their equivalent.

There are commensals, of course, one of them being distinctive in that it is a small clam, *Pseudopythina rugifera,* which attaches to the underside of the tail of its host. The little crab (*Scleroplax granulata*) that lives with the innkeeper, *Urechis,* and with the ghost shrimp, *Callianassa,* is another. There is also a scale worm similar to the ones that are commensal with the innkeeper and the ghost shrimp, a new species of *Hesperonoë* (§306), and the goby, *Clevelandia ios,* occasionally seeks protection in the burrows.

Both *Callianassa* and *Upogebia* are in ill repute with the oyster men of Puget Sound, for the mud that they dig up smothers many of the young oysters, and their burrows cause drainage from the areas that have been diked in to keep the oysters covered at low water.

(c) Free-swimming in pools.

§314. Several familiar shrimps will be found in pools on the mud flats, and, more conspicuously, such fish as flounders, skates, and rays. The very presence of these fish furnishes interesting sidelights on the food chains of estuary regions, since all were in search of food when the ebbing tide trapped them on the flats. The skates and rays were after clams, which they are reported to root out and eat after crushing the shells with their powerful pavement teeth. The sting ray is to be avoided, and barefoot collectors should be particularly careful about stepping into pools. The wounds they inflict are never serious, but are said to be decidedly painful. Dr. Starks advises soaking the affected part in very hot water, and he adds, no doubt from experience, that the sufferer is perfectly willing to put his foot into water even hotter than he can painlessly tolerate.

Water brought into the laboratory from the Elkhorn Slough mud flats may contain free-swimming specimens of the active little amphipod, *Anisogammarus confervicolus,* associated also with eelgrass, which Dr. Shoemaker reports as one of the most common amphipods of the north Pacific. This was reported by Holmes from Sitka, and MacGinitie finds it abundantly in the *Enteromorpha* beds at Elkhorn

Slough. It is more common in brackish water than in oceanic salinity, especially in the Puget Sound region. Water taken similarly from the mud flats at Mission Bay near San Diego will be teeming at times with a very common opossum shrimp, *Mysidopsis californica,* similar to the form mentioned in §61, but apparently adapted to the stagnant water and fairly high temperatures of this nearly landlocked shallow bay.

Addendum: The Tomales Bay tidal flats

On rocky shores it is not always easy to make out the groupings of animals into communities (with the obvious exception of the mussel beds), for the animals are often jumbled together. A tidal flat on sandy or muddy bottom, however, is a striking contrast—here the animals are so characteristically grouped that it is possible to say, here is an area of worms or phoronids and there, a colony of mud shrimps. These groupings are called communities, and ecologists recognize various degrees of organization in a virtual hierarchy of such natural groupings. Thus, we have such terms as consocies, associes, and association. The arrangement of these groupings is a result of the complicated interplay of the physical factors of the environment: the nature of the substrate, of currents and tidal action, of the influx of fresh water, of salinity and temperature, and of the biological factors imposed by the animals on their environment (such as the binding of the sandy bottom by tube builders and the retention of water in burrows) and upon each other. In such a complex system of interrelationships, a change in any one factor may set in motion a whole train of changes which will be reflected by a perceptible change in the limits of the various communities. Thus, the communities of such an area as that of upper Tomales Bay will change from year to year in details, although the general aspect as well as a characteristic arrangement of zones may remain the same.

Or, to put it another way, the area of a tidal flat is a meeting ground between the sea and the land, a tension zone (as Pitelka and Paulson, 1941, have called it) where we can observe, as nowhere else, the reciprocal actions between organisms and their environment. It might also be pointed out that organisms capable of adjusting themselves to the fluctuating and sometimes drastic changes of such an environment as this have a much better chance for long-range survival than those adapted to a more precise set of conditions. A change in the factors, then, would wipe out the species. Here on the tidal flats, outposts and sometimes entire divisions are wiped out, but the territory is quickly regained when the balance swings back again. An estuarine environment may well be the most stable environment in the long run, and estuarine faunas are the oldest and most conservative.

The arrangement of the communities in Tomales Bay was worked out in 1941, but the map we present here has not been published before. Although the outlines of the communities and of the shore line are different today, the basic pattern can be expected to remain the same, unless the "inexorable march of progress" catches up with Tomales Bay, as it has with such areas as Mission Bay, Newport Bay, Elkhorn Slough, and other parts of this coast which were famous marine environments when this book was first written. Tomales Bay so far has not attracted the schemes of the engineers nor suffered the blight of industrialization. Let us hope that it remains the happy haunts of *Priapulus* and marine biologists, with the ghost of a railroad that lost the race for progress still haunting its western shore.

J. W. H.

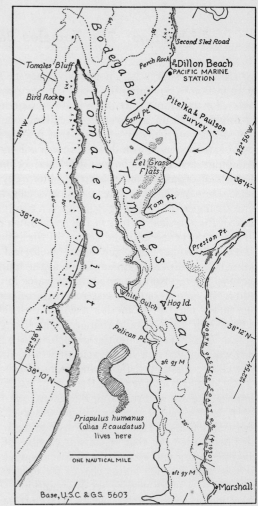

Courtesy of
Frank A. Pitelka

IV. WHARF PILING

Environmental Factors

WHILE work on this division was in progress, it was discovered that piling animals show variations apparently correlated with the degree of exposure to surf. Whether these differences are due actually to the presence or absence of wave shock, as is thought to be the case with rocky-shore animals, or to the different make-up of bay waters and open waters, cannot be stated. It is known that the waters of bays and harbors differ from oceanic waters materially in oxygen content, salinity, degree of acidity-alkalinity, and even temperature. It may be that we must look to these factors for the explanation of the faunal differences, but until more definite information is available the degree of protection from surf will serve as a convenient method of classification.

For obvious reasons no wharves or piers are built in fully exposed positions. Nevertheless, the outer piles of long piers, such as those at Santa Cruz and Santa Barbara, get pretty well pounded during storms, and it is noticeable that the animals most frequent on such piles are barnacles and California mussels, both referable to surf-swept rocky headlands and perfectly able to take care of themselves in rough weather. The piling fauna, therefore, will be considered under the two headings (A) *exposed* (using the term relatively) and (B) *protected*.

Piling offers a conspicuous means of observing depth zonation, although for some reason such zonation is not as obvious and clearcut on the Pacific as it is on the Atlantic. Dr. Allee speaks of the piles at Vineland Haven, Massachusetts, as having four distinct bands, recognizable by their color. Apparently very few West-coast workers have been interested in the ecology of wharf pilings, and much of the data reported below is more or less tentative. It would take several more years of work to establish the dividing line between the fauna of protected and exposed piling—or even to determine if there is such a thing, strictly speaking, or if we must look elsewhere for the explanation of the faunal differences. All that can be said is that the following information seems to be correct for the limited areas we have collected over.

317

A. Exposed Piles

Zones 1 and 2. Spray- and storm-wetted area and high-tide horizon.

§315. Very few *Littorina* are to be found on piling, and the highest animals encountered are very small barnacles, often under ¼″ in diameter. They occur sparsely, and almost flush with the wood. Typical individuals taken from the Monterey wharf and sent to the National Museum were identified as *Balanus balanoides,* a species named by Linnaeus in the eighteenth century and probably known on the coasts of Europe for many hundreds of years. So far as we know, this small circumpolar barnacle has not been recorded previously south of Sitka. It is strange to find it the commonest small barnacle on piling as far south as Monterey.

Intermingled with these barnacles, and a little below them, are a few preliminary and unhappy-looking clusters of California mussels. With the mussels, and a bit below them, some of the smallest examples of the rather prettily colored warty anemones (the aggregated phase of *Cribrina*) are likely to occur. A few of the little rock crabs (*Pachygrapsus*) may be seen walking about here, retreating, when danger threatens, into the larger mussel clusters just below.

Zone 3. Mid-tide horizon.

§316. This zone (and the upper part of the lower) is characterized by lush growths of an almost white hydroid, *Obelia;* by large clusters of big California mussels; and by the great barnacle *Balanus nubilis.* The hydroid *Obelia longissima* (Pl. XLV) and similar smaller species form long trailers or furry growths, usually on barnacle or mussel shells but also on the bare wood where the area is not already occupied—a rare situation. *Obelia longissima* is the commonest hydroid of the piling environment in British Columbia, and is common in Puget Sound also (§332), ranging northward to Alaska and southward to San Pedro. The stalks of *Obelia* branch and rebranch in every plane. Each little "branchlet" is terminated by a cuplike hydrotheca that protects the retracted tentacles. When other larger sacs, the gonangia, are swollen, they should be watched for the birth of minute jellyfish (Fig. 103). The young medusae, usually having twenty-six tentacles, are given off most abundantly during the summer, but reproduction continues throughout the year. The newly born jellyfish swim away with all the assurance in the world, propelling themselves with little jerks. It is a pity that they are so small, for they are delicate, diagrammatic, and beautiful; they can barely be seen with the unaided eye if the containing jar is held against the light. If they were larger and correspondingly better known we should probably eat our outdoor summer luncheons against a background design of *Obelia* medusae on the paper napkins.*

The growth of hydroids is very rapid—so rapid that many of them pass through several generations in a year. In one instance six weeks sufficed for *Obelia* to cover a raft moored at sea, and a single month is sometimes long enough for a newly hatched larva to become a hydroid and release medusae.

Associated with these piling *Obelia* colonies there is almost invariably a minute sea spider, *Halosoma viridintestinale,* not much larger than the zooids on which it probably feeds. There are also minute nudibranchs that look like small editions of *Hermissenda* (Fig. 97), possibly *Galvina olivacea* of §271.

This zone also, like the one still lower, is characterized by a furry brown endoproct, *Barentsia,* with a spongy texture, which often completely covers the piling and grows also over barnacles, leaving them barely room to protrude their feeding legs. Anemones frequently attach to this bryozoan matting instead of to the wood, and when they do so can be easily removed. Another bryozoan, *Alcyonidium mytili,* likewise brown and furry but very close-cropped, very often encrusts the insides of empty barnacle and mussel shells.

§317. *Balanus nubilus* is the largest barnacle on our coast and probably one of the largest in the world. It ranges on this coast from Southern Alaska to San Quintín, Lower California. It is commonly 2½″ to 3″ high, with a basal diameter exceeding the height, and in some places specimens grow on top of each other until they form great clusters. We have such clusters from the Santa Cruz wharf that are more than a foot high. The animal's great size and accretionary habits are not entirely helpful to it, since clusters get so large and heavy that they often carry away the bark or part of the disintegrating wood and sink to the bottom, where it is likely that the barnacles cannot live. The shell of *nubilus* is frequently covered with the bryozoan *Barentsia,*

---

* There is a good description and an original figure in Johnson and Snook (1927), page 61. We have taken this exceedingly abundant form once on rocks (in the enclosed and muddy Crab Bay near Sitka), on Alaska *Zostera,* and hundreds of times on floats and wharf pilings north and south, but particularly in northern quiet waters (§332).

and may provide an attachment base for anemones and tube worms also. The mantle through which the cirri or feeding legs are protruded is gorgeously colored with rich reds and purples. *B. nubilus* is another of the long series of barnacles originally described by Darwin. His description still stands correct—a tribute to the carefulness of the work put on this difficult group by a thoroughly competent mind.

A smaller but even more striking barnacle that is characteristic of boat bottoms and is occasional on wharf piling and even on rocks is *Balanus tintinnabulum* (Fig. 104). The nearly cylindrical shell is a pinkish red with white lines, and the "lips" of the mantle, as with *nubilus,* are vividly colored.

§318. The big-clawed porcelain crab, *Pachycheles rudis* (Fig. 105), ranging from British Columbia to Lower California, seeks crevices, nooks, and interstices, and is often at home in the discarded and *Alcyonidium*-lined shells of barnacles. It is about the same size as the porcelain crab of rocky shores (*Petrolisthes*) but may be distinguished from the latter by the granulations on the upper surface of the big claws. We have found ovigerous specimens in February, March, and July, and probably eggs are borne by at least a few individuals in every month of the year.

§319. Crawling about on these same empty barnacle shells are specimens of *Pycnogonum stearnsi* (Fig. 106), the largest and ungainliest of all local sea spiders. A border design of these grotesque yet picturesque animals might surround the pen-and-ink representation of a nightmare. Most sea spiders spend part of their tender youth in close juxtaposition to a coelenterate—the larvae, in fact, usually feed on the juices of their hydroid or anemone host. This sea spider, white to pale salmon pink in color, is found in a variety of habitats—*Aglaophenia* fronds, *Clavelina* clusters and the like, and around the bases of the large, green *Anthopleura*. It is especially common among the anemones of the caves and crevices of Tomales Bluff, Marin County; sometimes half a dozen occur on a single anemone.

§320. There are a few clusters of goose barnacles on the outer piles, and some large solitary specimens of the great green anemone *Cribrina*. Under the mussel clusters there are many acquaintances from other environments; among them the common scale worm (§49) of many loci, and the ubiquitous pile worm of the bait-gatherer and of the small boy, resembling *Nereis vexillosa* (§163) but smaller than those on more northern outer coasts, rarely more than 2″ to 4″, called *Nereis mediator.*

Zone 4. *Low intertidal.*

§321. The anemone, *Metridium senile* (Pl. XLV), usually white but occurring in several definite color patterns, prefers bare piling. Small specimens, however, may be found on dead shells and even on the shells of living barnacles and the club-shaped tunicate *Styela*. Several times we have taken, from piling, kelp crabs that carried *Metridium* on their backs and claws. The largest specimens occur subtidally, extending clear to the bottom in water twenty or twenty-five feet deep, but small specimens extend definitely into the intertidal, where, at low tide, they hang fully relaxed and pendulous. Expanded, they are delicate and lovely.

Entire clusters of this anemone may be colored a rich brown, and reddish-yellow specimens are not uncommon. The fact that specimens of one color seem to segregate themselves is accounted for by the common method of reproduction via basal fragmentation. This asexual method, actually a form of division, explains the presence of the many little specimens that seem to have been splattered about near larger individuals. *Metridium* reproduces itself sexually, also, unisexual individuals discharging eggs and sperm from the body cavity through the mouth. The chance unions of these products result in free-swimming larvae that carry the fair breed of *Metridium* far and wide—pretty well throughout the world in the Northern Hemisphere. On this coast we know them to extend from Sitka to Santa Barbara on wharf piling. Gigantic exhibition specimens are dredged from deep water; one specimen, from 60 fathoms, filled a ten-gallon crock when expanded. Piling specimens will average around 2″ in diameter, but 6″-specimens have been taken.

Metridium is a fascinating animal to physiologists, who have used it in many experiments. The most recent of these are described by Pantin (1950), who has leveled a movie camera at this seemingly stolid and motionless animal. When speeded up sixty times, his motion pictures reveal that *Metridium* is seldom motionless, and that its movements follow a well-defined pattern. When it is stimulated by a whiff of food, the movement is accelerated and the pattern changed. "We may conclude," writes Dr. Pantin, "that the very slow responses of *Metridium* involve a complex neuro-muscular pattern of inherent activity involving reciprocal inhibition and the successive activities of two antagonistic muscular systems. The system is normally active in varying degrees in different animals. . . . . The whole pattern is already there in the normal animal, though usually only released by the presence of food." So much for *Metridium*'s "instinctive" reaction to the promise of a square meal!

§322. Where it occurs at all, the stalked simple tunicate *Styela montereyensis* (Fig. 107) may be present in such numbers as to be a feature of the tidal "pile-scape." Although it was described originally from rocky-shore specimens a couple of inches long, the most luxuriant growths are found on such piers as those at Santa Cruz and Santa Barbara, where the water is fairly uncontaminated. Here occasional specimens may be more than a foot in length, and some are gorgeously festooned with growths of the ostrich-plume hydroid, with other tunicates, and even with anemones. They are dark red in color, except on the lower part of the body, which is lighter. The siphons are distinct, and the range is from British Columbia to San Diego.

Slabs of *Amaroucium* (§99), the "sea pork" of seashore children, occur in varying sizes and shapes, and their reds, yellows, or browns add touches of color to the piling assemblages. Locally there may be numbers of a simple tunicate, probably *Corella,* related to the *Molgula* so common on East-coast piling. The single animals are almost circular but are usually so crowded together as to form polymorphic clusters, and the test, where not covered by sand or bits of seaweed, is water-clear.

All these tunicates are the degenerate adults of free-swimming, tadpole-like larvae that indicate the group's relationship with the vertebrates. The free-swimming stage is very brief, and those tadpoles that do not find a suitable attachment surface quickly must perish. It has been determined for Atlantic *Amaroucium* larvae that at first they swim toward the light and away from the pull of gravity; later they swim away from the light and toward gravitational influence. Just how this affects their ultimate position in the low intertidal of piling is uncertain. Those that attach in the high-tide area must die of exposure, and those that drift down to the bottom of the piles, where conditions would seem to be satisfactory, die for some other reason, adults rarely or never being found there. Apparently, then, only those that happen, in the course of their vertical migrations, to touch a suitable spot on the right level have any chance of survival.

Adult tunicates feed on microscopic particles in the water, keeping currents of water circulating through the body by the waving action of great numbers of cilia. The food particles become entangled in mucus and are then transferred by other cilia to the digestive part of the gut.

§323. The kelp that grows on piling in this zone has the usual concomitants of life in a crowded environment. Most of it is plastered and encrusted with unbidden guests: *Aglaophenia, Obelia,* and sertularians among the hydroids; the omnipresent *Membranipora* and tiny colonies of the tubed *Tubulipora* among bryozoa. Even the single-celled *Ephelota gigantea*, a stalked suctorian protozoa a fraction of an inch tall, furs the blades of kelp with minute vases of white protoplasm, finding these swaying plants an ideal attachment site. These protozoa are related to the animals we find occurring in the respiratory trees of the cucumber *Stichopus*, more distantly to the barely visible infusoria that haunt stagnant swamps and hay infusions, and still more distantly to the host of protozoa that are infamous as agents of malaria, tropical dysentery, sleeping sickness, etc.

§324. The infrequent bare spots on piling are furred and plumed with the usual hydroids—the same that occur on kelp and the hard tests of tunicates. *Bugula neritina* (Pl. XLV), a red or yellow-purple bryozoan in sparse palmate clusters, seems to be characteristic of bare spots on piling or on boat bottoms. We have often found it on submerged wood, never on rock. Another bryozoa, the encrusting *Cryptosula pallasiana*, seems also to be specific to wood. It occurs in thin white watery sheets, sometimes slightly separated from the support, and will be recognized as a near relative of the bryozoan (such as *Eurystomella bilabiata*, Pl. XXIII) that encrusts the under side of rocks. There are a good many others, some characteristic of piling on this coast but many cosmopolitan forms known on pilings literally around the world. In this case universal distribution is easily explained by the fact that ships always, unless they are fresh from dry-dock, carry growths of attached animals on their hulls. Deep-water vessels take care of the intercontinental aspects, and smaller coastwise vessels carry on the distribution, for there is always a likelihood that some of the attached animals will be discharging sexual products or larvae while the vessel lies at the wharf.

§325. The starfish found on piling all attain their maximum abundance elsewhere. Considerable numbers of the common starfish (*Pisaster ochraceus*) are attracted by the easy picking in the way of mussels, and in the lower levels a few of the quiet-water *Pisaster brevispinus* will be found. The brilliantly colored sea bat *Patiria* occurs also, and the little six-rayed *Leptasterias* may be abundant.

Another echinoderm occurs, the white cucumber *Eupentacta quinquesemita* (§235), but as an almost exclusively subtidal form.

Also chiefly subtidal is the rock oyster *Pododesmus* (§217), which belies its popular name by preferring piling to rocks in the regions south of Puget Sound.

§326. The chunky little shrimp *Betaeus harfordi*, some ¾″ long, may often be found on piling. Like its relative of the southern tide pools (Fig. 18), this form has a carapace that extends over its eyes. No doubt this device affords protection to the eyes, but it must also be a considerable handicap in greatly limiting the animal's field of vision. *B. harfordi* has been reported from Point Arena to Laguna Beach.

§327. The kelp crab, *Pugettia producta* (§107), is quite as characteristic of piling as it is of rocky tide pools. At low tide it will usually be found at least a few inches below the surface, and even when the tide rises it seems to prefer this low zone. This fairly large member of the spider crab group is also one of the most active, but it is the most likely, of all the crabs on this coast, to be infected with the strange parasite *Heterosaccus californicus*. This creature is a crustacean, actually a degenerate barnacle which, in its free-swimming larval stages, looks very much like any other crustacean nauplius. It is incapable of developing independently, however, and must find a crab host in order to complete its life cycle. It attaches itself to a hair on the crab's body or legs, penetrates the base of the hair with its feelers, and then enters the crab by the nightmarish method of slipping through its own hollow feelers. This is possible only because the degenerative process is already well advanced, the legs, the bivalve shell, and some of the inner organs having been shed and the body consequently reduced to a fraction of its larval size. Once inside, the sacculinid migrates through the blood stream to the gut, attaches itself near the crab's stomach, and begins to grow. Its ramifications are considerable, both morphologically and physiologically. Avoiding the vital organs, the roots of its tumor-like sac extend throughout the crab's body, even into the claws; and the crab, its energies drained to feed the intruder, becomes sluggish. The crab moults just once after the parasite has gained entrance, and during that moult the parasite pushes out through the temporarily soft shell and assumes its final shape and position as a brownish mass under the crab's abdomen. Thereafter the host is unable to moult until the parasite has completed its life cycle and died—a matter of some three or four years. Usually the crab is unable to survive; but if it does, it becomes normal again after the parasite disappears.

Sacculinids attack both males and females, and one of the strangest effects is to modify the sex of the afflicted crab. Both sexes are rendered sterile, but the only other effect on the female is to speed up her assumption of adult sex characters. The male, however, develops various female characteristics, such as a broad curved abdomen and smaller claws; and if he survives the life cycle of the parasite he may then produce eggs as well as sperm, having become a male hermaphrodite. If he has been only slightly feminized by the parasite, he may regenerate normal male generative organs. The mechanism of this transformation is still incompletely understood. Reinhard, in his most recent paper (1950, *Biol. Bull.* **98**) suggests that the normal male crab is the result of a balance between the male and female substances, and that the sacculinid upsets this balance. The effect of this is the removal of the inhibition of "femaleness" in the male and the stimulation of "femaleness" in the female, resulting in hyperfeminization of the female.

On the California coast usually less than 10 per-cent but more than one per-cent of the kelp crabs are found to be infected. Infestation becomes more abundant with the increase in latitude on this coast. On the Atlantic coast sacculinids are rare except on the Gulf coast, where infestation is common on mud crabs in Louisiana and on the blue crab in Texas waters.

§328. To many well-informed persons the biological connotations of wharf piling all center around the word "teredo." These wood-borers have been the bane of shipping for at least two thousand years, for they were known, unfavorably, by the ancient Greeks and Romans. It seems quite possible that the early Mediterranean custom of hauling boats ashore when they were not in use was motivated, in part at least, by an understanding of the fact that frequent drying would protect them from attack by the shipworms. The species of *Teredo* and their near relatives are still, after many years of scientific research as to preventives, the cause of tremendous destruction to marine timbers—destruction that often runs into millions of dollars a year in a single seaport.

The term "shipworm," which is popularly applied to the whole group, is a misnomer, for the animal is actually a clam, although its small calcareous shell—its boring tool—covers only the "head" end of its long, worm-like body. They are highly efficient wood-workers, but countless generations of protected life in timber has made them helpless outside of that element, and once removed from their burrows they cannot begin a new one. In these days of steel hulls they have had to confine their activities to wharf piling and other marine timbers, but that has affected neither their aggressiveness nor their numbers.

In open water the true *Teredo* rarely occurs, but the one shipworm that is native to this coast, the giant *Bankia setacea* (Pl. XLVI), known as the Northwest shipworm, operates in relatively exposed piles from at least as far north as Kodiak Island to as far south as San Diego, although below Monterey Bay it does little damage. In San Francisco Bay proper it has been known since the earliest days of shipping, but since it is less resistant to lowered salinity than other shipworms it does not extend its activities into the brackish waters of the adjoining San Pablo and Suisun bays, or into similar enclosed bays in other regions. Neither has it ever been as destructive, according to a report by the San Francisco Bay Piling Committee, as the true *Teredo* that suddenly appeared there about 1910–1913.

The work of the shipworm is begun by a larva, which drills a hole that is barely visible to the naked eye. For the next few months the animal grows rapidly, enlarging the burrow as it grows but leaving the entrance very small. A few inches inside the wood the burrow turns, usually downward, so as to follow to some extent the grain of the wood. The animal turns aside, however, to avoid obstructions such as nails, bolts, and knots, and to avoid penetrating the burrows of neighbors. Thus the actual course of the burrows is nearly always sinuous. *Bankia* concentrates its attack at the mud line, digging out burrows that are sometimes three feet long and almost an inch in diameter. The shipworm's method of boring is very similar to that employed by the rock-boring clams; see §337 for an account of *Teredo navalis*. A heavy attack will reduce a new untreated pile to the collapsing point in six months, and survival for more than a year is unlikely. The life of a pile may be prolonged to three or four years by chemical treatment, such as creosoting, but nothing keeps the animals out for long. Copper sheathing, which did good service in protecting ships for so many years, is impractical on piles because of its expense, the likelihood of its being stolen, and the ease with which it is damaged by contact with boats and driftwood. Also the sheathing cannot extend below the vulnerable mud line, and the mud line is likely to be lowered by eroding currents. Numerous other jacketings have been tried, but not even concrete jackets are entirely satisfactory, for when the wood borers are thus thwarted the concrete borers (§242) come to their assistance. Steel and iron piling has numerous disadvantages, aside from its great expense, so the battle between man and the shipworm goes on, with the shipworm still getting somewhat the best of it (Pl. XLVI).

Bankia setacea likes low-water temperatures, and extrudes its eggs, in San Francisco Bay at least, at that time of the year when the water temperature is lowest—from February or March to June. In southeastern Alaska it breeds about a month earlier, as indicated by the attack on a test block at Petersburg. Fertilization is external to the burrow and a matter of chance. It has been suggested by Hill and Kofoid, the editors-in-chief of the *Report of the San Francisco Bay Marine Piling Committee,* that this inefficient reproductive method may account for the inferiority as a pest of *Bankia* to *Teredo.* Further considerations relating to the similar *Teredo* will be found in §§337, 338.

§329. Dampier, the English buccaneer, who was something of a naturalist also, is said to have written that his wormy ship was being attacked also by small white animals resembling sheep lice. Undoubtedly he was referring to a wood-boring isopod, the gribble, of which there are three species on this coast: *Limnoria lignorum, L. quadripunctata,* and *L. tripunctata*. Shipworms perform their work on the inside of wood; *Limnoria* works, with almost equal efficiency, from the outside, attacking piles at all levels from the middle intertidal down to depths of forty feet or more (Pl. XLVI).

These animals are so tiny—scarcely an eighth of an inch long —that hundreds of them may occur in a square inch of heavily infested wood. Their legs are adapted to holding to wood in the face of severe currents. The digging operation is performed with the mouth parts, and the wood is eaten as fast as it is gouged out, passing so rapidly through the intestine that a given particle remains in the digestive tract only an estimated eighty minutes. This speed of passage is what would be expected in an animal that derives all its nourishment from wood, as *Limnoria* apparently does, for the food content is very low. There is no mechanism for filtering the contained plankton out of the water, and nothing but wood has ever been found in the digestive tract. This is a unique situation, for cellulose is highly indigestible and remains unchanged by animal digestive juices unless, as in the case of the termites, there are intestinal protozoa to aid in the conversion. In one experiment, however, specimens of *Limnoria* ingested pure cellulose in the form of filter paper and lived nearly twice as long as controls that were unfed.

When digging, the animals jerk their heads backward and forward, turning them slowly at the same time. They can completely bury themselves in from four to six days, starting their burrows at a rather flat angle. Presumably because of the difficulty of obtaining oxygen, they seldom go more than half an inch below the surface. Probably breathing in a solitary burrow would be difficult even at that depth, but the burrows of different individuals are usually connected by small openings that permit freer circulation of water than could be obtained in an isolated burrow. There can be little doubt about the function of these openings, for they are not large enough to permit the passage of the animals themselves.

The females of *Limnoria* carry, on the average, only nine or ten eggs, but breeding is continuous throughout the year. The newly hatched animal, unlike the larvae of shipworms, does not swim at all, but gradually acquires some swimming ability as it grows. Experiments recorded in the *San Francisco Bay Marine Piling Report* show that at no stage of its life is the animal positively attracted to wood. Presumably they do not fasten on wood unless they accidentally touch it, but as they are never very good swimmers those that fail to make such contact probably die. At any stage, however, again unlike the shipworms, they may be transferred to new locations without harm. Thus driftwood floating among piling is assumed to be an important factor in their distribution, the work being begun by adult animals instead of by free-swimming larvae. The taking in and discharging of ballast water by ships may aid them in spreading from port to port.

Limnoria lignorum is primarily a cold-water animal, occurring on the Scandinavian coast, within the Arctic Circle, and on this coast from Kodiak Island to as far south as Point Arena. *L. quadripunctata* occurs on this coast from Tomales Bay to San Diego, and *L. tripunctata* from San Francisco to Lower California. The various species are responsible for damage to piling in most of the great harbors of the world, and the warmer water species, *L. tripunctata*, is undeterred by the creosote with which most piling is treated to protect it from such depredations.

§330. Whoever frequents wharves, piers, and floats, especially at not-quite-respectable hours, will be certain to see some of the more obvious free-swimming invertebrate animals that haunt the harbors. While such pelagic animals are not within the scope of this work, it would be a pity not to mention the bell-shaped jellyfish *Polyorchis* (Fig. 108), because its transparent white against the dark of under-wharf waters makes it very conspicuous. It swims beautifully and rather well by kicking the manubrium—a knee-like veil within the bell. The average diameter is an inch or more. The gonads and some other internal organs are variably colored from yellow-brown to purple.

In quiet bays in Puget Sound and British Columbia the jellyfish, *Aurelia* (Fig. 109), nearly colorless, except for its four horseshoe-shaped brown gonads, sometimes occurs in such immense numbers that it is impossible to dip an oar without striking several of the beautiful pulsating animals. A boat seems to glide through a sea of jellyfish rather than through water. Such tremendous aggregations are but a brief phenomenon, usually lasting during one flood tide only. A few hours later it may be difficult to find a dozen specimens. Similar swarms occur in Tomales Bay during the summer months.

The ubiquitous *Nereis vexillosa* (§163) occurs in this environment also whenever clusters of mussels extend so far down, but a smaller worm, probably *Platynereis agassazi*, seems to be both abundant and characteristic, especially in its free-swimming or heteronereis stage. We discovered the interesting periodicity of this form quite by accident, in connection with a proclivity for roaming about at odd hours, no doubt very annoying to conventional night-watchmen. Swarming takes place in Monterey harbor during the spring and summer months when, on moonless nights, the extreme high tides occur about midnight. At first only one or two of the vividly white and wriggly worms will be in sight; by the end of half an hour there may be two or three score, apparently concentrated into the area of observation by the rays of the flashlight. The male comes first—a tiny animal a half inch long or less—followed by the female, sometimes more than an inch long and having red after-segments. When the two sexes are together, the heteronereis go completely crazy, swimming about in circles at furious speed, and shedding eggs and sperm the while. Only one who has tried to capture them with a dip net knows how rapidly and evasively they swim. Specimens brought into the laboratory have continued this activity all night, although in their natural environment the swarming seems to last only a few hours at the height of the tide. In the morning, captive specimens look withered and worn out, no doubt an accurate reflection of their condition. In this connection, see also §163.

Finally there will be dozens, possibly hundreds, of smaller, free-swimming organisms of various types — micro-crustacea, minute jellyfish, larval stages of worms and mollusks and echinoderms—all outside the province of this book. It might be mentioned that one of the usually high-seas euphausiids, *Thysanoëssa gregaria,* or perhaps *Th. longipes,* distantly related to the opossum shrimps (§61), has been taken abundantly in Monterey harbor, within a stone's throw of the shore.

B. Protected Piles

As previously stated, we can draw only a vague line between relatively exposed and fully protected piling. Between the obvious extremes there is probably great overlapping, and we have to remind the reader that this classification is offered tentatively. Further work may justify it as a working hypothesis or may show that other factors than exposure are the primary ones.

Depth zonation is apparent here as on more exposed piling, but the distinctive animals are so few in number that they will be treated without formal zonal classification.

§331. We were surprised to learn, from the identification of specimens sent to the National Museum, that the common small barnacles of protected piling in two test spots, Berkeley and Newport Bay, are the omnipresent *Balanus glandula* (§4). For some reason the small barnacles of this coast have been almost entirely overlooked by collectors, so that until someone works them over carefully it is impossible to make any general remarks that further investigation may not refute.

§332. The California mussels of the more exposed piling are replaced in these quiet waters by the smaller and cosmopolitan bay mussels, *Mytilus edulis* (§197). In favorable environments they often form great bunches that double the diameter of the piles on which they grow, and they may be found in probably every suitable port between the Bering Sea and northern Mexico. They attain their maximum development in the middle zone, so they are very obvious, even at half tide.

This small mussel worm, *Nereis mediator* (§163), will be found here no less frequently than in open-shore mussel clusters, only the mussels are different. The quiet-water shield limpet, *A. cassis olympica* (§195), occurs on these pilings just as on rocks and gravel, minute specimens occupying the highest populated zone along with the small barnacles.

Interspersed among such clusters are several bay and harbor hydroids. The cosmopolitan *Obelia commissuralis* was reported by Torrey (1902) from San Francisco Bay, where it was adapted to the estuary conditions of dirty water and lowered salinity. Clusters of *Obelia* may still be found in these situations about the ferry wharves in Oakland, in water so filthy that all animal life would seem to be precluded, and *commissuralis* is presumed to be the species involved. There is an excellent illustration of a living Atlantic-coast colony in Nutting (1915, Pl. 21).

A pycnogonid (sea spider) occurs in hydroid clusters of this sort: *Achelia nudiuscula.* In a personal communication, J. W. Hedgpeth says of it: "abundant on *Obelia* on pilings and junk along the east shore of San Francisco Bay—in very filthy water." It is known only from this, the type locality. There is a good illustration in Hall (1913).

In cleaner stretches of quiet water, particularly up north, the tenuous *O. longissima* (§316) is known to be the predominant shore hydroid, avoiding pollution and direct sunlight, but tolerating some fresh water, with *Clytia* comprising up to 90 per cent of the littoral hydroid population of this region. (The rest is made up mostly of *Gonothyraea,* and of the smaller and more hidden *O. dichotoma,* §271.) On continually submerged floats, the situation seems to be that the very common and bristling *Clytia edwardsi* (illustrated in Nutting, 1915, Pl. 4) occurs in the face of considerable sunlight, but that the lush clusters of *O. longissima* are either underneath the float or on portions protected from direct sunlight by some of the superstructure. In late July 1935, the *Clytia* in southeastern Hood Canal were producing round, four-tentacled medusae. Of *O. longissima,* Fraser (1914, p. 153) says: "the commonest shallow water campanularian in the region. It grows throughout the year on the station float, Departure Bay, and medusae are freed at many times during the year."

On floats in the Puget Sound region (as at Port Madison, releasing medusae in July 1932), and on bell buoys, boat bottoms, etc., along the open coast at Monterey, the small and sparkling *Obelia dubia* (Pl. XLV) occurs, so similar to *dichotoma* (§271) that some authorities consider them identical. We have never knowingly taken this on fixed piling, where the latter frequently occurs. It seems to be intolerant equally to stagnation, lowered salinity, pollution, and tidal exposure—a "touchy" form, difficult to preserve expanded unless narcotized within a few minutes after capture. This is the form which we have been calling *O. gracilis* in Monterey Bay, according to determinations by Dr. Fraser, who says (1914, p. 151): the juveniles are sometimes impossible to distinguish from juvenile *longissima.*

Four of the five commonest hydroids so found release free-swimming medusae, thus increasing many times the opportunities for wide distribution of the race. Each hydroid colony produces thousands of minute active jellyfish which can be carried far from the parent hydroid by currents before reaching sexual maturity. The union of the jellyfish's eggs and sperm results in planulae, free-swimming larvae which can drift still farther before they attach again as hydroids.

Gonothyraea clarki (illustrated in Nutting, 1915, Pl. 17) resembles *Obelia,* but differs in that it develops medusae which are perfectly functional but which for some strange reason are never released. Four or five of these little captives pop out of each vaselike gonangium and pulsate ineffectually at the end of their stalks, releasing germ cells and eggs which are united by chance currents. In British Columbia and Puget Sound, *Gonothyraea* is plentiful in spring and early summer, growing on rocks as well as on floats and piling, but dies out later and is not to be found. It extends as far south as San Francisco.

§333. In the extreme low-tide zone enormous bushy clusters of the naked hydroid, *Tubularia crocea* (Pl. XLVI), will be found banding the piles or floating landings with delicate pinks or reds. Its nearest relative is the small solitary *T. marina* of rocky shores, but this clustered form, which may extend six inches out from the piles, is far more spectacular. It is the "heads" that provide the color; the supporting stems looking like small flexible straws. The heads, or hydranths, autotomize readily, and seem to break off as a regular thing if the water gets warm or the conditions are otherwise unfavorable, after which, if conditions improve, the stem regenerates a new head within a few days. The sexual medusae are never liberated. We have found *T. crocea* in Newport Bay, Elkhorn Slough, and San Francisco Bay, and it is known from many regions to the northward and from both sides of the Atlantic.

Hilton found the *Tubularia* clusters at Balboa heavily populated with a small sea spider, *Anoplodactylus erectus* (which we have found rarely on compound tunicates at Pacific Grove). He worked out the life history. The eggs, which are produced in the summer, develop into larvae that pierce the body wall of *Tubularia* and enter the digestive tract, there to live parasitically until further grown.

Flatter, tangled clusters of another naked hydroid are often interspersed with *Tubularia,* but the two will be differentiated easily. The tiny bulbous heads of *Syncoryne mirabilis* (Fig. 110) bear clubbed tentacles, and bud off their free-swimming medusae from the lower part of the heads. Agassiz found this form in San Francisco Bay in 1865. There is at least a distinct possibility that it is a relic of the days of wooden ships, for the same species occurs on the East coast, and it seems unlikely that its natural distribution would account for its occurrence on this coast also. If it was so imported it probably became established at several different places, since it now ranges the entire coast as far south as Chile.

IV. WHARF PILING

§§ 315–338, Figures 103–112, Plates XLV–XLVI

View of Point Conception, where northern and southern faunas
overlap. U.S. Navy Photo.

334

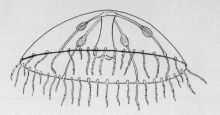

Fig. 103
A jellyfish from the hydroid, *Obelia;*
greatly enlarged (§ 316).

Fig. 104
The red and white
barnacle of wharf pil-
ings, *Balanus tintinna-*
bulum (§ 317).

¾

PLATE XLV (Opposite page)

WHARF-PILING INHABITANTS

1. Magnified portion of the hydroid, *Obelia dubia* (§ 332).
2. The hydroid, *Obelia longissima* (§ 316).
3. A white specimen of the anemone, *Metridium senile*; top view, showing mouth (§ 321). Photo by Woody Williams.
4. The bryozoan, *Bugula neritina* (§ 324).

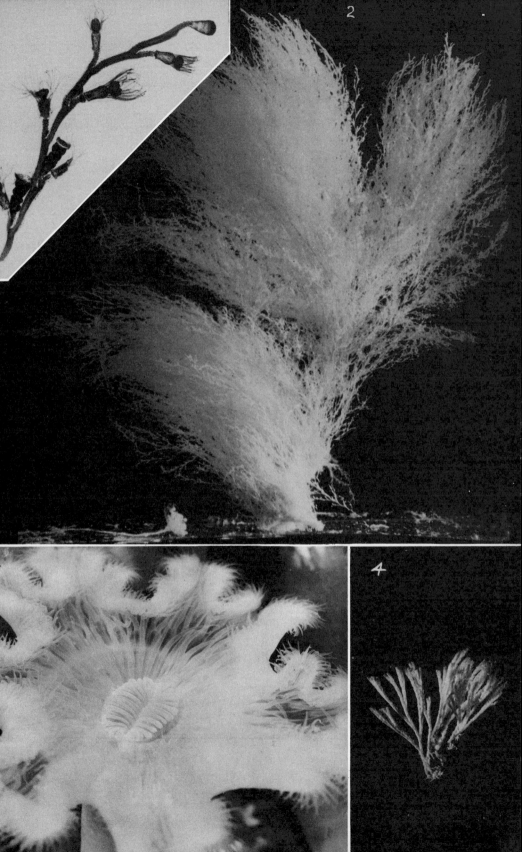

336

Fig. 105
The big-clawed porcelain crab, *Pachycheles rudis;* natural size (§ 318).

Fig. 106
A sea spider, *Pycnogonum stearnsi;* enlarged about two and a half times (§ 319).

Fig. 107
A stalked tunicate of wharf pilings, *Styela montereyensis;* natural size (§ 322).

PLATE XLVI

WHARF-PILING BORERS AND THEIR WORK

(1, 2, 4, and 5, from C. L. Hill and C. A. Kofoid, *Marine Borers and Their Relation to Marine Construction on the Pacific Coast*)

1. *Bankia setacea,* entire animals.
2. *Teredo diegensis:* (1) Posterior ends, showing pallets and siphons; (2) Pallets with corneous tips removed; (3) Normal pallets; (4) Entire animals, showing enlarged brood sac, with enclosed larvae.
3. A cluster of the naked hydroid, *Tubularia crocea* (§ 333). Photo by Woody Williams.
4. *Limnoria quadripunctata,* photographed alive in position.
5. Dolphin pile from Richmond Municipal Pier, driven December, 1917, broken out July, 1920: (1) Showing large tubes of *Bankia* and smaller ones of *Teredo navalis* and erosion by *Limnoria* at breaking level; *Sphaeroma* also present; breaking zone exposed at low tide; (2) Section of same pile, one foot above break.

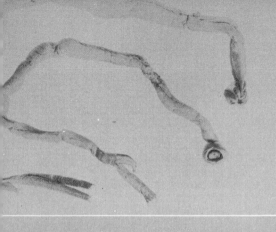

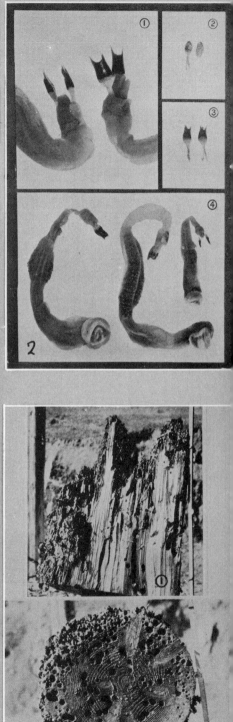

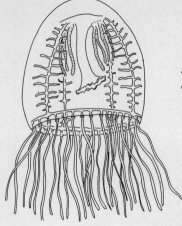

Fig. 108
The jellyfish, *Polyorchis*;
one-half natural size (§ 330).

Fig. 109
The jellyfish, *Aurelia*; about
one-tenth natural size
(§ 330).

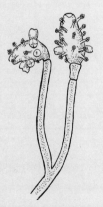

Fig. 110
A naked hydroid, *Syncoryne
mirabilis*, greatly enlarged
(§ 333).

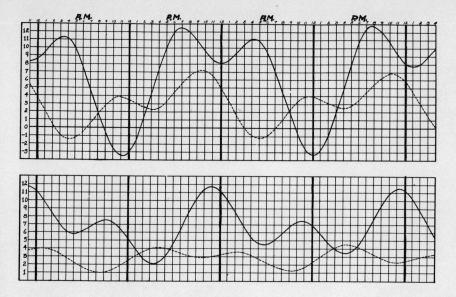

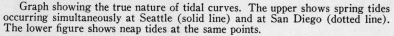

Fig. 111

Graph showing the true nature of tidal curves. The upper shows spring tides occurring simultaneously at Seattle (solid line) and at San Diego (dotted line). The lower figure shows neap tides at the same points.

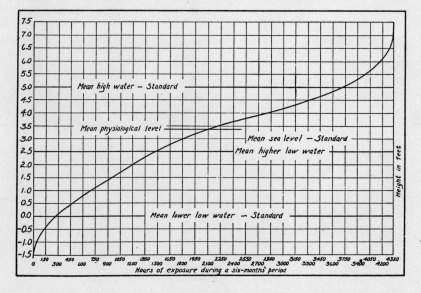

Fig. 112

Exposure curve for the six-months period, January 1 to June 30, 1931, comprising an analysis of a tidal curve drawn from hourly heights as recorded by the Coast and Geodetic Survey tide machine at Crissy Wharf in San Francisco Bay.

Bed of *Crassostrea virginica* in Tomales Bay. Note the stake fence to keep out sting rays and

§334. Crawling about on the piling throughout the intertidal zone, but keeping fairly well under water whatever the height of the tide, any of several crabs may be seen. Practically all of the rocky-shore forms have been reported, and two spider crabs seem to be characteristic. In Monterey Bay and southward to Panama a thoroughly attenuated, gangly form, *Pyromaia tuberculata* (formerly *Inachoides tuberculatus*), a half inch or less in carapace width, is fairly common. Sponges and seaweeds mask this sluggish little crab so that it will seldom be noticed until what appears to be a bit of the fixed piling growth moves slowly away from the observer.

Oregonia gracilis is very similar, but twice the size of the *Pyromaia*. It may be seen occasionally on wharf piling in Puget Sound and in eelgrass beds, whence it ranges northward to Bering Sea and southward, but in deeper water, to Monterey. The masking habit of this group of crabs is discussed in §131.

Several cucumbers occur, in the Puget Sound area especially. Huge *Stichopus californicus* (§77) crawl about on the pilings frequently enough to be considered characteristic here, but keep pretty well below the low-tide line.

§335. On these fully protected piles we find a good many of the animals already mentioned as occurring on more exposed piling: The omnipresent starfish *Pisaster,* both the common (§157) and the *brevispinus* (§209) forms, and the usually white anemone, *Metridium* (§321). There are the usual tunicates, although the large-stalked *Styela* (§322) seems never to occur in harbors. The elongate simple tunicate *Ciona intestinalis* reaches a length of from 4 to 5 inches. Its translucent green siphons are long and glassy, the basal portion being often covered with debris. It is well distributed throughout the Northern Hemisphere but requires pure water. Some of the small rock-loving tunicates, notably the red *Cnemidocarpa* (§216), are found on Puget Sound piling, and the gelatinous clusters of the compound *Botrylloides diegensis,* in reds, yellows, and purples, are features of the piling in San Diego Bay.

Referring to another tunicate, *Pyura haustor johnsoni,* which is almost identical in appearance with the Puget Sound *P. haustor* (§216, Pl. XXXII), Ritter remarks: "A striking thing about this species is its great abundance in San Diego Bay, and the large size reached there by individuals, as compared with what one finds on the open shores. Its favorite habitat appears to be the piles of wharves where, at times, it makes almost a solid coating. Although it must be counted as a native of the whole littoral zone, we have found only occasional specimens at outside points."

§336. Boring forms are as common here, and as destructive as

on less-sheltered piling. The boring isopods, *Limnoria* (§329), operate quite indiscriminately in these quiet waters, assisting the shipworms to make life miserable for harbor engineers. Another isopod
of ill fame is the larger *Sphaeroma pentodon* (up to nearly ⅜"
long), which cannot, however, compete with *Limnoria* in destruc-
tiveness. Wood is for it apparently only a secondary habitat, for
the animal (which resembles *Cirolana*, Fig. 14) is found in great
numbers in clay and friable rock. It seems rarely to attack piling
until the wood has been riddled by shipworms, hence is not of much
economic importance. It bores for protection only, making oval
openings up to nearly one-half inch in diameter, that give the pile
a pitted appearance. Boring is accomplished with the mouth parts,
as with *Limnoria,* but the loosened material (at least in the case of
an observed specimen boring in chalk) is passed backward by the
feet and washed out by the swimmerets. The fact that very little
wood is found in the intestines of wood-boring specimens indicates
that wood particles are handled in the same manner. Algae and
other growths constitute the food supply.

Eggs are carried under the abdomen of the female for a time,
and young have been found with the adults in the spring, summer,
and fall in San Francisco Bay, probably breeding all the year.

§337. Twenty years ago the European shipworm, *Teredo navalis,*
was altogether unknown on this coast. Just when or how it gained
a foothold is not known, but in 1914 it was discovered that piling at
Mare Island, in the northern part of San Francisco Bay, had been
extensively damaged. The attack was repeated in 1917, and within
three years the damage reached unprecedented and catastrophic
proportions. Ferry slips collapsed, and warehouses and loaded
freight cars were pitched into the Bay. All piling was attacked and
most of it destroyed. Since then *Teredo navalis* has spread to all
parts of the Bay. The animals can stand much lower salinity than
other shipworms, which accounts for their devastating attacks in
the northern parts of the Bay where piling was largely untreated
because it had been supposed that the influx of fresh water from the
Sacramento and San Joaquin rivers afforded immunity from borers.
The fresh water does kill them off during seasons of heavy rain-
fall, but when conditions improve they come back in force.

These animals are usually hoist by their own petard within six
months, for their honeycombing of timber is so complete that by the
end of that time it begins to disintegrate, the resulting exposure
causing their deaths. They can reach a length of more than 4" in
four months, however, and one fourteen-months-old specimen was
nearly a foot long. The rate of boring is more rapid in compara-

tively young animals; a three-months-old specimen bores about three-fourths of an inch a day. Thus the animals can ruin a pile during their short lives, making ample provision in the meantime for another generation to take care of the next set of piles.

Unlike *Bankia,* this *Teredo* breeds during late summer and early fall, the last lot of larvae being attached by December. The sexes are separate, but the same individual is first male, then finally female.* Eggs are retained in the gill cavity until fertilized by spermatozoa contained in the incoming water. They are then stored in a brood pouch that forms in the gills until they are ready to be discharged through the parent's siphons as free-swimming bivalves known as "veliger" larvae. Apparently the breeding period is continuous for some weeks, for the brood pouch contains larvae in various stages of development, while at the same time the ovaries are enlarged with unfertilized eggs. Since the ovaries may contain an estimated million or more eggs at one time, the tremendously rapid spread of the animals is easy to understand.†

In the first century, A.D., Pliny the Elder conjectured that teredos bored by means of their shells. His theory went unchallenged until 1733, when the Dutch naturalist, Sellius, announced that, since the shells appeared to be inadequate for the work, the boring must be accomplished by the foot. Recent investigations have vindicated Pliny. Dr. R. C. Miller, working for the San Francisco Bay Marine Piling Committee, succeeded in cutting into a burrow and covering the opening with a piece of glass. Through this window observers watched *Teredo navalis* at work. The animal rasps the wood with its shell by rocking on its foot as do the rock-boring pholids, repeating the motion rhythmically eight to twelve times per minute. Also like the pholids, it rotates, so that a perfectly cylindrical burrow is cut. Inter-

---

* Coe (1933) discovered at Woods Hole that, although the primary gonad is bisexual, *T. navalis* is "essentially protandric, nearly all females passing through a functional male phase before reaching the definitive phase of sexuality." This means that when the current year's brood is young, early in the season, there is a preponderance of males, any specimens left over from the previous season, however, being females. Later, as this brood ages, practically all the individuals in the colony will be females. But still later, when the new generation liberates its larvae and the second filial generation attaches and matures, there will be ample extruding males to fertilize all the available eggs. Some oysters are known to reverse sex still a second time, but so far as known the first female phase is definitive with *Teredo.*

† Working with this species at Woods Hole, Massachusetts, Grave (1928) found that spawning, during the summer and early fall, was a function simply of water temperature, 11° to 12° C. or more. There was no evidence of tidal influence or of stimulation due to the presence of the other sex. In its life history, *Teredo* spends five weeks developing, the first half of this period in the gill chamber of the mother and the next as a free-swimming veliger. The largest specimens found were 40 by 1 cm. Sexual maturity is attained at a length of 4 to 5 cm., about two months after settling. The normal adult size is reached the first year, and death ensues in the second.

estingly, there are two distinct grades of rasping surface on the shell, and the animal's intestinal contents show two correspondingly different sizes of wood particles.

All the wood removed from the head of the burrow passes rapidly through the animal's stomach into its intestine, and is finally removed via the siphons. *Teredo* probably extracts some nourishment from the wood en route but certainly not enough to keep it alive. Its chief food supply comes, as with all bivalves, from the plankton contained in the respiratory water.

All other means of controlling the *Teredo* having failed, there is some hope left in parasitology. Miss Pickard has found three ciliates (protozoa) parasitic in the gill chamber, the commonest of them, *Boveria teredinidi,* present in nearly all adult specimens; but unfortunately they are not harmful to the host. If only a decidedly injurious parasite could be found in some of these borers the solution to the problem would be found with it, for pure cultures released near recently infected piling would wipe out every individual that had gained a foothold.

It is presumed that *Teredo navalis* is the Puget Sound species also, but we can get no definite information, and without the ministering attentions of a pile-puller and a gang of equipped men it is almost impossible to obtain specimens.

§338. In Los Angeles and San Diego harbors, and in Hawaii also, the havoc-working shipworm is the small *Teredo diegensis* (Pl. XLVI). Reaching a length of 5″ but averaging nearer 2″, it is the smallest shipworm occurring on the Pacific coast. Breeding apparently takes place throughout the year, but the heaviest infections by larvae take place when the water is warmest, that is, from April to October. This is just the opposite of what takes place with *Bankia,* and differs somewhat from the breeding of *T. navalis.* As with *T. navalis,* the young are retained within a brood pouch until well along in their development, but they are larger and fewer in number. In the brood pouch of an average female 490 were counted. The brown-shelled, nearly globular larvae are plainly visible through the distended body wall of the parent.

This *Teredo* has been found (1920) at one spot in San Francisco Bay—a small inlet near South San Francisco, where, apparently, it found survival conditions after being accidentally introduced from the south or from Hawaii. Within four years after its discovery there its numbers were considerably depleted, and it is possible that it has already disappeared. Even if it survives it is unlikely ever to become an important destructive factor in San Francisco Bay's relatively cold waters.

V. PLANKTON

Marine Plankton of the Pacific Coast

I

MOST tide-pool life depends ultimately on plankton, the most primitive foodstuff in the ocean. Marine plankton is basic, the first link in the food chains which culminate in whales, fish, starfish, and humans. But although many of the relationships in these chains are direct, tracing them is another and more difficult matter.

The term *plankton* is used to include all the living organisms, plant or animal, usually minute, that swim weakly or drift about on or in the water. Large and active free-swimmers such as fish, squid, seals, and whales are never included within the term, but are called nekton.

The diatoms, microscopic plants of which there are many types, usually are regarded as the most primitive of these organisms, and first in the ecological series. The various species occur in regional associations, with characteristic proportions of local and cosmopolitan forms. Diatoms are the prime plankton-producers of the ocean.

Next in this series are the dinoflagellates, minute one-celled animals which resemble plants in elaborating their own food supply photosynthetically, and which for this reason are often treated along with the phytoplankton—the plant plankton. It seems to be pretty well established that dinoflagellates find their optimum conditions in water depleted by diatoms, and the peaks of production follow one another in a nice economy. Both in numbers and total production, the dinoflagellates are distinctly inferior in most temperate regions, and are scarcely to be found at all for a good part of the time in the more northern waters.

Quite recently, however, Atkins suggests that the ultra-minute *nannoplankton,* organisms too small for netting—mostly self-nourishing dinoflagellates—"make up the greatest proportion of the oceanic biota."[*] Developing *that* line of inquiry would be a truly herculean task.

Third in the plankton chain are the micro-crustacea, copepods, mysids, etc., and the arrow-worms and minute tunicates, which feed on the smaller organisms. Here, however, the food chain becomes more diffuse, for many fish, as well as the larger planktonic animals,

[*] *Biological Abstracts,* 4405, February 1946.

feed on copepods or smaller forms indiscriminately. Other fish, such as adult California sardines, feed on the diatoms and dinoflagellates directly. In point of fact, everything feeds on almost everything else. But little is known about the actual relationships.

Though many hours have been devoted to plankton study during the past generation, no orderly picture has yet emerged. Great effort has been expended, some discoveries have been made, and certain trends seem to have become clear. But as the work expands, anomalies tend to appear. Thirty years ago it was generally supposed that (a) production was relatively constant with the latitude, high in the north and low in the tropics; (b) the plankton calendar of any given year repeated itself over and over at the same place—in other words, that any one year was representative for that station; and (c) the sole limiting factors were sunlight and the amount of the two or three nutrient salts considered to be fertilizers. The first two of these suppositions seem pretty much to have gone the way of discarded hypotheses. The third is in dispute.

Recent work seems to have substantiated other ideas held originally. Production is great in summer and slight in winter, especially in the high latitudes. The northern (and presumably the far southern) latitudes show two sharp seasonal peaks against the more rounded single peak of the tropics. And coastal areas are much more productive than the high seas, more so even than was formerly supposed.

This is all in conformity with the photosynthetic activity of the diatoms. For, like grain and grass and root crops on land, the growth of these primary products of oceanic pastures bears a direct relation to sunlight and fertilizer. Only the upper layers of water receive enough light to permit this plant growth. In southern California the maximum production is reported by Moberg (1928)* at 30–35 meters. Allen (1945, p. 24) writes that production in the La Jolla region is "much alike at 20–50 M depths offshore, a little less at 10 M and at the surface, and much less at 60 M." At Friday Harbor, according to Phifer (1934a, p. 94), the greatest production occurs in the upper 25 meters with a maximum at 10 meters.

The original source of the above-mentioned fertilizers seems to be the run-off waters from the land. At any rate, peaks of plankton production in India and Egypt have been shown to follow the discharge of river floods into the sea.†

This plant growth, once the sunlight starts to increase in the spring, is normally so rapid that the fertilizer is depleted and the plant colonies

* See References in the Appendix.

† Hornell and Nayudo, 1924, *Madras Fisheries Department, Bulletin*, **17** (5): 129–97; and el Saby, 1937, quoted by Hickling, 1945, p. 136, from *Journal Marine Biological Association*, **26**.

die out as a result. At least this is the classical theory and usually it seems to be justified. Graham (1943, p. 7) sums it up when he notes that, at the start of a production cycle, the population is small against a large concentration of nutrient salts. As the population increases the nutrients decrease until, at the diatom peak, they are insufficient to support further production. As the organisms die out, the nutrients become totally depleted, and we end up with the positive relation which obtained before the start of the pulse. Phifer and Thompson (1937, p. 57), however, referring to the nutrient salts at Friday Harbor, remark: "It is unique that their concentration did not diminish sufficiently to become a limiting factor in phytoplankton productivity." More recently, Harvey (1942) suggests that constituents of sea water other than the known fertilizers may be importantly involved, and Sverdrup, Johnson, and Fleming (1942, p. 769), discuss "growth substances," undetermined elements involved in diatom growth. In any case, whether the factors are completely external, or whether these serve merely to trigger off some inherent population rhythm, rich productivity does seem to be associated with the so-called new-water just up from the depths.

As the plant colonies die out, their disintegration releases the nitrates, phosphates, and silicates, and perhaps other fertilizing compounds. The resulting rain of particles constantly enriches the dark deeper layers.

On the California coast (and along a very few Western shores elsewhere in the world with great depths close offshore) winds from the land push the coastal waters out to sea in horizontal currents. To maintain equilibrium, vertical currents—upwellings—are created, bringing up from the depths cool fertilizer-laden water-masses which enrich the surface layers, thus maintaining a high standard of fertility during the critical spring and summer months. Since the dying plants will have left spores everywhere waiting and ready to take advantage of favorable conditions, these waters are often blooming.

Upwelling varies from day to day and from year to year. Some correlations between it, the winds, the production of plankton, and even the temperature of coastal surface waters could be expected. And this can be shown.

Obviously the water recently brought up from the cool depths will have a lower temperature than that which has been warmed by the sun at the surface. This explains the relative coldness of the summer sea water along the California coast north of Point Conception, as compared with what we should normally expect at that latitude. This is well illustrated by the isotherm charts reproduced as Figs. 113 and 114. (Further temperature data will be found in Fig. 117, in

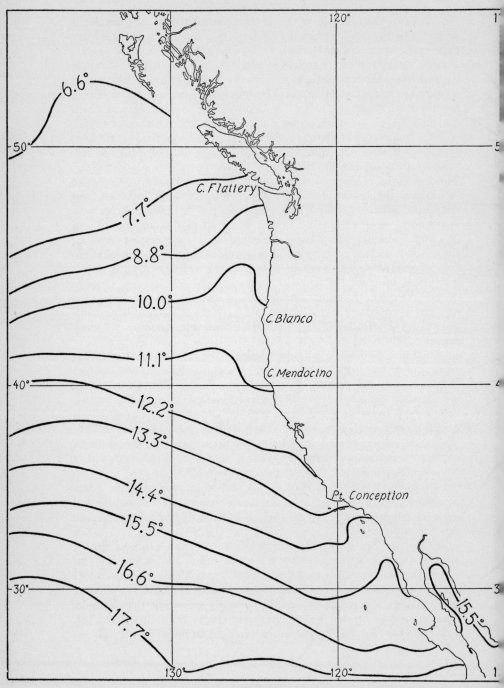

Fig. 113

Smoothed isotherms (Centigrade) for March along the Pacific Coast.

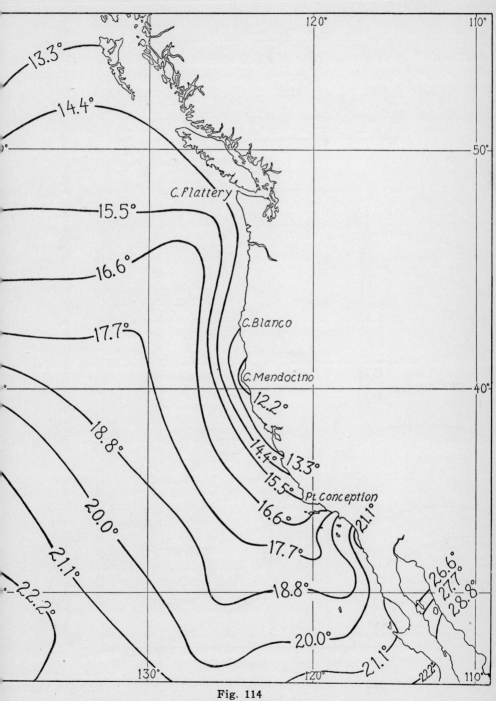

Fig. 114

Smoothed isotherms (Centigrade) for August along the Pacific Coast.

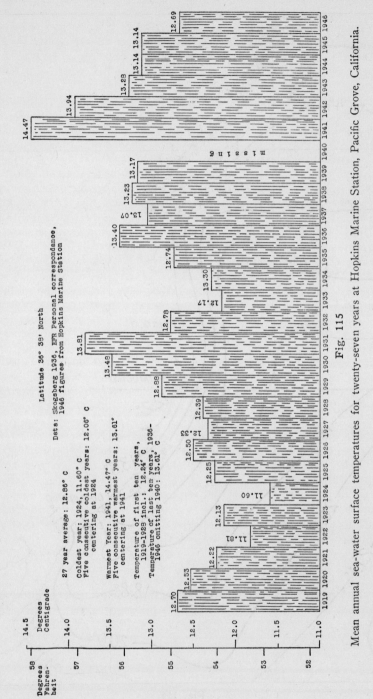

Latitude 36° 39' North

Data: Skogsberg 1936, EFR personal correspondence,
1946 figures from Hopkins Marine Station

27 year average: 12.86° C

Coldest year: 1924, 11.60° C
Five consecutive coldest years: 12.06° C
centering at 1924

Warmest Year: 1941, 14.47° C
Five consecutive warmest years: 13.61°
centering at 1941

Temperature of first ten years,
1919-1928 incl.: 12.24° C
Temperature of last ten years, 1936-
1946 omitting 1940: 13.61° C

Fig. 115

Mean annual sea-water surface temperatures for twenty-seven years at Hopkins Marine Station, Pacific Grove, California.

the references cited there, and in Tully, 1937). It is common knowledge among the fishermen near the centers of upwelling, at Cape Mendocino, at Monterey, or in northern Lower California, that in order to get into warmer water they need only sail west for a few hours.

According to this reasoning, cold-water years should be unusually productive of plankton. And the occasional warm years eventually will leave their marks even on the permanent life of the sea. Note the correlation between the high-temperature years, Fig. 115, and years of low diatom-productivity, Fig. 116. Tide-pool animals will suffer in their turn. Plankton-feeders will be affected directly. Year-classes born during the following season will be sparse, since it can be assumed in the fish so far studied with respect to this factor that all the excess food, stored in the form of fat, is converted into eggs and sperm.* All the life in the sea co-ordinates to this important plankton-production calendar.

But of the calendar itself little is known. We cannot even be certain that all the chief correlatives have been discovered. Sunlight certainly. But the photic differences between the Aleutians and southern California are such that we must wonder how it is that yearly diatom populations in these distant places come to peak in exactly the same week as we shall see in Figs. 118 and 124. As previously indicated, even the paramount importance of the known nutrients is in some doubt. It may be that we are confronted with a biological rather than with a strictly physico-chemical factor, since the profoundly peaked rhythms occur even where turbulence and upwelling constantly replenish the fertilizer, which has been assumed to be the chief limiting factor.

The erratic nature of the subject matter is chiefly to blame for the fact that so much about diatom production seems to be anomalous. For the yield may vary from a few hundred cells per liter to many hundred thousands in the course of a few days or a few miles. Cycles may and probably do occur, but the cyclic effect is so small in comparison with the erratic variables that a very long-term program must have matured before oceanographers can develop any mathematically dependable ideas as to the underlying orderliness.

II

Such knowledge as we have is the work of a few groups.

At Friday Harbor, although the gaps are large, a foundation at least has been laid. Unfortunately, the plankton calendar scheduled

---

* Hickling, 1940 and 1945, *Journal Marine Biological Association,* 24: 619–32; and 26: 115–38.

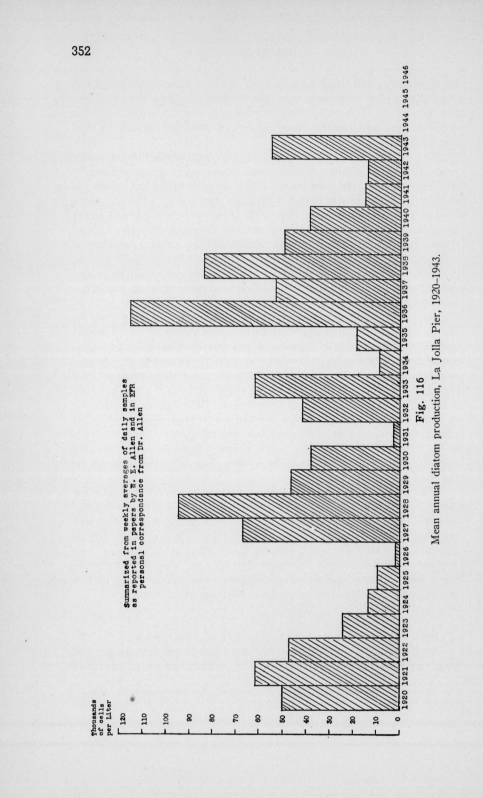

Thousands
of cells
per liter

Summarized from weekly averages of daily samples
as reported in papers by W. E. Allen and in EFR
personal correspondence from Dr. Allen

Fig. 116

Mean annual diatom production, La Jolla Pier, 1920-1943.

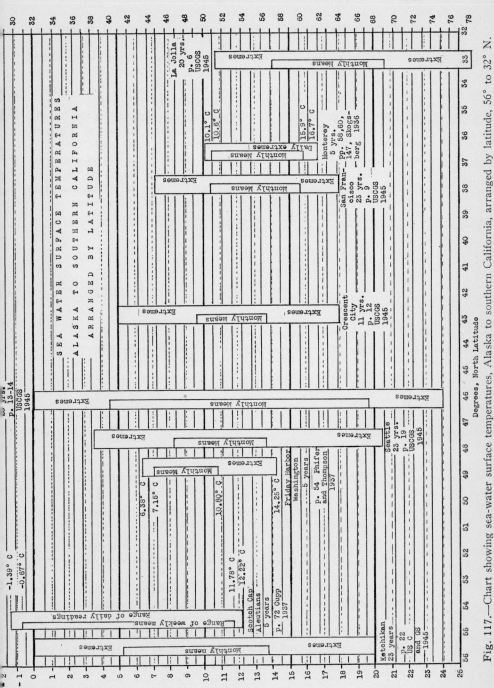

Fig. 117.—Chart showing sea-water surface temperatures, Alaska to southern California, arranged by latitude, 56° to 32° N.

for prompt appearance in 1937 (Phifer and Thompson, p. 34) has
not yet been published. The Canadians have been surveying the
Fraser River mouth, and the Japanese have worked in the Aleutian
and Bering Sea regions. But it is due chiefly to Dr. Allen and his
group at the Scripps Institution of Oceanography that the Pacific
Coast plankton has been studied perhaps more intensively, and certainly for a longer continuous period, than anywhere else in the world.

The work to date falls into several categories—shore and offshore
plankton studies, surface and subsurface counts, analyses of sampling
technics, and work of a general nature. Most of the plankton charts
reproduced herein are based on work done by Dr. Allen and his
students, who analyzed also samples collected in the Aleutians and
elsewhere and shipped already preserved for study at La Jolla.

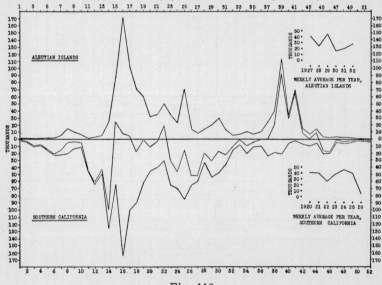

Fig. 118

Chart by Ed Ricketts, Jr., showing mean calendars of diatom production,
Aleutian Islands, 1927–32, and southern California, 1920–26.

The detail charts, Figs. 119, 120, and 121, illustrate the huge
production variations, and show how little orderliness can be adduced
from the data as reported.

Fig. 119 was chosen as an example of the greatest divergence in
yearly calendars at the *same stations*. Fig. 120 illustrates the production differentials between closely adjacent stations in the same
general region at the *same time*. Fig. 116 has already shown us how
greatly the *mean* annual diatom production at a given region can

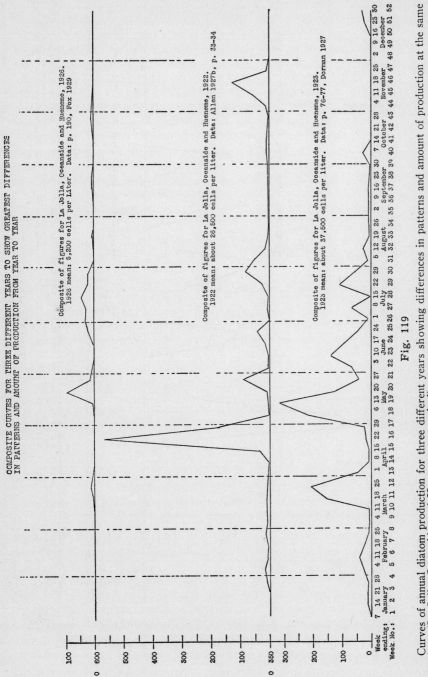

COMPOSITE CURVES FOR THREE DIFFERENT YEARS TO SHOW GREATEST DIFFERENCES
IN PATTERNS AND AMOUNT OF PRODUCTION FROM YEAR TO YEAR

Composite of figures for La Jolla, Oceanside and Hueneme, 1926.
1926 mean: 5,200 cells per liter. Data: p. 190, Fox 1929

Composite of figures for La Jolla, Oceanside and Hueneme, 1922.
1922 mean: about 26,500 cells per liter. Data: Allen 1927b, p. 33-34

Composite of figures for La Jolla, Oceanside and Hueneme, 1923.
1923 mean: about 37,500 cells per liter. Data: p. 76-77, Dorman 1927

Fig. 119

Curves of annual diatom production for three different years showing differences in patterns and amount of production at the same
stations (La Jolla, Oceanside, and Hueneme composited).

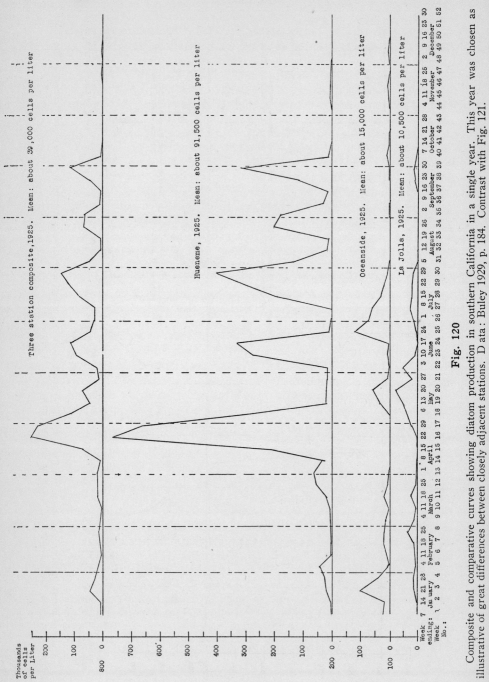

Fig. 120

Composite and comparative curves showing diatom production in southern California in a single year. This year was chosen as illustrative of great differences between closely adjacent stations. Data: Buley 1929, p. 184. Contrast with Fig. 121.

vary from year to year. And almost any of the detail charts exhibit instances of large *short-period* (weekly, etc.) variations.

But a nebulous pattern comes through despite these differences. Most of the graphs come to peak sometime in the first half of the year; the winter production is low. And relations usually can be traced in adjacent stations around the same time. The Hueneme pulse in Fig. 121 at Week 13 can be seen to have spread more than a hundred miles by Week 15, to Oceanside. The following week it can be picked up still farther south at La Jolla, where it blooms even more intensely. Something of the sort often can be found in even the most dissimilar patterns.

To differentiate the fortuituous from the truly repetitive, the small local from the large regional patterns, there should be daily counts from a dozen points up and down the coast for fifty years or more. At best we have only a fraction of this, and from two or three points only. Although Dr. Allen has been making daily and composited weekly counts from southern California for more than twenty years, details have been published only for the first seven. Through his co-operation we have some added manuscript figures. But it stands as a charge against a great educational institution that most of this detail lies unpublished and fallow.

Similar detail is available for parts of eight years in the Aleutians, six years consecutively, with a few small but most unfortunate gaps. This is for a single station only. Typical graphs, to show greatest similarities and greatest differences, will be found in Fig. 122. We should have data from several closely adjacent stations, so as to compensate for purely local pulses. But here again we must use what we have—and regard ourselves fortunate here on the Pacific for having even this much.

In a search for the fundamental patterns hinted at by some of the graphs, we decided to combine the figures into mean curves, allowing at the same time for the limitations of this method. The results certainly seem to justify it as a tool surprisingly useful for such a purpose.

In testing the concept of the mean curve with reference to this material, two things became apparent. First, that a mean curve over a period of years is probably an adequate expression for combined figures from several stations in the same general region. And second, that for a single station, even for a considerable number of years, this method must be used with caution. In Fig. 123, the seven-year mean curve for three southern California stations combined, was contrasted with a six-year curve for the same stations in which only the atypical year 1924 was omitted. It will be seen that the differences are

358

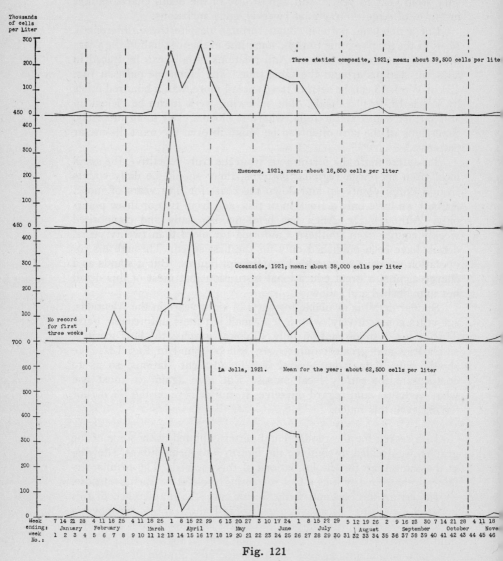

Thousands
of cells
per Liter

Three station composite, 1921; mean: about 39,500 cells per liter

Hueneme, 1921, mean: about 18,500 cells per liter

Oceanside, 1921; mean: about 38,000 cells per liter

No record
for first
three weeks

La Jolla, 1921.   Mean for the year: about 62,500 cells per liter

Week
ending: 7 14 21 28 4 11 18 25 4 11 18 25 1 8 15 22 29 6 13 20 27 3 10 17 24 1 8 15 22 29 5 12 19 26 2 9 16 23 30 7 14 21 28 4 11 18
           January   February   March   April   May   June   July   August   September   October   Nove
week
No.:   1 2 3 4 5 6 7 8 9 10 11 12 13 14 15 16 17 18 19 20 21 22 23 24 25 26 27 28 29 30 31 32 33 34 35 36 37 38 39 40 41 42 43 44 45 46

Fig. 121

Composite and comparative curves showing diatom production at closely adjacent stations in southern California, 1921. This year was chosen as illustrative of great similarity between closely adjacent stations. Data: Allen 1927a, p. 21–22. Contrast with Fig. 120.

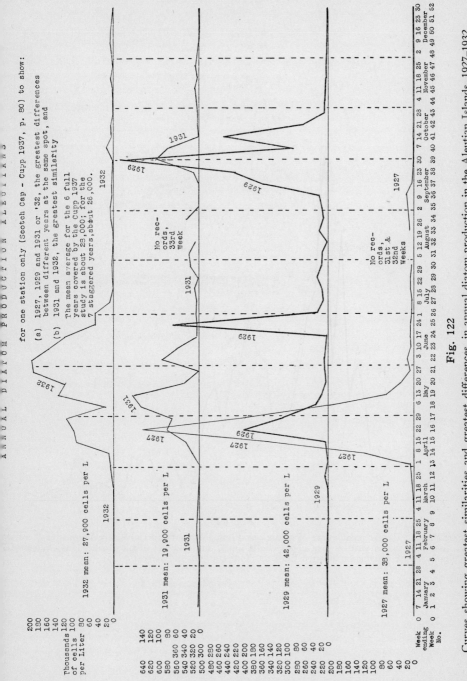

Fig. 122

Curves showing greatest similarities and greatest differences in annual diatom production in the Aleutian Islands, 1927–1932.

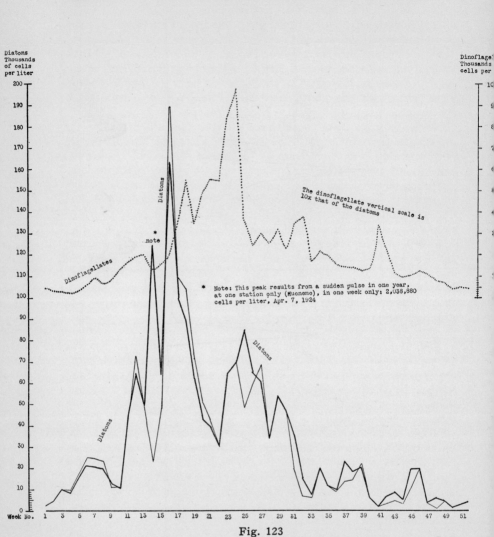

Fig. 123

Chart showing 7-year mean curve of annual production of southern California diatoms at three sta (heavy line) contrasted with 6-year mean (light line), omitting the atypical year 1924 and with 7 mean dinoflagellate production (dotted line) at same stations and same time.

few. The figures for 1924 are unique in featuring a phenomenal pulse
of more than two million cells per liter. This occurred at one station
only, and during only the single week, yet its weight was such that it
affected markedly the total pattern for all three stations for all seven
years. Obviously, if we had to deal only with a single station during
these years, and that station had been Hueneme, we should have
ended up with a graph typical neither for Hueneme, nor for southern
California, nor for those times. The data from La Jolla point this up
for even a longer period. Through the kindness of Dr. Allen, we
have been able to examine figures (for this one station only) covering
a period of twenty-four consecutive years. Unfortunately, this information covers lunar months rather than weeks, so that it can be
compared only within itself. From it, we constructed mean curves for
the odd- and for the even-numbered years, reasoning that skew
results of a systematic sort could arise only through a two-year cycle.
That could be checked by mean curves for the first, second, and third
eight-year periods. These were also constructed, compared with each
other, and with the curves for the odd- and even-numbered years. All
showed considerable variation, hence this method was held suspect
with reference to a single station. However, we were forced to use
it in the case of the Aleutians, since only a single station has been
studied in that region.

We were tempted to treat this information by means of logarithms,
which Dr. Allen uses entirely, and which are far easier to handle than
the original numbers. However, for anyone except a mathematician,
the distortions are too great. The large variations, which after all are
the important ones biologically, stand out less obviously. But it was
these, which we particularly wanted to point up, that logs play down,
while at the same time they overemphasize the differences in the
lower ranks of figures. Anything from ten to a thousand cells per
liter represents merely a latent or seeding influence, which we can
assume is always present. But the difference between ten thousand
and six hundred thousand, a subtle variation in a graph of logs, is the
difference between a sparse and a rich production—a vital difference
to plankton-feeders, and this should be obvious in the graphic repre-
sentations. A further disadvantage of logs is that the combinings
cannot be translated back into actual numbers for further combinings,
as we discovered in attempting to evaluate some copepod figures (see
page 282).

Also it would have been preferable, in constructing mean curves,
to employ data from the whole twenty-four years, instead of from the
seven on which information has been published. These data perhaps
could have been obtained through the kindness and patience of Dr.
Allen, if time had allowed us to spend a few weeks at La Jolla (preferably with a charming secretary).

Besides being highly rewarding at a personal level, a program of this sort could provide information valuable to pure and to applied biology. Studies of this kind should be made also of the dinoflagellates—and particularly of the copepods—food production predominantly important to fisheries research. But the compiling of data of this sort is a task both tedious and thankless. And what is there to support financially the student so engaged?

In any case, we reproduce herewith, as Fig. 124, mean curves for southern California and for the Aleutians. The figures are tabulated in our Fig. 125. Data for Scotch Cap, Alaska, are from Cupp (1937).* The first five of the seven-year studies of southern California are summarized by Allen (November 1928), in which paper will be found references to the five yearly reports. The two latter years are detailed in Buley (1929) and in Fox (1929). No further details have been published so far as known, although the counts and studies were continued for seventeen additional years.

The comparable food-getting advantages at any given time, in the north and in the south, to a plankton-eating animal, are indicated by the position of the central line in Fig. 118. Seen in this light, the significance of the annual summer northern migration of the California sardine is quite apparent, as is the return to the south in the late fall, after the autumn peak in the north has been harvested. The circular figure (Fig. 126) points up these differentials more clearly.

Considering the erratic nature of the details, the degree of order hinted at by the mean curves is rather surprising. We have emphasized the mirror-like nature of the peaks by parallel caption-letters. Even the complex labeled *f*, the northern secondary peak in the fall, seems to be weakly reflected in southern waters.

The 24-year mean is potentially accessible in work already done but never published. If it should substantiate the present correlations, a basic underlying pattern for the whole open Pacific could be suggested, more fundamental even than the factors of sunlight and fertilizer, perhaps some primitive biological pulse working through these permitting factors.

The Friday Harbor region offers some unique features for plankton study. Turbulence there is such as to "retard any sudden increase or decrease in the quantity of nutrient salts in solution" (Phifer and Thompson, [1933], p. 69). It will be noted nevertheless from the charts reproduced as our Fig. 127 that the peaks and troughs of total plankton production (arising from diatom foundations) are just as sharp there as in localities not subject to this steadying influence.

* See references at the end of this section, p. 284.

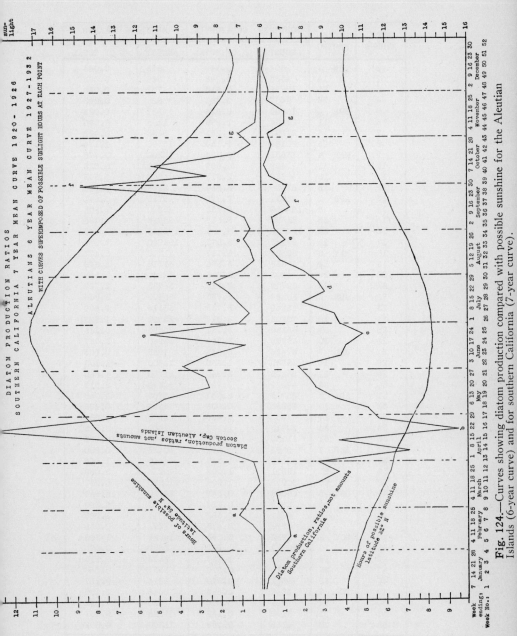

Fig. 124.—Curves showing diatom production compared with possible sunshine for the Aleutian Islands (6-year curve) and for southern California (7-year curve).

364

WEEK NUMBER	WEEK ENDING	SOUTHERN CALIFORNIA		ALEUTIAN ISLANDS	
		AMOUNT	% OF TOTAL	AMOUNT	% OF TOTAL
1	JAN 7	2604	0.149	828	0.063
2	14	4335	0.248	866	0.066
3	21	10725	0.613	771	0.059
4	28	8467	0.484	828	0.063
5	FEB 4	16201	0.926	857	0.065
6	11	22537	1.289	1185	0.090
7	18	21697	1.241	5585	0.426
8	25	20181	1.154	15385	1.174
9	MAR 4	13531	0.774	10200	0.778
10	11	11492	0.657	6900	0.526
11	18	45633	2.611	1875	0.143
12	25	63866	3.654	3228	0.246
13	APR 1	48531	2.776	5785	0.441
14	8	124650	7.132	25000	1.908
15	15	63597	3.639	88928	6.786
16	22	164350	9.403	172220	13.142
17	29	99143	5.673	103940	7.932
18	MAY 5	89427	5.117	71710	5.472
19	12	62328	3.566	61310	4.679
20	19	44603	2.553	32960	2.515
21	26	38709	2.215	35733	2.727
22	JUN 2	30286	1.733	50400	3.846
23	9	65249	3.733	35116	2.680
24	16	70203	4.017	23580	1.799
25	23	85130	4.781	70580	5.386
26	30	65809	3.765	13980	1.067
27	JUL 7	61466	3.517	7933	0.605
28	14	33739	1.930	14500	1.106
29	21	53295	3.049	21750	1.660
30	28	47552	2.721	30360	2.317
31	AUG 3	35775	2.047	13700	1.045
32	10	15895	0.909	5283	0.403
33	17	7453	0.426	6900	0.526
34	24	20413	1.167	11600	0.885
35	31	11830	0.676	7642	0.583
36	SEP 7	9994	0.572	10485	0.800
37	14	23550	1.347	24450	1.866
38	21	18511	1.002	40214	3.069
39	28	20975	1.200	113570	8.667
40	OCT 5	6048	0.347	34700	2.648
41	12	2213	0.127	70240	5.360
42	19	6851	0.392	16614	1.268
43	26	8276	0.473	7271	0.555
44	NOV 2	4953	0.283	14528	1.109
45	9	20292	1.162	3800	0.290
46	16	20741	1.187	2814	0.215
47	23	4120	0.279	3357	0.256
48	30	6622	0.379	2914	0.222
49	DEC 7	4645	0.266	2085	0.159
50	14	1853	0.106	1285	0.098
51	21	3199	0.183	1328	0.101
52	28	4155	0.238	1300	0.099

YEARS' TOTAL 1,747,700   1,310,378

Fig. 125

Table by Ed Ricketts, Jr., showing average number of diatom cells per liter per week for six to seven years in the Aleutian Islands and in southern California.

The diatoms represent but a small fraction of the total volume, making it impossible to compare these detail charts with those from southern California. Data are too scanty to justify constructing a mean curve. A great diatom pulse, with its resultant effect on the total population, might have arisen and declined without record, between any two of the more widely spaced readings. Or it might have been swept into surrounding channels by the strong currents characteristic of this region.

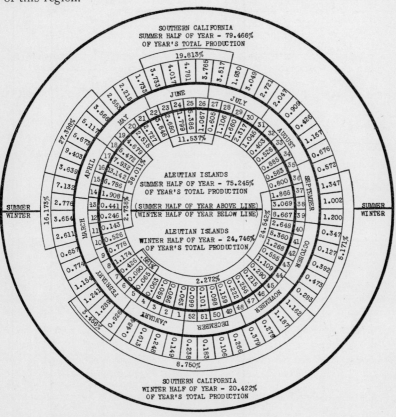

Fig. 126

Chart by Ed Ricketts, Jr., showing seasonal diatom production by half-years in the Aleutian Islands and in southern California.

There is also a graph (Fig. 128) to show silicate and phosphate readings correlated with total volumetric plankton production; but only for a single year. Another one-year study, of diatoms only, graphed on Fig. 129, might have provided the most important single contribution

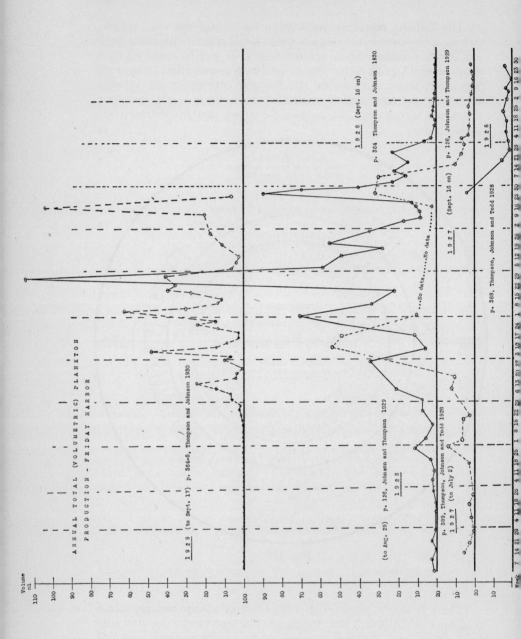

ANNUAL TOTAL (VOLUMETRIC) PLANKTON
PRODUCTION - FRIDAY HARBOR

to date if it had been continued for several consecutive years. This shows the great peak in the fall, just the opposite of what we found both in the Aleutians and in southern California (and hence not a function of latitude). Whether that year was anomalous, or whether the inland conditions at Puget Sound regularly favor such a harvest time, cannot be estimated from the insufficient information. Figures for a single year are valueless except for comparison with other years at the same place.

III

Students of plankton have devoted a great deal of effort to developing and checking the various sampling technics on which the studies are based. After the kinks had been worked out of the actual physical samplings at La Jolla, it remained to determine whether or not pier samples taken at the surface of the water represented a "fair" quota. Studies by Allen (November 1923, San Diego to Cortes Bank; 1924, San Diego to Seattle), by Allen and Lewis (1927, on the high seas) and by Lewis (1927, off the Oregon coast) indicate that the phytoplankton sometimes flowers in very sudden bursts. Occasionally these bursts are highly local, as we have seen from the Fig. 123 situation with reference to Hueneme. But often they are fairly widespread, "operative over an area nearly ninety miles in width" (p. 447, Allen, November 1923). The over-all results were such as to give confidence in the practice of sampling from piers.

Subsurface collections were reported in Allen (October 1923, with bibliographic reference to an account in *Ecology,* 1923) and in Dorman (1927). These accounted for a three-year investigation intended to cast light on subsurface conditions offshore as compared with surface conditions inshore, and lent further confidence to the shore operators.

Many other studies, but especially those reported by Allen (June 1923), and Moberg and Allen (1927) could be considered as checks on the sampling methods used, although unfortunately there seem to be no long-series tests in which the three chief divergent methods are compared. Friday Harbor has employed chiefly the volumetric methods of Gran for the determination of the total plankton. This is in contrast to the Scripps Institution method (Allen, January 1930, 1939, 1940) in which the number of diatom (or dinoflagellate) cells per representative liter of water is actually counted in a manner comparable to that used by clinical technicians for human blood. At Friday Harbor, Phifer reports a series of actual diatom counts by this method, already referred to in our Fig. 126, but the scant information both for the volumetric and for the counted series admits no just comparisons.

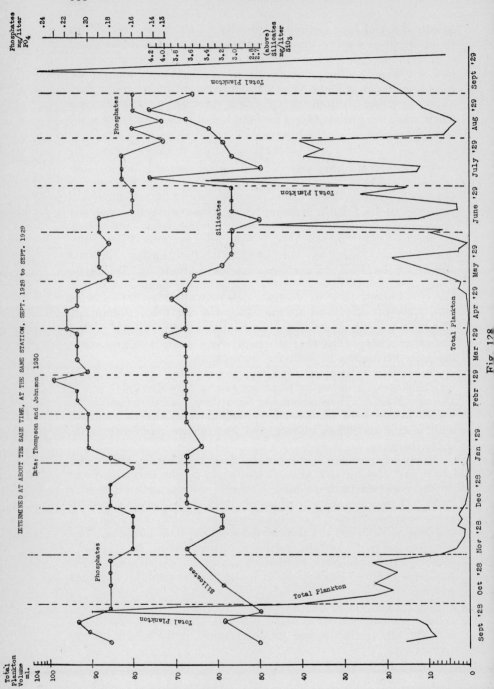

DETERMINED AT ABOUT THE SAME TIME, AT THE SAME STATION, SEPT. 1928 to SEPT. 1929

Data: Thompson and Johnson 1930

Fig 128

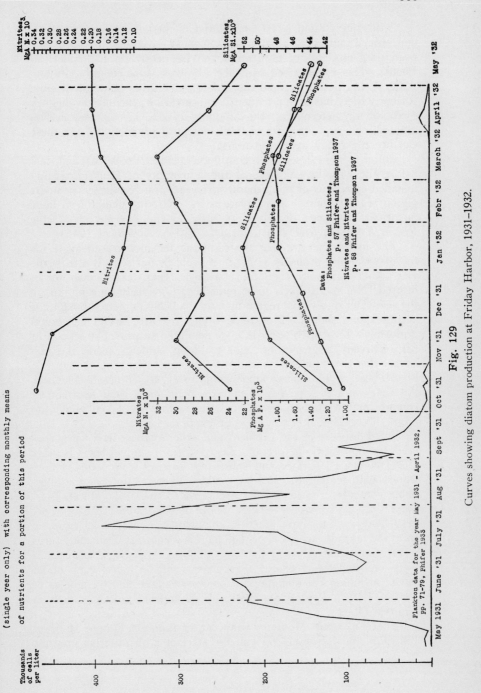

Fig. 129

Curves showing diatom production at Friday Harbor, 1931-1932.

A third very rapid, quasi-quantitative method, involving both plant-
and animal-pigment evaluation by chemical means, is in wide European use, but has not been employed frequently on the American
Pacific. This is described by Riley (1938). More recently Graham
(May 1943) details a rapid method for measuring chlorophyll only.
Recently there has been a tendency to use various chemical evaluatory
methods for determining the amounts of carbon, oxygen, carbon
dioxide, etc., as a measure of total biological productivity, but these
can be only rough approximations.

Phifer in 1934 described a continuous plankton-collector, and, just
before the war, investigators at the University of Hull (England)
installed apparatus of this general sort in several North Sea steamers
plying regular routes. An apparatus for collecting plankton in huge
quantities has been described recently in the *Journal of Marine
Research* (1944; *Biological Abstracts,* 21075, November 1945).

The indications are that the sampling technics are adequate for
the material and probably as good as could be devised. But from the
viewpoint of physico-chemical standards, they leave much to be
desired. Nor is this likely to be remedied. Obviously we can't stir up
the sea water of a whole region by a mechanical sampler, although, for
accuracy, we should. Planktonic organisms are rarely distributed
uniformly. They often occur in huge delimited swarms, like schools of
fish. Already a generation ago, plankton students made the discovery that two similar nets hauled for an equal time, one on each side
of the boat, would collect amounts differing sometimes by one-half.
All that we can hope for is that our samplings shall be frequent
enough, and widely enough distributed within the given region, to
offset the occasional erratic local or temporary pulses.

Other aspects of the problem and other regions have been covered by the La Jolla group. Sleggs (1927) and Allen (January
1928) compared surface and subsurface catches from local offshore
waters with temperature readings and with evaluations of the phosphate contents. Alaska catches are reported in Allen (March 1927,
June 1929, and October 1930). Some of the summer catches were
very heavy, while those taken in the winter, as would be expected
from the latitude, are quite negligible. As a contrast, Panama figures
were reported by Allen in February 1939. Certain very large yields
were reported there also. Other papers will be found cited under
Allen, including recent important summaries and offshore studies as
1940*a*, 1945*a*, 1945*b*; as Sverdrup and Allen (1939), and as
Graham (1941).

There is some Monterey Bay information on diatom statistics
(Bigelow and Leslie, 1930) and the start of a quantitative program

is reported for the Vancouver Island region by Lucas and by Hutchinson (1927–29). Phifer (1934*a*) reports on Puget Sound diatoms other than at Friday Harbor, and Thompson and Phifer (1936) correlate the conditions of the sea water and the amount of the plankton, including diatoms, in the Hood Canal region. Other papers from this region have been considered in connection with Friday Harbor, and on the captions of the Friday Harbor graphs.

IV

Much generalized work, essential to an understanding of the whole plankton situation, has become recently available. In chapters 16 to 19 of Sverdrup, Johnson, and Fleming (1942) there is a very good summary and review, and another in Harvey (1942).

Aikawa (1936) has shown in the Aleutians that the various regional diatom associations can be differentiated by analyzing quantitatively their make-up. And he shows also that the driftings of these societies can be traced seasonally and biogeographically.

Diatom systematics have been treated for southern California by Cupp (1943); for the Friday Harbor region by Gran and Angst (1931); for the Bering Sea by Aikawa (1936) and by Mann (1925).

Dinoflagellates were considered statistically along with the diatoms by the Scripps group and there is a fine summary by Allen (November 1941) with a mean lunar-month log curve. But no details have been published recently. It seems to be pretty well substantiated that dinoflagellates can bloom in waters having fertilizer concentrations below the minimal requirements of most diatoms, hence they are correctly to be regarded as the second step in ecological succession. Certainly the mean curve we reproduce (Fig. 123), showing an initial and largest dinoflagellate peak at the 24th week, would bear that out. By blooming to the point where they produce "red water" they exercise an adverse influence on higher organisms, killing fish and crustacea, perhaps by suffocation (Sommer and Clark, 1946).

[In experiments with fish in tanks containing noxious dinoflagellates, Gunter *et al.* (1948) killed fish under oxygenated conditions, indicating a direct poisoning effect. While the mechanism of "red water" in killing fish and invertebrates is inadequately understood, the phenomenon itself is widespread and well known. The names Red Sea and Vermilion Sea (an old name for the Gulf of California) suggest plankton blooms. The most spectacular recent occurrence is the Florida "red tide" of 1946–47, which killed porpoises, barnacles, and oysters as well as fishes, coincident with a bloom of the dinoflagellate *Gymnodinium*. Windrows of dead fish piled up on the beaches, and had to be buried with bulldozers. In Walvis Bay on the southwest coast of Africa a peculiar combination of circumstances brings about an annual phytoplankton bloom and mass mortality in the restricted waters of the bay (Brongersma-Sanders, 1948). The South African and Californian red tides occur on coasts with upwelling; elsewhere they occur with mixture of water masses (Peru), or possibly influx of nutrients from the land following heavy rains (Florida?). The most plausible explanation of these outbreaks is that they are the result of unusual supplies of nutrients coincident with physical conditions favorable to rapid increase of the organisms, but this again is only a descriptive hypothesis.

The red tides, with their consequent havoc, are only the most spectacular of fluctuations in the sea. Our sardines have been undergoing some sort of fluctuation apparently unrelated to the fishing pressure; following the recent decline, an investigation combining the efforts of the California Academy of Sciences, the California Division of Fish and Game, Scripps Institution of Oceanography, and the U.S. Fish and Wildlife Service was under way in 1949. The scope, methods, and preliminary results of this investigation (much of it perforce concerned with plankton) are described in the 1950 Progress Report of the Marine Research Committee (1950).

Some of the fluctuations observed in marine plants and animals may be cyclic, as Burkenroad (1946) has suggested for the starfish *Asterias forbesi* (14 years), others are, so far as we know, erratic. The surprising outbreak of *Ascidia ceratodes* in Tomales Bay in 1950 may be such an example. (On a few days in late July of that year the waters on the flats of upper Tomales Bay were pink with *Noctiluca*—an incidental coincidence?) Smith and Gordon (1948) in their paper on marine mollusks of Monterey Bay comment upon the large increase in the population of the jumbo squid, *Dosidicus gigas,* and upon the falling off of the giant kelp beds. According to fishermen, this decline in *Nereocystus* has also taken place along the Marin and Sonoma coasts. Lesser variations in abundance are common, and a great deal of valuable information could be gained if records were kept of populations of a few of the more conspicuous plants and invertebrates on selected plots at the various marine stations along the coast. Even a few rough counts a year on approximate areas would be better than the subjective impressions we have now.]

The larger and less ephemeral planktonic organisms have been studied sporadically at La Jolla, Friday Harbor, and Nanaimo. For Monterey Bay there is only the single very good general paper of Bigelow and Leslie (1930). Though outside the limits of this present study, we should note that a Russian, Okul (1943), reports rather completely on total production in the Sea of Azov, with tabular breakdown.* There is a very large program in full swing at the University, Hull, England, in connection with the commercial fisheries—this is as it should be!—and the publications emanating from this investigation promise to go further than anything else to date. Already some of the results have been applied to the herring fishery with rather striking success.

Dr. Esterly reported on the taxonomy of California copepods from 1905 to 1914, and again in 1924. From 1911 to 1928 he considered their habits and ecology, and the statistics of their distribution. Had he lived to continue this work, by now we should know something of their underlying pattern. But from what has been done already, it appears that they migrate nightly to the surface, chiefly in response to an inner or physiological rhythm. "Responses to external stimuli, at any rate, do not afford an adequate explanation" (Esterly [1923], p. 413). A two-year study showed that the peak of abundance, all species considered, was in the spring (February to May, Esterly [1928], p. 339). Since our mean diatom graph shows a peak at Week 16, the abundance of copepods seems not to follow that of the diatoms on which they feed. But in the years of the copepod study (September 1916 through August 1918), the diatoms may also have peaked earlier. Diatom data for these years, or larger data on the copepods, would be required to settle this question. In any case, logically it must be assumed that copepod peaks are dependent on diatom production.

From these papers, we had hoped to construct a mean graph for total copepod occurrence along the lines of the diatom curve, to see how the peaks compared in time and in size. But the data are insufficient for quantitative study. Esterly's combined figures are expressed as logs, and without further information they cannot be transposed back into the original numbers needed for further combinings.

Since then, the Vancouver Island copepods have been studied by Campbell (1929 and 1934), and papers on oceanic forms have appeared by M. W. Johnson from 1934 to 1939.

Dr. Esterly worked also on the occurrence of schizopods (May 1914), and papers on the systematics of *Mysis*, and others will be found cited elsewhere herein (p. 436). The pelagic larvae of shore- and bottom-living animals—the temporary plankton—has been studied only incidentally and in certain groups, mostly from the taxonomic angle.

Of the larger permanent planktonic animals, Dr. Esterly reported on the Ctenophores (April 1914), and Michael on the Chaetognaths (1911, 1913). Something is known about the pelagic tunicates through

* *Zoological Journal*, 20 (2), abstracted as No. 10044A, *Biological Abstracts*, 19 (6).

Essenberg (1922–26), Dr. Myrtle Johnson (1910), Michael (1918), and Ritter (1905).* Otherwise, the medusae (Bigelow [1914], Foerster [1923], Little [1914]), siphonophores, ctenophores (Torrey [1904], Mortensen [1927]), and the pelagic mollusks are known on the Pacific only through systematic studies or not at all.

As for the peaks and troughs in the production of these larger animals, and their place in the larger picture, practically nothing is known. The information is too negligible even for theorizing, especially since the presently accepted hypotheses of even the better-studied smaller forms rest on such doubtful foundations. (Even the classic idea that production in general is greater in high than in low latitudes is being strongly questioned, the most recent negative evidence coming from Graham [1941] for diatoms.)

Only one large thesis can be stated with any degree of certainty. The idea of hierarchy is implicit. Rank behind rank, societies stand in mutual interdependence. From the most minute and ephemeral bacteria and diatoms, clear up to the fish, seals, and whales, each rank is supported by the abundance of smaller and more transient creatures under it. Each in turn contributes to the series next above it. Ascending ranks have each a little more leeway in the matter of food storage, a little more resilience, a little more freedom of movement in the environment. Although the individuals are larger, their numbers are smaller. And their spores—the resting stages—are less significant in the life history. Finally, at the top of the hierarchy, the disintegrating body of the whale supports astronomical hordes of bacteria, busily engaged in breaking down the complex and slowly assembled proteins into simpler units which fertilize the waters for the oncoming crop of diatoms—James Joyce's *recorso* theme in its original manifestation.

Each higher order, instead of ruling the ranks of individuals below, is actually ruled by them. Each rank is completely at the mercy of its subjects, dependent on their abundance or accessibility. All the schemes which our social order prides itself on having discovered have been in use by societies of marine animals far back into the dim geological past. The units comprising human society very commonly claim to be one thing and are another. Not the least of the many values of marine sociology is the fact that the sea animals can be only themselves.

---

* Thompson ([1942] *Australia, Council for Science and Industrial Research, Bulletin*, 153) has shown that the production of tunicates may be important in the Australian plankton picture.

VI. INTERTIDAL ZONATION AND RELATED MATTERS

NOTE

A complete revision of this book according to Ed Ricketts' plans is obviously impossible. His intention was not only to revise this book, but to cross-reference it with *Sea of Cortez* (eventually revising that book as well*), and further, to write a third book on the Queen Charlottes and possibly the Aleutians, to be cross-indexed to the other two. An elaborate set of filing cards in various colors was devised and printed to facilitate this triune task. There are eight species, in two genera, for these cards; and it must be admitted that, if faithfully kept up, the system would have been useful and time-saving. A reasonably intelligent secretary, however, is a *sine qua non* for such a system. Undoubtedly a thorough revision of *Between Pacific Tides* would also have included liberal cross-referencing to the MacGinities' *Natural History of Marine Animals*. It is enough, for this edition, to remind the reader that further information about the life histories of many Pacific coast invertebrates, especially those occurring in the vicinity of Corona del Mar, will be found in the MacGinities' book; citations would become monotonously repetitious.

It need hardly be added that *Between Pacific Tides* is a dichotomous book: the text, as John Steinbeck has said in the Foreword, is for laymen and beginners; the Appendix is not only a guide for beginners who would like to go on, but is also a useful tool for the practitioners of what Joseph Wood Krutch somewhat disdainfully (so it seems to us) calls "official science." There is not—and there should not be—a sharp division between beachcombers and professors lined up to tug each other across some invisible line like the yokels at the village fair, and this book vacillates back and forth across that hazy border line. The author expected people to be interested enough to look things up for themselves, if they were interested enough to read his book, or he would not have gone to all the work of preparing the Appendix and Bibliography.

Among the things which Ed Ricketts was particularly interested in was the subject of zonation and its relation to the tides. For a long time he worked over a paper on the subject, but never published it. Certainly

* The recent appendectomized *Log of the Sea of Cortez* is not quite what Ricketts had in mind.

a book titled *Between Pacific Tides* should go into this problem in more detail, and probably such a discussion would have been part of the eventual revision he had planned. No pretense is made that the short review of recent work which follows is what he had in mind—it is a contribution by the editor of this edition which, it is hoped, will satisfy at least some of the constructive critics of this book and present the problems in such a way as to dispel the impression that there is practically nothing left to be done in this field.

I

Although one of the most obvious aspects of a rocky sea coast in the temperate zones is the arrangement of its sessile and sedentary life in bands or zones, *Between Pacific Tides* was (and remains) the first popular treatise on seashore life to describe this zonation along an entire sea coast and to discuss the distribution of the animals according to this zonation. Intertidal zonation was not, of course, a discovery of E. F. Ricketts. The zonal arrangement of plants and animals was described in detail by the French zoölogists, J. V. Audouin and Henri Milne-Edwards, in 1832. They recognized five zones: (1) Balanus, (2) seaweed, (3) coralline, (4) Laminaria, and (5) oyster zone. Algal zonation had been recognized even earlier; for a historical survey, up to 1929, of the literature and ideas on zonation and marine ecology generally, see the excellent summary by Gislén (1930).

Since the time of Gislén's review, work on intertidal zonation has increased, it would seem, at a geometrical ratio. In 1931 T. A. Stephenson began his survey of the South African intertidal region. Covering a coast line of more than 1200 miles and a period of ten years, this is the first large-scale study of zonation. It has been reported in detail, especially the descriptive aspects, by Stephenson and his colleagues (see Stephenson, 1947, for summary and bibliography). In this same year, 1931, Hewatt began his study of an "ecological transect" at the Hopkins Marine Station. While this work was in progress, Colman published his study of zonation in relation to tide levels (1933), the first critical work of its kind, and Elmhirst contributed a brief but significant note (1934) on the relation of tidal flow to zonation.

Hewatt had been preceded at Pacific Grove by Torsten Gislén, who investigated the California coast during the winter and spring of 1930–31. Gislén's observations were not published, however, until after those of Hewatt (Hewatt, 1937; Gislén, 1943, 1944). Gislén's studies are of particular interest inasmuch as they are concerned with comparisons of the coast of California and Japan at similar latitudes, and inasmuch as he utilizes (as does Hewatt) some of Ricketts' unpublished work. This discussion, based in part on this unpublished paper, "The

Tide as an Environmental Factor Chiefly with Reference to Ecological Zonation on the Pacific Coast," and the two graphs published in this book as Figures 111 and 112, are all that is now available of Ricketts' study (Hewatt published, as his Figure 7, a simplified version of Figure 112). Between the publication of Hewatt's and Gislén's studies, both so intimately associated with the local scene at Pacific Grove, the first edition (1939) of *Between Pacific Tides* appeared—although essentially completed in 1936.

During the summers of 1936, 1937, and 1938, Rigg and Miller made detailed studies of the zonation at Neah Bay, Washington, which were not published until recently (Rigg and Miller, 1949). Thus, this work is more closely related to the Puget Sound studies of Shelford *et al.* (1935), and is in some ways complementary to them. Early in the 1940's (apparently), a study of intertidal zonation of the coast of New South Wales comparable in scope to the Stephenson survey was begun, and the results are now available (Dakin *et al.*, 1949). Also at this time a study of the algal ecology of Kangaroo Island off the South Australian coast near Adelaide was being carried out (Womersley, 1947). In 1946 Doty published his paper on critical tide factors, which he has since supplemented with an experimental test of the hypothesis set forth in the earlier paper (Doty, 1946; Doty and Archer, 1950). Since 1947 a school of algal ecology has been at work on the New Zealand shores under the leadership of V. J. Chapman, who began his work in England (Chapman, 1950; Beveridge and Chapman, 1950; Dellow, 1950).

This brief historical summary is principally concerned, as the reader must have realized by now, with the study of intertidal zonation in the Pacific Ocean. Important recent studies of zonation in the Atlantic and Mediterranean will be found in the papers published in Volume VII of the Société de Biogéographique's memoirs (1940), which includes a bibliography (pp. 421–34) carrying on from Gislén's review. The work on marine algal ecology has been summarized and listed by Chapman (1946). Recent zonation work in England has been done by Evans (1947a, b). The most recent work on the American Atlantic is that of Dr. and Mrs. Stephenson; so far only the installments on the Florida Keys (1950b) and northern Florida and the Carolinas (1952) have been published. Following this anti-clockwise program, the Pacific Coast work will be the last of the series.

Inspection of these recent papers reveals a few shortcomings common to most of them, which we would like to point out as a constructive criticism. Some of these can be remedied by the authors in future papers in brief notes; others may require a more extended supplement:

1. Photographs lose much of their value as data without indication

of the date of exposure. A sharp view of zones and associations at an easily identifiable location deserves a date. One need only examine the photographs in D. P. Wilson's paper on *Zostera* (1949) to realize this.

2. The dates on which the field studies were made are, more often than not, omitted.

3. Discussions of intertidal zonation should be accompanied, when possible, by easily read tide graphs ("marigrams"), showing not only the sequence of tides, but the time of day, in relation to season, at which maximum exposure occurs. (Cf. Doty, Fig. 1, for a good example, although this should be somewhat larger.)

4. The terms "spring" and "neap" properly apply to the strict semi-diurnal tide pattern of the North Atlantic, South African, and New Zealand coasts. For the mixed tidal pattern of the North Pacific and Australian coasts the terms for the greatest and smallest ranges are "tropic" and "equatorial" (Cf. Marmer, *The Tide*, chap. v). The figure presented below (130) is not meant to be an example of the ideal diagram for all purposes, but indicates that tidal extremes are more closely related to the moon's transits than to her phases in this region. This is not a plea for punctilious hairsplitting but for more adequate recognition of certain ecologically significant differences attributable to differences in tidal regimes on the various coasts.

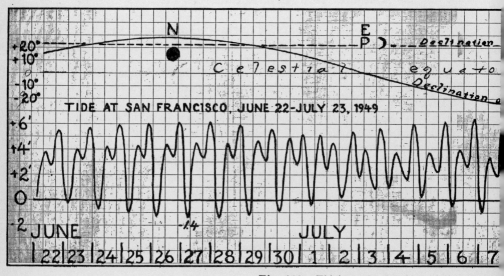

Fig. 130.—Tidal graph, showing relation of moc

II

That zonation occurs is obvious to all, and enough had been published on it by 1938 to cause MacGinitie to express an opinion that the subject had "been decidedly overdone" (1939, p. 45). In view of what has been published since then, it would seem that discussion of the subject has hardly started. T. A. Stephenson, in collaboration with his wife, is now working upon an entire book, to be completed in "five or ten years," on the zonation of rocky shores throughout the world.

MacGinitie, at least in 1938, recognized three zones, somewhat equivalent to the three basic zones of Stephenson (*vide infra*), but in "Natural History of Marine Animals," discussion of the subject is conspicuously lacking. This represents one extreme; the other is that of the Shelford school with its array of biomes, associations, and faciations, "a positively terrifying outburst of terminology referring to communities" (in Stephenson's words) in which the zones have been submerged in a high tide of related but not exactly synonymous subdivisions.

The number of zones which may be recognized on a seashore is not only a function of the complex variables of tide, climate, and the life subject to these variables, but is also dependent on the degree of refinement the student seeks to attain. In Figure 131 some of the various

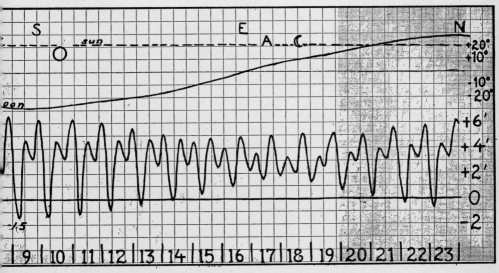

nsits and phases in the mixed tidal pattern.

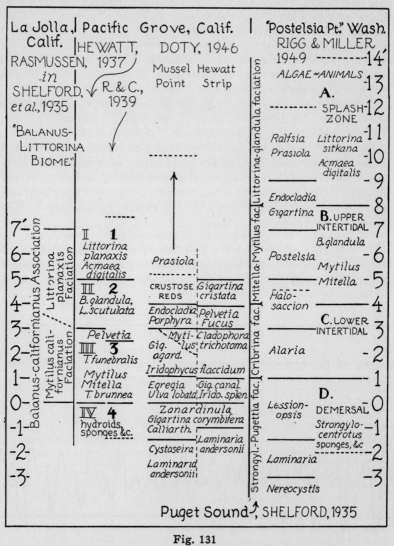

Fig. 131
Zonation on the Pacific Coast, as observed by various authors.

ways in which zonation has been recognized on the Pacific coast are represented. At first glance, this appears hopelessly complex. Even Hewatt and Ricketts, working in the same locality, do not quite agree. The samples from Doty's study, however, show the differences which may occur in algal zonation in the same locality under different conditions of exposure. Rigg and Miller set up two schemes of zonation, one for algae and the other for invertebrates. These zones indicate the essential similarity to central California despite the much greater tidal range at Neah Bay. As they state, "The major difference is one of nomenclature, the present writers having regarded mid-tide not as a zone but as the boundary between the upper and lower intertidal regions. A very little vertical displacement would bring the two sets of concepts into harmony." To these various zonal arrangements we have added, principally for historical interest, the community terms of Shelford *et al.*

A few words of caution about these diagrams (Figs. 131 and 132) are in order. First, they are, especially as presented in this interpretation, highly schematic, and it is, in a way, doing the authors an injustice to fix these zones on a scale of tidal heights. We are actually dealing with proportions related to tidal heights at specific localities, which are quite different from the levels based on a datum established for a gauging station. Hence, the measurements of Hewatt, Ricketts, and Doty, as referred to tidal levels at San Francisco, are abstractions or idealizations of conditions which may not even occur on the rocks near the gauging station. The water levels of the schemes of Yonge and Stephenson in Figure 132 are not strictly comparable with those at San Francisco in the center of the figure, an indication of the difficulties inherent in reconciling the semidaily and mixed tidal patterns. Zonation, like everything else in nature, is not a simple pattern, although we should like, sometimes, to have it so. Zones may overlap; they are quite different on a vertical face and a gently sloping reef—other things being equal—and, in the case of some algae, they may change with the seasons.

Nevertheless, the zones in the rocky intertidal region look pretty much the same in England, South Africa, Australia, and California, as anyone who examines the excellent (but undated) photographs in various books and papers will discover. A coniferous forest in Russia and in the United States also look the same in photographs. Such climax developments, the most stable sort of growth which can be produced under given climatic or physiographic conditions, are known in ecological terminology as biomes. Beveridge and Chapman (1950) seem to be the first to apply this term clearly to the rocky intertidal: "the biome of the rocky seashore represents a physiographic climax since it is dependent upon the tide rather than upon the climate" (p. 188). We might argue a bit about "physiographic" here; the tide is a component of what might be termed the "hydrographic climate." Application of the term biome (i.e., as equivalent to the terrestrial "climatic climax") to the sea is as yet undecided; it may perhaps apply to coral reefs, but the term means more than simply a larger, more inclusive rank in the hierarchy of communities. Perhaps the term "ecosystem" would be better for the three-dimensional conditions in the sea.

Virtually all students of zonation agree that one break is well de-fined. This is the approximate 0.0 of tide datum, or mean-lower-low-water, below which is found the zone of Laminarians (and *Phyllospadix* on our coast). There is also agreement as to the zone above the average high tide (or mean-higher-high-water of the Pacific coast), frequented by certain littorines and limpets. These two regions are (roughly) the infra- and supra-littoral fringes of Stephenson's terminology, the *D* and *A* of Rigg and Miller, sub- and upper-littoral of Beveridge and Chapman, littoral-sub-littoral fringe and supra-littoral zone of Dakin *et al.*, and, of course, the "4" and "1" of this book (Fig. 1). We shall leave further synonymy of these zones to the Stephensons.

There remains the intervening zone or zones, the mid-littoral zone of Stephenson's proposed universal system. Because of the dual application of zone to both the inclusive littoral (= intertidal) and the sub-sidiary mid-littoral in this classification, we have reduced "mid-littoral zone" to "mid-littoral." Since it separates the fringes, and one can hardly call the zone between two fringes a fringe, it is simpler to leave the term an unadorned adjective. The gap between Stephenson's supra-littoral and littoral zones is, according to him (*in litt.*), an incon-sistency of nature rather than of his classification.

As can be seen from Figure 132, the broad mid-littoral of Stephen-son has at least two natural divisions on this coast, the break occurring at mean sea level (3.0′) according to Hewatt, at 2.5 according to Ric-ketts. Stephenson, during his trip to the Pacific coast in 1947, recognized this division, and tentatively called the two parts, upper and lower Bala-noid zones, in his privately printed *Report on Work Done in North America During 1947–48* (1948). The terminology is now abandoned; he would now call them upper and lower mid-littoral. Doty's scheme can be reconciled with the four-zone system of this book by considering his zone of Endocladia-Pelvetia-Fucus a lower subdivision of Zone 2, 2*b*, perhaps; and similarly his zone of Corallinas, etc., becomes 3*b*.

Desirable as it may be to have a universal scheme of zonation of the sort proposed by Stephenson, it may require modification for the different types of tidal patterns. As yet there has been no study of a coast subject to a daily type of tide. The west coast of Japan is the only temperate coast where this type of tide occurs; it is common in

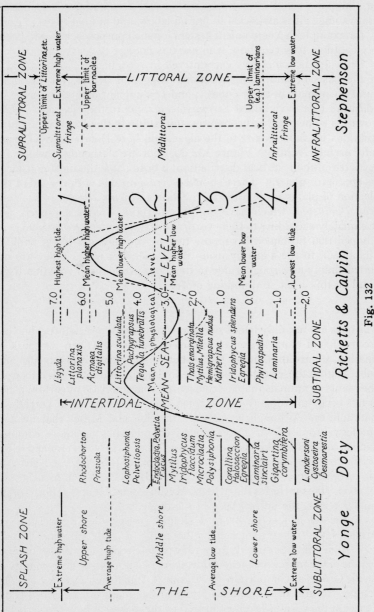

Fig. 132

Comparison of various schemes of intertidal zonation.

the Philippines and East Indies. Elaborate terminology has another disadvantage : it is awkward to put on labels, and in field notes. "Zone 1," for example, is a convenient system for such purposes, and will probably continue to serve those who use this book.

Difficulty is sometimes encountered in recognizing Zones 2 and 3 on the basis of animal distribution. Rigg and Miller, for example, found no animals in their Zones *C* and *D* abundant enough to serve as indicators (we have added *Strongylocentrotus* to the diagram) ; algal growth is so heavy that it obscures animal life at this locality. In such situations we must resort to the algae, and here Doty's work is especially useful. Although Figure 132 does not list all the algae which are restricted in their vertical distribution, it does name the most conspicuous species or genera. These should be recognizable with the aid of the selection of plates from Gilbert M. Smith's *Marine Algae of the Monterey Peninsula,* which have, for this purpose, been rearranged, approximately according to their vertical distribution (pages 385–93). It is hoped that no one will suppose that he can now get along without a handbook to the algae by using this handful of plates; they are intended simply as a rough guide to the more pronounced zonation to be found on this coast, and nothing more.

III

Zones are not only bands of organisms along the seashore; they are also groups of biotic aggregations or communities. When we speak of zonation, we are thinking of the vertical distribution of plants and animals. Within these vertical limits we find horizontal differences as well. The plants or animals that are considered characteristic of certain zones do not occur universally in the zones they indicate, but in patches or communities. Although we agree with Rigg and Miller that the terminology proposed for Puget Sound communities is "more complex than is required for the present purpose," it does serve to emphasize the community aspects of zonation. Occasionally Ricketts used some of this terminology—for example, *"Pisaster-Mytilus-Mitella* association" (p. 165). This includes the Mitella-Mytilus faciation of Shelford, or, in simpler terms, the mussel beds of the outer coast.

A mussel bed is far from a simple grouping of mussels, goose barnacles, and hungry starfish, as this name *"Pisaster-Mytilus-Mitella* association" might imply. Figure 133 (p. 394) represents the occurrence of some of the more conspicuous members of a mussel-bed community at Pacific Grove, as compiled by Dr. Frank A. Pitelka for a marine zoölogy lecture. Several of the animals found in this mature mussel bed could not live at the various levels embraced by the mussel zone on bare rock— for example, the little flat crab, *Petrolisthes,* the isopod *Cirolana,* and

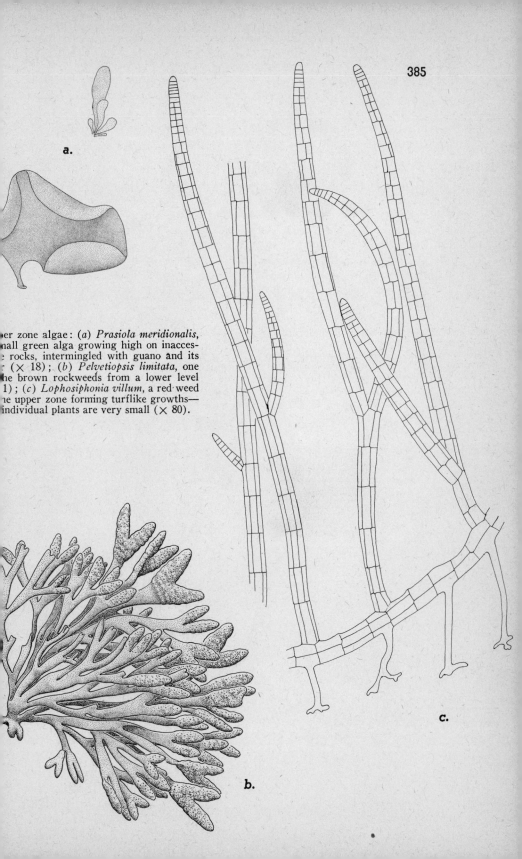

a.

er zone algae: (*a*) *Prasiola meridionalis*,
nall green alga growing high on inacces-
e rocks, intermingled with guano and its
 (× 18); (*b*) *Pelvetiopsis limitata*, one
he brown rockweeds from a lower level
1); (*c*) *Lophosiphonia villum*, a red weed
he upper zone forming turflike growths—
individual plants are very small (× 80).

b.

c.

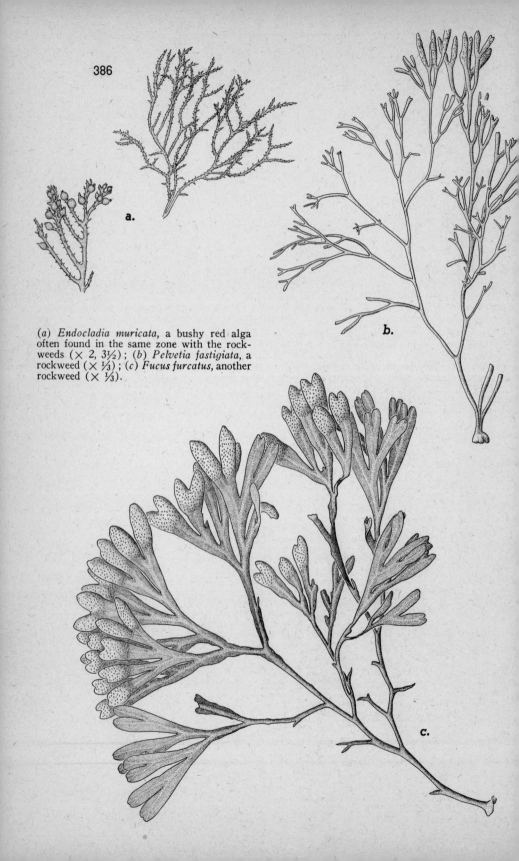

(*a*) *Endocladia muricata*, a bushy red alga often found in the same zone with the rockweeds (× 2, 3½) ; (*b*) *Pelvetia fastigiata*, a rockweed (× ⅓) ; (*c*) *Fucus furcatus*, another rockweed (× ⅓).

a.

b.

c.

d.

e.

Algae of the middle zones: (*a*) *Cladophora graminea*; (*b*) *C. trichotoma*, green algae which form characteristic tufts on the rocks—these drawings are details of the small individual fronds ($\times$ 6); (*c*) *Polysiphonia pacifica*, a red alga forming turflike patches ($\times$ 80); (*d*) *Iridophycus flaccidum*, a large red alga with an oily, iridescent surface ($\times$ ⅜); (*e*) *Microcladia boreale*, one of the smaller bushy reds ($\times$ 1½).

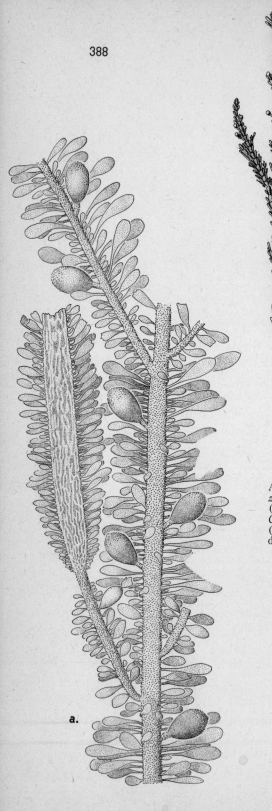

b.

Algae of the lower middle zones : (a) *Egregia Menziesii*, one of the largest of the intertidal browns (× ⅜)—the holdfast is the indicated level; (b) *Corallina gracilis* (× 3) and *C. chilensis* (× 1) (reds) ; (c) *Halosaccion glandiforme* (× ½), a bladderlike red alga.

a.

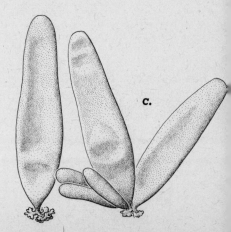

c.

Algae of the "Laminaria" zone: (a) *Prionitis lanceolata* (× ⅓); (b) *P. australis* (× ½); (c) *P. Andersonii* (× ⅕)—the Zanardinulas of some recent authors—the last species is more characteristic of sheltered coves than open rocks; (d) *Iridophycus splendens* (× ¼).

Two of the Laminarians: (*a*) *Laminaria Andersonii* (× ¼); (*b*) *Laminaria Farlowii* (× ¼). These are brown algae, or "kelp."

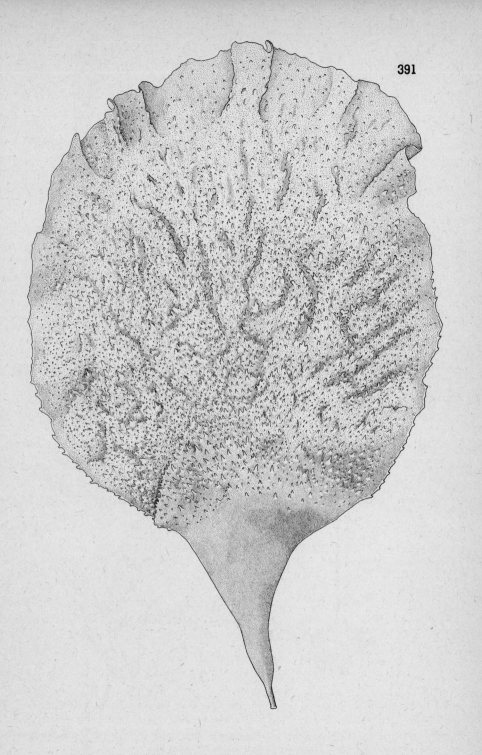

Gigartina corymbifera, a large red alga of the lower zone (× ½).

Cystoseira osmundacea, a brown seaweed growing just below the lowest tide level (× ⅜).

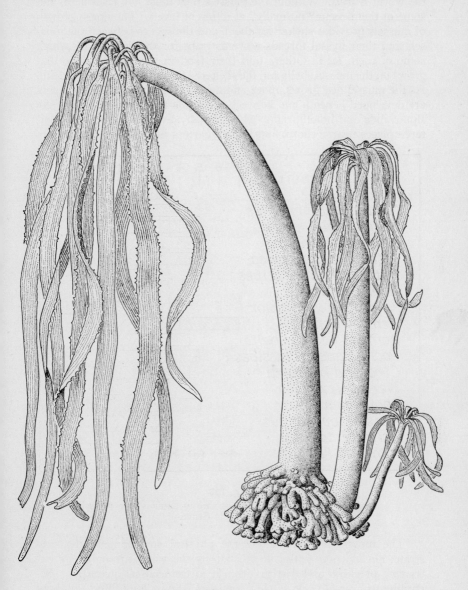

Postelsia palmaeformis, the brown, "palm tree" seaweed, growing in the lower
zone in regions of extreme wave shock (× ½ .

the worm *Nereis*. Without the mussels they must live elsewhere, and some of them occur "normally" at different levels. The dense growth of mussels provides shelter for them, and the spaces between the mussels and their byssal threads serve as traps for the detritus on which some of them feed. Others find their food in the film of algae that grows on the mussel shells and the sheltered areas of rock beneath them. As the mussel bed grows, more and more crevices and sheltered spots are developed beneath and between the shells until some animals, like sipunculids and holothurians, which usually live under rocks in sheltered places nearer shore, find living quarters in the mussel bed.

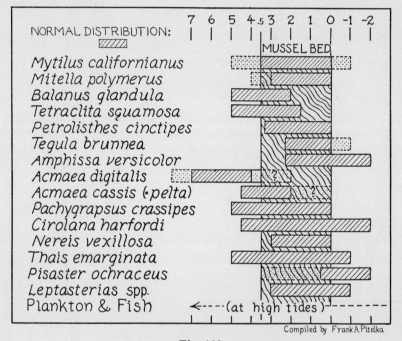

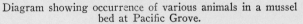

Compiled by Frank A. Pitelka

Fig. 133

Diagram showing occurrence of various animals in a mussel bed at Pacific Grove.

The mussel not only alters the physical environment, the substrate, on which it settles, it also affects the water around it by extracting plankton and detritus from it in tremendous quantities. According to Fox and Coe (1943), a mussel 70 mm. long filters, at about 60 percent efficiency, the plankton and suspended detritus out of 60 liters of water a day, or 22,000 liters a year. This is the activity of a single mussel; the turnover of water and accumulation of body and shell weight by a million mussels, as calculated by Dr. Fox at the Scripps Institution, is enormous. For those with a taste for such figures, we present his table (somewhat modified) here:

	Weight (tons)		Increment (tons)
	At one year	At two years	
Total	51.2	117.6	66.4
Dry weight tissues	2.3	6.4	4.1
Weight shell	26.0	77.7	51.7

Minimal quantity of water filtered per year (22,000 liters per mussel)	22,000,000 tons
Minimal quantity of organic matter removed from water per year (5 mg. per liter)	121 tons
Inert materials filtered from water	c. 400 tons

Approximate efficiency (maximal): $\dfrac{4.1}{121} \times 100 = 3.3\%$

Ecologists have a useful shorthand system for illustrating the interrelationships of such a community as this, called the "food chain." For a mussel bed, it would look something like this:

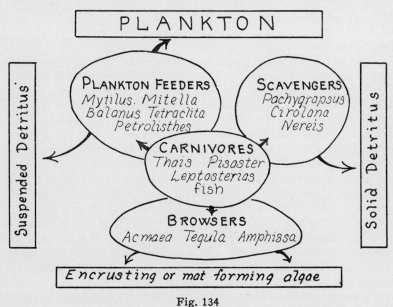

Fig. 134
Diagram illustrating the food chain of the mussel bed.

Contrary to what might be expected at first guess, the mussel bed does not start with young mussels settling on a bare rock. It is not exactly a matter of "getting thar fustest with the mostest." Hewatt, as part of his work at Pacific Grove, scraped a square yard of mussel bed bare in November, counting the animals he removed, and made subsequent counts every few months for a year. His results are best summarized in the form of a table:

	1931	1932						
	Nov. 23	Feb. 19	Mar. 4	Apr. 25	June 3	July 18	Oct. 13	Dec. 26
Algae		xxx						
Acmaea spp.	319	61	232	314	353	331	997	792
Amphissa versicolor	39							
Balanus glandula	872		95	2126	1967	1904	2175	2374
Cirolana harfordi	926							
Leptasterias aequalis	6							
Lottia gigantea	10	1	7	8	11	11	15	15
Mitella polymerus	356		76	109	109	109	109	108
Mytilus californianus ...	1612			55	51	7	53	89
Nuttallina californica					2	34	14	9
Pachygrapsus crassipes ..	14							
Petrolisthes cinctipes ...	416							
Phascolosoma agassizii..	327							
Tegula brunnea	17							
Tetraclita squamosa	78		423	416	378	371	359	329
Thais emarginata	218			2	7	367*	47	59

* Average size, 5 mm.

As can be seen from this table, the first event was the growth of a film of algae, accompanied by a vanguard of limpets grazing upon it. Then came the barnacles. At the end of the observation period, the barnacles were still in the majority, and none of the shelter required by the crevice-loving animals was yet available. Unfortunately, Hewatt was unable to follow this through until the test square had returned to normal, but this is enough to indicate how the mussel dominates its environment and its neighbors when firmly established.

There is apparently an orderly progression in the mussel bed, a replacement of one group by another as the first group makes living conditions suitable for the next, leading finally to the stable or climax condition. This orderly change, involving a sequence of dependencies, is known as succession, and it is to be remembered that it depends not on the physical environment, but on the animals and plants themselves. Thus, the conditions leading to the change are generated within the community by the members of the community.

The interactions of animals in a community is an important, but not the only, influence leading to the zonation of certain animals, which, as free-swimming larvae, would seem to have an equal chance of settling anywhere in the intertidal region. If the larvae settle too high, they are exposed too long, and die off; if they settle too low, they may be exposed to the abrasive action of sand, or if on piling in harbors, to silt near the bottom. Apparently some larvae manage to stay at the proper depth, possibly by reaction to light; others may be released only at certain stages of the tide and settle within a short time. These, of course, would be larvae which become attached or which metamorphose as soon as they strike a suitable substrate; and also the spores of algae. A few larvae have time enough to do a bit of searching about for their place, but the competition for a place to settle down is the most desperate of all the many contests on the seashore. The race is not to the swiftest, but to the best adapted, and the causes of zonation are basically the physical forces and conditions that cull out the "less favored races."

The evidence that this selection may in part be impressed upon larval behavior, to the extent that substrate requirements may be as specific as those of a parasite for its host species, has been summarized by Wilson (1952) for bottom-living invertebrates. It is possible that such specific substrate requirements may obtain for tidal levels as well as for the physical nature of the substrate.

IV

It is most frequently suggested that zonation is a result of exposure, i.e., that organisms are arranged in order of their ability to resist the desiccation or wave action attendant on such exposure. Some organisms, especially certain barnacles, require exposure to wave action to live. But zonation occurs where desiccation is not a problem, and is often so sharply marked (see, for example, the abrupt lower edge of the *Mytilus* in the photograph opposite page 189) as to suggest the operation of some more precise factor than wave action. Colman (1933) suggested that competition between species was the selective agent, yet zones ending abruptly on bare rock with unoccupied space above or below are common on every coast. Another curious facet of this competition aspect is the alternation between zones of plants and animals that so often occurs in the upper parts of the intertidal region. No one has offered an explanation for this.

There is a pronounced difference in the velocity of the tidal current—the ebb and flood—through the cycle, resulting in a velocity through the middle part of the tidal cycle twice, or more than twice, the velocity of the tidal current near the high or low of the cycle. Observing the establishment of organisms on the concrete slopes of a new seawall, Moore and Sproston (1940) found that the middle zone, most subject to the tidal currents, was the last to reach the climax condition, whereas the extremes developed first. Again, as with wave action, we are at a loss to explain how this difference in tidal flow could produce the sharp breaks observed.

The degree to which organisms, especially plants, may require light is undoubtedly an influential factor. Recent work at Hopkins Marine Station confirms the old idea that brown algae are actually more efficient in water of certain depths than the green, since their pigment stops more light than the unaided chlorophyll of such greens as *Ulva,* and transfers the energy to the chlorophyll of the brown seaweeds. This gives them a competitive advantage over the greens in the lower levels, at least in the temperate zone. It may be some such relationship as this which influences the sharp but narrow zonation observable in comparatively tideless regions. Colman (1943) has commented upon this zonation at Tortugas, Florida. It is also conspicuous on jetties in Texas, where the upper zone consists of seasonal greens (which die off in winter), followed by a zone of reds about six inches to a foot wide, and, finally, by a slightly broader zone of browns. Then the algae end abruptly, and the next zone is one of encrusting sponges. The tidal range in this region is about two feet, but the pattern is complex.

The emphasis on "intertidal theory," if we may so call it, is now on "critical levels." Colman (1933) and Evans (1947a, b) have determined such levels for various algae in England, and Beveridge and Chapman in New Zealand. Doty (1946) has attacked this problem of critical levels in a slightly different manner. He considers that the vertical distribution of algae, in particular, is correlated with the sudden increases in maximum time of single exposure that occur at certain parts of the tidal cycle or, conversely, to sudden increases in the period of exposure to submergence. Ricketts recognized the striking difference in exposure at the 3.5′ level in central California (Cf. Gislén, 1943, p. 23), where maximum single exposure below this level is only half as long as exposure immediately above it. This coincides roughly with the "mean physiological level" of his diagram in this book (Fig. 112). Ricketts was considering "mean" or "average" conditions; Doty is concerned with the differences in exposure during a given time, and his tide factors are combinations of both tidal levels and time. They become "critical levels" when they coincide with other, secondary, factors to act upon the organisms. Doty has found, on the basis of his study of the vertical distribution of algae and the tidal curves, that these sudden changes in the tidal cycle occur at LHHW (4.7′), LLHW (3.5′), HHLW (3.0′), LHLW (1.0′), MLLW (0.0′), and LLLW (−1.5′). The figures in parentheses refer to predicted San Francisco tide levels for 1945 and are simply conventions, since obviously these levels vary from place to place and with time.

In more recent studies (Doty and Archer, 1950), an experimental test of this change in gradient or "tide factor hypothesis" has been made by submerging algae for prolonged periods. These experiments consisted of exposing algae in temperatures 5 degrees above normal, and indicated, according to the authors, that when they doubled or tripled the time "at which only just significant injury took place, death occurred sufficiently frequently to indicate acceptability of the tide factor hypothesis." These are the cautious words of science, and, equally cautiously, we venture to suggest that the experiments are promising. It is to be hoped, however, that conditions more comparable to those found in nature can be reproduced in future tests. The oyster biologists have developed an apparatus for reproducing tide effects which might be applied in this sort of thing. With so many variables in the equation, it is desirable to control as many of them as possible, for as C. M. Yonge says in his recent book, "We still have much to learn about the interplay of forces on the shore."

VIa. Newcomers to the Pacific Coast

One of the problems of particular interest to students of the geographical distribution of plants and animals is biogeography : the colonization of new areas by organisms which have in some manner strayed from their native haunts. A man named Guppy, for whom a certain little fish was named, devoted several large volumes to the subject of plant dispersal, one of them concerned entirely with the floating leguminous seeds of the West Indies, the famous "sea beans." We do not propose to add more pages than necessary to this already bulky volume, but it is of particular interest to take note of several of the exotic animals which have, in one way or another, made their way to the Pacific coast. Most of these have hitchhiked their way with oysters, either from the Atlantic coast or from Japanese waters (see p. 260). Usually these immigrants have become well established before their presence is noticed, which, as in the case of undesirable aliens, is too late.

On the other hand, efforts to establish desirable invertebrates from other waters have been on the whole unsuccessful. Fish have succeeded —some of them too well—from surprisingly small plantings, among them the striped bass, the shad, and various catfishes and basses. The most spectacular failure, to return to invertebrates, was that of the Atlantic lobster, which was brought across the Continent in the 1870's and dumped into the Pacific off the Golden Gate. It has since been determined that the larvae of this lobster require a minimum temperature of about 15° C. although the adults can do very well in low temperatures and sometimes stray into the waters around Iceland. Since temperatures off the Golden Gate are rarely above 13° C. on the average during the summer months, it is not surprising that the lobsters planted off the Golden Gate have never been seen again. The critical requirements for spawning, or for the larvae themselves, in temperature, particular food, or some other factor, are the biggest stumbling blocks in the introduction of an invertebrate to these waters.

Efforts to establish the Eastern or Virginia oyster, *Crassostrea virginica*, have for the most part failed (there are some small colonies in Willapa Bay), and the Japanese oyster, *Crassostrea gigas* (now ambiguously called "Pacific oyster" by the trade), is precariously established, under supervision, in Hood Canal, and recently, in Drake's Estero. About once every three years there is a successful spatfall in Willapa Bay. The bulk of the Japanese oyster production in American waters, however, is still from spat imported from Japan and raised in our coastal waters.

With the Japanese oysters has come the Japanese oyster drill, *Tritonalia japonica* (or *Ocenebra japonica*), now established in Puget Sound as a serious pest. It has not become naturalized in California waters. This unwelcome guest was preceded by the related Atlantic drill, *Urosalpinx cinereus*, reported to be common in San Francisco and Tomales bays, and the dog whelk, *Ilyanassa obsoleta*, in San Francisco Bay. A possibly more sinister immigrant from Japan is the parasitic copepod, *Mytilicola orientalis*, reported to be a minor oyster pest in Puget Sound. This, or a similar copepod, has wiped out the mussel industry of France and the Low Countries in the last few years. Since 1947, spat inspectors have been stationed in Japan to prevent the continued introduction of Japanese drills and other pests.

Two slipper limpets have survived the long trip across the Continent to become naturalized. *Crepidula fornicata* (see p. 33) is reported by Dr. J. E. Lynch to be pestiferously abundant in southern Puget Sound, and has been reported from San Francisco and Tomales bays, although Dr. Coe (1949) says its survival "at present is doubtful." The other species, *Crepidula plana*, very similar to the native *C. nummaria* (formerly *C. nivea*), is established in Puget Sound.

The wanderings of *Diadumene luciae* have been mentioned on page 221; a few years ago (1947), this anemone turned up on the Texas coast. Where it will be found next is anyone's guess.

There are some neutral immigrants from the Atlantic coast, the most spectacular of which is the conch, *Busycon pyrum*, which has recently been collected several times in San Francisco Bay. Another is the little brackish water crab, *Rhithropanopeus harrisi*, reported from the same locality by Jones (1940). In 1950 Dr. James A. Macnab found this crab in the sloughs south of Coos Bay. In the summer of

1949 Dr. Lynch found the Atlantic tunicate, *Molgula manhattensis*, on the piling at Marshall, in Tomales Bay.

Some years ago (1939) Dr. G. Dallas Hanna prepared a list of exotic mollusca introduced into California. At that time there were at least ten marine species, including, in addition to those already named, the Eastern gem clam, *Gemma gemma*, the horse mussel, *Modiolus demissus*, the infamous shipworm, *Teredo navalis* (presumed to be non-native at the time), and the Eastern soft shell clam, *Mya arenaria*. His list does not include *Busycon*, or the Japanese littleneck clam mentioned below.

It is pleasant to conclude our roster of undesirable and indifferent invaders with a mention of one of some value, at least by our homocentric standards. This is the Japanese "littleneck" clam, *Protothaca philippinarum* (also known as *Tapes semidecussata*), now widespread and common enough in Puget Sound to appear on the market. It was first noticed in British Columbia waters about 1939, when it was described as a new species, *Paphia bifurcata*. It has become abundant in Puget Sound within the last eight or nine years. Its presence in California waters was noticed some years earlier; there is a note by Bonnot (Nautilus, **49**: 1–2) indicating its arrival in central California at least as early as 1930. It is now abundant in San Francisco Bay. Somewhat smaller than its relative, *Protothaca staminea*, it is considered to be better flavored than the native species. In appearance it is more elongate, with brownish to bluish banding on one end, indicating the source of one of its names, *semidecussata*.

APPENDIX

Annotated Systematic Index
and Bibliography

For this new edition we (the editor and his helpful colleagues) have tried to add important and interesting new papers, published through 1951, to straighten out some of the names which have been changed since this book first went to press, and, here and there, to add new material. The treatment for some groups, notably hydroids, echinoderms, and decapod crustacea, remains almost unchanged from the previous edition. This does not mean that perfection was attained in 1948, but that there has been no one working critically with these groups, and that what work is being done is still too incomplete to permit revision of these pages at this time.

That happy millennium when each invertebrate group will have been monographed is not yet here; a few monographs, notably Osburn's work on the bryozoa, are in progress. The fashion these days is not single-handed, elaborate monographs, but symposium volumes, by a minimum of three authors, on an entire field. Thus we have Sverdrup, Johnson, and Fleming (oceanography), Allee *et al.* (ecology), and Prosser *et al.* (physiology). These are very fine, but we hope that the student who approaches marine biology through this book will at least realize how much detailed work, especially in systematics, remains to be done, and how many unanswered questions are raised in each sweeping symposium that seeks to tell him all he needs to know; in short, how much is yet unknown. That the literature on Pacific coast marine invertebrates is widely scattered is a lament we need hardly reiterate from the previous editions of this book (and from *Sea of Cortez*, p. 285), and it continues to be scattered in journals both foreign and domestic. The most acute literature problem involves material published in Russia and Japan. Russian scientific literature is becoming increasingly parochial; the number of papers accompanied by summaries in an accessible language is steadily decreasing; and, if this were not enough, the journals are hard to track down, are poorly represented in our libraries, and, when represented, are thoroughly hidden by the peculiar filing system of libraries. It seems to us that matters would be simpler if both librarians and students were to learn and use the Russian alphabet, and master the rudimentary vocabulary of journal

403

titles, instead of using the obfuscating and inaccurate scheme of transliteration now in vogue. Our knowledge of Japanese publications has not yet caught up with the wartime gap in communications, and much wartime work of Japanese investigators is waiting publication.

We have tried to adhere to the standards of citation established in previous editions but make no pretense for comprehensiveness. The number of new titles added is rather small, although the printers may think otherwise. The plankton bibliography has been moved into the Appendix, the echinoderms have been moved over to the exalted position they enjoy in modern texts, and some lesser changes have been made. The various paragraphs of acknowledgment have been removed, since some of the people mentioned have died, and others have changed their addresses. This does not mean that we are less indebted to the specialists, but in more than one instance the impression was given that a specialist was more responsible for the contents of a particular section than was actually the case. Responsibility for errors, as usual, must fall on us rather than on the people who have helped us.

Our thanks are due to the following, for helpful advice, recommendations for changes or additions, citing of errors, and, in some cases, scrutiny of the sections in their specialities:

Dr. Donald P. Abbott (tunicates), Mr. Zach Arnold (Foraminifera), Mr. J. Laurens Barnard (Amphipoda), Dr. S. Stillman Berry (Mollusca, especially chitons), Dr. Rolf L. Bolin (fish), Dr. Elisabeth Deichmann (Alcyonaria), Dr. Maxwell S. Doty (algae), Dr. J. Wyatt Durham (corals), Dr. Walter K. Fisher (echiurids and sipunculids), Dr. Cadet H. Hand (anemones), Dr. Olga Hartman (polychaetes), Dr. A. Myra Keen (Mollusca), Dr. James E. Lynch (general), Dr. Robert J. Menzies (Isopoda), Dr. Raymond C. Osburn (Bryozoa), and Dr. Frank A. Pitelka (birds).

We wish to thank Dr. Frank A. Pitelka for permission to use the map of communities at Tomales Bay and his diagram of the mussel bed, Mr. John R. Hendrickson and Dr. Martin W. Johnson for photographs, and also to acknowledge the assistance of Dr. Joe W. Johnson in obtaining the Navy photographs, which were taken by Willard N. Bascom. We are indebted also to Dr. Gilbert M. Smith for the use of the plates of algae from his book, and to Dr. Alden E. Noble, director of Pacific Marine Station, for the use of specimens illustrated in some of the new drawings. The drawings of isopods and bryozoa which replace former figures are used with the permission of Dr. Robert J. Menzies. Several mollusk drawings have been contributed by Sam Hinton. The color photograph is by Ross Commings. Most of the new photographs in this edition are by Woody Williams of Inverness.

To Mrs. Fred G. Strong of Carmel the editor owes a debt of thanks, both for some of the information about her brother which is included in the Preface, and for her generous assistance with typing copy for this revision.

PLANTS

This is, of course, a book about animals; and a surprisingly small number of them are directly related to the intertidal algae as grazers or browsers, although the seaweeds are one of the major sources of organic detritus in the intertidal, and provide refuge in one way or another for many species of animals. Algae are also important indicators of intertidal zonation, as brought out in Section VI. The literature on Pacific coast marine algae is large and is steadily growing; certain papers dealing principally with algal ecology are cited in Section III of the Bibliography. The following references are useful guides, and Smith's book in particular contains a comprehensive bibliography of systematic literature on Pacific coast algae.

References:

CUPP, EASTER E. 1943. "Marine plankton diatoms of the West coast of North America," Bull. Scripps Inst. Oceanogr., 5 (1): 1–238, 5 plates, 168 figures.
   Seventy years or so ago it was the fashion to collect diatoms and mount them in designs on slides, which were then admired at the meetings of the local microscopical society. An amiable pastime now gone the way, it seems, of the free lunch and the horse-drawn trolley.

DAWSON, E. YALE. 1946. "A guide to the literature and distributions of the marine algae of the Pacific coast of North America," Mem. S. Calif. Acad. Sci., 3 (1): 134 pages.
   A useful check list.

DOTY, MAXWELL S. 1947. "The marine algae of Oregon," I, Chlorophyta and Phaeophyta. Farlowia, 3 (1): 1–65, 10 plates; II, Rhodophyta, ibid., 3 (2): 159–215, pls. 11–14.

SANBORN, ETHEL I., and DOTY, MAXWELL S. 1947. "The marine algae of the Coos Bay–Cape Arago region of Oregon," Ore. State Monogr., Bot., 8: 66 pages, 4 plates.

SMITH, GILBERT M. 1944. Marine algae of the Monterey Peninsula, Stanford University Press. 622 pages, including 98 plates.
   Because the majority of the algae known from the Pacific coast of the United States and Canada occur at Monterey, this becomes a handbook for the whole coast.

——— (ed.) 1951. Manual of phycology, Chronica Botanica, Waltham, Mass., xi + 375 pages.
   A symposium treatment of the algae in the broadest sense, including the flagellates, with a long chapter on intertidal algal ecology by Feldmann. Excellent bibliographies.

In addition to the algae, there are three species of higher plants commonly found intertidally on this seacoast, the eel grasses. Rather than refer the reader to a flora, devoted primarily to terrestrial plants, the following key or synopsis of the Zosteraceae is offered:

1. Flowers unisexual but borne on the same spike; fruit ovoid, hornless. Plants growing on sand or mud in bays and similar protected situations; leaves 5–7-nerved (*Zostera*) 2

    Flowers unisexual but borne on different spikes; fruit heart-shaped with prominent horns at the base. Plants growing on rocky, exposed or semiprotected situations; leaves 3-nerved (*Phyllospadix*) 3

2. Leaves usually 2–8 mm. broad; fruit subsessile; seed distinctly ribbed; Atlantic and Pacific oceans, known from San Pedro to Alaska on the Pacific coast of North America....................................*Zostera marina* Linné

    Leaves usually 6–12 mm. broad; fruit distinctly stipitate; seed ribless; Santa Barbara to Puget Sound.............*Zostera marina* var. *latifolia* Marong

3. Leaves usually 1–2 mm. broad, thin, flat, indistinctly 3-nerved; seed-bearing spikes, several, scattered along the stem; Lower California to Mendocino County....................................*Phyllospadix Scouleri* Hook.

    Leaves usually 2–4 mm. broad, elliptical in cross section, distinctly 3-nerved; seed-bearing spike, usually one (rarely two spikes), attached near the base of the stem; Santa Barbara to Vancouver Island, Japan
    Phyllospadix Torreyi Wats.

Since fruiting stages of these plants are seldom seen, at least by unobservant zoölogists, we must rely upon habitat and general appearance for field determination. The varieties of *Zostera* are of "doubtful distinctness," according to one botanist; only the variety *latifolia* is recognized, from Marin County, in Howell's flora, and is probably the common phase of the central California coast. Of the *Phyllospadix*, *Scouleri* seems to prefer more exposed, wave-beaten conditions than *Torreyi*.

PLANKTON

There has been no attempt to make this list complete, even for the Pacific; that would require too much space. The aim has been instead to provide a suggestive bibliography, which, followed out, should lead the investigator into a fairly complete list.

Perhaps attention should be called to the fact that the "University of California Publications in Oceanography" were originally entitled and issued as *Bulletin of the Scripps Institution of Oceanography, La Jolla, California, Technical Series.*

AIKAWA, H. 1936. "On the diatom communities in the waters surrounding Japan," Rec. Ocean. Works Japan, **8** (1): 1–159.

ALLEN, W. E. 1923 (June). "Some tide-water collections of marine diatoms taken at half-hour intervals near San Diego, California," University Calif. Pub. Zool., **22**: 413–16.

———. 1923 (Oct.). "Studies on marine diatoms and dinoflagellates caught by aid of the Kofoid Bucket in 1922," University Calif. Publ. Zool., **22**: 435–45.

———. 1923 (Nov.). "Statistical studies of marine diatoms of the San Diego region collected by the U.S.S. *Pioneer* in midwinter 1923," University Calif. Publ. Zool., 22: 445–48.

———. 1924. "Surface catches of marine diatoms and dinoflagellates made by the U.S.S. *Pioneer* between San Diego and Seattle in 1923," University Calif. Publ. Zool., 26: 243–48.

———. 1927. "Surface catches of marine diatoms and dinoflagellates made by the U.S.S. *Pioneer* in Alaskan waters in 1923," University Calif. Publ. Ocean., 1: 39–48.

———. 1928 (Jan.). "Catches of marine diatoms and dinoflagellates taken by boat in southern California waters in 1926," University Calif. Publ. Ocean., 1: 201–46.

———. 1928 (Nov.). "Review of five years of studies on phytoplankton at southern California piers, 1920–24 inclusive," University Calif. Publ. Ocean., 1: 357–401.
   The bibliography cites the 1922a Introduction (fall, 1919, figures) and the 1920–24 annual details, 1922b, 1927a, 1927b, Dorman 1927, and Allen 1928b, which must be used in any statistical analysis.

———. 1929. "Surface catches of marine diatoms and dinoflagellates made by the U.S.S. *Pioneer* in Alaskan waters in 1924," University Calif. Publ. Ocean., 2: 139–53.

———. 1930. (Jan.). "Methods in quantitative research on marine microplankton," University Calif. Publ. Ocean., 2: 319–29.

———. 1930 (Oct.). "Quantitative studies of surface catches of marine diatoms and dinoflagellates . . . . Alaskan waters . . . . 1927–28 and 1929," University Calif. Publ. Ocean., 2: 389–99.

———. 1939. "Surface distribution of marine plankton diatoms in the Panama region in 1933," University Calif. Publ. Ocean., 4: 181–96.

———. (1939) 1940. "Methods of field and laboratory procedure in phytoplankton research . . . . ," Proc. 6th Pac. Sci. Congr., 3: 525–28.

ALLEN, W. E. (1939) 1940a. "Summary of results of twenty years of researches on marine phytoplankton," Proc. 6th Pac. Sci. Congr., 3: 577–83.

———. 1941. "Depth relationships of plankton diatoms in sea water," Jour. Marine Res., 4 (2): 107–11.

———. 1941a. "Ocean pasturage in California waters," Sci. Monthly 52: 261–64.

———. 1941b. "Twenty years' statistical studies of marine plankton dinoflagellates of southern California," Amer. Midl. Nat., 26: 603–35.

———. 1945 (Jan.). "Occurences and abundances of marine plankton diatoms offshore in southern California," Trans. Amer. Micro. Soc., 64: 21–24.

———. 1945 (Aug.). "Vernal distribution of marine plankton diatoms offshore in southern California in 1940," Univ. Calif. Publ. Ocean., 5: 335–70.
   Bibliography cites the previous 1945 paper on the 1938 findings.

ALLEN, W. E., and LEWIS, R. 1927. "Surface catches of marine diatoms and dinoflagellates from Pacific high seas in 1925 and 1926," Univ. Calif. Publ. Ocean., 1: 197–200.

BIGELOW, H. B. 1914. "Notes on the medusan genus Stomolophus from San Diego," Univ. Calif. Publ. Zool., 13: 239–42.

BIGELOW, H. B., and LESLIE, M. 1930. "Reconnaissance of the waters and plankton of Monterey Bay, July 1928," Bull. Mus. Comp. Zool., 70: 429–581.

Brongersma-Sanders, Margaretha. 1948. "The significance of upwelling to vertebrate paleontology and oil geology," Verh. Konink. Nederl. Akad. Wetensch., Natuurk, (2) 45 (4): 1–112, 7 figures.

Buley, H. M. 1929. "Quantitative studies on inshore diatoms and dinoflagellates of the California coast in 1925," Univ. Calif. Publ. Ocean., 2: 181–87.

Burkenroad, Martin D. 1946. "Fluctuations in abundance of marine animals," Science, 103: 684–86, 1 figure.

Campbell, M. H. 1929. "Some free swimming copepods of the Vancouver Island region," Trans. Roy. Soc. Can., (3), Sec. 5, 23: 303–32.
    Bibliography cites Currie, 1918, Poppe, 1884, and Willey, 1920, apropos papers for the region involved.

———. 1934. "The life history and post-embryonic development of the copepods *Calanus tonsus* Brady and *Euchaeta japonica* Marukawa," Jour. Biol. Bd. Can., 1: 1–65.

Cupp, Easter E. 1937. "Seasonal distribution and occurrence of marine diatoms and dinoflagellates at Scotch Cap, Alaska," Univ. Calif. Publ. Ocean., 4: 71–100.

———. 1943. "Marine plankton diatoms of the west coast of North America," Univ. Calif. Publ. Ocean., 5: 238 pages.

Davis, Charles C. 1949. "The pelagic copepoda of the northeastern Pacific Ocean," Univ. Wash. Publ. Biology, 14: 1–118, 15 pls.

Dorman, H. P. 1927. "Studies on marine diatoms and dinoflagellates caught with the Kofoid Bucket in 1923," Univ. Calif. Publ. Ocean., 1: 49–61.

Essenberg, C. 1922. "The seasonal distribution of the Appendicularia in the region of San Diego," Ecology, 3: 55–64.

———. 1924. "The incomplete digestive tract of Appendicularia sicula," Univ. Calif. Publ. Zool., 26: 263–66.

———. 1926. "Copelata from the San Diego region" and "Observations on the gradual disintegration and death of Copelata," Univ. Calif. Publ. Zool., 28: 399–525.

Esterly, C. O. 1911. "Third report on the Copepoda of the San Diego region," Univ. Calif. Publ. Zool., 6: 313–52.
    Bibliography cites the first two reports, 1905 and 1906.

———. 1912. "The occurrence and vertical distribution of the Copepoda of the San Diego region . . . .," Univ. Calif. Publ. Zool., 9: 253–340.
    Bibliography cites two 1911 apropos papers.

Esterly, C. O. 1913. "Fourth taxonomic report on the Copepoda of the San Diego region," Univ. Calif. Publ. Zool., 11: 181–96.

———. 1914 (April). "A study of the occurrence and manner of distribution of the Ctenophora of the San Diego region," Univ. Calif. Publ. Zool., 13: 21–38.

———. 1914 (May). "The vertical distribution and movements of the Schizopoda of the San Diego region," Univ. Calif. Publ. Zool., 13:123–45.

———. 1916. "The feeding habits and food of pelagic copepods and the question of nutrition by organic substances in solution in the water," Univ. Calif. Publ. Zool., 16: 171–84.

———. 1917. "The occurrence of a rhythm in the geotropism of two species of plankton copepods when certain recurring external stimuli are absent," Univ. Calif. Publ. Zool., 16: 393–400.

――――. 1919. "Reactions of various plankton animals with reference to their diurnal migrations," Univ. Calif. Publ. Zool., 19: 1–83.

――――. 1924. "Freeswimming copepods of San Francisco Bay," Univ. Calif. Publ. Zool., 26: 81–129.

――――. 1928. "The periodic occurrence of Copepoda in the marine plankton of two successive years at La Jolla, California," Univ. Calif. Publ. Ocean, 1: 247–345.
Bibliography includes the 1923 preliminary report and others.

FOERSTER, R. E. 1923. "The hydromedusae of the west coast of North America, with special reference to the Vancouver Island region," Cont. Can. Biol., n.s., 1: 219–77.

Fox, D. 1929. "Quantitative studies on inshore marine diatoms and dinoflagellates at five stations on the east Pacific coast in 1926," Univ. Calif. Publ. Ocean., 2: 189–96.

GRAHAM, H. W. 1941. "Plankton production in relation to character of water in the open Pacific," Jour. Marine Res., 4: 189–97.

――――. 1943 (May). "Chlorophyll-content of marine plankton," Jour. Marine Res., 5: 153–60, figure.

――――. 1943 (July). "The Phytoplankton," in: Sci. Results of Cruise VII of the *Carnegie* . . . . , Biology IV (No. 1): 1–13, figures.

GRAN, H. H., and THOMPSON, T. G. 1930. "The diatoms and the physical and chemical conditions of the sea water of the San Juan archipelago," Publ. Puget Sound Biol. Sta., 7: 169–204.

GRAN, H. H., and ANGST, E. C. 1931 "Plankton diatoms of Puget Sound," Publ. Puget Sound Biol. Sta., 7: 417–519.

GUNTER, GORDON, WILLIAM, R. H., DAVIS, C. C., and SMITH, F. G. W. 1948. "Catastrophic mass mortality of marine animals and coincident phytoplankton bloom on the west coast of Florida, November 1946 to August 1947," Ecol. Monogr. 18: 309–24, 2 figures.

HARVEY, H. W. 1942. *Production of life in the sea. A review summary.* Biol. Rev., Cambr. Phil. Soc., 17 (3).

HUTCHINSON, A. H. 1928. "A bio-hydrographical investigation of the sea adjacent to the Fraser River mouth," Trans. Roy. Soc. Can., (3) 22: 293–310.

HUTCHINSON, A. H., LUCAS, C. C., and McPHAIL, M. 1929. "Seasonal variation in the chemical and physical properties of the waters of the Strait of Georgia in relation to phytoplankton," Trans. Roy. Soc. Can., (3) 23: 177–83.

JOHNSON, MYRTLE E. 1910. "A quantitative study in the development of the Salpa chain in *Salpa fusiformis-runcinata,*" Univ. Calif. Publ. Zool., 6: 145–76.

JOHNSON, MARTIN W. 1932. "Seasonal distribution of plankton at Friday Harbor, Washington," Univ. Wash. Publ. Ocean., 1: 1–38.

JOHNSON, MARTIN W. 1934. "The life history of the copepod *Tortanus discaudatus* . . . . ," Biol. Bull., 67: 182–200.

――――. 1934a. "The developmental stages of the copepod *Epilabidocera amphitrites* . . . . ," Biol. Bull, 67: 466–83.

――――. 1936. "*Pachyptilus pacificus* and *Centraugaptilus porcellus,* two new copepods from the north Pacific," Univ. Calif. Publ. Ocean., 4: 65–70.

――――. 1937. "The developmental stages of the copepod *Eucalanus elongatus* var. *bungii* Giesbrecht," Trans. Amer. Micro. Soc., 54: 79–98.

———. 1938. "Concerning the copepod *Eucalanus elongatus* Dana and its varieties in the northeast Pacific," Univ. Calif. Publ. Ocean., **4**: 165–80.

———. 1939. "*Pseudodiaptomus . . . . euryhalinus*, a new subgenus and species of Copepoda, with preliminary notes on its ecology," Trans. Amer. Micro. Soc., **58**: 349–55.

JOHNSON, M. W., and THOMPSON, T. G. 1929. "The sea water at the Puget Sound Biological Station from September 1927 to September 1928," Publ. Puget Sound Biol. Sta., **7**: 119–28.

LEPESCHKIN, W. W. 1931. "Some experiments on the influence of light and poisons on marine copepods, with reference to their daily migration," Univ. Calif. Publ. Ocean., **3**: 33–35.

LEWIS, RALPH. 1927. "Surface catches of marine diatoms and dinoflagellates off the coast of Oregon by the U.S.S. *Guide* in 1924," Univ. Calif. Publ. Ocean., **1**: 189–96.

LITTLE, S. V. 1914. "The structure of the ocelli of Polyorchis penicillata," Univ. Calif. Publ. Zool., **11**: 307–28.

LUCAS, C. C., and HUTCHINSON, A. H. 1927. "A bio-hydrographical investigation of the sea adjacent to the Fraser River mouth," Trans. Roy. Soc. Can., (3) **21**: 485–520.

MANN, ALBERT. 1925. *Marine diatoms*. Rep. Can. Arc. Exped., 1913–18, **4** (F): 33 pages.

MARINE RESEARCH COMMITTEE, CALIFORNIA DEPARTMENT OF NATURAL RESOURCES. 1950. "California co-operative sardine research program. Progress report, 1950." 54 pages, 37 figures.

MICHAEL, E. L. 1911. "Classification and vertical distribution of the Chaetognatha of the San Diego region," Univ. Calif. Publ. Zool., **8**: 21–186.

———. 1913. "*Sagitta californica*, n.sp., from the San Diego region including remarks on its variation and distribution," Univ. Calif. Publ. Zool., **11**: 89–126.

———. 1918. "Differentials in behavior of two generations of *Salpa democrita* relative to the temperature of the sea," Univ. Calif. Publ. Zool., **18**: 239–98.

MILLER, R. C. (1939) 1940. "Plankton investigations at the University of Washington," Proc. 6th Pac. Sci. Congr., **3**: 585–86.

MOBERG, ERIK G. 1928. "The interrelation between diatoms, their chemical environment, and upwelling water in the sea off the coast of southern California," Proc. Natl. Acad. Sci., **14**: 511–18.

MOBERG, E. G., and ALLEN, W. E. 1927. "Effect of tidal changes on physical, chemical, and biological conditions in the sea water of the San Diego region," Univ. Calif. Publ. Ocean., **1**: 1–17.

MORTENSEN, TH. 1927. "Two new ctenophores," Vidensk. Medd. fra Dansk naturh. Foren., **83**: 277–88.

PHIFER, L. D. 1929. "Littoral diatoms of Argyle Lagoon," Publ. Puget Sound Biol. Sta., **7**: 137–49.

PHIFER, L. D. 1933. "Seasonal distribution and occurrence of planktonic diatoms at Friday Harbor, Washington," Univ. Wash. Publ. Ocean., **1**: 39–81.

———. 1934. "Continuous phytoplankton collection," Science, **79**: 298–99.

———. 1934a. "Vertical distribution of diatoms in the Strait of Juan de Fuca," Univ. Wash. Publ. Ocean., **1**: 83–96.

————. 1935*b*. "Phytoplankton of East Sound, Washington, February to November, 1932," Univ. Wash. Publ. Ocean., **1**: 97–110.

PHIFER, L. D., and THOMPSON, T. G. 1937. "Seasonal variations in the surface waters of San Juan Channel during the five-year period . . . . ," Jour. Marine Res., **1**: 34–59.

RILEY, GORDON A. 1938. "The measurement of phytoplankton," Int. Rev. ges. Hydrobiol. Hydrogr., **36**: 371–73.

RITTER, W. E. 1905. "The pelagic Tunicata of the San Diego region, excepting the Larvacea," Univ. Calif. Publ. Zool., **2**: 51–112.

SKOGSBERG, T. 1936. "Hydrography of Monterey Bay, California. Thermal conditions, 1929–1933," Trans. Amer. Phil. Soc., **29**: 1–152.

SLEGGS, G. F. 1927. "Marine phytoplankton in the region of La Jolla, California, during the summer of 1924," Univ. Calif. Publ. Ocean., **1**: 93–117.

SOMMER, H., and CLARK, FRANCES N. 1946. "Effect of red water on marine life in Santa Monica Bay, California," California Fish and Game, **32**: 100–101.

SVERDRUP, H. U., and ALLEN, W. E. 1939. "Distribution of diatoms in relation to the character of water masses and currents off southern California," Jour. Marine Res., **2**: 131–44.

SVERDRUP, JOHNSON, and FLEMING. 1942. *The Oceans* . . . . (Prentice-Hall, Inc., New York), especially chapters 16, 17, 18, and 19, pp. 762–945.

THOMPSON, T. G., JOHNSON, M. W., and TODD, S. P. 1928. "The sea water at the Puget Sound Biological Station from September 1926 to September 1927," Publ. Puget Sound Biol. Sta., **6**: 371–94.

THOMPSON, T. G., MILLER, HITCHINGS, and TODD. 1929. "Studies of the sea water near the Puget Sound Biological Station during the summer of 1927," Publ. Puget Sound Biol. Sta., **7**: 65–99.

THOMPSON, T. G., and JOHNSON, M. W. 1930. "The sea water at the Puget Sound Biological Station from September 1928 to September 1929," Publ. Puget Sound Biol. Sta., **7**: 345–68.

THOMPSON, T. G., and ROBINSON, R. J. 1934. "The sea water of the Puget Sound region," Proc. 5th Pac. Congr., pp. 2,101–2,107.

THOMPSON, T. G., and PHIFER, L. D. 1936. "The plankton and the properties of the surface waters of the Puget Sound region," Univ. Wash. Publ. Ocean., **1**: 111–34.

TORREY, H. B. 1904. "The ctenophores of the San Diego region," Univ. Calif. Publ. Zool., **2**: 45–51.

TULLY, JOHN P. 1937. "Oceanography of Nootka Sound," Journal Biological Board Canada, **3** (1): 43–69.

United States Coast and Geodetic Survey. 1945. "Surface water temperatures . . . . Pacific Coast," Publ. TW-2, 33 pages. Washington, D.C.

WILSON, CHARLES B. 1942. "The copepods of the plankton gathered during the last cruise of the *Carnegie*," Publ. 536, Carn. Inst. Wash., 327 pages.

Phylum **PROTOZOA**

Single-celled animals, being ordinarily too small for naked-eye observance, have been deliberately omitted, except for the inclusion of a few which may add interest.

References:

LYNCH, JAMES E. 1929. "Studies on the ciliates from the intestine of *Strongylocentrotus*. I," Univ. Calif. Publ. Zoöl., **33**: 27–56 (*et seq.*).

MACLENNAN and CONNELL. 1931. "The morphology of *Eupoterion per - nix* . . . .," Univ. Calif. Publ. Zoöl., **36**: 141–56.
Ciliate from limpet gut.

MOHR, JOHN LUTHER. 1948. *"Trichochona lecythoides,* a new genus and species of marine Chonotrichous ciliate from California, with a consideration of the composition of the order Chonotrichia Wallengren, 1895," Occ. Pap. Allan Hancock Found., No. 5 : 20 pages, 1 plate.
Ciliates attached to pleopods of amphipods.

MYERS, EARL H. 1940. "Observations on the origin and fate of flagellated gametes in multiple tests of *Discorbis* (Foraminifera)," Jour. Mar. Biol. Assoc., **24**: 201–26, 3 plates.
Beautifully illustrated paper on a group of benthic tide-pool Foraminifera well represented on the California coast. Species occurring at La Jolla, Monterey, and Moss Beach are discussed.

STEVENS, N. M. 1901. "Studies on ciliate infusoria," Proc. Calif. Acad. Sci., Ser. 3, Zoöl., **3** : 1–42.

Boveria subcylindrica Stevens (in the holothurian *Stichopus*) . . . . § 77

B. teredinidi Nelson . . . . §337
Reference:
PICKARD, E. A. 1927. "The neuromotor apparatus of *Boveria teredinidi* Nelson, a ciliate from the gills of *Teredo navalis,*" Univ. Calif. Publ. Zoöl., **29**: 405–28.

Ephelota gemmipara (Hertwig), suctorian occurring on *Abietinaria* (hydroid) . . . . § 83

E. gigantea Noble . . . . §323
Reference:
NOBLE, A. E. 1929. "Two new species of . . . . *Ephelota* from Monterey Bay," Univ. Calif. Publ. Zoöl., **33**: 13–26.

Gromia oviformis Dujardin . . . . not treated
References:
ARNOLD, ZACH M. 1951. "Occurrence of *Gromia oviformis* Dujardin in California (Testacea)," Wasmann Jour. Biol., **9** (3) : 351–53.
JEEPS, MARGARET W. 1926. "Contributions to the study of *Gromia oviformis* Dujardin," Quar. Jour. Micr. Sci., n.s., **70**: 701–19, 3 plates.
This large (2–3 mm.) foram, mistaken by some for "fecal pellets," is common, especially among *Phyllospadix* holdfasts, from Pacific Grove to Dillon Beach and probably elsewhere. It is an ivory-white, conspicuous (for a protozoan!) object.

Licnophora macfarlandi Stevens (in *Stichopus*) . . . . § 77

Trichamoeba schaefferi Radir . . . . § 64
Reference:
RADIR, PAUL I. 1927. *"Trichamoeba schaefferi,* a new species of

large ameba from Monterey Bay, California," Arch. f. Protis.,
59: 289–300.

Phylum (?) MESOZOA

Reference:
McConnaughey, Bayard H. 1949. "Mesozoa of the family Dicyemidae from
  California," U. Calif. Publ. Zool., **55 (1)**: 1–34, 8 plates.
Curious animals of doubtful position, parasitic in the kidneys of octopus. Several species are known from California cephalopods.

Phylum PORIFERA.   Sponges

References:
Laubenfels, M. W. de. 1928. "Interspecific grafting, using sponge cells,"
  Jour. of Elisha Mitchell Scientific Society, **44**: 82–85.

——. 1932. "The marine and fresh-water sponges of California," Proc.
  U.S. Nat. Mus., **81**: 1–140.

——. 1935. "Some sponges of Lower California (Mexico)," Amer. Mus.
  Novit., No. **799**: 14 pages.

——. 1936. "A discussion of the sponge fauna of the Dry Tortugas . . . .
  with material for a revision of the families and orders of the Porifera,"
  Publ. No. 467, Carnegie Institution of Washington. 225 pages, etc.
  The most indispensable modern sponge reference.

——. 1948. "The order Keratosa of the phylum Porifera—a monographic
  study," Allan Hancock Publ., "Occ. Papers," **3**: 217 pages, 30 plates, 31 figures in text.
  Concerns the bath sponges and their relatives; mostly tropical and warm-water forms.

Parker, G. H. 1914. "On the strength and the volume of the water currents produced by sponges," Jour. Exper. Zoöl., **16**: 443–46.

Choanites suberea var. *lata* (Lambe), as *Suberites latus* . . . . §225
Cliona celata Grant, Boring Sponge . . . . §217
Esperiopsis originalis de L., Red Sponge . . . . §140
Halichondria panicea (Pallas), Crumb-of-Bread Sponge . . . . § 97
Haliclona permollis Bowerbank (formerly considered *Reniera cineria*) . . . . . § 31
H. rufescens (Lambe), as *Reniera rufescens* . . . . §198
Halisarca sacra de L., Slime Sponge . . . . §238
Hymeniacidon sinapium de L. . . . . §183
Isociona lithophoenix (de L.), Red Sponge . . . . § 32
Leuconia heathi (Urban), as *Leucandra heathi* . . . . § 95
Leucosolenia eleanor Urban . . . . § 93
L. nautilia de L. . . . . §229
Lissodendoryx noxiosa de L. . . . . § 97
Mycale adherens Lambe, and *Ectyodoryx parasitica* (Lambe) on *Pecten* . . . §220
M. macginitiei de L. . . . . §238

Class HYDROZOA.   Hydroids and Hydromedusae

References:

FRASER, C. McL. 1914. "Some hydroids of the Vancouver Island region," Trans. Roy. Soc. Can., Biol. Sci., (3) **8**: 99–215.
    The most useful single work. Bibliography covers such previous papers as Fraser 1911, Nutting 1900, 1904, and Torrey, 1902, 1904, the listings of which need not be repeated here.

———. 1925. "Some new and some previously unreported hydroids, mainly from the California coast," Univ. Calif. Publ. Zoöl., **28**: 167–72.

———. 1935. "Hydroids from the west coast of Vancouver Island," Can. Field Natur., **49**: 143–45.

———. 1936. "Hydroids from the Queen Charlotte Islands," Jour. Biol. Bd. Can., **1** (b) : 503–7.

———. 1937. *Hydroids of the Pacific Coast of Canada and the United States.* University of Toronto Press. 207 pages.

———. 1940. "Some hydroids from the California coast, collected in 1939." Trans. Roy. Soc. Canada, Ser. 3, Sec. **V**: 39–44
    From the San Francisco Bay area, and from Santa Cruz Island off southern California. One new species from the latter. All littoral.

———. 1940a. "Hydroid distribution in the Pacific," 6th Pac. Sci. Congress, **3**: 495–500.

———. 1941. "New species of hydroids . . . ," Proc. U.S. Nat. Mus., **91**: 77–89, pls. 13–17.

HYMAN, L. H. 1947. "Two new hydromedusae from the Californian coast," Trans. Amer. Micr. Soc., **66**: 262–68.

NUTTING, C. C. 1915. "American hydroids, Pt. III," U.S. Nat. Mus. Spec. Bull. No. 4.

REES, W. J. 1950. "On *Cladonema myersi,* a new species of hydroid from the Californian coast," Proc. Zool. Soc. London, **119** (4) : 861–65, 4 figures.

SKOGSBERG, TAGE. 1948. "A systematic study of the family Polyorchidae (Hydromedusae)," Proc. Calif. Acad. Sci., 4th ser., **26** (5) : 101–24, 2 figures.
    Describes, as *Polyorchis montereyensis,* the species common in Monterey Bay, and also a rare species, *P. haplus.* Redescription of *P. pencillatus,* the species found in San Francisco Bay, p. 244.

STECHOW, E. 1923. "Zur Kenntnis der Hydroiden Fauna des Mittelmeers, Amerikas und andere Gebiete. II," Zool. Jahrb. Abt. f. Syst., **47**: 29–270.

Mentions only four Monterey and Vancouver forms, one of them new. A previous paper (Pt. I, 1919, 42:1–172) describes a new species of *Orthopyxis* [*Eucopella*] from Vancouver, p. 69.

There remains much work to be done with Pacific coast hydroids; new discoveries await the alert student at every turn. A fascinating example is that of the hydroid "Lar," which we cite below, under *Proboscidactyla*. Since we lack at present a student of Pacific coast hydroids, this section must stand uncorrected.

Order **Gymnoblastea**

Corymorpha palma Torrey..§288
    Much used for physiological work on polarity, etc. See papers by
    Torrey and by Parker listed on p. 610 of Johnson and Snook (1927 ed.),
    and by Childs, 1927–28, Biol. Bull.

Eudendrium californicum Torrey, and other species......................§ 79

Garveia annulata Nutting...§ 81

Hydractinia milleri Torrey...§ 82

Proboscidactyla sp. ....Pl. XXXIV
    References :
    HAND, CADET, and HENDRICKSON, JOHN R. 1950. "A two-tentacled,
        commensal hydroid from California (*Limnomedusae, Probos-
        cidactyla*)," Biol. Bull., **99** (1) : 74–87, 5 figures, 2 plates.
        This quaint little creature lives around the rim of the tube of the sabellid,
        Pseudopotamilla ocellata, and, like a bureaucrat, dips its hands into the food grooves
        of its host. It occurs in the Monterey area. The young medusae are also described
        in this excellent paper. Two other species, including the northern one of the fol-
        lowing reference, occur on this coast.
    UCHIDA, TOHRU, and OKUDA, SHIRO. 1941. "The hydroid *Lar* and the
        medusa *Proboscidactyla*." J. Fac. Sci. Hokkaido Imp. Univ., Zool.,
        7 (4) : 431–40, 11 figures.
        Describes hydroid and medusa stages of *Proboscidactyla flavicirrata*, the
        species in northern Japan; it also occurs in the Pugent Sound region.

Syncoryne mirabilis (Agassiz)..§333

Tubularia crocea (Agassiz)..§333

T. marina Torrey..§ 80

Order **Calyptoblastea**

Abietinaria amphora Nutting, and *A. anguina* (Trask)..................§ 83

A. greenei (Murray)...§ 83

A. turgida (Clark)..§173

Aglaophenia inconspicua Torrey, and *A. latirostris* Nutting..........§ 84

A. struthionides (Murray), Ostrich-Plume Hydroid......................§173

Campanularia and *Halecium* spp. ....§ 78
    C. *urceolata* Clark occurs abundantly on the open coast from Mon-
    terey Bay to Sitka, and *H. annulatum* Torrey is common at Monterey,
    both furring over larger hydroids. Many other species are listed for
    the Pacific coast, but all are small, their differentiation requires careful
    microscopic examination, and no attempt will be made to consider them
    here, despite abundance.

Clytia bakeri Torrey, on the bean clam and on the Pismo clam..........§188

C. edwardsi (Nutting) ....§332
Eucopella caliculata (Hinks), also known as *Orthopyxis*.................§ 85
E. everta (Clark), also as *Orthopyxis everta,* furring over stems.........§ 78
Gonothyraea clarki (Marktanner-Turneretscher).......................§332
Lafoea dumosa (Fleming) and *L. gracillima* (Adler)....................§ 86
Obelia commissuralis McCrady.......................................§332
O. dichotoma (Linn) ....§271
O. dubia Nutting ....§332
> This is the commonest Monterey Bay *Obelia,* formerly considered to be *O. gracilis,* on bell buoys, boat bottoms, and on stipes of *Macrocystis.*
O. longissima (Pallas)..§316
Plumularia lagenifera Allman..§ 78
P. setacea (Ellis)...§ 78
Sertularella turgida (Trask), *S. fusoides* Stechow, or similar............§ 86
Reference:
> STECHOW, E. 1926. "Einige neue Hydroiden," Zool. Anz., 48: 96–108.
Sertularia furcata Trask (=*S. pulchella* [D'Orbigny] of Patagonia?).....§ 86
Thuiaria dalli Nutting ....§173

Order **Hydrocorallina**. Hydroid-corals

Reference:
> FISHER, W. K. 1938. "Hydrocorals of the North Pacific Ocean," Proc. U.S. Nat. Mus., 84: 493–554.

Allopora porphyra (Fisher) (as *Stylantheca porphyra*)...................§ 87
Reference:
> FISHER, W. K. 1931. "California hydro-corals," Ann. Mag. Nat. Hist., Ser. 10, 8: 391–99.
>> The Alaska hydrocoral which occurs littorally on the exposed shore near Sitka turns out to be *A. petrograpta* Fisher.

Order **Trachymedusae**

Gonionemus vertens A. Agassiz ....§283
Reference:
> RUGH, R. 1929. "Egg laying habits of *Gonionemus murbachii* in relation to light," Biol. Bull., 57:261–66.

Class SCYPHOZOA. The Scyphomedusae, usually large Jellyfish
Order **Stauromedusae**

Haliclystus stejnegeri Kishinouye.....................................§273
Reference:
> KISHINOUYE, K. 1899. "A new species of stalked medusa . . . .," Proc. U.S. Nat. Mus., 22: 125–29.

Order Semaeostomeae

Scyphistoma of scyphozoan...§228
Reference:
> GALIGHER, A. E. 1925. "On the occurrence of the larval stages of
> Scyphozoa . . . .," Amer. Nat., **59**: 94–96.

Class ANTHOZOA

References:
> VERRILL, A. E. 1868–70. "Review of the corals and polyps of the west coast
> of America," Trans. Conn. Acad. Arts and Sci., **1**: 377–557.
>> Includes the hydro-corals; mostly obsolete, but still useful for spp. of *Sagartia*
>> and other anemones, and essential for the corals.

> ———. 1922. "Alcyonaria and Actiniaria," in Rep. Canad. Arc. Exped.,
> 1913–18, **8 (G)**. 164 pages, etc.

Subclass ALCYONARIA

References:
> HICKSON, S. J. 1915. "Some Alcyonaria and a Stylaster from the west
> coast of North America," Proc. Zool. Soc. London for **1915** (4) : 541–58,
> 1 plate.
>> Mostly dredged material from Oregon, British Columbia, and Alaska.

> KÜKENTHAL, W. 1913. "Über die Alcyonarian Fauna Californiens . . . .,"
> Zool. Jahrb., Abt. f. Syst., **35**: 219–70.
>> Corrects and revises the paper of Nutting cited below, more than half of whose
>> species are reported to have been incorrectly determined.

> NUTTING, C. C. 1909. "Alcyonaria of the California coast," Proc. U.S. Nat.
> Mus., **25**: 681–727. (See above.)

See also Alcyonaria reference in Hickson 1917, on p. 293 above.

Order Stolonifera

Clavularia sp. (new species according to Professor Hickson)..............§144

Clavularia sp. (formerly listed as *Telesto ambigua* Nutting)..............§144
Reference:
> NININGER *et al.* 1918. "Coelenterates from Laguna Beach," Pom.
> Jour. Entom. and Zoöl., **10**: 59.

Order Alcyonacea

Eunephthya rubiformis (Pallas), Sea Strawberry, also as *Gersemia rubiformis* ....§173

Order Pennatulacea

Acanthoptilum gracile (Gabb) ....Pl. XL
> Known from shallow water in Tomales Bay (12–20 feet) and Monterey
> Bay (to 50 fathoms). In both localities it occurs with *Stylatula elongata*.
> The southern species, found near Corona del Mar, is *A. scalpellifolium*
> Moroff.

Leioptilus guerneyi (Gray) (as *L.,* or *Ptilosarcus quadrangulare* in 1948 ed.)
                                                                          not treated
Reported to occur in the low intertidal from Puget Sound northward
to Prince Rupert, B.C. The expanded animal is a translucent, pale-orange
color, and may attain a length of more than two feet.

Renilla köllikeri Pfeffer, Sea Pansy, formerly considered to be the more
   southern *Renilla amethystina* Verrill...............................§248
   References:
   PARKER, G. H. 1919–20. Three papers cited on p. 610, Johnson and
      Snook (1927 ed.).
   PFEFFER, GEORG. 1886. "Neue Pennatuliden des Hamburger Natur-
      historischen Museum," Jahrb. Wis. Aust. Ham., III, Beilage
      Jahresb. Naturh. Mus. Ham., 1885: 53–61.
   This species ranges from Wilmington to Cedros Island.

Stylatula elongata (Gabb), slender sea pen.........................§289
   The known range of this species is from Tomales Bay to San Diego,
possibly further south, from low tide to 35 fathoms. It is abundant in
Tomales Bay.

Virgularia bromleyi Kolliker and *V. galapagensis* Hickson are reported
by Deichmann (*in litt*) as occurring in the vicinity of Corona del Mar in
shallow water (less than 12 fathoms); two species of *Balticina, B. californica*
(Moroff) and *septentrionalis* (Gray) are shallow-water forms (20 fathoms
to deep water); *septentrionalis* possibly at lesser depths in Burrows Inlet near
Vancouver.

Order Gorgonacea

Muricea californica Aurivillius..§218
   Reference:
   AURIVILLIUS, MAGNUS. 1931. p. 111. "The Gorgonarians from Dr.
      Sixten Bock's expedition to Japan and the Bonin Islands, 1914,"
      Kungl. Svenska Vetenskabs-Akademiens Handlingar, Ser. 3,
      9 (4): 1–337.

Subclass ZOANTHARIA. Anemones and Corals
References:
   STEPHENSON, T. A. *The British sea anemones.* Ray Society, London. Vol I,
      1928, 148 pages, 14 plates. Vol. II, 1935, 426 pages, 19 plates.
         The vade mecum for anemone students. Several of the forms considered occur
      here also. Excellent color plates.
   TORREY, H. B. 1902. "Anemones. Papers from the Harriman Alaska Ex-
      pedition. XXX," Proc. Wash. Acad. Sci., 4: 373–410.

There is no up-to-date general account of Pacific shore Zoantharia; a most
obvious need. There are recent considerations of Alaska and California forms
in the following.

   CARLGREN, OSKAR. 1931. "Zur Kenntnis der *Actiniaria Abasilaria,*" Arkiv.
      Zool., K. Sven. Vet., 23a (3): 1–48. (See pages 22, 33, and 39.)
   ———. 1934. "Zur Revision der Actiniarien," *ibid.,* 26a (18): 1–36 (Page 16,
      Evactis artemisia from Wrangell, Alaska.)
   ———. 1934. "Some Actiniaria from Bering Sea and Arctic waters,"

Jour. Wash. Acad. Sci., **24** (8) : 348–53. (*Anthopleura xanthogrammica* from Wrangell, Alaska, etc.)

———. 1936. "Some West American sea anemones," Jour. Washington Acad. Sci., **26 (1) :** 16–23.

Corynactis californica and two other new species, dredged from Monterey Bay.

———. 1949. "A survey of the Ptychodactiaria, Corallimorpharia, and Actiniaria," Kungl. Svenska Vetens. Handl., (4) **1** (1), 121 pages, 4 plates.

Diagnoses and keys to the genera and families of anemones; an indispensable reference but requiring a specialist's knowledge to use. Lists most of the described species.

McMurrich, J. P. 1913. "On two new actinians from the coast of British Columbia," Proc. Zool. Soc. London for 1913 : 963–76, 1 plate.

The anemones present one of the most difficult problems in invertebrate taxonomy, requiring tedious examination of nematocysts and prepared sections. The central California species are now being monographed, but this will be only a beginning.

Order **Cceriantharia**

Reference:

Torrey and Kleeberger. 1909. "Three species of *Cerianthus* from Southern California," Univ. Calif. Publ. Zoöl., **6** : 115–25.

Cerianthus aestuari Torrey and Kleeberger.............................§256

Cerianthus sp. ....§256

Order **Actiniaria**

References:

McMurrich, J. P. 1901. "Report on the Hexactiniae of the Columbia University Expedition to Puget Sound," Ann. N.Y. Acad. Sci., **14** : 1–52.

Torrey, H. B. 1904. "On the habits and reactions of *Sagartia davisi*," Biol. Bull., **6** : 203–16.

A small San Pedro and San Diego Bay form, in clusters on *Chione* shells near the surface of the sand. This species is actually *Diadumene luciae.*

Solitary *Anthopleura xanthogrammica* (Brandt)..........................§ 64

(Considered also variously as *Evactis, Bunodactis, Cribrina,* etc.)

Aggregated *Bunodactis* (= *elegantissima* [Brandt] ?) (also as *C. xanthogrammica*) ....§ 24

Charisea saxicola Torrey...§202

Evactis artemisia (Pickering) (also as *Cribrina xanthogrammica*).........§258

References:

Gee, W. 1913. "Modifiability in . . . . *Cribrina xanthogrammica,*" Jour. An. Behav., **3** : 305–28.

Parker, G. H. 1917. "The power of suction in the sea-anemone *Cribrina,*" Jour. Exper. Zoöl., **24** : 219–22.

Torrey, H. B. 1906. "The California shore anemone. . . . ," Univ. Calif. Publ. Zoöl., **3** : 41–45.

Corynactis californica ....§ 40

Diadumene luciae (Verrill) or similar (see pp. 101–4, Johnson and Snook [1927 ed.], for two spp. *Sagartia*)................................§224

This widespread anemone has been variously called *Sagartia, Dia-*

dumene, or *Aiptasiomorpha luciae* (Carlgren prefers the last name). Although its occurrence at such places as Puget Sound, Hokkaido, and Woods Hole suggests a cold-temperate distribution pattern, records from such localities as the Suez Canal and Port Aransas, Texas, suggest that it is a eurythermal species as well as a euryhaline one.

References:

Hausman, Leon Augustus. 1919. "The orange striped anemone (*Sagartia luciae,* Verrill). An ecological study," Biol. Bull., **37**: 363–71.

Uchida, Tohru. 1932. "Occurrence in Japan of *Diadumene luciae,* a remarkable actinian of rapid dispersal," Jour. Fac. Sci. Hokkaido Imp. Univ., (6) **2** (2): 69–82, 4 figures, 1 plate.

    Suggests that the original home of this widespread anemone is the coast of Japan and Asia, where sexually reproducing phases are found. Elsewhere, reproduction is usually by budding.

Reference:

McMurrich, J. P. 1913. "A new species of *Edwardsiella* from Southern California," Proc. U.S. Nat. Mus., **44**: 551–53.

References:

Batham, E. J., and Pantin, C. F. A. 1950. "Muscular and hydrostatic action in the sea-anemone *Metridium senile* (L)," Jour. Exp. Biol., **27** (3 & 4): 264–89, 9 figs., 1 pl.; "Inherent activity in . . . ," *ibid.,* 290–301, 6 figs.; "Phases of activity in . . . and their relation to external stimuli," *ibid.,* 377–99, 11 figs.

————. 1951. "The organization of the muscular system of *Metridium senile,*" Quar. Jour. Micr. Sci., **92** (1) : 27–54, 12 figs., 2 pls.

Pantin, C. F. A. 1950. "Behaviour patterns in lower invertebrates," Symposia Soc. Exper. Biology, **4**: 175–95. (Academic Press, New York.) 3 figures.

Many papers by G. H. Parker; see list on p. 610, Johnson and Snook (1927 ed.). We found his 1916 "Effector system of Actinians" (Jour. Exper. Zoöl., **21**: 461–84) particularly interesting.

Order **Madreporaria.** Stony Corals

References:

Durham, J. Wyatt. 1947. "Corals from the Gulf of California and the North Pacific coast of America," Geol. Soc. Amer. Mem., **20**: 68 pages, 14 plates, 2 figures.

    Well-illustrated monograph; based on hard parts.

Durham, J. Wyatt, and Barnard, J. Laurens. 1952. "Stony corals of the eastern Pacific collected by the *Velero III* and *Velero IV,*" Allan Hancock Pac. Exp., **16** (1) : 1–110, 16 pls.

Vaughan, T. W., and Wells, J. W. 1943. "Revision of the suborders, families, and genera of the Scleractinia," Geol. Soc. Amer. Spec. Paper, **44**: 363 pages, 51 plates, 39 figures.

Astrangia lajollaensis Durham..§ 39
   Reference:
      Boschma, H. 1925. "On the feeding reactions . . . . of *Astrangia*,"
         Biol. Bull., **49**: 407–39.
Balanophyllia elegans Verrill..§ 39
   Reference:
      Yonge, C. M. 1932. "A note on *Balanophyllia regia* . . .," *Jour.*
         Mar. Biol. Assoc., **18**: 219–24.
Caryophyllia alaskensis Durham..§ 39

Phylum PLATYHELMINTHES

Class TURBELLARIA.   Flatworms, Planarians

Order Polycladida.   Polyclad Worms

References:
   BOCK, SIXTEN. 1925. "Planarians, Pt. IV," No. 28 in: Papers from Dr. Th.
      Mortensen's Pacific Expedition, 1914–16, Vidensk. Medd. fra Dansk
      Naturh. Foren., **79**: 97–184.
      Describes *Kraburakia excelsa* sp. nov., from Nanaimo littoral, p. 132.

   BOONE, E. S. 1929. "Five new Polyclads from the California coast," Ann.
      Mag. Nat. Hist. (10), **3**: 33–46.

   FREEMAN, DANIEL. 1930. "Three polyclads from the region of Pt. Fermin,
      San Pedro, Calif.," Trans. Amer. Micros. Soc., **49**: 334–41.
      Described as *P. molle,* the southern polyclad mentioned by Johnson and Snook
      as a new species probably of *Prosthiostomum.*

   Idem. 1933. "The polyclads of the San Juan region of Puget Sound," Trans.
      Amer. Micros. Soc., **52**: 107–46.
      Describes twelve new species, most of them littoral and several common.

   HEATH and McGREGOR. 1912. "New polyclad worms from Monterey Bay,
      California," Proc. Acad. Nat. Sci. Phil., **64**: 455–88.

   HYMAN, L. H. 1939. "New species of flatworms from North, Central and
      South America," Proc. U.S. Nat. Mus., **86**: 419–39, figs. 47–51.
      Including *Leptoplana vesiculata,* n.sp. from Puget Sound. On p. 437 there is a
      plea for revision in this group. All the Pacific Coast species cited in our treatment
      of the polyclads are stated by Miss Hyman in a personal communication to have been
      inadequately treated in the source literature.

Much critical work remains to be done with Pacific coast polyclads; there are
many undescribed species; and life histories are unknown.

Cryptophallus magnus Freeman ....§235

Leptoplana acticola Boone..§ 17
   Reference:
      HARMAN & STEBBINS. 1928. "The maturation and segmentation of
         the eggs of *Leptoplana* (sp.)," Publ. Puget Sound Biol. Sta.,
         6: 239–51.

Notoplana segnis Freeman ....§235

Planocera californica Heath & McGregor..§ 3

Order Rhabdocoelida

Reference:
> LEHMAN, H. E. 1946. "A histological study of *Syndisyrinx franciscanus* gen. et sp. nov., an endoparasitic rhabdocoel of the sea urchin *Strongylocentrotus franciscanus*," Biol. Bull., **91 (3)**: 295–311, 8 figures.

Order Acoela

References:
> COSTELLO, H. M. and D. P. 1938. "A new species of *Polychoerus* from the Pacific Coast," Ann. Mag. Nat. Hist., (11) **1**: 148–55.
> GARDINER, E. G. 1895. "Early development of *Polychoerus caudatus* Mark," Jour. Morphol., **11**: 155–71.

Phylum **NEMERTEA**. Ribbon Worms

References:
> COE, W. R. 1904. "Nemerteans," Harriman Alaska Series, **11**: 220 pages.
> ———. 1905. "Nemerteans of the west and northwest coasts of America," Bull. M.C.Z., **68**: 318 pages.
> ———. 1930. "Asexual reproduction in nemerteans," Physiol. Zoöl., **3**: 297–308.
> ———. 1938. "A new genus and species of Hoplonemertea having differential bipolar sexuality," Zool. Anz., **124**: 220–24.
> ———. 1940. "Revision of the Nemertean fauna of the Pacific coasts of North, Central, and northern South America," Allan Hancock Pac. Exp., 2 (13): 247–323, pls. 24–31, 2 colored.
> ———. 1944. "Geographical distribution of the Nemerteans of the Pacific coast of North America, with descriptions of two new species," Jour. Wash. Acad. Sci., **34 (1)**: 27–32.

Reference:
> COE, W. R. 1930. "Two new species of nemerteans belonging to the family Cephalotrichidae," Zool. Anz., **89**: 97–103.

Reference:
> WILSON, C. B. 1900. "The habits and early development of *Cere-*

bratulus lacteus (Verrill)," Quart. Jour. Micros. Soc., n.s., **43**: 97–198.

Emplectonema gracile (Johnston) ....§165

Lineus vegetus Coe ....§139
References:
COE, W. R. 1929. "Regeneration in nemerteans," Jour. Exper. Zoöl., 54: 411–60.
———. 1931. "A new species of nemertean (*Lineus vegetus*) . . . . ," Zool. Anz., 94: 54–60.

Malacobdella grossa (Müller) ....§189
Reference:
GUBERLET, J. E. 1925. "*Malacobdella grossa* from the Pacific coast of North America," Publ. Puget Sound Biol. Sta., 5: 1–14.

Micrura sp. (of Elkhorn Slough)..§312

Micrura verrilli Coe ....§139

Paranemertes peregrina Coe ....§139

Phylum BRYOZOA (POLYZOA)

References:
OSBURN, RAYMOND C. 1950. "Bryozoa of the Pacific coast of America. Part 1. Cheilostomata-Anasca," Allan Hancock Pacific Exp., **14** (1): 269 pages, 29 plates. 1952. Part 2. "Cheilostoma-Ascophora," *ibid.*, **14** (2): 271–611, pls. 30–64.
The first installments of a three-part monograph. The bibliography lists all important Pacific coast references for the entire group.
ROBERTSON, ALICE. 1902. "Some observations on *Ascorhiza occidentalis* Fewkes, and related Alcyonidia," Proc. Calif. Acad. Sci., (3) **3** (3): 99–108, 1 plate.
———. 1903. "Embryology and embryonic fission in the genus *Crisia*." University of California Publ. Zool. 1 (3): 115–56, pls. 12–15.

Although recent practice recognizes the Entoprocta as a distinct phylum, sometimes called Calyssozoa, the entoprocts are usually treated together with the bryozoa, and for convenience of citations we retain the system of the former editions.

Class ENTOPROCTA, 1, 2, and 3. Class ECTOPROCTA,
all the rest

Alcyonidium mytili Dalyell...§111
(1) *Barentsia* sp., probably *gracilis* var. *nodosa* (Lomas)................§316
(2) *B. ramosa* (Robertson), formerly *Gonypodaria ramosa*..............§115
Bugula californica Robertson ....§113
Reference:
GRAVE, B. H. 1930. "The natural history of *Bugula flabellata* . . . . ," Jour. Morph. and Physiol., **49**: 355–84.

Phylum BRACHIOPODA

Reference:
DALL, H. D. 1920. "Annotated list of the recent Brachiopoda in the collection of the United States National Museum," Proc. U.S. Nat. Mus.,
57: 261–377. See also the Smith and Gordon (1948) reference, under
Mollusca.

Phylum PHORONIDA

References:
HILTON, W. A. 1930a. "Phoronida from the coast of southern California,"
Jour. Entom. and Zoöl., 22: 33–35.

———. 1930b. "A new *Phoronopsis* from California," Trans. Amer. Micros.
Soc., 49: 154–59.

PIXELL, H. L. M. 1912. "Two new species of Phoronidea from Vancouver
Island," Quart. Jour. Micros. Sci., n.s., 58: 257–84.

TORREY, H. B. 1901. "On *Phoronis pacifica* sp. nov.," Biol. Bull., 2: 283–88.
Eight specimens from Humboldt Bay and Puget Sound; apparently not found
since.

Phylum ANNELIDA (ANNULATA). Segmented Worms

The Annelida may be recognized for three classes, the marine worms or Polychaeta, including the aberrant Archiannelida and the parasitic Myzostomida, the

freshwater and terrestrial worms or the Oligochaeta, and the leeches or Hirudinea. The Polychaeta constitute by far the largest group of the marine annelids. The Archiannelida are small reduced forms usually occurring in intertidal sands; species of several genera may be found along the western shores of North America, but the specific details for any of them remain to be worked out. MARCUS (1948, Com. Zool. Mus. Hist. Nat. Montevideo, 2 (48) : 1–17, 5 plates) has recently made an important contribution to this group of worms and includes an extensive bibliography. The Myzostomes are largely parasitic upon or within echinoderms, especially crinoids, and easily overlooked because of their small size. The few Oligochaeta that may occur in marine habitats are limited to the upper levels of the beaches.

Subclass ARCHIANNELIDA

Reference:
HILTON, W. A. 1922. "The occurrence of *Polygordius* adult at Laguna Beach," Pomona College Jour. Entom. and Zoöl., 14, No. 4.
Very active, like an attenuated roundworm, but with characteristic antennae at head region. In sand with amphioxus.

Class OLIGOCHAETA

Reference:
ALTMAN, LUTHER C. 1931. "*Enchytraeus pugetensis* (n. sp.), a new marine enchytraeid from Puget Sound," Trans. Amer. Micros. Soc., 50: 154–63 (including natural-history notes).

Class POLYCHAETA

The literature on polychaetes is vast, according to Dr. Olga Hartman; her bibliography, *The literature of the polychaetous annelids: Part 1, Bibliography and subject analysis* (Los Angeles, privately printed, 1951, vi + 290 pages), contains more than 1,300 authors and about 4,000 titles. This bibliography includes an analytical index with twenty subjects most frequently consulted. The authors mostly or entirely concerned with polychaetes of the northeast Pacific are these: Berkeley, E., and C.; Bush, K. J.; Chamberlin, R. V.; Essenberg, C.; Guberlet, J. E.; Hartman, O.; Johnson, H. P.; Johnson, M. W.; MacGinitie, G. E., and N.; Moore, J. P.; Skogsberg, T.; and Treadwell, A. L. Of principal importance to Pacific coast workers are, of course, the many revisionary papers by Dr. Hartman, published principally in the "Allan Hancock Pacific Expeditions" series from 1939 on. We hope that this work will find its eventual culmination in a single, comprehensive monograph dealing with Pacific coast polychaetes.

In addition, monographs or manuals of major importance include: Fauvel, P., "Polychètes errantes" (1923) and "Polychètes sedentaires" (1927) in the *Faune de France*, Vols. 5, and 16, and McIntosh, W. C., 1900–24, Monograph of the British Marine Annelids. Ray Society Monographs. There is also the recent manual by Berkeley and Berkeley: *Canadian Pacific fauna*, 9, "Annelida"; 9b (2), "Polychaeta sedentaria." Univ. Toronto Press, 139 pages, 292 figures (1952).

Amphitrite robusta Johnson, also as *Terebella robusta* or *Neoamphitrite robusta* ....§232
Arctonoë fragilis (Baird), includes *Polynoë fragilis*......................§207
A. pulchra (Johnson), originally as *Polynoë*...............................§ 77
A. vittata (Grube), includes *Lepidonotus lordi* Baird.......................§ 76

References:
DAVENPORT, DEMOREST. 1950. "Studies in the physiology of com-

mensalism. I. The polynoid genus Arctonoë," Biol. Bull., **98** (2) : 81–93. 2 figures.

DAVENPORT, D., and HICKOCK, JOHN E. 1951. ". . . 2. The polynoid genera Arctonoë and Halosydna," *ibid.*, **100** (2) : 71–83.

> By the use of an ingenious arrangement of tubing, leading to tanks with and without the echinoderm hosts, the author found that the worms will, more often than not, travel toward their hosts, if the hosts are uninjured. Authors conclude that "a rather tenuous bond exists between host and commensal," and have not determined the source of the chemical agent involved; preparations of the test or viscera fail to attract the worms. Worms are attracted to the tank from which the host has been removed for a very short period only. These experiments indicate that the attractive agent—or agents—is very unstable, and that it may be masked by other substances released when the host is injured or disturbed.

Anaitides medipapillata (Moore) as *Phyllodoce* ....§153

Arabella iricolor (Montagu) ....§153

Arenicola pusilla Quatrefages, formerly *A. claparedii*, the Lugworm ....§310

Armandia bioculata Hartman ....§265

Axiothella rubrocincta (Johnson), formerly *Clymenella rubrocincta* ....§293

Boccardia proboscidea Hartman ....§152

Capitella capitata (Fabricius) ....§293

Chaetopterus variopedatus (Renier), includes *C. pergamentaceus* Cuvier....§309

References :

> BERRILL, N. J. 1927. "The control of the beat of the fan segments in *Chaetopterus variopedatus,*" Nature, **119**: 564–65.
> FAULKNER, G. H. 1931. "Notes on the feeding mechanism, and on intestinal respiration in *Chaetopterus variopedatus,*" Biol. Bull., **61**: 472–77.
> See MACGINITIE and MACGINITIE. 1949. *Natural History of Marine Animals*, pp. 203–5 for description of feeding methods.

Cirriformia luxuriosa (Moore), originally *Cirratulus luxuriosus* ....§ 16

C. spirabrancha (Moore), originally *Cirratulus spirabranchus* ....§293

Colonial chaetopterid similar to *Phyllochaetopterus prolifica* Potts..........§118

Dodecaceria fistulicola Ehlers, includes *Dodecaceria pacifica* (Fewkes)......§ 63

Eudistylia polymorpha (Johnson), originally as *Bispira polymorpha* ....§129

> The colonial habits of the nearly related *E. vancouveri* (Kinberg) have been described for a beach near Vancouver, B.C., by O'DONOGHUE, 1924, Cont. Can. Biol. and Fish, n.s., **1**: 441–53

Eupolymnia heterobranchia (Johnson), as *Lanice*, and other terebellids......§ 53

Glycera americana Leidy, including *G. rugosa* Johnson, Proboscis Worm....§280

G. robusta Ehlers, the large Proboscis Worm............................§311

Halosydna brevisetosa Kinberg, including *Lepidonotus insignis* Baird.......§ 49

H. johnsoni (Darboux), including *Polynoë californica* Johnson..............§ 49

Hemipodus borealis Johnson ....§234

Hesperonoë adventor (Skobsberg), as *Harmothoë adventor*..............§306

Reference :

> FISHER, W. K. 1946. Proc. U.S. Nat. Mus., **96**: 277–78 and pl. 37, has given an account of the relations of this with its host and other commensals.

Hesperonoë complanata (Johnson), as *Harmothoë complanata*...........§292

Hesperonoë, sp., commensal with *Upogebia* ....§313

Hololepidella tuta (Grube), as *Polynoë tuta*...............................§234

Lubrineris erecta (Moore), as *Lumbriconereis erecta* ....§153

L. zonata (Johnson), as *Lumbriconereis zonata* ....§293

Marphysa stylobranchiata Moore ....§129

Mesochaetopterus taylori Potts ....§265
  Reference:
    MacGinitie and MacGinitie. 1949. *Natural History of Marine Animals* (p. 205), have described the methods of feeding in a related species, *M. rickettsi.*

Naineris dendritica (Kinberg), formerly *N. laevigata*....................§191

Neanthes brandti (Malmgren) ....§164

N. lighti Hartman...not treated
  Reference:
    Smith. Ralph I. 1950. "Embryonic development in the viviparous nereid polychaete, Neanthes lighti Hartman," Jour. Morph. 87 (3) : 417–65, 38 figures.
        Detailed study of the reproductive life history of a polychaete occurring in oversaline to almost fresh water in the Salinas estuary (and similar situations in central California). The worm appears to be a self-fertilizing hermaphrodite, at least in so far as the Salinas population is concerned.

N. virens (Sars) ....§311
  Reference:
    Feeding behavior and modifications have been described by Copeland and others, 1924, Biol. Bull., 47:231–38; and 1934, Biol. Bull., 67 : 356–64.

Nephtys spp., sometimes as *Nephthys* ....§265

Nereis mediator Chamberlin, the small Mussel Worm................§163, 320

N. procera Ehlers ....§274

N. vexillosa Grube, the large Mussel Worm........................§163, 320
  Reference:
    Johnson, Martin W. 1943. "Studies on the life history of the marine annelid *Nereis vexillosa,*" Biol. Bull., 84 (1) : 106–14.

Notomastus tenuis Moore ....§293

Odontosyllis phosphorea Moore and similar syllids ....§151

Pareurythoë californica (Johnson), originally as *Eurythoë*...............§311

Pectinaria sp...§281
    A common intertidal species in beaches of the northeast Pacific is *Cistenides brevicoma* (Johnson) ; its tube is curved and constructed of coarser sand.

Phragmatopoma californica (Fewkes), originally as *Sabella californica*....§166

Platynereis agassizi (Ehlers), originally as *Nereis agassizi*.............§153, 330

Sabellaria cementarium Moore ....§166

Salmacina sp., Serpulid Worm, sometimes *Filograna* ....§183

Serpula vermicularis Linnaeus, including *S. columbiana* Johnson...........§213

Spirorbis sp., the sinistral *Spirorbis*, small Serpulid Worm.................§ 22
   Reference:
      SCHIVELY, M. A., 1897. "The anatomy and development of *Spirorbis*
      borealis," Pros. Acad. Nat. Sci. Phil., 1897 : 153–60.

Stylarioides papillata (Johnson), originally as *Trophonia papillata*.........§233
   Reference:
      SCHLIEPER, CARL. 1927. *"Stylarioides plumosus, eine monograph-*
      ische Darstellung," Zeit. Wiss. Biol., Abt. A., Zeit. Morph. u Ökol.
      Tiere, 7 : 320–83.

Terebella californica Moore ....§311

Thelepus crispus Johnson ....§ 53
   References:
      SCOTT, J. W. 1911. "Further experiments on the methods of egg
      laying in *Amphitrite*," Biol. Bull., **20**: 252–65.
      WELSH J. H. 1934. "The structure and reactions of the tentacles
      of *Terebella magnifica* W.," Biol. Bull., **66**: 339–45.

Thoracophelia mucronata (Treadwell) ....§191
   References:
      DALES, R. PHILLIPS. 1952. "The larval development and ecology of
      Thoracophelia mucronata (Treadwell)," Biol. Bull., **102** (3) : 232–
      42, 7 figs.
      FOX, DENIS L., CRANE, S. C., and MCCONNAUGHEY, BAYARD H.
      1948. "A biochemical study of the marine annelid worm *Thoraco-*
      phelia mucronata. Its food, biochromes and carotenoid metabo-
      lism," Jour. Mar. Research, **7**: 565–85.
      MCCONNAUGHEY, BAYARD H., and FOX, DENIS L. 1949. "The
      anatomy and biology of the marine polychaete *Thoracophelia mu-*
      cronata (Treadwell)," Opheliidae. Univ. Calif. Publ. Zool.,
      47 (12) : 319–40, pls. 26–30.
      FOX, DENIS L. 1950. "Comparative metabolism of organic detritus by
      inshore animals," Ecology, **31**(1) : 100–8.
         This beach worm occurs in extensive beds at La Jolla, where it lives on the
      colloidal organic matter in the sand. It is estimated that colonies of these worms
      move tons of sand annually through their alimentary tract, thus exerting a con-
      siderable influence on both the character of the water and the bottom.

Phylum SIPUNCULOIDEA. Gephyreans. Sipunculid Worms

Reference:
   FISHER, W. K. 1952. "The sipunculid worms of California and Baja California," Proc. U.S. Nat. Mus., **102**: 371–450, fig. 87, plates 18–39.
      The definitive opus for our region; we hope it is not Dr. Fisher's "chanson
   de cygne!"

Dendrostoma perimeces Fisher..§282

D. pyroides Chamberlin (= *D. petraeum* Fisher) ....§125
   Reference:
      FISHER, W. K. 1928. "New Sipunculoidea from California," Ann.
      Mag. Nat. Hist., Ser. 10, **1**: 194–99.

D. zostericolum Chamberlin (as *D. zostericola*)........................§145
   Reference:
      PEEBLES and FOX. 1933. "The structure, functions, and general re-
      actions of the marine sipunculid worm *Dendrostoma zostericola*,"
      Bull. Scripps Inst. Ocean., Tech. Ser., **3**: 201–24.

Golfingia hespera (Chamberlin) ....§293
References:
    FISHER, W. K. 1950. "The Sipunculid genus *Phascolosoma*," Ann.
    & Mag. Nat. Hist., **(12)** 3 (30) : 547–52.

        Phascolosoma, as recently used, is erroneous; this name properly belongs to
    the animals referred to under *Physcosoma*; for the animals known as *Phascolosoma*
    the available name is Lankester's *Golfingia*, in honor of an afternoon on the
    St. Andrew's links with Prof. McIntosh! This does not mean, as a bystander might
    suppose, that zoologists cannot make up their minds about the name of an animal,
    but that some people have not played according to the rules.

    GEROULD, J. H. 1906. "The development of *Phascolosoma*," Zool.
    Jahrb., Abt. f. Anat., **23**: 77–162.

        Referring mostly to *Ph. gouldii* of the Atlantic.

Phascolosoma agassizii Keferstein (= *Ph. japonicum*)....................§ 52

Sipunculus nudus Linn. ....§308

Phylum **ECHIUROIDEA.**   Echiurid Worms

References:
    FISHER, W. K. 1946. "Echiuroid worms of the North Pacific Ocean," Proc.
    U.S. Natl. Mus., **96**: 215–92, pls. 20–37, text figures.

    GISLÉN, TORSTEN. 1940. "Investigations on the ecology of Echiurus," Lunds
    Universitets Årsskript, N F Avd. 2, Bd. **36**, Nr. 10, pp. 3–39, 6 plates.
        Also as: Kungl. Fysiografiska Sällskapets Handlingar, N F, Bd.51, Nr.10.

    NEWBY, W. W. 1940. "The embryology of the echiuroid worm *Urechis
    caupo*," Mem. Am. Phil. Soc., **16**: 219 pages, 85 text figures.

        Perhaps the most important embryological paper of recent years. Records for the
    first time the complete development of a representative of this group previously uncer-
    tain as to phyletic relations. Formally proposes the erection of a separate phylum for
    the echiuroids. The short bibliography covers much of the *Urechis* literature, certainly
    all the embryological items.

Echiurus echiurus alaskensis Fisher ....§306

Listriolabus pelodes Fisher ....§307

Ochetostoma octomyotum Fisher ....§307

Urechis caupo Fisher and MacGinitie..................................§306
References:
    FISHER, W. K. 1947. "New genera and species of echiuroid and sipun-
    culid worms," Proc. U.S. Natl. Mus., **97**: 351–72, pls. 8–15.

    FISHER and MACGINITIE. 1928. "A new echiuroid worm from Cali-
    fornia," Ann. Mag. Nat. Hist., Ser. 10, **1**: 199–203; also "The
    natural history of an echiuroid worm," *ibid.*, 204–13.

    MACGINITIE, G. E. 1935*a*. "Normal functioning and experimental
    behavior of the egg and sperm collectors of the echiuroid, *Urechis
    caupo*," Jour. Exp. Zoöl., **70**: 341–54.

    ———. 1935*b*. "The fertilization of eggs and the rearing of the
    larvae of *Urechis caupo* within the blood cavity of the adult ani-
    mals," Jour. Exp. Zoöl., **71**: 483–87.

    NEWBY, W. W. 1932. "The early development of the echiuroid
    Urechis," Biol. Bull., **63**: 387–99.

Urechis is being used extensively for embryological and physiological
experimentation. (See A. TYLER. 1931. Biol. Bull., **60**: 187–211, *et seq.*)

Phylum **ARTHROPODA**

Class (or Subphylum) PYCNOGONIDA. Sea Spiders

References:

COLE, L. J. 1904. "Pycnogonida of the west coast of North America," Harriman Alaska Exped., **10** : 249–98, 16 plates.

Still an essential reference.

HEDGPETH, JOEL W. 1941. "A key to the Pycnogonida of the Pacific coast of North America," Trans. San Diego Soc. Nat. Hist., **9**(26) : 253–64, pls. 9–11.

Key paper for this group within the area involved—Alaska to southern California. Species described in later preliminary notes by Hilton require further description and figures before they can be recognized. It should be pointed out, however, that the genus *Endeis* is still unknown from this coast; his *Endeis compacta* from Dillon Beach is actually an abnormal specimen of *Halosoma viridintestinale*.

———. 1947. "On the evolutionary significance of the Pycnogonida," Smithson. Miscel. Collections, **106** (18) : 1–53, 1 pl., text figs.

Bibliography lists most papers to 1947, supplementing the comprehensive bibliography of the Bronns Tierreich monograph (Helfer and Schlottke, 1935). A few papers were missed, notably the Okuda reference, below.

———. 1948. "Report on the Pycnogonida collected by the Albatross in Japanese waters in 1900 and 1906," Pros. U.S. Nat. Museum, **98** : 233–321, 33 figures.

Includes general discussion of the zoögeographical relations of this group in the North Pacific.

———. 1951. "Pycnogonids from Dillon Beach and vicinity, California, with descriptions of two new species," Wasmann Jour. Biol., **9** (1) : 105–17, 3 pls.

OKUDA, SHIRO. 1940. "Metamorphosis of a pycnogonid parasitic in a hydromedusa," Jour. Fac. Sci. Hokkaido Imper. Univ., (6) **7** (2) : 73–86, 10 figures.

Describes development of *Achelia alaskensis* in the Japanese *Polyorchis karafutoensis*. Although local medusae have not been observed to harbor pycnogonids, they have not been adequately examined.

SCHMITT, W. L. 1934. "Notes on certain pycnogonids . . . . ," Jour. Wash. Acad. Sci., **24** (1) : 61–70.

Pycnogonum rickettsi, from dredged *Metridium,* and a list of Monterey Bay species, littoral and dredged.

Class ARACHNIDA
Order Acari

The minute but supramicroscopic animals of the seashore are almost unexamined on our coast; the two papers cited below are the second and third (the first, in 1912, cited therein) concerning them. The 1949 reference proposes two new genera and three species from the coasts of Oregon and California; the second redescribes one of the 1912 species from the California coast and adds five new species from Alaskan shores. The field is open for the hand-lens naturalist.

References:

NEWELL, IRWIN M. 1949. "New genera and species of Halacaridae (Acari)," Amer. Mus. Novit., **1411**: 22 pages, 63 figures.

———. 1951. "*Copidognathus curtus* Hall, 1912, and other species of *Copidognathus* from Western North America (Acari, Halacaridae)," *ibid.*, **1499**: 27 pages, 91 figs.

Order Chelonethida Pseudoscorpions

Several species of these quaint creatures, especially of the genus *Garypus*, frequent the high beaches, living among stones. The common beach species on this coast appears to be *Garypus californicus* (Banks), found from Ensenada to Monterey, on San Nicholas Island, and also in the Tomales Bay area, especially on Hog Island. The body is about 3–4 mm. long, making it fairly conspicuous for a pseudoscorpion. A monster, *Garypus giganteus* Chamberlin, occurs on Lower California beaches, and another species occurs on beaches in the Gulf of California. These animals build little inverted dome-shaped huts of sand grains on the undersurfaces of rocks. Another pseudoscorpion, *Halobisium occidentale* Beier, occurs on Salicornia flats and debris-littered flats of bays and estuaries from San Francisco Bay to Alaska, possibly intergrading with *H. orientale* of the Siberian coast. The curious "mating waltz" observed in some pseudoscorpions has not been reported for these halophilous forms, but would be well worth confirming. It is a ceremony which would have delighted the late Ed Ricketts.

References:

CHAMBERLIN, J. C. 1921. "Notes on the genus *Garypus* in North America," Canad. Ent., **53**: 186–91, pl. 7.

———. 1924. "The giant Garypus of the Gulf of California," Nature Magazine, Sept., 1924: 171–72, 175, 6 figs.

———. 1931. "The Arachnid order Chelonethida," Stanford Univ. Publ. Biol. Sci., **7**: 1–284, 71 figs.

Morphology and phylogeny, with key to genera and bibliography. *Garypus californicus* figured (Fig. 3); toto-figure of *Halobisium*, fig. 56.

Class CRUSTACEA

References:

BAKER, C. F. 1912. "Notes on the crustacea of Laguna Beach," 1st Ann. Report, Laguna Marine Lab., 100–17.

A *Mysis* is mentioned; a new cumacean, a new copepod, and two new marine ostracods are described.

CALMAN, W. T. 1898. "On a collection of crustacea from Puget Sound," Ann. N.Y. Acad. Sci., **11**: 259–84.

Decapods, amphipods, isopods, and one rhizocephalan.

CALMAN, W. T. 1909. "Crustacea," in: Lankester's Treatise on Zoölogy, 7: 346 pages.

HOLMES, S. J. 1900. "Synopsis of the California stalk-eyed crustacea," Occ. Papers Calif. Acad. Sci., 7: 262 pages.

———. 1904. "On some new and imperfectly known species of west American crustacea," Proc. Calif. Acad. Sci., Ser. 3, 3: 307–24.

MACGINITIE, G. E. 1937. "Notes on the natural history of several marine crustacea," Amer. Midland Nat., 18: 1031–37.

NIERSTRASZ and BRENDER À BRANDIS. 1930. "Three new genera and five new species of parasitic crustacea," Proc. U.S. Nat. Mus., 77: 1–9.
  Parasitic isopods, rhizocephalans, and uncertain forms, mostly from deep-water shrimps of the Pacific coast.

WALKER, A. O. 1898. "Crustacea collected by W. A. Herdman, F.R.S., in Puget Sound . . . .," Trans. Liverpool Biol. Soc., 12: 268–87.
  Decapods, isopods, amphipods, and one schizopod.

Order Anostraca (Fairy Shrimps)

Although not an intertidal animal, the brine shrimp, *Artemia*, is well known to amateur aquarists and visitors to the evaporation ponds of salt works, where it is associated with the red unicellular green alga *Dunaliella*, upon which it feeds.

Reference:
KUENEN, D. J. 1939. "Systematical and physiological notes on the brine shrimp, Artemia," Arch. Néerl. Zool., 3 (4) : 365–449, 25 figs.
  Based on studies of material hatched from eggs collected at Marina, near Monterey, and European material. Author suggests that there are at least two species. *Artemia salina* (L.) of Europe, and *A. gracilis* Verrill of America (Monterey, San Francisco Bay, Great Salt Lake), and near the Caspian Sea.

Order Cladocera

Reference:
BAKER, HARRIET M. 1938. "Studies in the Cladocera of Monterey Bay," Proc. Calif. Acad. Sci., (4) 23 (23): 311–65.

Order Ostracoda

References:
LUCAS, V. Z. 1931. "Some Ostracoda of the Vancouver Island region," Contr. Canad. Biol. and Fish., 7: 397–416.

SKOGSBERG, T. 1928. "Studies on marine ostracods," Occ. Papers Calif. Acad. Sci., 15: 1–154.
  We list none of these almost microscopic bivalved crustacea. Skogsberg records five littoral species of *Cythereis* from calcareous algae and from the roots of eelgrass at Monterey, but they are not taken frequently.

———. 1950. "Two new species of marine ostracoda (Podocopa) from California," Proc. Calif. Acad. Sci., (4) 26 (14) : 483–505, pls. 27–30.

Order Copepoda

References:
CAMPBELL, MILDRED H. 1930. "Some free swimming copepods of the Vancouver Island region. II," Trans. Roy. Soc. Can., Sec. 5 (Biol.), 24 (1) : 177–83.
  Records three new species; pelagic, hence considered here only incidentally.

FRASER, J. H. 1936. "The occurrence, ecology and life history of *Tigriopus fulvus* (Fisher)," Jour. Mar. Biol. Assoc., **20**.

————. 1936a. "The distribution of rock pool copepods according to tidal level," Jour. Animal Ecol., **5**.

ILLG, P. L. 1949. "A review of the copepod genus *Paranthessius Claus*," Proc. U.S. Nat. Mus. **99**: 391–428, 6 figures.

JOHNSON, MARTIN W., and OLSON, J. BENNET. 1948. "The life history and biology of a marine harpacticoid copepod, *Tisbe furcata* (Baird)," Biol. Bull., **95** (3) : 320–32, 2 plates.

LANG, KARL. 1948. "Monographie der Harpacticiden," Lund, Håkan Ohlssons Boktryckeri, 2 vols. 1683 pp., 605 figs., 371 distr. maps.

LIGHT, S. F., and HARTMAN, O. 1936. "A review of the genera *Clausidium* Kossmann and *Hemicyclops* Boeck (*Copepoda*) with the description of a new species from the northeast Pacific," Univ. Calif. Publ. Zoöl., **41**: 173–88.

MONK, C. R. 1941. "Marine harpacticoid Copepods from California," Trans. Amer. Micros. Soc., **60** (1) : 75–99, 3 plates.

WILSON, C. B. 1908. "North American parasitic copepods : A list of those found upon the fishes of the Pacific coast . . . .," Proc. U.S. Nat. Mus., **35**: 431–81.
    Parasitic, and on deep-water fish mostly.

————. 1912. "Parasitic copepods from Nanaimo, B.C. . . . . ," No. IX in Contrib. Canad. Biol., **1906–1910**: 85–102.

————. 1935. "Parasitic copepods from the Pacific coast," Amer. Midland Nat., **16**: 776–97.

Clausidium vancouverense (Haddon), on *Callianassa* and *Upogebia* . . . . §292

Hemicyclops callianassae Wilson, on gills of Callianassa . . . . §292

Lamippe sp., parasitic in *Renilla* polyps . . . . §248
Reference :
    ZULUETA, ANTONIO DE. 1911. "Los copépodos parásitos de los ce-lentéreos," Mem. real Soc. Esp. Hist. Nat., **7**: 58 pages.

Modiolicola gracilis Wilson, on *Mytilus edulis* gills . . . . §197

Pseudomolgus navanacis Wilson . . . . §294

Scolecimorpha huntsmani Henderson, in the tunicate *Styela gibbsii* . . . . §216
Reference :
    HENDERSON, JEAN T. 1930. "A new parasiticcopepod (Scolecimorpha huntsmani n.sp.)," Contr. Canad. Biol. and Fish., **6**: 215–24.

Tigriopus californicus (Baker) . . . . § 8
Reference :
    MISTAKIDIS, M. 1949. "A new variety of *Tigriopus lilljeborgii* Norman," Dove Marine Lab. Report, 3d s., no. **10**: 55–70, 3 pls.
        Gives comparison tables of known species, including *T. californicus* (as *T. triangularis*); Lang. 1948, p. 342, uses *T. californicus,* however.

Class CIRRIPEDIA

Order **Thoracica.** Barnacles

References :
BOHART, R. M. 1929. "Observations on the attachment of *Balanus crenatus* Bruguiere, found in the waters of Puget Sound," Amer. Nat., **43**: 353–61.
BROCH, H. 1922. "Studies on Pacific cirripeds," No. 10 in : Papers from Dr.

Th. Mortensen's Pac. Exp., 1914–16, Vidensk. Medd. fra Dansk naturh. Foren., **73**: 215–58, 77 text figures.

CORNWALL, I. E. 1925. "Review of the Cirripedia of the coast of British Columbia," Contr. Canad. Biol. and Fish., n.s., **2**: 469–502.

———. 1927. "A new species of barnacle from the coast of California," Ann. Mag. Nat. Hist., (10), **20**: 233–35.

———. 1930. "A barnacle (*Scalpellum columbianum*) from Departure Bay, B.C.," Contr. Canad. Biol. and Fish., n.s., **5**: 215–17.

———. 1936. "On the nervous system of four British Columbian barnacles (one new species)," J. Biol. Bd. Can., **1**: 469–75.

HENRY, DORA PRIAULX. 1940. "Notes on some pedunculate barnacles from the north Pacific," Proc. U.S. Natl. Mus., **88**: 225–36.

———. 1940a. "The Cirripedia of Puget Sound, with a key to the species," Univ. Wash. Publ. Ocean., 4 (1): 1–48, 4 plates.

———. 1942. "Studies on the sessile Cirripedia of the Pacific coast of North America," Univ. Wash. Publ. Ocean., 4 (3): 95–134, 4 plates, figures.

HERON-ALLEN, EDWARD. 1928. "Barnacles in nature and myth." Oxford Univ. Press, xv + 180 pages, illus.
"This volume . . . has no reason whatever for existence, it serves no useful purpose, and supplies no want, long-felt or otherwise" (from the Preface).

HERZ, LUDWIG E. 1933. "The morphology of the later stages of *Balanus crenatus* Bruguiere," Biol. Bull., **64**: 432–42.
Some data also on Monterey Bay littoral barnacles, the larvae of which were found to be too delicate from the aeration standpoint for practical culture methods. *B. glandula* of the San Francisco Bay sloughs was found to breed only until June.

PILSBRY, H. A. 1907. "The barnacles (Cirripedia) contained in the collections of the U.S. National Museum," Bull. U.S. Nat. Mus., No. **60**: 122 pages.

———. 1916. "Sessile barnacles (Cirripedia) contained in the collections of the U.S. National Museum," Bull. U.S. Nat. Mus., No. **93**: 366 pages.

———. 1921. "Barnacles of the San Juan Islands, Washington," Proc. U.S. Nat. Mus., **59**: 111–15.

For ecological data in connection with barnacle communities, note a series of papers by Shelford, Towler, Worley, and Rice, 1930, in Vol. 7, Publ. Puget Sound Biol. Sta.

Order **Rhizocephala**

References:

BOSCHMA, H. 1930–31. "Rhizocephala," No. 55 in: Papers from Dr. Th. Mortensen's Pacific Expedition, 1914–16, Vidensk. Medd. fra Dansk Naturh. Foren., **89**: 297–380.

———. 1933. "New species of Sacculinidae in the collection of the U.S. Natl. Mus." Tijdschrift der Ned. Dierkundige Vereeniging, (3) **3** (4).
   Including *Heterosaccus californicus*, sp.n. on *Pugettia producta* from Santa Cruz, California.

———. 1934. "The relationship between the Sacculinidae of the Pacific and their hosts," Proc. 5th Pac. Sci. Cong., **5**: 4195–97.

See also the Nierstrasz and Brender à Brandis 1930 paper cited on our p. 315.

POTTS, F. A. 1912. "*Mycetomorpha*, a new rhizocephalan (with a note on the sexual condition of *Sylon*," Zool. Jahrb., Abt. f. Syst., **33**: 575–94.
   Parasitic on the shrimp *Crago communis* at Nanaimo. *Sylon* on *Spirontocaris, Pandalus*, etc., at Friday Harbor.

———. 1915. "On the rhizocephalan genus *Thompsonia* . . . .," Publ. Dept. Mar. Biol., Carnegie Institution **8**: 1–32.

REINHARD, EDWARD G. 1942. "Studies on the life history and host-parasite relationship of *Peltogaster paguri*," Biol. Bull., **83** (3): 401–15.

———. 1944. "Rhizocephalan parasites of hermit crabs from the northwest Pacific," Jour. Wash. Acad. Sci., **34** (2): 49–58.

———. 1950. "An analysis of the effects of a sacculinid parasite on the external morphology of *Callinectes sapidus* Rathbun," Biol. Bull., **98** (3): 277–288.
   See pp. 240–41; the effect of sacculinid parasitism suggests the peculiar phenomenon of sex determination in the echiurid *Bonellia*. In this worm, larvae which settle by themselves become females; if a larva settles on a female, however, it becomes a small parasite-like male which lies within the nephridium of its mate. There is some substance, hormone-like in action, secreted by the female, which inhibits the larva, although all young Bonellias are potentially female.

   Sacculina, Peltogaster, and/or other rhizocephalans increase in abundance with the increase in latitude. At Monterey they are rare, at Sitka abundant, where *Lophopanopeus* and *Cancer oregonensis* are commonly infected.

Class MALACOSTRACA

Subclass LEPTOSTRACA

Order **Nebaliacea**

References:

CANNON, H. G. 1927. "On the feeding mechanism of *Nebalia bipes*," Trans. Roy. Soc. Edinburgh, **55**: 355–69.

CLARK, A. E. 1932. "*Nebaliella caboti*, n.sp., with observations on other Nebaliacea," Trans. Roy. Soc. Canada, (3) Sec. 5, **26**: 217–35.

LA FOLLETTE, R. 1914. "A *Nebalia* from Laguna Beach," Jour. Entom. and Zoöl., **6**: 204–6.
   Appendages and entire drawing of *N. bipes.*

   See the Clark (1932) reference. Identified as the Atlantic *Nebalia bipes* in former editions; while the females are almost inseparable from *bipes*, the males are so distinct that Clark considered a new genus justified. There may be other species, especially in the south.

Subclass HOPLOCARIDA (STOMATOPODA)

References:

BIGELOW, R. P. 1894. "Report upon the crustacea of the order *Stomatopoda* ....," Proc. U.S. Nat. Mus., **17**: 489–550.

SCHMITT, WALDO L. 1940. "The Stomatopods of the west coast of America," Alan Hancock Pac. Exp., **5** (4): 129–225, 33 text figures.
    Monographic for the region covered, chiefly the Panamic area. Includes species occurring in California.

Pseudosquilla lessonii (Guèrin) ....§146

Squilla polita Bigelow ....§146

Subclass PERACARIDA

Order Schizopoda (Obs.)

Euphausiacea and *Mysidacea,* comprising the obsolete order *Schizopoda;* the first is entirely pelagic, mostly on the high seas, so treated scantily here.

References:

BANNER, ALBERT H. 1948–49. "A taxonomic study of the Mysidacea and Euphausiacea (Crustacea) of the northeastern Pacific." 1948. "Part I. Mysidacea from family Lophogastridae through tribe Erythropini," Trans. Roy. Canad. Inst., **26**: 345–99, 9 plates. 1948. "Part II. Mysidacea, from tribe Mysini through subfamily Mysidellinae," *ibid,* **27**: 65–124, 7 plates. 1949. "Part III. Euphausiacea, *ibid.,* **28**: 1–62, 4 plates.

ESTERLY, C. O. 1914. "The *Schizopoda* of the San Diego region," Univ. Calif. Publ. Zoöl., **13**: 1–20.
    Taxonomy only, no distribution or natural history; the bibliography cites Hansen, 1913, and Ortman, 1908, which need not be repeated here.

HANSEN, H. J. 1915. "The Crustacea *Euphausiacea* of the United States National Museum," Proc. U.S. Nat. Mus., **48**: 59–114.

TATTERSALL, W. M. 1932. "Contribution to a knowledge of the *Mysidacea* of California. I (La Jolla). II (San Francisco)," Univ. Calif. Publ. Zoöl., **37**: 301–14, 315–47.

———. 1933. *"Euphausiacea* and *Mysidacea* from western Canada," Contr. Canad. Biol. and Fish., **8**: 181–205.

Note also the Calman, 1909 (in Lankester's Treatise), and the Holmes, 1900, citations on our p. 315.

Order Mysidacea

Reference:

TATTERSALL, WALTER M. 1951. "A review of the Mysidacea of the United States National Museum," U.S. Nat. Mus., Bull., **201**: 292 pages, 103 figs.

Acanthomysis costata (Holmes), originally as *Mysis costata*..............§ 61
    Reference:
    CANNON, H. G. 1927. "On the feeding mechanism of a mysid crustacean," Trans. Roy. Soc. Edinburgh, **55**: 219–54.

Archaeomysis maculata (Holmes), originally as *Callomysis maculata*.....§187

Mysidopsis californica Tattersall..§314

Order **Cumacea**

References :
CALMAN, W. T. 1912. "The crustacea of the order *Cumacea* in the collection of the United States National Museum," Proc. U.S. Nat. Mus., **41**: 603–76.
HART, JOSEPHINE F. L. 1931. "Some Cumacea of the Vancouver Island region," Contr. Canad. Biol. Fisheries n.s., **6** (3) : 25–40, 5 figures.
ZIMMER, CARL. 1936. "California crustacea of the order *Cumacea*," Proc. U.S. Nat. Mus., **83**: 423–39.

None of these sometimes common but usually small ($\frac{1}{2}$") grotesque shrimplike crustaceans is treated here. Two species are fairly common inshore in the region involved, and several extend northward from southeastern Alaska. One, *Colurostylis occidentalis* Calman, has just turned up at Corona del Mar.

Order **Chelifera** (**Tanaidacea**)

Small, chelate, isopodlike animals, especially common in mussel beds; usually treated in systematic papers with the isopods. (Cf. Hatch, 1947.) *Leptochelia* is a genus commonly represented on this coast.

Reference:
MENZIES, ROBERT J. 1949. "A new species of apseudid crustacean of the genus *Synapseudes* from northern California (Tanaidacea)," Proc. U.S. Nat. Mus., **99**: 509–15.

Order **Isopoda**. Pill bugs, etc.

References:
FEE, A. R. 1926. "*Isopoda* of Departure Bay . . . .," Contr. Canad. Biol. and Fish., n.s., **3**: 15–46.
HATCH, MELVILLE A. 1947. "The Chelifera and Isopoda of Washington and adjacent regions," Univ. Wash. Publ. Biol., **10** (5) : 155–274.
HOLTHUIS, L. B. 1949. "The Isopoda and Tanaidacea of the Netherlands, including the description of a new species of Limnoria," Zool. Mededel. Leiden, **30** (12) : 163–90, 4 figs.
    Describes *Limnoria quadripunctata* from Dutch coast and points out that the "*Limnoria lignorum*" of the San Francisco Bay piling report is actually this species.
JOHNSON, MARTIN W. 1935. "Seasonal migrations of the wood borer *Limnoria lignorum* (Rathke) at Friday Harbor, Washington," Biol. Bull., **69**: 427–38.
MALONEY, J. O. 1933. "Two new species of isopod crustaceans from California," Jour. Wash. Acad. Sci., **23**: 144–47.
    Synidotea macginitiei and *Pentidotea montereyensis,* Monterey Bay littoral.
MENZIES, ROBERT J. 1950. "Notes on California isopods of the genus *Armadilloniscus*, with the description of *Armadilloniscus coronacapitalis* n. sp.," Proc. Calif. Acad. Sci., (4) **26** (13) : 467–81, 5 plates.
———. 1950a. "A remarkable new species of marine isopod, *Erichsonella crenulata* n. sp., from Newport Bay, California," Bull. S. Calif. Acad. Sci., **49** (1) : 29–35, 3 plates.
———. 1951a. "New marine isopods, chiefly from northern California, with notes on related forms," Proc. U.S. Nat. Mus., **101** (3273) : 105–56, 33 figs.
———. 1951b. "A new species of *Limnoria* (Crustacea : Isopoda) from southern California," Bull. So. Calif. Acad. Sci., **50** (2) : 86–88, pl. 30.
    This is *Limnoria tripunctata*, invading creosoted wood in southern California.
———. 1951c. "A new genus and new species of asellote Isopod, *Caecijaera*

horvathi, from Los Angeles–Long Beach Harbor," Amer. Mus. Novitates, 1542: 7 pages, 3 figs.

MENZIES, ROBERT J., and BARNARD, J. LAURENS. 1951. "The isopodan genus *Iais* (Crustacea)," Bull. So. Calif. Acad. Sci., 50(3) : 136–51, pls. 42–50.

RICHARDSON, H. 1905. "Isopods of North America," Bull. U.S. Nat. Mus., No. 54: 727 pages.

———. 1909. "Isopods collected in the northwest Pacific . . . . ," Proc. U.S. Natl. Mus., 37: 75–129.

STAFFORD, B. E. 1912. "Studies in Laguna Beach Isopoda," First Ann. Rept. Laguna Marine Lab., pp. 18–33.

———. 1913. "Studies in Laguna Beach Isopoda," Pomona Jour. Entom. and Zoöl., 5: 161–72, and 182–88.

Three species of wood-boring *Limnoria* occur on the Pacific coast: *L. lignorum* from Alaska to Point Arena, *L. quadripunctata* from Tomales Bay to San Diego, and *L. tripunctata* from San Francisco Bay to San Quintin, Lower California. The last two species occur in San Francisco Bay; the species of the piling report, at least as illustrated, is *L. quadripunctata*, from the colder waters of the bay; *L. tripunctata* occurs in slightly warmer waters and is capable of boring into creosoted timbers. All three species are widely distributed else-where in the world. In addition to the wood-boring *Limnoria*, there is a species on the Pacific Coast which acts as a parasite, boring into the living hold fasts of the large kelps.

Sphaeroma pentodon Richardson..§336

Reference:

BARROWS, A. L. 1919. "The occurrence of a rock-boring isopod along the shore of San Francisco Bay, California," Univ. Calif. Publ. Zoöl., **19**: 299–316.

Tylos punctatus Holmes & Gay..§184

Order **Amphipoda**. Beach Hoppers, Sand Fleas, Skeleton Shrimps, etc.

References:

ALDERMAN, A. L. 1936. "Some new and little-known amphipods of California," Univ. Calif. Publ. Zoöl., **41**: 53–74.

BOECK, A. 1871. "Bidrag til Californiens Amphipodefauna," Vidensk. Selsk. Christiana, **1871**: 32–51.

BRADLEY, J. C. 1908. "Notes on two amphipods of the genus Corophium from the Pacific coast," Univ. Calif. Publ. Zoöl., **4**: 227–52.

CHEVREUX, ED., and FAGE, L. 1925. "Amphipodes," Faune de France, **9**: 488 pages, 438 figures.

The most recent monograph on the group; since many species are cosmopolitan, many species occurring here are treated.

CRAWFORD, G. I. 1937. "A review of the Amphipod genus *Corophium*, with notes on the British species," Jour. Mar. Biol. Assoc., **21** (2) : 589–630, 4 figures.

With keys to sections of the genus, including species occurring locally.

HOLMES, S. J. 1904. "Amphipod crustacea," Harriman Alaska Exped., **10**: 231–46.

———. 1908. "The Amphipoda collected by the U.S. Bureau of Fisheries Steamer 'Albatross' off the west coast of North America . . . . ," Proc. U.S. Nat. Mus., **35**: 489–543.

LA FOLLETTE, R. 1915. "Caprellidae from Laguna Beach. II," Pomona Jour. Entom. Zoöl., **7**: 55–60.

And previous report, Pt. I, not available for consultation.

SHAW, M. 1916. "Caprellidae from Laguna Beach," *ibid.*, **8**: 86–87.

SHOEMAKER, C. R. 1916. "Description of three new species of Amphipods from southern California," Proc. Biol. Soc. Wash., **29**: 157–60.

———. 1925. "XV: The Amphipoda collected . . . . chiefly in the Gulf of California," Bull. Amer. Mus. Nat. Hist., **52**: 21–61.

———. 1926. "Amphipods of the family Bateidae . . . . ," Proc. U.S. Nat. Mus., **68**: 1–26.

———. 1931. "A new species of amphipod crustacean . . . . ," **78**: 1–8.

———. 1934. "Two new species of Corophium from the west coast of America," Jour. Wash. Acad. Sci., **24**: 356–60.

One dredged Monterey Bay; the other from Peru to Bering Sea may occur inshore.

———. 1938. "Three new species of the amphipod genus *Ampithoë* from the west coast of America," Jour. Wash. Acad. Sci., **28** (1) : 15–25, 4 text figures.

————. 1949. "The amphipod genus *Corophium* on the west coast of America," Jour. Wash. Acad. Sci., **39** (2) : 66–82, 8 figures.

————. 1952. "A new species of commensal amphipod from a spiny lobster," Proc. U.S. Nat. Mus., **102** (3299) : 231–33, fig. 83.

STOUT, V. R. 1912. "Studies in Laguna Amphipoda. I," First Ann. Report, Laguna Marine Lab., pp. 134–49.

————. 1913. "Studies in Laguna Amphipoda. II," Zool. Jahrb., Abt. f. Syst., **34**: 633–59.

THORSTEINSON, ELSA D. 1941. "New or noteworthy amphipods from the north Pacific coast," Univ. Wash. Publ. Ocean., **4** (2) : 50–96.

Note also the references: CALMAN, 1898, HOLMES, 1904, and WALKER, 1898, on p. 315.

Ampithoe sp. and *Atylopsis* sp. (formerly often as *Amphithoe*)..............§ 42

Anisogammarus confervicolus (Stimpson) ....§314

Aorides columbiae Walker ....§153

Caprella kennerlyi Stimpson ....§ 89

C. equilibra Say ....§ 89
    A number of species, usually referred to as *Caprella acutifrons*, occur on this coast. One of them is *C. equilibra*.

C. scaura Templeton..§272

Elasmopus rapax Costa...§165

Eurystheus tenuicornis (Holmes)......................................§153

Hyale sp. or spp..§153
    In nineteen lots as sent to the National Museum, chiefly in their numbers 99/493, 110/306, 110/391.

Melita palmata (Montagu)..§ 20

Orchestia sp. (U.S. Nat. Mus., No. 110/306)...........................§ 50

O. traskiana Stimpson...§ 2

Orchestoidea benedicti Shoemaker......................................§155
    Reference:
        SHOEMAKER, C. R. 1930. "Description of two new amphipod crustaceans (*Talitridae*) from United States," Jour. Wash. Acad. Sci., **20**: 107–14.

O. californiana (Brandt)..§185

O. corniculata Stout..§154
    Reference:
        SMALLWOOD, M. E. 1903. "The Beach Flea *Talorchestia longicornis*," Brooklyn Inst. Arts and Sci., Cold Spring Harbor Mon., No. **1**: 27 pages.
            A comprehensive account of an Atlantic beach hopper comparable in form and probably in habits to the Pacific *Orchestoidea*.

Polycheria antarctica (Stebbing)......................................§100
    Reference:
        SKOGSBERG and VANSELL. 1928. "Structure and behavior of the amphipod *Polycheria osborni*," Proc. Calif. Acad. Sci., **(4) 17**: 267–95.

The amphipods comprise one of the most abundant, and at the same time least known, components of our intertidal fauna. Revisionary work, now in progress, is not available at this time, hence we are unable to do more than submit a list of common species.

These species build tubes of soft mud, frequently on pilings in harbors: *Jassa falcata* (Montagu), *Corophium acherusicum* (Costa), *C. insidiosum* Crawford, *C. spinicorne* Stimpson, and *Podocerus brasiliensis* (Dana). In bays or harbors, among hydroids, *Stenothoë marina* (Bate) is common. Also in bays, found in borings which it possibly enlarges from *Limnoria* borings, is *Chelura terebrans* Philipi.

Common intertidal species of the coast include the following: *Allorchestes angustus* Dana, *Amphilochus neapolitanus* Della Valle, *Ampithoë indentata* (Stout), *A. dalli* Shoemaker, *A. humeralis* Stimpson, *Anisogammarus pugettensis* (Dana), *Elasmopus antennatus* (Stout), *Ericthonius brasiliensis* (Dana), *Hyale frequens* (Stout) [possibly the *Hyale* sp. of our §153?], *Maera dubia* Calman, *M. simile* Stout, *Melita fresnelii* (Audouin), *Paragrubia uncinata* (Stout), *Parallorchestes ochotensis* (Brandt).

Subclass EUCARIDA
Order **Euphausiacea**

Thysanoëssa gregaria G. O. Sars ....§330

According to Banner (1949, III), records for this species from off northern California to British Columbia actually refer to *Th. longipes* Brandt, and implies that *gregaria* may not occur here at all. See his paper for consideration of other euphausiids commonly found near shore, especially along the coasts of Washington and British Columbia.

Order **Decapoda**. Shrimps, Lobsters, and Crabs

References:
GLASSELL, STEVE A. 1935. "New or little-known crabs from the Pacific coast of northern Mexico," Trans. San Diego Soc. Nat. Hist., **8 (14)**: 91–106.

———. 1938. "New and obscure decapod Crustacea from the West American coasts," Trans. San Diego Soc. Nat. Hist., **8 (33)**: 411–54, pls. 27–36.

HART, JOSEPHINE F. L. 1930. "Some decapods from the southeastern shores of Vancouver Island," Canadian Field Naturalist, **44 (5)**: 101–9.
Describes a new species of *Spirontocaris*.

———. 1940. "Reptant decapod Crustacea from the west coasts of Vancouver and Queen Charlotte Islands, B.C.," Canadian Jour. Research, D, **18**: 86–105.

RATHBUN, MARY J. 1904. "Decapod crustaceans of the northwest coast of North America," Harriman Alaska Series, **10**: 1–210.
Useful especially for northern *Spirontocaris*.

SCHMITT, W. L. 1921. "Marine decapod crustacea of California," Univ. Calif. Publ. Zoöl., **23**: 1–470.

WAY, W. F. 1917. "Brachyura and crab-like Anomura of Friday Harbor, Washington," Publ. Puget Sound Biol. Sta., **1**: 349–96.

Suborder NATANTIA. Shrimps and Prawns

References:
BERKELEY, A. A. 1929. "Commercial shrimps of British Columbia," Museum and Art Notes, **4 (3)**: 109–15.

BONNOT, PAUL. 1932. "The California shrimp industry," Fish Bulletin 38, Div. Fish and Game of California, 22 pages.

Hynes, Frank W. 1929. "Shrimp fishery of southeastern Alaska," Bur. Fish. Doc. 1052, 18 pages.

Needler, A. Berkeley. 1934. "Larvae of some British Columbia *Hippolytidae*," Contr. Canad. Biol. and Fish., **8**: 237–42.
Spirontocaris paludicola, *S. brevirostris*, etc., *Hippolyte californiensis.*

Similar in appearance and habitat.
Reference:
> Israel, H. R. 1936. "A contribution toward the life histories of two California shrimps . . . .," Div. Fish and Game of Calif., Fish Bull. No. **46**: 28 pages.

Reference:
> Johnson, Martin W., Everest, F. A., and Young, R. W. 1947. "The role of snapping shrimp (*Crangon* and *Synalpheus*) in the production of underwater noise in the sea," Biol. Bull., **93** (2) : 122–38, 8 figures.

Reference:
> Chace, Fenner A., Jr. 1951. "The grass shrimps of the genus *Hippolyte* from the west coast of North America," Jour. Wash. Acad. Sci., **41** (1) : 35–39, 1 fig.
> Restricts range of *H. californiensis* to Gulf of California to Bodega Bay; the species found from Puget Sound to Alaska is described as *H. clarki.*

Reference:
> Berkeley, A. A. 1930. "The post-embryonic development of the common pandalids of British Columbia," Contr. Canad. Biol. and Fish., n.s., **6 (6)**: 79–114 and 115–63.

Suborder Reptantia
Tribe PALINURA.   Spiny Lobsters

References:
> Allen, B. J. 1916. "Notes on the spiny lobster," Univ. Calif. Publ. Zoöl., **16**: 139–52.

WILSON, ROBERT C. 1948. "A review of the southern California spiny lobster fishery," Calif. Fish & Game, 34 (2) : 71–80, 6 figures.

Tribe ANOMURA. Hermit Crabs, Ghost Shrimps, Mud Shrimps, Porcelain Crabs, etc.

References:

BANNER, A. H., and McKERMAN, D. L. 1943. "A record of *Emerita analoga* from the Washington coast," Science, 97 (2509) : 119.

GLASSELL, STEVE A. 1945. "Four new species of North American crabs of the genus Petrolisthes," Jour. Wash. Acad. Sci., 35 (7) : 223–29.

HART, JOSEPHINE F. L. 1937. "Larval and adult stages of British Columbian Anomura," Canadian Jour. Research, D, 15: 179–220.

JOHNSON, M. W., and LEWIS, W. M. 1942. "Pelagic larval stages of the sand crabs . . . . ," Biol. Bull., 83 (1) : 67–87.

MACKAY, D. C. G. 1932. "Description of a new species of crab of the genus *Paralithodes*," Contr. Canad. Biol. and Fish., 7 : 335–40.
   P. rostratus from 15 fathoms, near Prince Rupert, B.C.

STEVENS, B. A. 1925. "Hermit crabs of Friday Harbor, Washington," Publ. Puget Sound Biol. Sta., 3 : 273–310.

———. 1927. "*Orthopagurus*, a new genus of Paguridae from the Pacific coast," *ibid.*, 5 : 245–52.
   O. schmitti, dredged from shallow water near Friday Harbor.

———. 1928. "*Callianassidae* from the west coast of North America," Publ. Puget Sound Biol. Sta., 6 : 315–69.

References:

MACGINITIE, G. E. 1934. "The natural history of *Callianassa californiensis* Dana," Amer. Midland Nat., 15 (2) : 166–77.

TOLLEFSON, H., and MARRIAGE, L. D. 1949. "The ghost shrimp fishery," Ore. Fish Comm. Shellfish Invest. Progress Report 16, 6 pages.
   The fishing method is a portable pump, forcing the animals out of their burrows by pressure. They are sold as bait.

References:

JOHNSON, MARTIN W. 1940. "The correlation of water movements and dispersal of pelagic littoral animals, especially the sand crab, *Emerita*," Jour. Ma. Research, 2 (3) : 236–45, 4 figures.

MACGINITIE, G. E. 1938. "Movements and mating habits of the sand crab, *Emerita analoga*," Amer. Midland Nat., 19 : 471–81.

SNODGRASS, R. E. 1952. "The sand crab *Emerita talpoida* (Say) and some of its relatives," Smiths. Misc. Colls., 117 (8) : 34 pages, 11 figs.
   The structural anatomy, from the viewpoint of functional adaptations, in the various sand crabs, including *E. analoga.*

WEYMOUTH, F. W. 1919. "Notes on the habits and use of the small sand crab (*E. analoga*)," Calif. Fish and Game, 5 : 171–72.

Tribe BRACHYURA. The True Crabs: Shore Crabs, Pea Crabs,
Spider Crabs, Edible Crabs, Fiddler Crabs, etc.

References:
GLASSELL, STEVE A. 1933. "Descriptions of five new species of Brachyura
collected on the west coast of Mexico," Trans. San Diego Soc. Nat. Hist.,
7 (28): 331–44.
HART, JOSEPHINE F. L.1935. "The larval development of British Columbia
Brachyura. I," Canadian Jour. Research, **12**: 411–32, figures.
McKAY, DONALD C. G. 1942. "The Pacific edible crab, *Cancer magister,*"
Fish. Res. Bd., Can., Bull., **62**: 32 pages.
MENZIES, ROBERT J. 1948. "A revision of the brachyuran genus *Lophopano-
peus,*" Occ. Pap. Allan Hancock Found., No. 4: 44 pages, 6 plates, 3 graphs.
RATHBUN, MARY J. 1918. "The grapsoid crabs of America," U.S. Natl. Mus.
Bull., **97**: 461 pages, 161 plates, 172 figures.
——. 1925. "The Spider crabs of America," *ibid.,* **129**: 613 pages, 283 plates,
153 figures.
——. 1930. "The cancroid crabs of America of the families Euryalidae,
Portunidae, Atelecyclidae, Cancridae, and Xanthidae," *ibid.,* **152**: 609 pages,
230 plates, 85 figures.
——. 1937. "The oxystomatous and allied crabs of America," *ibid.,* **166**: 278
pages, 86 plates, 47 figures, and tailpiece.
WELLS, W. W. 1928. "*Pinnotheridae* of Puget Sound," Publ. Puget Sound
Biol. Sta., **6**: 283–314.
——. 1940. "Ecological studies on the Pinnotherid crabs of Puget Sound,"
Univ. Wash. Publ. Ocean., **2** (2): 19–50.

Similar to *magister*, but with more rounded, smoother carapace, and somewhat smaller. Intertidal, especially from Dillon Beach northwards, and offshore in the south. Somehow overlooked in previous editions.

C. magister Dana...§152
Reference:
> MacKay and Weymouth. 1935. "The growth of the Pacific edible crab, *Cancer magister* Dana," Jour. Biol. Bd. Can., 1: 191–212.

C. oregonensis (Dana) ....§231

C. productus Randall...§106

Cycloxanthops novemdentatus (Lockington).............................§133

Fabia subquadrata (Dana), commensal with *Mytilus californianus*........§159
Reference:
> Stauber, Leslie A. 1945. "Pinnotheres ostreum, parasitic on the American oyster, *Ostrea (Gryphaea) virginica*," Biol. Bull., 88 (3) : 269–91, 4 plates.
> The borderline between commensalism and parasitism is very narrow in this case. It would be worthwhile to examine mussels occupied by *Fabia* for signs of injury and debilitation.

Hemigrapsus nudus (Dana)..§ 27

H. oregonensis (Dana)...§285

Heterocrypta occidentalis (Dana)....................................§249

Lophopanopeus bellus (Stimpson).....................................§231

L. frontalis (Rathbun) ....§132

L. leucomanus heathii Rathbun ....§132

Loxorhynchus crispatus Stimpson.....................................§131
Reference:
> Dembrowska, W. S. 1926. "Study of the habits of the crab *Dromia vulgaris* M.E.," Biol. Bull., 50: 163–78.
> Behavior of a masking crab not closely related to *Loxorhynchus*.

Mimulus foliatus Stimpson...§132

Opisthopus transversus Rathbun, commensal with *Stichopus*, Keyhole Limpets, *Cryptochiton*, etc. ....§ 76

Oregonia gracilis Dana..§334

Pachygrapsus crassipes Randall......................................§ 14
Reference:
> Hiatt, Robert M. 1948. "The biology of the lined shore crab, *Pachygrapsus crassipes* Randall," Pacific Science, 2 (3) : 135–213, 2 plates, 18 figures.
> Exhaustive and comprehensive study—the last word on the subject.

Parapinnixa affinis Holmes, commensal in giant southern *Amphitrite*......§311
Reference:
> Glassell, Steve A. 1933. "Notes on *Parapinnixa affinis* Holmes and its allies," Trans. San Diego Soc. Nat. Hist., 7 (27) : 319–30.

Paraxanthias taylori (Stimpson) (formerly *Xanthias*)................§133

Pilumnus spinohirsutus (Lockington).................................§133

Pinnixa barnharti Rathbun, commensal in the Sea Cucumber *Molpadia*....§264

P. eburna Wells...§310

P. faba (Dana), commensal in *Schizothaerus*........................§300

    Reference:
        PEARSE, A. S. 1913. "On the habits of crustacea found in *Chaetop-
        terus* tubes . . . . ," Biol. Bull., **24**: 102–14.
          An account of the natural history of certain pea crabs.

    Reference:
        DEMBROWSKI, J. B. 1926. "Notes on the behavior of the fiddler
        crab," Biol. Bull., **50**: 179–201.
          Considers also the previous work of Pearse, 1914.

Class (or Subphylum) LABIATA

Class INSECTA

Order Coleoptera

Intertidal insects are either rare or seldom sought after, but certain small
beetles occur in the rocky intertidal especially at Moss Beach and near Dillon
Beach (where the editor found one associated with a sponge). Five genera, in
four families, are represented on the Pacific coast: *Thalassotrechus* (Carabidae) ;
Liparocephalus, Diaulota (Staphylinidae) ; *Endeodes* (Melyridae) ; and *Eury-
stethes* (Eurystethidae). Because of the considerable ecological interest of this
group, despite which almost nothing is known of the life histories of these animals,
we list the available literature. Perhaps this will stimulate someone to investigate
them.

Referenčes:
        BLACKWELDER, R. E. 1932. "The genus *Endeodes* Leconte (Coleoptera,
        Melyridae)," Pan-Pac. Ent., **8** (3) : 128–36.
        CHAMBERLIN, L. C., and FERRIS, G. F. 1929. "On *Liparocephalus* and
        allied genera," *ibid.*, **5** (3) 137–43; **5** (4) : 153–62.
        SAUNDERS, L. G. 1928. "Some marine insects of the Pacific coast of Can-
        ada," Ann. Ent. Soc. Amer., **21** (4) : 521–45.
        USINGER, R. L., LaRIVERS, IRA, CHANDLER, H. P., and WIRTH, W. W.
        1948. "Biology of aquatic and littoral insects," Univ. Calif. Syllabus SS,

Entomology **133**: 244 pages (mimeo).
With keys to genera, literature, collecting methods, etc.

VANDYKE, E. C. 1918. "New inter-tidal rock-dwelling Coleoptera from California," Ent. News, **29**: (8) : 303–8.

Order **Diptera**

Many flies, of course, frequent the beaches; of these the kelp flies, *Fucellia rufitibia* and *F. costalis*, which frequent the masses of decaying kelp on the beach are the most noticeable and are at times so numerous as to make a visit to the shore (especially on a calm day) unpleasant. The first is a small fly with red tibiae, the second, somewhat larger, is predaceous, and may bite.

References :

SMITH, LESLIE M., and LOWE, HOMER. 1948. "The black gnats of California," Hilgardia, **18** (3) : 157–83, 16 figs.

Describes the life history of the Bodega black gnat (*Holoconops kerteszi* Kieffer) which breeds in sand near the sea. This biting gnat is sometimes unpleasantly abundant at Dillon Beach and is also known from Great Salt Lake and North Africa.

WIRTH, W. W. 1949. "A revision of the Clunionine midges with descriptions of a new genus and four new species. (Diptera: Tendipedidae)," Univ. Calif. Publ. Entom., **8** (4) : 151–82, 7 figures.

These midges are often extremely abundant (especially during the winter months) on rocks in the intertidal. Some of the species are completely flightless, in some the males have functional wings, and in others both sexes are capable of flight. Immature stages are to be sought among *Enteromorpha* and similar green algae in the high intertidal.

―――. 1952. "The Heleidae of California," *ibid.*, **9** (2) : 95–266, 33 figs.

Monograph of the biting midges; assigns *Holoconops* to *Leptoconops*, discusses *Culicoides tristriatulus* (pp. 173–175) as a severe pest along parts of Alaska coast, especially at Valdez. It breeds in salt marshes in Alaska and northern California.

Phylum **MOLLUSCA**

References :

BURCH, JOHN Q. (ed.). 1944–46. "Distributional list of the West American marine mollusks from San Diego, California, to the polar sea." Minutes Conch. Club. So. Calif., Nos. **45–63**.

Mimeographed bulletins, also issued separately as Parts I and II, the latter in two volumes, with comprehensive index.

GRANT, U. S., IV, and GALE, H. R. 1931. "Catalogue of the marine Pliocene and Pleistocene Mollusca of California and adjacent regions. . . . ," Mem. San Diego Soc. Nat. Hist., **1** : 1–1036.

A fairly definitive source for the terminology and taxonomy of local molluscs, despite its palaeontological outlook.

HANNA, G. DALLAS. 1939. "Exotic mollusca in California," Bull. Calif. State Dept. Agr., **28** (5) : 298–321, 4 plates, 2 figures.

KEEN, A. MYRA. 1937. "An abridged checklist and bibliography of west American marine Mollusca." Stanford University Press, Photolith, 88 pages.

KEEP, JOSIAH. 1935. "West coast shells." Revised by Joshua L. Baily, Jr. Stanford University Press, 1935. 350 pages.

NEWELL, IRWIN M. 1948. "Marine molluscan provinces of western North America: a critique and a new analysis," Proc. Amer. Phil. Soc., **92** (3) : 155–66, 7 figures.

Criticism of Schenck and Keen, 1936, 1937 and 1940.

OLDROYD, IDA S. 1924. "Marine shells of Puget Sound and vicinity," Publ. Puget Sound Biol. Sta., **4**: 1–272.

————. 1924–27. "Marine shells of the west coast of North America," Stanford Univ. Publ., Univ. Ser., Geol. Sci., I; II, Parts 1, 2, and 3.

PACKARD, E. L. 1918. "Molluscan fauna from San Francisco Bay," Univ. Calif. Publ. Zoöl., 14: 199–452.

QUALE, D. B. 1941. "The edible mollusks of British Columbia," Rep. British Columbia Comm. Fish. for 1940: 75–87.

SCHENCK, HUBERT G., and KEEN, A. MYRA. 1936. "Marine molluscan provinces of western North America," Proc. Amer. Phil. Soc., 76 (6) : 921–38.

————. 1937. "An index method for comparing molluscan faunules," Proc. Amer. Phil. Soc., 77 (2) : 161–82.

————. 1940. "Biometric analysis of molluscan assemblages," Société biogéographique, 7 : 379–92, 2 plates.

SMITH, ALLYN G., and GORDON, MACKENZIE, JR. 1948. "The marine mollusks and brachiopods of Monterey Bay, California, and vicinity," Proc. Calif. Acad. Sci., (4) 26 (8) : 147–245, 2 plates, 4 figures.
     Comprehensive checklist, with descriptions of several new species, and notes on ecology and distribution. Already "out of print."

YONGE, C. M. 1947. "The pallial organs in the aspidobranch Gastropoda and their evolution throughout the Mollusca," Phil. Trans. Royal Soc. London, (B) 232 (591) : 443–518, 1 plate, 40 figures.
     A splendid paper by a master zoölogist; by far the most interesting part of a mollusk is that which leaves the empty shell behind.

No effort is made to present a "comprehensive" bibliography of Pacific coast mollusks. The papers previously cited, especially Keen, 1937, and the Burch catalogue contain literature summaries. There is, alas, no handy single volume, suitable for use in the field, on Pacific coast shells. The Baily revision of Keep (cited above) is the nearest approximation although many of the illustrations are venerable antiques; a field guide for Western shells by Percy Morris has been promised by an Eastern publisher.

Class AMPHINEURA
Order **Polyplacophora.**   Chitons (Sea Cradles)
References:

BERRY, S. STILLMAN. 1911. "A new California chiton," Proc. Acad. Nat. Sci. Philadelphia for 1911: 487–92, 1 plate.

————. 1917 and 1919. "Notes on west American chitons. I and II," Proc. Calif. Acad. Sci., (4) 7: 229–48; and (4) 9: 1–36.

————. 1922. "Fossil chitons of western North America," Proc. Calif. Acad. Sci., (4) 11 (18) : 399–526, pls. 1–16, text figures.
     Of the 33 species treated, 25 are Recent also. There are detail illustrations, geographic and bathymetric ranges of these living species, making this as near as there is to a handbook of Pacific Recent species.

————. 1925. "The species of Basiliochiton," Proc. Acad. Nat. Sci. Philadelphia for 1925: 23–29, 1 plate.

————. 1925a. "New or little-known southern California Lepidozonas," Proc. Malacol. Soc., 16 (5) : 223–31, 1 plate.

————. 1927. "Notes on some British Columbian chitons," Proc. Malacol. Soc., 17 (4) : 159–64, 1 plate.

————. 1931. "A redescription, under a new name, of a well-known Californian chiton," Proc. Malacol, Soc., 19 (5) : 255–58, 1 plate.

————. 1946. "A re-examination of the chiton Stenoplax magdalenensis (Hinds), with description of a new species," Proc. Malacol. Soc., 26 (6) : 161–66, pls. 4 and 5.

DALL, W. H. 1919. "Description of new species of chitons from the Pacific Coast of North America," Proc. U.S. Natl. Mus., **55**: 499–516.

No illustrations. Short descriptions, including 17 intertidal species, mostly from southern California.

HEATH, H. 1905. "Breeding habits of chitons of the California coast," Zoöl. Anz., **29**: 390–93.

YONGE, C. M. 1939. "On the mantle cavity and its contained organs in the Loricata (Placophora)," Quar. Jour. Micr. Sci., **81** (3) : 367–90, 6 figures.

The term Loricata also applies to the group of crustaceans which includes the spiny lobsters, and to the crocodiles and alligators as well as to the chitons. Slightly confusing.

Callistochiton crassicostatus Pilsbry ....§128

Cryptochiton stelleri (Middendorff) ....§ 76

Reference :

OKUDA, SHIRO. 1947. "Notes on the postlarval development of the giant chiton, *Cryptochiton* stelleri (Middendorff)," Jour. Fac. Svo. Hokkaido Imper. Univ. (6) Zoöl., **9** (3) : 267–75, 14 figures.

Cyanoplax dentiens (Gould) ....§237

Ischnochiton regularis (Carpenter) ....§128

Katharina tunicata (Wood) ....§177

Lepidochitona keepiana Berry ....§237

Reference :

BERRY, S. STILLMAN. 1948. "Two misunderstood west American chitons," Leaflets in Malacology, **1** (4) : 13–15.

L. keepiana ranges from Monterey southward; *Cyanoplax dentiens* from Monterey northward. The two had been confused under the name *Lepidochitona dentiens*.

Lepidozona cooperi (Carpenter) ....§128

L. mertensii (Middendorff) ....§128

Mopalia ciliata (Sowerby) and *lignosa* (Gould) ....§128

M. muscosa (Gould) ....§221

Nuttallina californica (Reeve) ....§169

Placiphorella velata Carpenter ....§128

Stenoplax conspicua (Carpenter) ....§127

S. heathiana Berry ....§127

Tonicella lineata (Wood) ....§ 36

Class GASTROPODA.　Snails, Limpets, Nudibranchs, Sea Hares, etc.

Reference :

KEEN, A. MYRA, and PEARSON, JOHN C. 1952. "Illustrated key to west North American Gastropod genera," Stanford University Press, 39 pages, photolith.

The long awaited companion to the pelecypod key; only the *shelled* forms are treated, however. Hence it is a guide for conchologists.

Subclass PROSOBRANCHIA. Most of the Marine True Snails

References :

CARLISLE, JOHN G., JR. 1945. "The technique of inducing spawning in *Haliotis rufescens* Swainson." Science (N.S.) **102**: 566. Nov. 30.

More recently, Carlisle (who should not be held responsible for these inferences) has been good enough to convey to the senior author the substance of some of his unpublished work still in progress. The evidence seems to me indicative that the game laws *may* need radical revision with reference to this commercially valuable mollusk. Spawning has been induced in all the summer months. The present closed season is in spring. It may be also that these abalones come inshore to spawn, as do certain other mollusks such as *Cryptochiton*. In the interests of conservation, work of this sort should be continued; abalones are rapidly becoming scarce.

COLMAN, JOHN. 1932. "A statistical test of the species concept in *Littorina*," Biol. Bull., **62** (3) : 223–43, 11 figures.

HEWATT, WILLIS G. 1940. "Observations on the homing limpet, *Acmaea scabra* Gould," Amer. Midl. Nat., **24** (1) : 205–8.
Finds evidence of homing.

JENSEN, AD. S. 1951. "Do the Naticidae (Gastropoda Prosobranchia) drill by chemical or by mechanical means?" Widensk. Medd. Danks. naturh. Foren., **113**: 251–61, 2 figs.
Favors boring by mechnical action with the radula, suggesting that acid is too weak to be of use in boring holes rapidly enough. The last word on this problem has not been said, however.

KEEN, A. M., and DOTY, C. L. 1942. "An annotated checklist of the Gastropods of Cape Arago, Oregon," Ore. State Monographs, Stud. in Zool., **3**: 16 pages.

MORITZ, C. E. 1939. "Organogenesis in the Gastropod *Crepidula adunca* Sowerby," Univ. Calif. Publ. Zool., **43** (11): 217–48, 22 text figures.
Also the previous anatomical account, Moritz, 1938.

ORTON, J. H. 1928. "Observations on *Patella vulgata*. Part III. Habitat and habits," Jour. Marine Biol. Assoc., n.s., **16**: 277–88.
Also see previous papers on *Patella*, a European and tropical west coast of America genus related to our *Acmaea* and similar in habitat.

———. 1946. "Biology of *Patella* in Great Britain," Nature, **158**: 173, 1 figure.

SHOTWELL, J. ARNOLD. 1950. "Distribution of volume and relative linear measurement changes in *Acmaea*, the limpet," Ecology, **31** (1): 51–61, 11 figures.
Does not find that height of shell is correlated with zonal distribution.

———. 1950a. "The vertical zonation of *Acmaea*, the limpet," *ibid.*, (4) : 647–49, 3 figures.
Suggests desiccation as the primary factor in distribution of *Acmaea*.

TEST, A. R. (G.) 1945. "Description of new species of *Acmaea*," Nautilus, **58** (3): 92–96.

———. 1945a. "Ecology of California *Acmaea*," Ecology, **26** (4): 395–405.

———. 1946. "Speciation in limpets of the genus Acmaea," Contr. Lab. Vert. Zool., Univ. Michigan, **31**: 24 pages.
Note on nomenclature: Various references to "Mrs. Grant" or "Grant (MS)" refer to personal communications to E. F. Ricketts or to her unpublished thesis on the genus Acmaea on file in the University of California library. References to "Dr. A. R. (Grant) Test" are to the published work cited above. This distinction is made, not in deference to whatever Mrs. Post may have to say on such matters, but to save students from a futile search of the literature.

TEST, FREDERICK H. 1945. "Substrate and movements of the marine gastropod *Acmaea asmi*," Amer. Midl. Nat., **33** (3): 791–93.

VILLEE, C. A., and GROODY, T. C. 1940. "The behavior of limpets with reference to their homing instinct," Amer. Midl., Nat., **24**: 190–204.
Finds no evidence of homing in the strict sense. Bibliography includes Richardson, 1934, and Wells, 1917, Pacific references to the same subject.

VOKES, H. E. 1936. "The gastropod fauna of the intertidal zone at Moss Beach, San Mateo County," Nautilus, **50**(2) : 46–50.

Order Aspidobranchia

In gastropods of this order the gills bear filaments on both sides of the axis and both kidneys are usually present, the gonad associated with one kidney or its duct.

Fertilization is external and the larvae are, of course, free living. These snails are characteristically dwellers on hard substrates in clear waters, and are rare in sandy or muddy regions. They comprise the majority of our intertidal gastropods.

Suborder PATELLACEA. The True Limpets

Our numerous species of *Acmaea* are in need of a thorough anatomical examination, according to Dr. Berry. During his stay at Scripps, Dr. Gunnar Thorson found one of the commonest gastropod larvae to be that of a Helcion, a genus not recognized on this coast. This can only mean, according to Dr. Berry, that one or more of our "supposed Acmaeids are really Helcions."

Acmaea asmi Middendorff, on the snail *Tegula* ....§ 13
A. cassis Eschscholtz ....§ 11
  According to a ruling of the International Commission on Zoological Nomenclature in 1948. *A. pelta* Eschscholtz now becomes a synonym, as *A. cassis* has page priority.
A. cassis olympica Dall (formerly *A. pelta olympica*) ....§195
A. depicta (Hinds), on quiet water eelgrass; Painted Limpet.............§274
A. digitalis Eschscholtz (formerly called *A. persona*) ....§ 6
A. fenestrata (Reeve) ....§117
A. insessa (Hinds), on the kelp *Egregia* ....§119
A. limatula Carpenter, typical form (*A. scabra* of Keep); File Limpet.....§ 25
  A distinct color variety of *limatula,* mistakenly called *A. scutum ochracea* Dall, occurs commonly at La Jolla as one of the highest limpets.
A. mitra Eschscholtz..§117
A. paleacea Gould, of open coast eelgrass...............................§119
A. pelta Eschscholtz (see note under *A. cassis pelta*).....................§ 11
A. persona Eschscholtz..§ 11
A. scabra (Gould) (the former *A. spectrum*)...........................§ 11
Acmaea sp., similar to *A. scabra*.......................................§ 25
A. scutum Eschscholtz (the former *A. patina*), Plate Limpet.............§ 25
Lottia gigantea Sowerby (*L. gigantea* [Gray] of authors), Owl Limpet......§ 7
  Reference:
    FISHER, W. K. 1904. "The anatomy of *Lottia gigantea* Gray," Zool. Jahrb., **20** (1): 1–66.

Order **Docoglossa**

Suborder TROCHACEA. Top Shells, Turbans

Astraea gibberosa (Dillwyn) (formerly *A. inequalis* [Martyn])...........§117
A. undosa (Wood), also as *Pomaulax*...................................§117
Calliostoma annulatum (Humphrey) ....§182
C. canaliculatum (Humphrey) ....§182
C. ligatum (Gould) (formerly *C. costatum* [Martyn]).....................§215
Norrisia norrisii (Sowerby)..§136
Tegula brunnea (Philippi), also as *Chlorostoma brunnea*.................§ 29

Suborder ZYGOBRANCHIA. Keyhole Limpets, Abalones

     References:

         BONNOT, PAUL. 1948. "The abalones of California," Calif. Fish and Game, **34** (4) : 141–69, 16 figures, color plate.

         CROFTS, D. R. 1929. "*Haliotis,*" Liverpool Mar. Biol. Committee Mem., **29**: 1–174.

         ————. 1937. "The development of *Haliotis tuberculata,* with special reference to organogenesis during torsion," Phil. Trans. Roy. Soc. London, (B) **228**: 219–68, pls. 21–27, figs. 39–52.

         PALMER, C. F. 1907. "The anatomy of California *Haliotidae,*" Proc. Acad. Nat. Sci. Phil., **59**: 396–407.

Order **Pectinobranchia**

The gill bears filaments on one side only, and is attached to the wall of the mantle cavity. One kidney is lost and the gonad is independent, thus permitting specialized reproductive organs, internal fertilization, and, in some cases, viviparity. Pectinobranchs are found in all sorts of habitats, and outnumber aspidobranchs in such regions as the South Atlantic and Gulf coasts.

Suborder TAENIOGLOSSA. Most Prosobranchs, including the Periwinkles, Slipper Shells, Cowries, Moon Shells, Horn Shells, Pelagic Heteropods, etc.

     Reference:

         HALL, R. P. 1925. "Twinning in a mollusc," Science, **61**: 658.

           As *Serpuloides vermicularis.*

     References:

         ORTON, J. H. 1912. "An account of the natural history of the slipper limpet (*Crepidula fornicata*) . . . . ," Jour. Mar. Biol. Assoc., n.s., **9**: 437–43; and "The mode of feeding . . . . ," *ibid.,* 444–78.

         COE, WESLEY R. 1948. "Nutrition and sexuality in protandric gastropods of the genus Crepidula," Biol. Bull., **94** (2) : 158–60.

         ————. 1949. "Divergent methods of development in morphologically similar species of prosobranch gastropods," Jour. Morphy., **84** (2) : 383–400, 10 figures.

CONKLIN, E. G. 1897. "The embryology of *Crepidula*," Jour. Morphol., **13**: 1–226.

GOULD, HARLEY N. 1952. "Studies on sex in the hermaphrodite mollusk Crepidula plana, IV. Internal factors influencing growth and sex development," Jour. Exp. Zool., **119** (1) : 93–164, 16 figs. 1 pl.

C. nummaria Gould (formerly *C. nivea* Adams) .... §215

C. onyx Sowerby .... §296

Cypraea spadicea Swainson .... §136

Fusitriton oregonensis (Redfield) (formerly *Argobuccinum oregonensis* [Redfield]) .... §214
Reference :
PHILPOTT, C. H. 1925. "Observations on the early development of *Argobuccinum oregonense*," Publ. Puget Sound Biol. Sta., **3**: 369–81.

Lacuna porrecta Carpenter and *L. variegata* Carpenter .... §274

Littorina planaxis Philippi .... § 14

L. (Melarhaphe) scutulata Gould .... § 10

L. sitkana Philippi (sometimes erroneously written *L. sitchana*) .... §195
(*L. rudis* Donovan of West coast authors is a variety of *L. sitkana* ; the name is a synonym of the Atlantic *L. saxatilis* [Olivi].)

The terrestrial tendencies of *Littorina* have made it the subject of much investigation. The following are some of the more recent accounts, the last of Puget Sound, the others on Atlantic forms :
GOWANLOCH and HAYES. 1926. "Contribution to the study of marine gastropods. I. *Littorina*," Contr. Canad. Biol. and Fish., **3**: 135–66.
HAYES, F. R. 1929. "Contribution to the study of marine gastropods. III. The development, growth and behavior of *Littorina*," Contr. Canad. Biol. and Fish., **6**: 415–30.
HUMPHREY and MACY. 1930. "Observations on some of the probable factors controlling the size of certain tidepool snails," Publ. Puget Sound Biol. Sta., **7**: 205–8.

Polinices draconis (Dall) (*Natica draconis*) (also as *Polynices*) .... §252

P. lewisii (Gould) .... §252

P. recluzianus (Deshayes) .... §252

Trichotropis cancellata Hinds .... §215

[Suborder GYMNOGLOSSA. *Melanella*, the Pyramidellids, etc.]

References :
DALL and BARTSCH. 1909. "Monograph of west American pyramidellid mollusks." Bull. U.S. Nat. Mus., No. 68.
FRETTER, V., and GRAHAM, A. 1949. "The structure and mode of life of the Pyramidellidae, parasitic opisthobranchs," Jour. Mar. Biol. Assoc., **28** (2) : 493–532, 12 figures.

None of these very common but minute shells is considered in this account. Recent work indicates that the pyramidellids are actually opisthobranchs and that they are pseudo-commensal parasites on tubiculous polychaetes or lamellibranchs. Species of

Odostomia possess long proboscides which may be inserted into the tissues of the host, or, in one case, directly into the alimentary canal of a worm. Investigation of the *Odostomia* associated with *Haliotus* in our region is indicated by this British research.

Suborder STENOGLOSSA

Tribe RACHIGLOSSA. Olives, Purples, Whelks, Mud Snails, etc.

Acanthina paucilirata (Stearns) . . . . §286
A. spirata (Blainville) . . . . §165
Amphissa versicolor Dall . . . . §137
Ceratostoma foliatum (Gmelin), also known as *Murex* and *Purpura* . . . . §117
C. nuttalli (Conrad) . . . . §296
Ilyanassa obsoleta (Say) (*Nassa obsoleta*) . . . . §286
  Reference:
    DIMON, A. C. 1905. "The mud snail, *Nassa obsoleta*," Cold Spring
    Harbor Monographs, No. **5**: 86 pages.
Nassarius fossatus (Gould) (*Nassa fossata, Alectrion fossatus*) . . . . §286
  Reference:
    MacGINITIE, G. E. 1931. "The egg-laying process of the gastro-
    pod *Alectrion fossatus* Gould," Ann. Mag. Nat. Hist., Ser. 10,
    8: 258–61.
N. tegula (Reeve) (*Alectrion tegula*) . . . . §270
Olivella baetica Carpenter, also known as *O. pedroana* and *O. intorta*) . . . . §253
O. biplicata (Sowerby) . . . . §253
Searlesia dira (Reeve) . . . . §200
Thais canaliculata (Duclos), also as *Purpura canaliculata* . . . . §200
  Reference:
    DALL, W. H. 1915. "Notes on the species of the molluscan sub-
    genus *Nucella* . . . . northwest coast of America," Proc. U.S.
    Nat. Mus., **49**: 557–72.
T. emarginata (Deshayes) . . . . §182
T. lamellosa (Gmelin) . . . . §200
Urosalpinx cinereus (Say) . . . . §286
  Reference:
    FEDERIGHI, HENRY. 1931. "Studies on the Oyster Drill (*Urosal-
    pinx cinerea*, Say)," Bull U.S. Bur. Fish., **47** (4): 85–115, 7 fig-
    ures.

Tribe TOXIGLOSSA. The Cones

Conus californicus Hinds . . . . §136

Subclass PULMONATA

Trimusculus reticulata (Sowerby) (formerly *Gadinia*) . . . . §147
  Reference:
    HUBENDICK, BENGT. 1947. "Phylogenie und Tiergeographie der Sip-
    honariidae. Zur Kenntnis der Phylogenie in der Ordnung Basom-
    matophora und des Ursprungs der Pulmonatengruppe," Zool. Bidr.
    Uppsala, **24**: 1–216, 107 figs.
    Includes discussion of the morphology of the Gadiniidae.

Subclass OPISTHOBRANCHIATA
Order Nudibranchia

References:

AGERSBORG, H. P. K. 1923. "Notes on a new cladohepatic nudibranch from Friday Harbor, Wash.," Nautilus, **36**: 133–38.
The dark brown *Olea hansineënsis,* from eelgrass.

HEATH, HAROLD. 1917. "The anatomy of an aeolid, *Chioraera dalli,*" Proc. Acad. Nat. Sci. Phil., **1917**: 137–48.
From the southeastern Alaska littoral.

MACFARLAND, F. M. 1906. "Opisthobranchiate mollusca from Monterey Bay," Bull. Bur. Fish., **25**: 109–51.
Colored plates, etc.

——. 1912. "The nudibranchiate family *Dironidae,*" Zool. Jahrb., Supp. **25**: (1)515–36.

——. 1923. "Morphology of the nudibranch genus *Hancockia,*" Jour. Morphol., **38**: 65–92.

——. 1923. "Acanthodoridae of the California coast," Nautilus, **39**: 1–27.

——. 1929. *"Drepania,* a genus of nudibranchiate mollusks new to California," Proc. Calif. Acad. Sci., **(4)18**: 485–96.

O'DONOGHUE, C. H. 1926. "A list of the nudibranchiate mollusca recorded from the Pacific coast of North America," Trans. Roy. Can. Inst., **15**: 199–247.

——. Various. "Notes on the nudibranchiate mollusca from the Vancouver Island region," in several issues of: Trans. Roy. Can. Inst., **14, 15,** and **16.**

——. 1927. "Notes on a collection of nudibranchs from Laguna Beach," Pomona Jour. Entom. and Zoöl., **19**: 77–117.

Order **Tectibranchia**. Sea Hares, etc.

Aglaja diomedea (Bergh) ....not treated
This small, dark-brown to black slug frequents estuarine flats. It has been reported from Elkhorn Slough, and is probably the species which occurs in large numbers on the "High Clam Flats" of Dillon Beach. At the Dillon Beach locality spawning occurs in July and August; eggs are deposited in pear-shaped masses on the flats. The large summer population of 1950 was reduced to a few scattered individuals by December. Another variety, or species, occurs in Puget Sound.
Bulla gouldiana (Pilsbry), also known as *Bullaria* and *Vesica*..............§287
Reference:
BERRILL, N. J. 1931. "The natural history of *Bulla hydatis* Linn.," Jour. Marine Biol. Assoc., 17: 567–71.
Habits, development, and feeding mechanism of a form related to ours.
Haminoea vesicula (Gould) (also as *Haminaea*)........................§274
References:
LEONARD, RUTH E. 1918. "Early development of *Haminea*," Publ. Puget Sound Biol. Sta., 2: 45–63.
SPICER, V. D. P. 1933. "Report on a colony of *Haminoea* at Ballast Point, San Diego, Calif.," Nautilus, 47: 52–54.
Ecological notes, with data on ovipositing, of a new subspecies.
Navanax inermis (Cooper) ....§294
Philine sp..§274
Phyllaplysia taylori Dall...§274
Tethys californica (Cooper), formerly *Aplysia californica*...............§104
References:
EALES, N. B. 1921. "*Aplysia*," Liverpool Mar. Biol. Committee Mem., 24: 84 pages.
MACGINITIE, G. E. 1934. "The egg-laying activities of the sea hare *Tethys californicus* (Cooper)," Biol. Bull., 67 (2): 300–303.
Tylodina fungina Gabb (1865, Proc. Calif. Acad. Sci., 3: 188)...........§ 98

Class PELECYPODA. Clams, Cockles, Mussels, Oysters, etc.

References:
BAUGHMAN, J. L. 1947. "An annotated bibliography of oysters with pertinent material on mussels and other shellfish and an appendix on pollution," Texas A. & M. Res. Found., College Station. 794 pages.
A prodigious compilation, which, if nothing else, demonstrates that the oyster is the most written about, if not the most studied, marine invertebrate. The abstracts must be used with caution.
BURCH, JOHN Q. 1945. "Distributional list of the west American Marine Mollusks . . . . I. Pelecypoda," Proc. Conch. Club Southern California.
CAHN, A. R. 1949. "Pearl culture in Japan," Fish and Wildl. Ser., Fishery Leaflet No. 357, 91 pages, 22 figures (photolith).
A complete account of the artificial propagation of pearls; the pearls, of course, are no less natural than the wild ones—in fact, they are a little better.

————. 1950. "Oyster culture in Japan," *ibid.*, No. **383**: 80 pages, 40 figures.
Also a complete account; both of these reports originally appeared as report Nos.
122 and 134, Natural Resources Section, Supreme Commander for Allied Powers, Tokyo.

Coe, Wesley R. 1941. "Sexual phases in wood-boring mollusks," Biol.
Bulletin, **81** (2): 168–76, 3 figures.

————. 1946. "A resurgent population of the Bay-mussel (*Mytilus edulis
diegensis*)," Jour. Morphol., **78** (1): 85–101, 2 pls.

————. 1948. "Nutrition, environmental conditions, and growth of marine
bivalve mollusks," Jour. Mar. Research, **7** (3): 586–601, 2 figures.
Summary of recent literature on this subject.

Coe, W. R., and Fox, D. L. 1944. "Biology of the California sea-mussel
. . . . III," Biol. Bull. **87**: 59–72

Fox, Denis L. (Editor). 1936. "The habitat and food of the California sea
mussel," Bull. Scripps Inst. Ocean., Tech. Ser., **4**:1–64.

Gunter, Gordon. 1950. "The generic status of living oysters and the scientific name of the common American species," Amer. Midl. Nat., **43** (2):
438–49.
Oysters with free larval development and estuarine habit should be referred to
genus *Crassostrea* (incl. *gigas* and *virginica*); those with fertilization and development
in mantle cavity and more maritime habit are in *Ostrea* s. str. (incl. the European
edulis and our *lurida*). There are also significant morphological differences.

Haas, Fritz. 1942. "The habits of some west coast bivalves," Nautilus,
55 (4): 109–13.

Hill and Kofoid. 1927. "Marine borers on the Pacific coast," Final Report,
San Francisco Bay Mar. Piling Committee, 1–357.

Keen, Myra A., and Frizzell, Don. 1939. "An illustrated key to west
North American pelecypod genera," Stanford University Press. Photolith, 28 pages.

Kincaid, Trevor. 1951. "The oyster industry of Willapa Bay, Washington."
Seattle: The Calliostoma Company, 45 pages, illus.

Korringa, P. 1949. "More light upon the problem of the oyster's nutrition?"
Bijdr. Dierk., **28**: 237–48.

————. 1951a. "On the nature and function of 'chalky' deposits in the shell of
Ostrea edulis Linnaeus," Proc. Calif. Acad. Sci., 4th s., 27 (5): 133–58, 2 figs.

————. 1951b. "The shell of Ostrea edulis as a habitat," Arch. néerl. zool.,
10 (1): 32–152, 13 figs., tables.

MacGinitie, G. E. 1941. "On the method of feeding of four pelecypods,"
Biol. Bull., **80** (1): 18–25.

Quale, D. B. 1939. "Notes on *Paphia bifurcata*, a new molluscan species
from Ladysmith Harbor, B.C.," Nautilus, **52** (4): 139.

————. 1941. "The Japanese 'Littleneck' clam accidentally introduced into
British Columbia waters," Pacific Biol. Sta. Progress Report, **48**: 17–18.

————. 1943. "Sex, gonad development and seasonal gonad changes in
Paphia staminea Conrad," Jour. Fish. Res. Bd. Can., 6 (2): 140–51, 5
figures.

Sommer, Hermann, and Meyer, Karl F. 1935. "Mussel poisoning," Calif.
and Western Medicine, **42** (6): 423–26.

Stauber, Leslie A. 1950. "The problem of physiological species with special
reference to oysters and oyster drills," Ecology 31 (1): 109–18, 2 figures.

Weymouth, F. W. 1920. "Edible clams, mussels, and scallops of California," Fish Bulletin, Calif. Fish and Game Comm., No. 4.

Weymouth, F. W., and Thompson, S. H. 1931. "The age and growth of
the Pacific cockle (*Cardium corbis* Martyn)," Bull. Bur. Fish., **46**: 633–41.

Whedon, W. Forest. 1936. "Spawning habits of the mussel *Mytilus californianus* Conrad . . . . ," Univ. Calif. Publ. Zool., **41** (5): 35–44, 1 plate.

YOCUM, H. B., and EDGE, E. R. 1929. "The ecological distribution of the Pelecypoda of the Coos Bay region of Oregon," Northwest Science, **5**: 65–71.

YONGE, C. M. 1939. "The protobranchiate mollusca; a functional interpretation of their structure and evolution," Phil. Trans. Roy. Soc. London, (B) **230**: 79–147, 39 figures, 1 plate.

———. 1949. "On the structure and adaptations of the Tellinacea, deposit-feeding Eulamellibranchia," *ibid.*, **234**: 29–76, 29 figures.

———. 1951. "Studies on Pacific coast mollusks. I–III," Univ. Calif. Publ. Zoöl., **55** (6–8) : 395–420, 13 figures.
Three species are considered: I, *Cryptomya californica*; II, *Platyodon cancellatus* (a rock borer); III, *Hinnites multirugosus* (*H. giganteus*).

YOUNG, R. T. 1941. "The distribution of the mussel (*Mytilus californianus*) in relation to the salinity of its environment," Ecology **22** (4): 379–386.

———. 1945. "Stimulation of spawning in the mussel (*Mytilus californianus*)" Ecology **26** (1): 58–69.

[Note on classification: The classification of the pelecypods is a difficult task, reflecting somewhat the difference in approach to the group by the students of the living animal (the malacologists) and the students of the empty shells (the conchologists). To the latter group must also be added the paleontologists, who have no other recourse but to classify bivalves according to their shell structure. Since this is primarily a treatise about living animals, we have rearranged the group to agree with the excellent studies of C. M. Yonge. Two orders are not represented in our intertidal catalogue: the **Protobranchia**, of which *Nucula* is the best-known genus, and the **Septibranchia**, which is comprised of deeper-water forms specialized possibly as scavengers (e.g., *Cuspidaria*).]

Order Filibranchia

Reference:

STOHLER, R. 1930. "Beitrag zur Kenntnis des Geschlechtszyklus von *Mytilus californianus* Conrad, Zool. Anz., **90**: 263–68.

See also the many papers by Fox *et al.* and Coe, summarized in Coe, 1948, cited under Pelecypoda.

Reference:

COE, WESLEY R. 1945. "Nutrition and growth of the California bay-mussel (*Mytilus edulis diegensis*)," Jour. Exp. Zool., **99** (1) : 1–14, 2 figures.

References:

DAKIN, W. S. 1909. *"Pecten,"* Liverpool Mar. Biol. Committee Mem., No. **17**: 132 pages.

GUTSELL, J. S. 1930–31. "Natural history of the bay scallop," Bull. Bur. Fish., **46**: 569–632.

Order Eulamellibranchia

    Reference:
        WILLIAMS, WOODBRIDGE. 1949. "The enigma of Mission Bay," Pacific
        Discovery, **2** (March–April): 22–23.
           A popular account, with excellent photographs, of a curious naked bivalve
           which looks like a nudibranch. Occurred in Mission Bay before progress in-
           vaded the place; may still be there. Reported as "rare" in the Monterey
           intertidal.

    Reference:
        FRASER, C. McLEAN. 1931. "Notes on the ecology of the cockle . . ."
        Trans. Roy. Soc. Can., Sec. 5, **25**: 59–72.

    References:
        COE, W. R. 1932*b*. "Sexual phases in the American oyster
        (*Ostrea virginica*)," Biol. Bull., **63**: 419–41.
        NELSON, T. C. 1924. "The attachment of oyster larvae," Biol.
        Bull., **46**: 143–51.
        ———. 1928. "Relation of spawning of the oyster to temperature,"
        Ecology, **9**: 145–54.
        YONGE, C. M. 1926. "Structure and physiology of the organs of
        feeding and digestion in *Ostrea edulis*," Jour. Marine Biol.
        Assoc., **14**: 295–386.
           A most important paper.

    Reference:
        GRAVE, B. H. 1927. "The natural history of *Cumingia tellinoides*,"
        Biol. Bull., **53**: 208–19.

    Reference:
        BERKELEY, C. 1923. "On the crystalline style as a possible factor in
        the anaerobic respiration of certain marine mollusks," Jour.
        Exper. Zoöl., **37**: 477–88.
           Reviews the work of Collip, 1921, etc.

Solen rosaceus Carpenter, Jackknife Clam..............................§260

S. sicarius Gould, Jackknife Clam.....................................§279
Reference:
    DREW, G. A. 1907. "Habits and movements of the razor clam *Ensis directus*," Biol. Bull., **12**: 127–40.

Tagelus californianus Conrad, Jackknife Clam..........................§304

Tellina bodegensis Hinds, and two related species.......................§260
Reference:
    STEPHENS, A. C. 1929. "Notes on the rate of growth of *Tellina tenuis* da Costa in the Firth of Clyde," Jour. Marine Biol. Assoc., **16**: 117–29.
        Refers to previous work on natural history 1928.

Teredo diegensis Bartsch, Shipworm...................................§338

T. navalis (Linné), Shipworm ....§337
References:
    COE, W. R. 1933. "Sexual phases in *Teredo*," Biol. Bull., **65**: 283–303.
    ———. 1934. "Sexual rhythm in *Teredo*," Science, **80**: 192.
    GRAVE, B. H. 1928. "Natural history of the shipworm, *Teredo navalis*, at Woods Hole, Mass.," Biol. Bull., **55**: 260–82.
    MILLER, R. C. 1924. "The boring mechanism of *Teredo*," Univ. Calif. Publ. Zool., **26**: 41–80.

Tivela (Pachydesma) stultorum (Mawe), Pismo Clam ....§190
References:
    COE, WESLEY R. 1949. "Nutrition, growth, and sexuality of the Pismo clam (*Tivela stultorum*)," Jour. Exper. Zool., **104** (1) : 1–24, 4 figures.
    FITCH, JOHN E. 1950. "The Pismo Clam," Calif. Fish and Game, **36** (3) : 285–312, 13 figures.
    HERRINGTON, W. C. 1930. "The Pismo clam," Fish Bull., Calif. Fish and Game Comm., No. 18: 1–69.
    WEYMOUTH, F. W. 1923. "Life history and growth of the Pismo clam," *ibid.*, No. 7.

Zirfaea pilsbryi Lowe (known formerly as *Z. gabbi* Tryon)..............§305
Reference:
    LOWE, H. N. 1931. "Notes on the west coast *Zirfaea*," Nautilus, **45**: 52–53.

Class CEPHALOPODA. Squids, Octopi, Nautili, etc

References:
    BERRY, S. S. 1910. "Review of the cephalopods of western North America," Bull. Bur. Fish., **30**: 269–336.
    ———. 1913. "Notes on some west American cephalopods," Proc. Acad. Nat. Sci. Phil. for **1913**: 72–77, text figures.
    FIELDS, W. GORDON. 1950. "A preliminary report on the fishery and on the biology of the squid, *Loligo opalescens*," Calif. Fish and Game, **36** (4) : 366–77, 6 figures.
    FOX, DENIS L. 1938. "An illustrated note on the mating and egg-brooding habits of the two-spotted octopus," Trans. San Diego Soc. Nat. Hist., **7**: 31–34, pl. 2.

PICKFORD, GRACE E., and McCONNAUGHEY, BAYARD H. 1949. "The *octopus bimaculatus* problem: a study in sibling species," Bull. Bingh. Oceanogr. Coll., **12** (4) : 66 pages, 28 figures.

A fine example of critical taxonomic study; establishes two sympatric species of two-spotted octopus, differing principally in egg size and ecological habitat. *O. bimaculatus* is subtidal in rocky habitats; *O. bimaculoides* is low intertidal, especially on mud flats. They also differ in their assemblage of mesozoans! Both species are known only between Los Angeles and Ensenada. Study also indicates genus Paroctopus is invalid.

ROBSON, G. C. 1929. *A monograph of the Recent Cephalopoda.* Part I. British Museum. 236 pages.

———. 1932. *A monograph of the Recent Cephalopoda.* Part II, Brit. Mus. (N.H.), 359 pages, 6 plates, 79 text figures.

Octopus apollyon Berry (also as *Polypus apollyon*, formerly considered to be *Polypus hongkongensis* Hoyle) ....§135
References:
FISHER, W. K. 1923. "Brooding habits of a cephalopod," Ann. Mag. Nat. Hist., (Ser. 9), **12**: 147–49.

———. 1925. "On the habits of an octopus," *ibid.,* (Ser. 9), **15**: 411–14.

O. bimaculoides Pickford and McConnaughey ....§135
See Pickford and McConnaughey paper already cited. The *O. bimaculatus* of previous editions and of the MacGinities' book is, of course, *bimaculoides.*

Phylum ECHINODERMA

References:
BUSH, M. 1921. "Revised key to the echinoderms of Friday Harbor, Washington," Publ. Puget Sound Biol. Sta., **3**: 65–77.

Includes description of a new ophiuran, *Amphiodia peloria,* very long armed, in sand. Nomenclature obsolete.

CLARK, H. L. 1913. "Echinoderms from Lower California," Bull. Amer. Mus. Nat. Hist., **32**: 185–236.

———. 1935. "Some new echinoderms from California," Ann. Mag. Nat. Hist., Ser. 10, **15**: 120–29.

Describes a new sand dollar subspecies from 15 fathoms off Coronado and two new brittle stars from subtidal Corona del Mar, *Ophiacantha eurythra* and *Amphiodia psara.*

EKMAN, SVEN. 1946. "Zur Verbreitungsgeschichte der Warmwasserechinodermen im Stillen Ozean (Asteroidea, Ophiuroidea, Echinoidea)," Nova Acta R. Soc. Sci. Upsaliensis, (4) **14** (2) : 42 pages, 1 figure.

HILTON, W. A. 1918. "Some echinoderms of Laguna Beach," Jour. Entom. and Zool., **10**: 78.

JOHNSON, MARTIN W., and LEILA T. 1950. "Early life history and larval development of some Puget Sound echinoderms," in Studies Honoring Trevor Kincaid, pp. 73–153, 4 plates.

ZIESENHENNE, FRED C. 1942. "Some notes on the distribution records of little known southern California echinoderms," Bull. South. Calif. Acad. Sci., **40** (3): 117–20.

Class ASTEROIDEA.   Sea Stars, Starfish

References:
FISHER, W. K. 1911–1930. "Asteroidea of the north Pacific," Part 1, 1911; Part 2, 1928; Part 3, 1930, Bull. U.S. Nat. Mus., No. 76.

O'DONOGHUE, C. H. 1924. "On the summer migration of certain starfish in Departure Bay, British Columbia," Contr. Can. Biol. and Fish., n.s., 1: 455–72.

PAINE, V. L. 1929. "The tube feet of starfish as autonomous organs," Amer. Nat., 43: 517–29.

Astrometis sertulifera (Xantus) .... § 72
Reference:
    JENNINGS, H. S. 1907. "Behavior of the starfish *Asterias forreri* de Loriol," Univ. Calif. Publ. Zoöl., **4**: 53–185.

Astropecten armatus Gray .... §250

Dermasterias imbricata (Grube) .... §211

Evasterias troschelii (Stimpson) .... §207

Henricia leviuscula (Stimpson) .... § 69

Leptasterias aequalis (Stimpson) .... § 68

L. hexactis (Stimpson) .... §210
Reference:
    OSTERUD, H. L. 1918. "Preliminary observations on the development of *Leptasterias hexactis,*" Publ. Puget Sound Biol. Sta., **2**: 1–15.

L. pusilla Fisher .... § 30

Linckia columbiae Gray .... § 71
Reference:
    MONKS, S. P. 1904. "Variability and autotomy of *Phataria,*" Proc. Acad. Nat. Sci. Phil., **51**: 596–600.

Orthasterias koehleri (de Loriol) .... §208

Patiria miniata (Brandt), formerly *Asterina miniata* .... § 26
Much used for embryological work.
References:
    NEWMAN, H. H. 1925. "An experimental analysis of asymmetry in the starfish *Patiria miniata,*" Biol. Bull., **49**: 111–38.
    MOORE, A. R. 1945. "The individual in simpler forms," Ore. State Monogr. Psychology, **2**: 143 pages, 13 plates, 9 figures. Chap. iv, "The aganglionic central nervous system," pp. 61–79.

Pisaster brevispinus (Stimpson) *f. paucispinus* (Stimpson) .... §209
Pisaster f. brevispinus occurs at Monterey only offshore, but at Crescent City it occurs on reefs. At Dillon Beach it is often seen on the eelgrass flats.

P. giganteus (Stimpson) .... §157

P. giganteus capitatus (Stimpson), the southern California subspecies ...... §142

P. ochraceus f. ochraceus (Brandt), chiefly on shores subject to wave impact .... §157

P. ochraceus f. confertus (Stimpson), of quiet water .... §199

P. ochraceus segnis Fisher, of southern California .... §157

Pycnopodia helianthoides (Brandt) .... § 66

Solaster dawsoni Verrill, and *S. stimpsoni* Verrill .... § 67

Class OPHIUROIDEA. Brittle Stars, Serpent Stars

References:
BERKELEY, A. 1927. "Preliminary list of the ophiurans of the Nanaimo district," Contr. Canad. Biol. and Fish., n.s., **3**: 319–22.
CLARK, A. H. 1921. "A new ophiuran of the genus *Ophiopsila* from southern California," Proc. Biol. Soc. Wash. **34**: 109–10.
CLARK, H. L. 1911. "North Pacific ophiurans . . . . ," Bull. U.S. Nat. Mus., No. **75**: 1–302.
———. 1915. "A remarkable new brittle star," Jour. Entom. and Zoöl., **7**: 64–66.
    Ophiocryptus maculosus, from kelp holdfasts at Laguna Beach, 16 mm. disk, arms 9 mm. long.
MAY, R. M. 1924. "Ophiurans of Monterey Bay," Proc. Calif. Acad. Sci., (4) **13**: 261–303.
McCLENDON, J. F. 1909. "Ophiurans of the San Diego region," Univ. Calif. Publ. Zoöl., **6**: 33–64.
NIELSEN, EIGEL. 1932. "Ophiurans from the Gulf of Panama, California, and the Strait of Georgia," No. 59 in: Papers from Dr. Th. Mortensen's Pacific Expedition 1914–16. Vidensk. Medd. fra Dansk Naturh. Foren. Köbenhavn, **91**: 241–346.
    Descriptions of new species, including *Ophiocryptus granulosus* and *Amphi-chondrius granulosus* from La Jolla, with keys and taxonomic descriptions of all the ophiurans known from these regions. *Ophiactis simplex* (LeConte) and *Amphipholis squamata* (Delle Chiaje) are reported from the La Jolla littoral.

Reference:
HILTON, W. A. 1918. "The central nervous system of a long-armed serpent star," Jour. Entom. and Zoöl., **10**: 75.

    With radial shields spiny. The related, littorally less common *O. rudis* Lyman has bare radial shields and smooth spines.

Class ECHINOIDEA. Sea Urchins, Sand Dollars, and Heart Urchins

References:
CLARK, H. L. 1925. "A catalogue of the recent sea urchins (*Echinoidea*) . . . . ." British Museum, 250 pages.
———. 1948. "A report on the Echini of the warmer eastern Pacific, based on the collections of the Velero III," Allan Hancock Pacific Exped., **8** (5): xii, 225–351, pls. 35–71, 3 figures.
    Since most of central California species range well down Baja California, this report discusses five of the eight species we list below. A bibliography of Clark's echinoderm papers is included.
GRANT, U. S. IV, and HERTLEIN, L. G. 1938. "The West American Ceno-

zoic Echinoidea," Publ. Univ. Cal. at L.A. in Math and Phys. Sci., **2**: 225 pages, 30 plates.

Although the emphasis is on paleontology, all the Recent Pacific Coast species are also cited, with synonymy, references and geographic range, often with descriptions and sometimes with illustrations.

KAHL, M. E. 1950. "Metabolism and cleavage of eggs of the sea urchin *Arbacia punctulata*. A review, 1932–1949," Biol. Bull., **98** (3) : 175–217.

A summary of the work done on this Atlantic coast species, with bibliography.

Dendraster excentricus (Eschscholtz)....................................§246

Echinarachnius parma (Lamarck)......................................§246
Reference:
PARKER and VAN ALSTYNE. 1932. "Locomotor organs of *Echinarachnius parma*," Biol. Bull., **62**: 195–200.

Lovenia cordiformis A. Ag..§247

Lytechinus anamesus A. Ag. and H. L. Clark..........................§269

L. pictus (Verrill)...§218

Strongylocentrotus dröbachiensis (O. F. Müller)......................§212
Reference:
WEESE, A. O. 1926. "Food and digestive processes of *Strongylocentrotus dröbachiensis*," Publ. Puget Sound Biol. Sta., **5**: 165–79.

S. franciscanus (A. Ag.)..§ 73
Reference:
JOHNSON, MARTIN W. 1930. "Notes on the larval development of *Strongylocentrotus franciscanus*," Publ. Puget Sound Biol. Sta., **7**: 401–11.

S. purpuratus (Stimpson)..§174

The three species of *Strongylocentrotus* have been the subject of physiological and embryological experimentation for years; there are certainly dozens, probably hundreds of scattered papers relating to them. Loeb's classic work on parthenogenesis was done with Monterey Bay urchins.

Class HOLOTHURIOIDEA. Sea Cucumbers, Sea Slugs

References:
CLARK, H. L. 1901. "Holothurians of the Pacific coast of North America," Zool. Anz., **24**: 162–71.
Nomenclature in part obsolete.

———. 1907. "The apodous holothurians," Smithsonian Contr. Knowl., **35**: 1–231.

———. 1924. "Some holothurians from British Columbia," Can. Field Nat., **38** (3) : 54–57.
Eleven species from shore and from shallow dredgings.

DEICHMANN, E. 1938. "New holothurians from the western coast of North America, and some remarks on the genus *Caudina*," Proc. New Eng. Zool. Club, **16**: 103–15, text figures.

EDWARDS, C. L. 1907. "The holothurians of the north Pacific coast of North America collected by the *Albatross* in 1903," Proc. U.S. Natl. Mus., **33**: 49–68.

HEDING, S. G. 1928. "Synaptidae," No. 46 in: Papers from Dr. Th. Morten-

sen's Pacific Expedition, 1914–16. Vidensk. Medd. fra Dansk Naturh. Foren., **85**: 105–323.
Describes four new *Leptosynapta* and three *Chiridota* from La Jolla and Nanaimo.
WELLS, H. W. 1924. "New species of *Cucumaria* from Monterey Bay," Ann. Mag. Nat. Hist., (9) **14**: 113–21.

Chiridota albatrossi Edwards...§245

Cucumaria curata Cowles...§176
References:
COWLES, R. P. 1907. *Cucumaria curata* sp. nov. Johns Hopkins Univ. Circ., No. **195**: 2 pages.
FILICE, FRANCIS P. "A study of some variations in *Cucumaria curata* (Holothuroidea)," Wasmann Jour. Biol., **8** (1) : 39–48, 2 figures.

C. lubrica H. L. Clark...§176

C. miniata (Brandt)...§235
Reference:
HALL, A. R. 1927. "Histology of the retractor muscle of *Cucumaria miniata*," Publ. Puget Sound Biol. Sta., **5**: 205–19.

C. piperata (Stimpson) ....§235

C. vegae Théel ....§235

Eupentacta pseudoquinquesemita Deichmann ....§235

E. quinquesemita (Selenka) (= *Cucumaria chronhlemi* Théel) ....§235

Leptosynapta albicans (Selenka) (= *L. inhaerens* [O. F. Müller]).......§ 55

Molpadia arenicola (Stimpson).......................................§264

Psolus chitonoides Clark...§226

Stichopus californicus (Stimpson)....................................§ 77
Reference:
COURTNEY, W. D. 1927. "Fertilization in *Stichopus californicus*," Publ. Puget Sound Biol. Sta., **5**: 257–60.

S. parvimensis H. L. Clark ....§ 77

Thyone rubra Clark..§141

Thyonepsolus nutriens Clark...§141

Phylum CHORDATA

Subphylum HEMICHORDATA (ENTEROPNEUSTA)

The Acorn-Tongue Worms, etc.

References:
BULLOCK, THEODORE H. 1945. "The anatomical organization of the nervous system of Enteropneustra," Quar. Jour. Micr. Sci., **86** (1) : 55–111, 7 plates, 1 figure.
DAVIS, B. N. 1908. "The early life history of *Dolichoglossus pusillus* Ritter," Univ. Calif. Publ. Zool., **4** (30): 187–226, pls. 4–8.
HILTON, W. A. 1918. "*Dolichoglossus pusillus* Ritter," Pomona Jour. Entom. and Zoöl., **10**: 76.
RITTER, W. E. 1900. "*Harrimania maculosa,* a new genus and species of *Enteropneusta* from Alaska . . . . ," Papers from the Harriman Alaska Exped. II, Proc. Wash. Acad. Sci., **2**: 111–32.
Records a very common intertidal form, not taken by the present writers, but which should be noted here, since it seems to be a feature of underrock collecting at

Kodiak and at Prince William Sound, Orca, and Valdez. This thick, dark, acorn-tongue worm, up to 6 inches in length, does not burrow as do most *Enteropneusta*, but lies under stones after the fashion of holothurians. Other species are mentioned, to be named *Balanoglossus intermedia, californicus,* but these apparently remain MS species to this day.

RITTER, W. E. 1902. "The movements of the *Enteropneusta* and the mechanism by which they are accomplished," Biol. Bull., 3: 255–61.
Two MS species mentioned; *D. pusillus,* described 1930 in Horst below; and *B. occidentalis,* stated to be abundant in Puget Sound. The latter is apparently still a MS species.

RITTER and DAVIS. 1904. "Studies on the ecology, morphology, and speciology of the young of some *Enteropneusta* of western North America," Univ. Calif. Publ. Zoöl., 1: 171–210.

WILLEY, ARTHUR. 1931. *"Glossobalanus berkeleyi,* a new enteropneust from the west coast," Trans. Roy. Soc. Canada, Series 3, 25 (Sec. 5) : 19–28.
Known from a single fragmentary specimen, 40 × 6 mm.

Saccoglossus pusillus (Ritter)...§267
Reference:
HORST, C. J. VAN DER. 1930. "Observations on some Enteropneusta," Papers from Dr. Th. Mortensen's Pac. Exped. 1914–16. II, Vidensk. Medd. fra Dansk Naturh. Foren., 87: 135–200.
Ritter's description is on p. 154.

Subphylum UROCHORDATA (TUNICATA)

Sea Squirts, Compound Ascidians, Tunicates

The large systematic literature on Pacific coast tunicates is catalogued in Van Name's monograph, and there is no need to cite scattered papers here.

References:
BERRILL, N. J. 1950. "The tunicata. With an account of the British species," Ray Society. 354 pages, 120 figures.
An essential reference for students of ascidiology.

MACGINITIE, G. E. 1939. "The method of feeding of tunicates," Biol. Bull., 77: 443–47.

MORGAN, T. H. 1941. "Further experiments in cross- and self-fertilization of *Ciona* at Woods Hole and Corona del Mar," Biol. Bull., 80 (3) : 338–53.

RITTER and FORSYTH. 1917. "Ascidians of the littoral zone of southern California," Univ. Calif. Publ. Zoöl., 16: 439–512.

VAN NAME, WILLARD G. 1945. "The North and South American Ascidians," Bull. Amer. Mus. Nat. Hist., 84: 476 pages, 31 plates, text figures.

Amaroucium californicum Ritter and Forsyth...........................§ 99
Reference:
GRAVE, CASWELL. 1920. *"Amaroucium pellucidum* forma *constellatum.* I. The activities and reactions of the tadpole larva," Jour. Exp. Zoöl., 30: 239–57.
Natural history of an Atlantic form comparable to *A. californicum.*

Ascidia ceratodes (Huntsman) ....not treated
Phytoplankton is not unique in its erratic fluctuations; this ascidian "bloomed" in Tomales Bay in the early spring of 1950 and died off by fall. The animals were not only abundant in all parts of the bay (including the intertidal), but specimens up to six inches in length were seen. The range of this species is southern California to British Columbia.

Botrylloides diegensis Ritter and Forsyth...............................§335

Subphylum CEPHALOCHORDATA. Lancelets

References:
> JORDAN, EVERMANN, and CLARK. 1929. As listed below.
> HUBBS, C. L. 1922. "A list of the lancelets of the world . . . .," Occ.
> Papers Mus. Zoöl., Univ. Michigan, No. 105.

Subphylum CRANIATA (VERTEBRATA)

Class PISCES. Fishes

Consideration of the fishes has been deliberately omitted, as in the case of the protozoa, except where it was thought that the mention of a few of the more obvious forms, especially those found under rocks and in the tide pools, would add to the interest or usefulness of this account.

References:
> ARORA, HARBANS L. 1948. "Observations on the habits and early life history
> of the batrachoid fish, *Porichthys notatus* Girard," Copeia, 1948 (2) : 89–93,
> 1 plate.
> BARNHART, P. S. 1936. "Marine fishes of southern California," University
> of California Press, 209 pages, 290 figures.
> BOLIN, ROLF L. 1944. "A review of the marine cottid fishes of California."
> Stanford Ichthy. Bull., **3** (1) : 135 pages including 40 figures.
>> With toto drawings of each species. Included are most of the common tidepool
>> fish. Descriptions of species rather than specimens, with practical keys.
> CLEMENS, W. A., and WILBY, G. V. 1946. "Fishes of the Pacific Coast of
> Canada," Fisheries Res. Bd. Canada, Bull., **68**: 368 pages, 253 figures.
>> An adequate and useful guide, in so far as tide-pool fishes are concerned, from
>> San Francisco, or possibly Monterey, northward.

HUBBS, CLARK. 1952. "A contribution to the classification of the blennioid fishes of the family Clinidae, with a partial revision of the Eastern Pacific forms," Stanford Ichth. Bull., 4 (2) : 41–165, 64 figs.
Includes toto-figures and descriptions of the various tide-pool blennies mentioned in this book.

JORDAN and EVERMANN. 1896–1900. "The fishes of north and middle America," Bull. U.S. Nat. Mus., No. 47. 4 volumes, 3313 pages, 392 plates.

JORDAN, EVERMANN, and CLARK. 1930. "Checklist of the fishes and fish-like vertebrates of north and middle America . . . . ," Report U.S. Comm. Fish. for 1928, Part II : 670 pages, etc.

MACGINITIE, G. E. 1939. "The natural history of the blind goby, *Typhlogobius californiensis* Steindachner," Amer. Midl. Nat., 21 (2) : 489–505, 2 plates.

MORRIS, ROBERT W. 1951. "Early development of the cottid fish, *Clinocottus recalvus* (Greeley)," Calif. Fish and Game, 37 (3) : 281–300, 27 figs.
One of the common "tide-pool johnnies" of the Central California coast.

NOBLE, ELMER R. 1941. "On distribution relationships between California tidepool fishes and their Myxosporidian (protozoan) parasites," Jour. Parasitol., 27 (5) : 409–14, 1 plate.

ROEDEL, PHIL M. 1948. "Common marine fishes of California," Calif. Div. Fish and Game Fish. Bull., 68 : 150 pages, 111 figures.

SCHULTZ, L. P. 1936. "Key to the fishes of Washington, Oregon, and closely adjacent regions," Univ. Wash. Publ. Biol., 2 (4) : 103–228, 48 text figures.

WALFORD, LIONEL A. 1937. *Marine game fishes of the Pacific coast from Alaska to the Equator*. University of California Press. xxix + 205 pages, map and frontispiece, and 69 plates, 37 of them colored.

Anoplarchus purpurescens Gill, Blenny .... §240
Reference :
    SCHULTZ and DELACY. 1932. "Nesting habits of . . . . *A. purpurescens*," Science, Oct. 7, 1932, p. 311.

Clevelandia ios (Jordan & Gilbert), Mud Goby .... §306

Epigeichthys atro-purpureus (Kittlitz), formerly *Xiphister*, Blenny .... § 51

Gibbonsia elegans (Cooper), Blenny .... § 51

Gillichthys mirabilis Cooper, Sand Goby .... §266

Hypsypops rubicunda (Girard), Garibaldi .... §149

Leuresthes tenuis (Ayres), Grunion .... §192
References :
    CLARK, F. N. 1925. "The life history of *Leuresthes tenuis,* an atherine fish with tide-controlled breeding habits," Fish Bull., Div. Fish and Game, Calif., 10 : 51 pages.
    ———. 1938. "Grunion in southern California," Calif. Fish and Game, 24 (1) : 49–54, 3 figures.
    OLSON, ANDREW C. 1950. "Ground squirrels and horned larks as predators upon grunion eggs," *ibid.*, 36 (3) : 323–27, 3 figures.
    WALKER, BOYD W. 1952. "A guide to the grunion," *ibid.*, 38 (4) : 409–20, 6 figures.

Oligocottus maculosus Girard, Sculpin, Tide-Pool Johnny .... §149

Porichthys notatus Girard, Midshipman, Grunter .... §240

Sicyogaster maeandrica (Girard), Clingfish .... § 51

Typhlogobius californiensis Steindacher, Blind Goby.....................§ 58
Xiphister mucosus (Girard), Blenny.....................................§ 51

Class AVES.

General references on distribution:

MUNRO, J. A., and COWAN, I. McT. 1947. "A review of the bird fauna of British Columbia," Brit. Columbia Provincial Mus., Spec. Publ., No. 2: 1–285.

GRINNELL, J., and MILLER, A. H. 1944. "The distribution of the birds of California," Pacific Coast Avifauna, No. 27: 608 pages.
With excellent habitat notes.

Selected references on ecological relations of birds of inshore waters and the intertidal zone:

BARTHOLOMEW, G. A., JR. 1942. "The fishing activities of double-crested cormorants on San Francisco Bay," Condor, 44: 13–21.

———. 1943. "The daily movements of cormorants on San Francisco Bay," Condor, 45: 3–18.

BOND, R. M. 1942. "Banding records of California brown pelicans," Condor, 44: 116–21.

KENYON, K. W. 1949. "Observations on behavior and populations of oyster-catchers in lower California," Condor, 51: 193–99.

LAWRENCE, G. E. 1950. "The diving and feeding activity of the western grebe on the breeding grounds," Condor, 52: 3–16.
Acmaea taken as prey on wintering waters.

McHUGH, J. L. 1950. "Increasing abundance of albatrosses off the coast of California," Condor, 52: 153–56.
See bibliography for other recent papers on albatrosses.

McKERNAN, D. L., and SCHEFFER, V. B. 1942. "Unusual numbers of dead birds on the Washington coast," Condor, 44: 264–66.

MARSHALL, J. T., JR. 1948. "Ecologic races of song sparrows in the San Francisco Bay region," Condor, 50: 193–215, 233–56.
Salt-marsh habitats described.

MILLER, A. H. 1943. "Census of a colony of Caspian terns," Condor, 45: 220–25.
On San Francisco Bay.

MOFFITT, J. 1941. "Notes on the food of the California clapper rail," Condor, 43: 270–73.

MURIE, O. J. 1940. "Food habits of the northern bald eagle in the Aleutian Islands, Alaska," Condor, 42: 198–202.

REEDER, W. G. 1951. "Stomach analysis of a group of shorebirds," Condor, 53: 43–45.
Records of prey taken at Sunset Beach and Point Mugu, California.

WEBSTER, J. D. 1941. "Feeding habits of the black oyster-catcher," Condor, 43: 175–80. (See corrections, Condor, 53: 54, 1951.)

———. 1941a. "The breeding of the black oyster-catcher," Wilson Bull., 53: 141–56. (See corrections, Condor: 53: 54, 1951.)

WILLIAMS, L. 1942. "Displays and sexual behavior of the Brandt cormorant," Condor, 44: 85–104.

Class MAMMALIA

Man is not the only mammal who raids the intertidal for food; the raccoon (*Procyon lotor*, various subspecies) visits the shore at low tide from Puget Sound to Lower California, feeding principally on crabs, leaving his tracks along the sand. In Lower California, where the barren back country offers little nourishment, the coyote is a consistent intertidal feeder. Various mice, ground squirrels (see grunion), and possibly the mink also visit the shore.

As for the strictly marine mammals, the representatives of two mammalian orders (exclusive of the whales) occur along the shores of California. The Carnivora are represented by the sea otter, *Enhydra lutris nereis*, a marine member of the weasel family (Mustelidae), which feeds principally on subtidal abalone, sea urchins, and crabs. The sea otter, once almost banished from California shores, still exists in small scattered herds along the less-frequented parts of the coast from Monterey to perhaps Sonoma County, and hope has been expressed for its return in sufficient numbers to justify harvesting for its valuable fur. This might mean competition with commercial abalone divers. Among the Pinnipedia, the seals and sea lions, we see most often the Steller sea lion, *Eumetopias stelleri*, and the smaller California sea lion, *Zalophus californianus* (the trained seal of the circus), members of the family Otariidae or eared seals. Commercial fishermen make the perennial claim that these animals destroy valuable fish, especially salmon (a complaint first made in the 1870's), but investigations have failed to substantiate this, at least to the degree that wholesale slaughter of the animals is justified. These animals, relatives of the famous Pribilof fur seal, have their principal breeding grounds or rookeries on the Channel Islands. The harbor seal, *Phoca vitulina*, is the only true seal likely to be seen by shorebound observers. Because it cannot turn its hind feet forward, it is clumsy on land and cannot climb rocks as do the sea lions. Small herds are to be seen in bays, where they "haul out" on sand bars. They are common in San Francisco and Tomales bays. The great sea elephant, *Mirounga angustirostris*, also a member of the true seals or Phocidae, was once reduced to a few small bands on the islands off Lower California, but it has recently been observed on the Channel Islands, and is "coming back."

References:

ANDREWS, ROY C. 1914. "Monograph of the Pacific Cetacea. I. The California gray whale (*Rachianectes glaucus* Cope)," Mem. American Museum Nat. Hist., n.s., **1** (5) : 227–87, 22 figs., pls. 19–27.

> Once thought to be nearly extinct, the California gray whale, which calves in bays and lagoons, is gradually returning; the present population consists of several thousand individuals. Calving is now restricted to the lagoons of Lower California, but during the winter months these whales migrate southward along the California coast and may often be seen from shore.

BOLIN, ROLF L. 1938. "Reappearance of the southern sea otter along the California coast," Jour. Mammal., **19** (3) : 301–6.

BONNOT, PAUL. 1928. "Report on the seals and sea lions of California," Calif. Fish Bull., **14** : 61 pages, 38 figures.

————. 1951. "The sea lions, seals and sea otter of the California coast," Calif. Fish and Game, **37** (4) : 371–89, 11 figs.

> "In common with all organisms in a natural environment the marine mammals were controlled by biological checks that maintained the populations in balance with all associated species. The advent of man into this orderly design demoralized it completely. The human animal is the most persistent and rapacious predator that has so far appeared on earth" p. 371.

FISHER, H. D. 1952. "The status of the harbour seal in British Columbia,

with particular reference to the Skeena River," Fish. Res. Bd. Canada,
Bull., **93** : 58 pages, 16 figs.

OGDEN, ADELE. 1941. "The California sea otter trade 1784–1848," University of California Press. xi + 251 pages, illustrations.
    Primarily concerned with the economics of the trade, but with life history information, an excellent photo (opp. p. 146) of a sea otter herd, and a color frontispiece.

SCAMMON, C. M. 1874. "The marine mammals of the northwestern coast of North America, described and illustrated. Together with an account of the American whale-fishery," J. H. Carmany, San Francisco. 319 pp., 27 pls.

SCOFIELD, W. L. 1941. "The sea otters of California did not reappear," Calif. Fish and Game, **27** (1) : 35–38.
    (They were there all the time.)

SELECTED LIST OF NON-SPECIFIC BOOKS
AND ACCOUNTS

The number of books about the seashore and the life of the oceans is astounding. Hundreds have been printed, and new ones appear almost monthly. A great many of them have been boiled over from their predecessors, and some, especially those intended for children, should not have been printed at all. During the last five years the percentage of noteworthy additions to seashore literature has been very high. Leading all the rest is C. M. Yonge's *The sea shore*, a book in the great tradition of British seashore biology. The reviews of oceanography by Coker, Colman, and Ommanney are also noteworthy. This five-year period saw also the publication of the MacGinities' book, a valuable record of firsthand studies with marine animals, and Miner's guide to Atlantic coast seashore life. Edmondson, Hylander, and Wilson have written fine books for younger readers. New editions of old favorites are in prospect. On the more technical side, the period is noteworthy for the publication of ZoBell's *Marine microbiology* and the texts in the comparatively new field of marine geology by Shepard and Kuenen.

In revising this list we have tried to include recent works, most of which should be still in print, together with certain old standbys which may be accessible only in libraries. Superseded works have been removed. We have added a section on marine geology and paleontology, presenting also a selection of works dealing with the "Pacific tides" of the past : handbooks, so to speak, of the better-known marine fossil beds. The citations are preponderantly of works published in England or the United States. Such provincialism is inevitable in these times when communications and exchange rates are haphazard. The editor of this edition, who has greater facilities than most of his colleagues for keeping up with this literature, has despaired of keeping track of publications in continental Europe and Russia. Nevertheless, it is hoped that this list will provide a reasonable selection of useful titles in the field, although it cannot be considered a "bibliography."

I. POPULAR BOOKS

ALLEE, W. C. 1938. *The social life of animals.* W. W. Norton, New York. 293 pages. (Rev. ed., 1951. *Cooperation among animals.* Henry Sherman, New York. xiv + 233 pages, ills.)
    ". . . . the most permanent contributions of our age appear to be the scientific discoveries.

. . . . These contributions are being made by extremely impractical research workers who are supported by a tiny splinter from the great block of capital gains. . . . ."
Consideration of "one of the most significant biological developments of recent years": the principle of biological co-operation. "It is my hope that from the work described in these pages, all social action may have a somewhat broader and more intelligent foundation." (Excerpts from pages 15 *et seq.*)

BEEBE, WM. 1938. *Zaca venture.* Harcourt, Brace, New York. 308 pages.
Lower California. Including interesting information on collecting and field-trip methods.

BERRILL, N. J. 1951. *The living tide.* Dodd, Mead & Co., New York. 256 pages, illus.
In chap. 21 there is a brief glimpse of "Doc" (as E. K. [!] Ricketts); we wish the author had said more about his visit to Cannery Row. The book is concerned mostly with seashore life on the Atlantic coast.

BUCHSBAUM, RALPH. 1948. *Animals without backbones. An introduction to the Invertebrata.* University of Chicago Press. Revised ed. 405 pages, illustrated.
Well-illustrated by amusing drawings and by plate gravures of photos. Written in alternate chapters, the first of which are addressed to the layman, the second to the student. Many of the photos were made at Pacific Grove and elsewhere on the Pacific Coast.

CALMAN, W. T. 1949. *The classification of animals.* John Wiley, New York. 54 pages.
This small volume, one of the Methuen monographs, is a concise introduction to the practice and problems of taxonomy by an accomplished taxonomist.

CARSON, RACHEL L. 1951. *The sea around us.* Oxford University Press, New York. vii + 230 pages.
Primarily a well-done popularization of oceanography with little reference to the life of the seas, this deservedly best-selling book has made oceanography famous to the extent that Hollywood has considered whipping up a movie under this title, with a courageous and pulchritudinous lady oceanographer and assorted sea serpents. An earlier book by Miss Carson, *Under the sea wind,* has been reissued by Oxford University Press; it describes, in slightly more tinted language, the life of birds, fish, and eels on the eastern coast. Unfortunately the glossary was not corrected, and the life-histories are more imaginative than necessary.

COLMAN, JOHN S. 1950. *The sea and its mysteries.* W. W. Norton, New York. xvi + 261 pages, illustrated.
One of the best of the recent summaries of oceanography, reprinted from the English edition without the colored frontispiece—a sad commentary on the high cost of American printing.

CORI, CARL. 1928. *Die Naturfreunde am Meeresstrande.* Emil Haim, Vienna. 2d edition. xi + 174 pp., 22 pls.
Considers interestingly some two hundred Mediterranean and Adriatic animals by type of shore (sand, mud, rock, etc.).

DOUGLAS, JOHN SCOTT. 1952. *The story of the oceans.* Dodd, Mead & Co., New York. ix + 315 pp.
Somewhat more lurid in spots than *The sea around us,* and with more about animals, this book seems to have been written primarily "for older boys." Since it is dedicated to that eminent diver and abalone ecologist Thomas Delmer Reviea (see *Fortnight,* Jan. 21, 1952, pp. 12–13), we wonder who is responsible for the idea that he would "be squeezed by tremendous water pressure" if the octopus ripped open his suit with its horny beak at "sixty feet below the sparkling blue waters of the mid-California coast (p. 181)." Such a gruesome scene is oddly out of place in a book which is, on the whole, surprisingly accurate in its popularization of zoology and in its general statements.

EDMONDSON, CHARLES H. 1949. *Seashore treasures.* Pacific Books, Palo Alto. 144 pages, illustrated.
Hawaiian shore life; for children.

GUBERLET, MURIEL L. 1936. *Animals of the seashore.* Metropolitan Press, Portland, Oregon. 412 pages, illustrated.
Descriptions, usually well illustrated, of 190 invertebrates of the Puget Sound region, of which 16 are pelagic, 17 dredged, and 157 intertidal. Short bibliography. The illustration on p. 96 labeled as *Sipunculus nudus* looks more like *Phascolosoma. Haliclystus sanjuanensis,*

pp. 46–47, seems to be still a manuscript species unless, under rules of nomenclature, this illustration and description constitute publication.

HYLANDER, CLARENCE J. 1950. *Sea and shore*. Macmillan, New York. 242 pages, illustrated.

An excellent introduction to seashore life for young readers, ages ten to fourteen, general enough to apply to both Atlantic and Pacific coasts.

MINER, ROY WALDO. 1950. *Field book of seashore life*. Putnam, New York. xv + 888 pages, 251 plates, incl. 24 in color.

Compact, concise guide to Atlantic coast invertebrates from New England to Beaufort, North Carolina. In preparation for twenty years, it supplants all previous Atlantic guides, although some of the nomenclature is not the most recent.

NEWBIGIN, M. 1919. *The study of the seashore*. Swann, Sonnenschein, London. Also in 1907 as *Life by the Seashore*, 344 pages; also in 1931 as *Life by the Seashore; an Introduction to Natural History*, rewritten and revised by R. Elmhirst. George Allen & Unwin, London. 296 pages.

So many genera are common to both regions that, by substituting only a few and bringing the synonymy to conform with American usage, this British seashore book could almost be used as a Pacific manual.

OMMANNEY, F. D. 1949. *The ocean*. Oxford University Press (Home University Library). 238 pages; illustrated.

This is a successor to the volume of this title by Sir John Murray, which is now rare in secondhand bookstores.

RICHARDS, HORACE G. 1938. *Animals of the seashore*. Bruce Humphries, Boston, 273 pages.

Although concerned with the rather limited New Jersey fauna, this has been rated as one of the best of the Atlantic seashore guides.

ROUGHLEY, T. C. 1937. *Wonders of the great barrier reef*. Angus and Robertson, Ltd., Sydney, Australia. 282 pages, 50 plates. (Reprinted, 1947, by Charles Scribner's Sons, New York, and since has been remaindered.)

Of the plates, comprising 52 illustrations, 35 are in full color, all but one from color photos of the living animals in water. The text includes much natural history information. Treatment is entirely popular in the sense that technical names are used rarely except in the glossary. This is unfortunate from the zoologist's standpoint, since many of the figures are unidentified except by popular names.

STEINBECK, JOHN, and RICKETTS, E. F. 1941. *Sea of Cortez. A leisurely journal of travel and research*. Viking Press, New York. 598 pages, with 40 plates of which 8 are colored.

A popular narrative comprises the first half. The account of an informal expedition into the Gulf of California by small boat, the object of which was to survey the shore animals of that inaccessible and, even to this day, little-known region. The latter half of the book is strictly technical, devoted mostly to lists, and consists of an annotated catalogue of the 550 species encountered, a résumé of the literature with a bibliography of some 479 titles, and a summary of the state of our knowledge with regard to the natural history of the Panamic faunal province, together comprising materials for a source book of the marine invertebrates of this region.

WELLS, HARRINGTON. 1942. *Seashore life*. California State Department of Education, Sacramento. 271 pages; illustrated.

WILSON, DOUGLAS P. 1935. *Life of the shore and shallow sea*. Ivor Nicholson and Watson, Ltd., London. 150 pages, 8 text figures, colored frontispiece, and 52 plates (7 x 9½ inches).

The finest book of the sort that has come to our attention until Yonge's. The 128 photographic illustrations of the living animals, reproduced generally very well by the plate-gravure process, are little short of superb. Treatment is ecological and semipopular. Sublittoral species are included. Southern England. (2d. ed., 1951, 213 pages, 44 pls., 10 figs.)

————. 1947. *They live in the sea*. Collins, London. 128 pages; illustrated.

For younger readers, illustrated with ninety fine photographs.

YONGE, C. M. 1944. *British marine life.* William Collins, London. 48 pages, 26 figures, 8 color plates.

A volume of the Britain in Pictures Series, illustrated with plates taken from old seashore books and monographs. The text is a précis of marine biology in Britain.

――――. 1949. *The sea shore.* Collins, London. 311 pages, 88 figures, 32 black and white, 40 color plates.

This is the finest book of this genre yet published; a *sine qua non* for the bookshelf of all who go to the shore. Our own shores are no less beautiful than those in the color photographs of this book, but our printers work shorter hours and charge more for their time. Most of the photographs are by Douglas P. Wilson. If the reader finds it hard to choose between Yonge and Wilson, we can only recommend that he buy both books.

II. SCIENTIFIC AND REFERENCE BOOKS

A. BIOLOGY

ALLEE, W. C., EMERSON, A. E., PARK, O., PARK, T., and SCHMIDT, K. P. 1949. *Principles of animal ecology.* W. B. Saunders, Philadelphia. 837 pages, 263 figures.

This milestone (in weight as well as content) of ecology is a mine of information which brings together a great mass of recent literature and digests it (pardon the metaphor!) for the reader with varying success. An indispensable reference, it nevertheless leaves much to be desired in regard to marine ecology, an indication, perhaps, of the comparative youth of this branch of the science. Nevertheless, it provides the best short summary of the development of marine ecology in the historical introduction, and provides much of the tangential information on terrestrial and lacustrine problems which must be scanned by the marine ecologist. Perhaps it should be pointed out that ecology, as understood by these authors, is not the practice of describing the phenomena of natural history in an esoteric terminology (the old-fashioned definition of ecology as "scientific natural history"), but the analytical study of the dynamics and interrelationships of groups of organisms in what Ed Ricketts was fond of calling the "holistic" manner.

BROWN, F. A., JR. (ed.). 1950. *Selected invertebrate types.* John Wiley, New York. xx + 597 pages, 234 figures.

A dissection and reference guide to Eastern types, static and disconnected in treatment, but with an excellent bibliography of recent summary papers dealing with morphology and anatomy.

BULLOUGH, W. S. 1950. *Practical invertebrate anatomy.* Macmillan, London. xi + 463 pages, 168 figures.

Similar to the above, but the work of a single author, with many standard forms re-examined and some not usually included in a one-volume text.

CARTER, G. S. 1948. *A general zoology of the invertebrates.* New and rev. ed.; Sidgwick and Jackson, London. xxviii + 509 pages, 172 figures.

A readable textbook of invertebrate physiology.

CENTRE NATIONAL DE LA RECHERCHE SCIENTIFIQUE. 1952. *Colloques Internationaux. XXXIII. Écologie.* Paris, C.N.R.S., 582 pages, illus.

The papers given at the international colloquium on ecology at Paris, 1950; also published in parts 2–7 of Année Biologique, vol. 27, 1951. A good summary of recent thought and work in ecology, especially on the nature of communities and the biocoenosis.

EALES, N. B. 1949. *The littoral fauna of Great Britain. A handbook for collectors.* 2d ed.; Cambridge University Press. 305 pages, frontispiece, 24 plates.

An annotated manual, with keys and diagnostic drawings, for most of the British shore animals. Bibliographies at the beginning of each chapter. We quote herewith, as being even more applicable to conditions in America, some of the remarks in the Foreword by Stanley Kemp: "One of the chief difficulties which lies in the way of a student who is beginning work on the marine fauna of the British coasts is the identification of the specimens which he collects. The information he wants is as a rule to be found in large monographs, or in papers scattered through long series of zoological journals; and these will almost always include descriptions of very many species that he is never likely to obtain. . . . . Only those who have worked on systematic zoology can realize the vast amount of labour which this book has entailed. . . . . Continental countries are much ahead of us in the production of such handbooks as this. . . . ." There is an appendix with practical hints and with a glossary.

EDMONDSON, C. H. 1946. "Reef and shore fauna of Hawaii," Bernice P. Bishop Museum, Spec. Publ., 22: 381 pages, 223 figures.
A useful guide to the Hawaiian fauna, provided with short keys.

EKMAN, SVEN. 1935. *Tiergeographie des Meeres.* Akad. Verlags. M.B.H., Leipzig. 542 pages.
Dr. Ekman is finishing a revision of this work, which is being translated into English by the British firm of Sidgwick and Jackson for publication in 1952.

FLATTELY, F. W., and WALTON, C. L. 1922. *The biology of the sea-shore.* Macmillan, London. 336 pages, 16 plates, 21 figures.
One of the three indispensable references and in some ways the best, its principles being applicable universally.

GAYEVSKAYA, N. S. (ed.). 1948. *Opredelitel' Fauny i Flory Severnykh Morei S.S.S.R.* Moskva: Gosudarstvennoye Izdatel'stvo "Sovetskaya Nauka." *(Manual of the Fauna and Flora of the Northern Seas of U.S.S.R.* State Publishing House, Moscow.) 740 pages, 136 plates, 77 text figures.
A well-illustrated "handbook" (it is about the size of a telephone directory!) of arctic and high boreal marine plants and invertebrates. Some of the species included occur within our range. This useful work—for those who read Russian—could well serve as a model for the sort of guide we need for our own shores.

HESSE, RICHARD. Translated and prepared by W. C. ALLEE and KARL P. SCHMIDT. 1937. *Ecological animal geography.* John Wiley, New York. 597 pages, 135 figures. 2d. ed., 1951. 715 pp., 142 figures.
Marine communities are extensively considered both for themselves and in connection with environmental limitations; methodology illuminated by the modern technic of holistic thinking.

HYMAN, LIBBIE H. 1940. *The Invertebrates: Protozoa through Ctenophora.* McGraw-Hill, New York, 726 pages, 221 text figures.
The first volume of what promises to be the most important invertebrate text of these times. Rather than the usual compilation, this is a review, digest, and re-evaluation based on much original work, combined with a critical examination of the literature. Traditional assumptions have been eliminated as their inherent incorrectnesses or limitations became apparent in the course of the work. The illustrations are mostly new, drawn for this purpose by the author. The treatment is monographic, with profuse sectional bibliographies. Obviously the work of a mind radical (in the sense of basic), disciplined, experienced, and exceptionally comprehensive.

——. 1951. *The Invertebrates. Vol. II. Platyhelminthes and Rhynchocoela. The acoelomate Bilateria.* McGraw-Hill, New York. vii +550 pages, 208 figures.

——. 1952. *The Invertebrates. Vol. III. Acanthocephala, Aschelminthes, and Entoprocta. The pseudocoelomate Bilateria. Ibid.,* vii + 572 pages, 223 text-figures.

JOHNSON, MYRTLE E., and SNOOK, HARRY J. 1927. *Seashore animals of the Pacific coast.* Macmillan, New York. 659 pages, 700 figures, 11 color plates.
An essential reference, now somewhat out of date and virtually unobtainable except at collectors' prices. Dr. Johnson is working on a new edition.

JOHNSTONE, JAMES. 1911. *Life in the sea.* Cambridge University Press. 150 pages.
A readable summary of the author's *Conditions of Life in the Sea* (Cambridge, 1908). The small, pink 1911 book still turns up in secondhand stores at a nominal price; the 1908 volume is getting rare.

LIGHT, S. F. 1941. *Laboratory and Field Text in Invertebrate Zoology.* Associated Student's Store, University of California. Photolith, 232 pages, by Stanford University Press.
An essential reference, well illustrated. The "Directions for the Study of Various Groups"

include many keys applicable to the San Francisco Bay area, and lists of species likely to be encountered at Dillon Beach and Moss Beach. An outgrowth of the *Zoology 112 Syllabus* previously cited, and one that should be expanded into a more available volume. It is a curious commentary on American zoology that this, the only work in this country so far as known which even attempts to approximate the Eales handbook 1939, in England, should apply to the little-known fauna of the Pacific coast.

At the time of his death in 1947, Dr. Light was gathering material for a new edition; this work has been continued at Berkeley, and the "more available volume" is in prospect for the near future.

MacGINITIE, G. E., and NETTIE. 1949. *Natural history of marine animals.* McGraw-Hill, New York. 473 pages, 282 figures.

This is essentially the record of the MacGinities' work at the Kerckhoff Marine Laboratory on Newport Bay and along the shores of southern California. Full of original observations on the behavior and habits of seashore animals, no student of the marine life of the Pacific coast can get along without it.

PROSSER, C. LADD. (ed.) 1950. *Comparative animal physiology.* W. B. Saunders, Philadelphia. 888 pages, 312 figures.

A monumental reference work, containing information about the physiology of many marine animals and excellent bibliographies to the large and scattered literature of the field.

RUSSELL, F. S., and YONGE, C. M. 1936. *The seas. Our knowledge of life in the sea and how it is gained.* Rev. ed.; Frederick Warne, London. 379 pages, 127 plates.

SCHEER, BRADLEY T. 1948. *Comparative physiology.* John Wiley, New York. vii + 563 pages, 68 figures.

Somewhat more readable than the Prosser text, but sometimes too general.

SCHENK, EDWARD T., and McMASTERS, JOHN H. 1948. *Procedure in taxonomy.* Rev. ed.; enlarged and in part rewritten by A. MYRA KEEN and SIEMON WILLIAM MULLER. Stanford University Press, vii + 93 pages.

Because so much of the invertebrate reconnaissance work here on the Pacific coast is constantly involved in taxonomic vexations, it seemed well for us to cite here this manual of procedure.

SOCIÉTÉ DE BIOGÉOGRAPHIQUE. 1940. *Contribution à l'étude de la répartition actuelle et passée des organismes dans la zone néritique.* Paul Lechevalier, Paris. 434 pages.

Memoir VII of the Société de Biogéographique; a symposium volume containing papers on Atlantic, Mediterranean, and Australian intertidal ecology, and a paper by Schenck and Keen on molluscan assemblages.

TRESSLER, DONALD K., and LEMON, JAMES McW. 1951. *Marine products of commerce. Their acquisition, handling, biological aspects of the science and technology of their preparation and preservation.* 2d ed. New York, Reinhold Publ. Corp., xiii + 782 pages, illus.

First published in 1923, this has long been considered a standard reference work. Many of the chapters have been satisfactorily brought up to date, but the sections on mussels, abalones, crabs, and the like appear to have been revised by the office boy. The section on abalones is a miserable joke, and the dangerous statement of the 1923 edition that "Mussels are best from December to July; they therefore may be used as a substitute for oysters during the early summer" has been repeated without making it clear which species or coast is meant (see p. 676).

ZoBELL, CLAUDE E. 1946. *Marine microbiology. A monograph on hydrobacteriology.* Chronica Botanica, Waltham, Mass. 240 pages, 12 figures.

Until the appearance of this volume, with its excellent bibliography, most marine biologists had been only dimly aware of the importance of bacteria in the economy of the sea.

B. OCEANOGRAPHY

COKER, R. E. 1947. *This great and wide sea.* xvii + 325 pages, 23 text figures, 91 plates. University of North Carolina Press.

Semipopular. The most up-to-date summary of oceanography.

FOWLER, G. HERBERT, and ALLEN, E. J. 1928. *Science of the sea. An elementary handbook of practical oceanography for travellers, sailors, and yachtsmen.* Clarendon Press, Oxford. xxiii + 502 pages, 216 figures.

GRIER, MARY C. 1946. *References on the physical oceanography of the western Pacific Ocean.* U.S. Navy, Hydrographic Office, Publ. 238. 174 pages.

HARVEY, H. W. 1945. *Recent advances in the chemistry and biology of sea water.* Cambridge University Press. vii + 164 pages.
Supplementary to the Harvey manual 1928, *Biological chemistry and physics of sea water.*

JOHNSTONE, JAMES. 1923. *An introduction to oceanography.* University Press of Liverpool, Ltd., Hodden & Stoughton, Ltd., London. 351 pages.
Comprehensive account of tide and tidal influences especially.

MARMER, H. A. 1926. *The tide.* 282 pages. Appleton, New York.
Indispensable.

MURRAY, JOHN, and HJORT, JOHAN. 1912. *The depths of the ocean.* Macmillan, London. xx + 821 pages, 575 figures, 9 plates.
A monumental source book, especially for the North Atlantic. It is now a collector's item, commanding exorbitant prices.

SVERDRUP, H. U., JOHNSON, M. W., and FLEMING, R. H. 1942. *The Oceans. Their physics, chemistry, and general biology.* Prentice-Hall Inc. New York. 1087 pages, illustrated.
Essential. Source book and summary. Extensive sectional bibliographies. Charts and tables. A review, but with considerable new work included.

C. GEOLOGY AND PALEONTOLOGY

ANDERSON, CHARLES A. and others. 1950. *1940 E. W. Scripps cruise to the Gulf of California.* Geol. Soc. Amer., Mem., **43**.
A collection of papers, independently paged, concerning geology, paleontology, and oceanography of the Gulf of California, by various authors, with an excellent bathymetric map. A suitable companion piece to *Sea of Cortez.*

ANDERSON, F. M. 1938. "Lower cretaceous deposits in California and Oregon," Geol. Soc. Amer. Spec. Paper **19**: x + 339 pages, 84 plates. (Pl. 84 is a map of principal beds.)
The fossil record along the Pacific coast is spotty. It jumps from the amazing Cambrian beds of the Burgess shale in British Columbia to the Lower Cretaceous, followed by a rich Tertiary. The Cambrian has not been treated in a single monograph, but can be sampled in the many papers by Walcott published principally in the Smithsonian Miscellaneous Series.

CAMP, CHARLES L., and HANNA, G. DALLAS. 1937. *Methods in paleontology.* University of California Press, xxiii + 153 pages, 58 figures.
A useful manual for handling fossils.

DALY, REGINALD ALDWORTH. 1942. *The floor of the ocean. New light on old mysteries.* University of North Carolina Press, x + 157 pages, 82 figures.
Written in a charming and persuasive style, it should not, however, be taken as the last word on the subject. Collateral reading, e.g., in Kuenen, is strongly recommended.

DAVIS, WILLIAM MORRIS. 1928. "The coral reef problem," American Geographical Society, Spec. Publ., **9**: 596 pages. 227 figures.
Monographic summary of the problem, with reviews of theories to 1928.

JENKINS, OLAF P. 1943. "Geologic formations and economic development of the oil and gas fields of California," California Div. Mines, Bull. **118**: 773 pages.
Some detailed accounts of principal beaches.

———. (ed.). 1951. "Geologic guidebook of the San Francisco Bay counties. History, landscape, geology, fossils, minerals, industry and routes to travel," Calif. Div. of Mines Bull., **154**: 392 pages, illus.
An excellent compilation of information, including a chapter on the Farallons and, *inter alia,* material on the central California sea coast. Here and there the touch of a biologist would have improved the text, but one cannot have everything in this world.

JOHNSON, D. W. 1919. *Shore processes and shore-line development.* John Wiley, New York. 584 pages.
A comprehensive source book with much ecologically applicable information; includes more data on waves and is more easily understandable popularly, than anything else we have found. Johnson's classification of shore lines as emergent and submergent is oversimplified, but, despite its signs of age, this book still remains the best available treatment of coastal geomorphology.

KEEN, A. MYRA, and BENTSON, HERDIS. 1944. "Check list of California Tertiary marine mollusca," Geol. Soc. Amer. Spec. Paper **56**: 280 pages.

KUENEN, P. H. 1950. *Marine geology.* John Wiley, New York. 568 pages, 246 figures, 2 charts.
With special emphasis on the Dutch East Indies. Contains an excellent chapter on coral reefs.

RATHBUN, MARY J. 1926. "The fossil stalk-eyed Crustacea of the Pacific slope of North America," U.S. Nat. Mus., Bull., **138**: 149 pages, 39 pls.

SCHENCK, HUBERT G., and KEEN, A. MYRA. 1950. *California fossils for the field geologist.* Stanford University Press. 88 pages, incl. 56 plates. Photolith, spiral-bound.
A handy guide, principally to mollusks. Intended to be used in the field, it needs a stronger binding to stand up.

SHEPARD, FRANCIS P. 1948. *Submarine geology.* Harper & Bros., New York. xvi + 348 pages, 105 figures, 1 chart.
With special reference to continental shelves and slopes and submarine canyons, hence complementary to the Kuenen text.

SHEPARD, FRANCIS P., and EMERY, K. O. 1941. "Submarine topography off the California coast: canyons and tectonic interpretation," Geol. Soc. Amer. Spec. Paper **31**: 171 pages, 42 figures, 4 charts.
The charts which accompany this monograph show, in layered colors, the bottom formations along the California coast, and are handsome examples of the cartographer's art.

WEAVER, CHARLES E. 1937. "Tertiary stratigraphy of western Washington and northwestern Oregon," Univ. Wash. Publ. Geol., **4**: 266 pages, 15 plates.
With good maps of the beds.

———. 1943. "Paleontology of the marine tertiary formations of Oregon and Washington," *ibid.*, **5**: 788 pages, 104 plates.
Monographic treatment of larger invertebrate fossils.

In addition to the above, see Grant and Gale (1931) cited under mollusca in this volume. Much useful and interesting work on the structure and formation of beaches is being printed in the *Bulletin of the Beach Erosion Board* (U.S. Engineers), in their *Technical Memoranda*, and in *Shore and Beach.* These journals are available in engineering and geology libraries. The annual reports of the committee on marine ecology of the National Research Council (under various names) contain, in addition to bibliographies of recent papers, longer articles on paleoecology. The committee, now formally titled "Committee on a Treatise on Marine Ecology and Paleoecology," is, as its current title implies, working on a symposium treatise which will combine our knowledge of marine ecology and paleontology.

III. ECOLOGICAL AND FAUNISTIC ACCOUNTS

A. PACIFIC COAST REFERENCES

ANDREWS, H. L. 1945. "The kelp beds of the Monterey region," Ecology, **26**: 24–37.

Coe, W. R. 1932. "Season of attachment and rate of growth of sedentary marine organisms . . . .," Bull. Scripps Inst. Ocean., Tech. Ser., 3: 37–86.

Coe, W. R., and Allen, W. E. 1937. "Growth of sedentary marine organisms on experimental blocks and plates for nine successive years at the pier of the Scripps Institution of Oceanography," Bull. Scripps. Inst. Ocean., Tech. Ser. 4: 101–36.

Doty, Maxwell, S. 1946. "Critical tide factors that are correlated with the vertical distribution of marine algae and other organisms along the Pacific coast," Ecology, 27 (4): 315–28, 6 figs.

Fraser, C. McL. 1932. "A comparison of the marine fauna of the Nanaimo region with that of the San Juan archipelago," Trans. Roy. Soc. Canada, 3d ser., 26 (Sec. 5): 49–70.

———. 1942. "The collecting of marine zoological materials in B.C. waters," Canad. Field Nat., 56: 115–20.

Gersbacher and Denison. 1930. "Experiments with animals in tidepools," Publ. Puget Sound Biol. Sta., 7: 209–15.

Gislén, Torsten. 1943–44. "Physiological and ecological investigations concerning the littoral of the northern Pacific." Sections 1–4. Lunds Univ. Ars. N F Avd. 2, 39 (5) and 40 (8): 63 and 91 pages, plates.
Comparisons between the fauna and the environmental factors of Pacific Grove, California, and Misaki, Japan, in the same latitude. Statement of the ecological associations, with correlations of temperature, wave-shock, etc., for the coasts of California and northern Lower California. Extensive information not elsewhere available.

Graham, H. W., and Gay, Helen. 1945. "Season of attachment and growth of sedentary marine organisms at Oakland, California," Ecology, 26: 375–86.

Grier, Mary C. 1941. "Oceanography of the north Pacific Ocean, Bering Sea and Bering Strait: A contribution towards a bibliography," Libr. Series, U. Wash. Publ., 2: 290 pages.
Includes zoölogy, botany, and explorations.

Grinnell, Joseph, and Linsdale, Jean M. 1936. "Vertebrate animals of Point Lobos Reserve, 1934–35." Carnegie Ist. Wash. Publ., 481: 159 pages, 39 plates.
Contains considerable information about marine mammals and shore birds, with excellent photographs.

Harrington and Griffin. 1927. "Notes on the distribution and habits of some Puget Sound invertebrates," Trans. New York Acad. Sci., 16: 152–65.

Hewatt, W. G. 1935. "Ecological succession in the *Mytilus californianus* habitat as observed in Monterey Bay, California," Ecology, 16: 244–51.

———. 1937. "Ecological studies on selected marine intertidal communities of Monterey Bay, California," Amer. Midl. Nat. 18 (2): 161–206.

———. 1938. "Notes on the breeding seasons of the rocky beach fauna of Monterey Bay, California," Proc. Calif. Acad. Sci., (4) 23 (19): 283–88.

———. 1946. "Marine ecological studies on Santa Cruz Island, California," Ecol. Monogr., 16: 185–210.
A survey involving more than 500 species, mostly intertidal.

MacGinitie, G. E. 1935. "Ecological aspects of a California marine estuary," Amer. Midl. Nat. 16 (5): 629–765, 20 figures.
Life in Elkhorn Slough before progress improved the place; some of the animal life is now making a comeback. In this work, little faith is placed in the mapping of communities and attempts to segregate them into zones. Whether it is the influence of this paper, or other factors, it is interesting to note that quantitative population studies have been scarce on this coast. When the papers of Shelford and his students, the work of Hewatt, and the unpublished work of Pitelka and Paulson (see our pp. 229–30) have been cited, that is about all we have.

One of the most important deterrents to such work is, of course, the bewildering complexity of our fauna and the taxonomic uncertainty in which so many of the species are involved.

———. 1939. "Littoral marine communities," Amer. Midl. Nat., 21 (1): 28–55.

RIGG, GEORGE B., and MILLER, R. C. 1949. "Intertidal plant and animal zonation in the vicinity of Neah Bay, Washington," Proc. Calif. Acad. Sci., (4), 26 (10) : 323–51, 8 figures.
The authors recognize four zones: splash, upper intertidal, lower intertidal, and demersal, corresponding to the 1–4 system of this book.

SCHEER, BRADLEY T. 1945. "The development of marine fouling communities," Biol. Bull., 89 (1) : 103–21, 4 figures.
The time table of establishment in Newport Bay, California.

SHELFORD and TOWLER. 1925. "Animal communities of the San Juan Channel and adjacent waters," Publ. Puget Sound Biol. Sta., 5: 33–74.
Application of community principles to Puget Sound waters; the animals only are considered.

SHELFORD et al. 1935. "Some marine biotic communities of the Pacific coast of North America," Ecological Monographs, 5: 251–345.

STOHLER, R. 1930. "Gewichtsverhältnisse bei gewissen marinen Evertebraten," Zool. Anz., 91: 149–55.
Tables of fresh weight, skeletal weight, and in some cases, weight of water, of "meat," etc., are given for such common Pacific forms as *Pisaster, Patiria* (as *Asterina*), *Pycnopodia,* urchins, *Acmaea,* chitons, snails, *Mytilus,* etc.

ZOBELL, CLAUDE E., and FELTHAM, CATHARINE B. 1942. "The bacterial flora of a marine mud flat as an ecological factor," Ecology, 23 (1) : 69–78, 1 figure.
Concerns the bacterial flora of Mission Bay.

B. EXTRA-LIMITAL AND GENERAL ACCOUNTS

ALLEE, W. C. 1923. "Studies in marine ecology, I and II," Biol. Bull., 44: 157–253.
One of the few comprehensive treatments of a restricted area in this country. Although concerned with the fauna of Woods Hole, it pictures a state of affairs applicable anywhere.

———. 1931. *Animal Aggregations.* University of Chicago Press.

ALLEN, E. J. 1899. "On the fauna and bottom deposits near the thirty-fathom line . . . .," Jour. Mar. Biol. Assoc., n.s., 5: 365–542.
Although dealing exclusively with dredged forms, this lengthy and excellent account is still valuable for general ecological information, factors of distribution, interrelations, etc. Type of bottom is considered an important factor.

ALLEN, TODD, et al. 1900. "Fauna of the Salcombe Estuary," Jour. Mar. Biol. Assoc., n.s., 6: 151–217.

———. 1902. "Fauna of the Exe Estuary," *ibid.,* 6: 295–343.
They classify the regions into areas predominantly sand, mud, gravel, etc., and give sample collecting hauls for representative stations.

BASSINDALE, R., EBLING, F. J., KITCHING, J. A., and PURCHON, R. D. 1948. "The ecology of the Lough Ine rapids with special reference to water currents. I. Introduction and hydrography," Jour. Ecology, 36 (2) : 305–22, 9 figures, 1 plate, chart.
See also Ebling *et al.*

BATCHELDER, G. H. 1926. "An ecological study of a brackish water stream," Ecology, 7: 55–71.
New Hampshire.

BEVERIDGE, W. A., and CHAPMAN, V. J. 1950. "The zonation of marine algae

at Piha, New Zealand, in relation to the tidal factor. (Studies in inter-tidal zonation 2)," Pacific Science, 4 (3) : 188–201, 14 figures.
See also Dellow, Chapman, below.

CASPERS, H. 1950a. "Der Biozönose und Biotopbegriff vom Blickpunkt der Marinen und Limnischen Synökologie," Biol. Zentralb., 69 (½) : 43–63.

―――. 1950b. "Die Lebensgemeinschaft der Helgoländer Austernbank," Helgol. Wiss. Meeresunters., 3 : 119–69, 15 figs.

―――. 1951a. "Biozönotische Untersuchungen über die Strandarthropoden im bulgarischen Küstenbereich des Schwarzen Meeres," Hydrobiologica, 3 (2) : 131–93, 15 figs.

―――. 1951b. "Quantitative Untersuchungen über die Bodentierwelt des Schwarzen Meeres im bulgarischen Küstenbereich," Arch. Hydrobiol., 45 : 1–192, 66 figs., 7 pls.
A useful series of papers, held up by wartime conditions until this time. The 1951a item is noteworthy as a contribution to the study of sandy shores, which are too often neglected by ecologists.

CHAMBOST, L. 1928. *"Essai sur la région littorale dans les environs de Salammbô,"* Bull. Sta. Oceanogr. Salammbô, 8 : 28 pages, 7 figures, 1 chart.
Missed in the various comprehensive bibliographies, but worth citing as a reference to a sandy, tideless environment.

CHAPMAN, V. J. 1946. "Marine algal ecology," Botanical Review, 12 : 628–72.
Literature review.

―――. 1950. "The marine algal communities of Stanmore Bay, New Zealand (Studies in inter-tidal zonation 1)," Pacific Science, 4 (1) : 63–68, 3 figures.
The three papers so far published in this series (Beveridge and Chapman, and Dellow) are principally concerned with ecology of algae.

COLMAN, JOHN. 1933. "The nature of the intertidal zonation of plants and animals," Jour. Mar. Biol. Assoc., n.s., 18 : 435–76.
Establishes close correlation between critical distributional horizons and tidal marks.

―――. 1943. "Some intertidal enigmas," Proc. Linn. Soc. London, 1941–42, (3) : 232–34.
Poses some critical questions about intertidal zonation, which still remain to be answered.

CROSSLAND, C. 1927. "Expedition to the South Pacific on the S. Y. St. George"; "Marine ecology, etc.," Trans. Roy. Soc. Edinburgh, 55 : 531–54.
Panama intertidal and upper subtidal.

DAHL, ERIK. 1948. "On the smaller Arthropoda of marine algae, especially in the polyhaline waters off the Swedish west coast," Unders. Öresund, 35 : 193 pages, 42 figures.
Another of these excellent, comprehensive Scandinavian papers (Cf. Gislén, below), beautifully printed, which are the product of a sound tradition in marine ecology and a well-known fauna.

DAKIN, W. J., BENNETT, ISOBEL, and POPE, ELIZABETH. 1948. "A study of certain aspects of the ecology of the intertidal zone of the New South Wales coast," Australian Jour. Scient. Research (B), 1 (2) : 176–230, 9 plates, 3 figures.
Excellently illustrated description and analysis of the Australian coast, with lists of species characteristic of the zones recognized. Of special interest is the information about the marine spider *Desis crosslandi*, living in the low intertidal.

DELLOW, VIVIENNE. 1950. "Inter-tidal ecology at Narrow Neck Reef, New Zealand (Studies in inter-tidal zonation, 3)," Pacific Science, 4 (4) : 355–74, 13 figures.

DEXTER, RALPH W. 1947. "The marine communities of a tidal inlet at Cape Ann, Massachusetts: a study in bio-ecology," Ecol. Monogr., 17 : 261–94, 17 figures.
Descriptive population ecology, with biomes and faciations and coaction diagrams.

EBLING, F. J., KITCHING, J. A., PURCHON, R. D., and BASSINDALE, R. 1948. "The ecology of the Lough Ine rapids with special reference to water currents. 2. The fauna of the *Saccorhiza* canopy," Jour. Animal Ecology, **17** (2) : 223–44, 14 figures.

The two papers on Lough Ine rapids describe a situation similar to the surge channels and narrow passages of the Puget Sound region, where comparable studies would be of interest.

EINARSSON, HERMANN. 1941. "Survey of the benthonic animal communities of Faxa Bay (Iceland)." Meddel. Komm. Danmarks Fisk. og Havunders. (Fiske.) **11** (1) : 46 pages, 19 figures, 6 tables.

ERCEGOVIĆ, A. 1934. "Wellengang und Lithophytenzone an der Ostadriatischen Küste," Acta Adriatica (Split, Jugoslavia), **3**: 1–20.

Stresses the significance of the wave, i.e., surf and astronomical or barometric tide, as a primary oceanographic factor, and emphasizes the importance of wave shock as a formative and segregating factor for lithophytic organisms.

EVANS, R. G. 1947. "The intertidal ecology of Cardigan Bay," Jour. Ecol., **34**: 273–309.

———. 1947a. "The intertidal ecology of selected localities in the Plymouth neighborhood," Jour. Mar. Biol. Assoc., **27**: 173–218.

These two papers are the beginning of series planned to describe, in Stephenson's manner, the coasts of England.

GISLÉN, TORSTEN. 1930. "Epibioses of the Gullmar Fjord. II," Kristin. Zool. Sta. 1877–1927, N : r **4**: 1–380.

Sweden west coast. Recognizes and enumerates the plant-animal communities starting from above mean sea level, in a tideless region, and working down. This "marine sociology" would seem to be the most correct system of ecological analysis yet devised; but one unfortunately not adapted to a popular treatise such as our book, and restricted furthermore to areas better known taxonomically and physically than the Pacific coast of North America.

———. 1931. "A survey of the marine associations in the Misaki district . . . . ," Jour. Fac. Sci. Imp. Univ. Tokyo, Sec. 4, **2**: 398–444.

Through the kindness of Dr. Gislén, we were able to read the manuscript of this account of the communities of a Japanese area, differing intertidally not greatly from those of Monterey Bay except in temperature.

GRAVE, B. H. 1933. "Rate of growth, age at sexual maturity, and duration of life in sessile organisms at Woods Hole," Biol. Bull., **65**: 375–86.

Finds that many prolific animals have a life span of less than one year, producing several generations during the summer, which accounts for the rapid rehabilitation of depleted areas.

GUILER, ERIC R. 1950. "The intertidal ecology of Tasmania," Pap. & Proc. Roy. Soc. Tasmania, **1949**: 135–201, 30 figs., 2 pls.

———. 1951a. "The intertidal ecology of Pipe Clay Lagoon," *ibid.*, **1950**: 29–52, 8 figs., 2 pls.

———. 1951b. "Notes on the intertidal ecology of the Freycinet Peninsula," idem., 53–70, 4 figs., 3 pls.

A series of excellent, well-illustrated papers; author suggests that conditions in Tasmania are more comparable to those of the South African coast than of New South Wales.

HEDGPETH, JOEL W. 1947. "Fishers of the Murex (Notes for a Bibliography of Marine Natural History)," Isis, 1947, **37** (107–8): 27–32.

HEEGAARD, P. 1944. "The bottom fauna of Praestø Fjord," Folia Geographica Danica, **3** (3) : 59–81, 7 figures, 5 tables.

HUNTSMAN, A. G. 1918. "The vertical distribution of certain intertidal animals," Trans. Roy. Soc. Canada, Ser. 3, **12** (Sec. 4): 53–60.

HUTCHINS, LOUIS W. 1947. "The bases for temperature zonation in geographical distribution," Ecol. Monogr., **17**: 325–35, 8 figures.

Recognizes four basic types of zonation for marine organisms in the northern Hemisphere based on temperature differences. Because of the importance of this paper, we consider a summary in this place inadvisable.

JOHNSON, MARTIN W. 1948. "Sound as a tool in marine ecology, from data on biological noises and the deep scattering layer," Jour. Mar. Research, 7 (3) :443–58, 4 figures.
One of the interesting and unexpected products of wartime research was the study of underwater noises by shrimp and fish. This paper summarizes and lists recent papers on the subject.

JOHNSON, D. S., and YORK, H. H. 1915. "The relation of plants to tide levels," Carnegie Institution Wash. Publ., 206: 162 pages.
Establishes the great importance of the tidal-exposure factor in the distribution of shore algae, emphasizing the fact that plants occur in zones through the operation of this factor, and that "the vertical range of a plant common to two localities with different ranges of tide will be found exactly proportional in each place to the local range of tide."

JONES, N. S. 1950. "Marine bottom communities," Biol. Reviews, 25: 283–313.
. Summary of the research and thought on bottom communities, especially in European waters, with comprehensive list of literature.

KLUGH, B. 1924. "Factors controlling the biota of tidepools," Ecology, 5: 192–96.

KORRINGA, P. 1947. "Relations between the moon and periodicity in the breeding of marine animals," Ecol. Monogr., 17: 347–81, 5 figures.
Review paper, with discussion of typical species showing periodism, especially oysters and polychaetes.

MOLANDER, A. 1928. "Animal communities on soft bottom areas in the Gullmar Fjord," Kristin. Zool. Sta., 1877–1927, N :r 2: 1–90.

NELSON, THURLOW C. 1947. "Some conditions from the land in determining conditions of life in the sea," Ecol. Monogr., 17: 337–46, 7 figures.

ORTON, J. H. 1920. "Sea temperature, breeding and distribution in marine animals," Jour. Mar. Biol. Assoc., n.s., 12: 339–66.

PEARSE, A. S., HUMM, H. J., and WHARTON, G. W. 1942. "Ecology of sand beaches at Beaufort, North Carolina," Ecol. Monogr., 12: 135–90, 24 figures.
California beaches are actually much richer in species-mass than the Beaufort beach, but little has been done with them except studies of the Pismo clam, Emerita, and the worm Thoracophelia (q.v.).

PETERSEN, C. G. JOH. 1918. The sea bottom and its production of fishfood. A survey of the work done in connection with valuation of the Danish waters from 1883–1917. Report Danish Biol. Station to the Board of Agriculture. 62 pages, 10 plates, map.
This is the summary paper of the classic work of Petersen and his colleagues, the first two installments of which, under the title of Valuation of the Sea appeared as reports 20 (1911) and 21 (1913) of the Danish Biological Station. Although the efficacy of Petersen's sampling methods has been criticized, the work remains the foundation of all subsequent work in marine population ecology. Of Petersen, Allee et al. (p. 51) say: "It is not always recognized that this man is among the great in the history of ecology and hydro-biology."

REID, D. M. 1932. "Salinity interchange between sea-water in sand, and overflowing fresh-water at low tide. II," Jour. Mar. Biol. Assoc., 18: 299–306.

STEPHEN, A. C. 1929–30. "Studies on the Scottish marine fauna; the fauna of the sandy and muddy areas of the tidal zone," Trans. Roy. Soc. Edinburgh, 56: 291–306, and 521–35.
Zonation and optimum areas per species.

STEPHENSON, T. A. 1947. "The constitution of the intertidal fauna and flora of South Africa," Annals of the Natal Museum, 11 (2): 207–324, illustrations.
Part III of the report of a ten-year survey. Bibliography.

STEPHENSON, T. A., and ANNE. 1949. "The universal features of zonation between tide-marks on rocky coasts," Jour. Ecology, 37 (2): 289–305, 4 figures, 1 plate.

————. 1950a. "Life between tidemarks in North America," Endeavour, **9** (33) : 3 pages, 4 color plates.

————. 1950b. "Life between tide-marks in North America. I. The Florida Keys," Jour. Ecology, **38** (2) : 354–402, 10 figs., pls. 9–15.

————. 1952. ". . . II. Northern Florida and the Carolinas," *ibid.*, **40** (1) : 1–49, 9 figs., pls. 1–6.

THORSON, GUNNAR. 1946. *Reproduction and larval development of Danish marine bottom invertebrates, with special reference to the planktonic larvae in the Sound (Øresund).* Meddel. Komm. Danmarks Fisk. og Havunders. (Plankton) **4** (1) : 523 pages, 198 figures.

————. 1950. "Reproductive and larval ecology of marine bottom invertebrates," Biol. Reviews, **25**: 1–45, 6 figures.
Correlates development of nonpelagic larvae with conditions unfavorable to larval feeding, i.e., short seasons of plankton production and low temperatures. An excellent review paper.

VATOVA, ARISTOCLE. 1940. *"Le zoocenosi della Laguna veneta,"* Thalassia, **3** (10) : 28 pages, 10 plates.

————. 1943. *"Le zoocenosi dell' Alto Adriatico presso Rovigno e loro variazioni nello spazio e nel tempo,"* *ibid.*, **5** (6) : 61 pages, 1 plate.

————. 1949. *"Caratteri di alcune facies bentoniche della Laguna Veneta,"* Nova Thalassia, **1** (4) : 14 pages, 1 plate.
The population ecology of the canals and lagoon of Venice.

VAUGHAN, T. W. 1940. "Ecology of modern marine organisms with reference to paleogeography," Bull. Geol. Soc. America, **51**: 433–68.

VERRILL and SMITH. 1871–72. "Report on the invertebrate animals of Vineyard Sound and adjacent waters," Report U.S. Fish Comm., **1871–72**: 295–778.
Out of date, but still surprisingly useful in principle, and excellent reading. They divide the fauna into animals predominantly inhabiting (*a*) bays and sounds, (*b*) estuaries, harbors, etc., and (*c*) ocean shores (comparable to the classification we employ), and each region is subdivided according to type of bottom—sand, mud, rock, etc.

WHITTEN, H. L., ROSENE, HILDA F., and HEDGPETH, J. W. 1950. "The invertebrate fauna of Texas coast jetties; a preliminary survey," Publ. Inst. Mar. Science Univ. Texas, **1** (2) : 53–87, 4 figures, 1 plate.
Describes the fauna of a little-known environment, peculiar in that it is artificially introduced upon a sandy littoral.

WILSON, DOUGLAS P. 1949. "The decline of *Zostera marina* L. at Salcombe and its effects on the shore," Jour. Mar. Biol. Assoc., **28**: 395–412, 4 plates, 1 figure.

————. 1951. "A biological difference between natural sea waters," Jour. Mar. Biol. Ass., **30**: 1–20, 2 pls.
Water from two different localities gave very different results in rearing certain marine invertebrates, but lacked any perceptible chemical difference.

————. 1952. "The influence of the nature of the substratum on the metamorphosis of the larvae of marine animals, especially the larvae of *Ophelia bicornis* Savingy," Annales l'Inst. Oceanogr., **27** (2) : 49–156, 2 figs.

WOMERSLEY, H. B. S. 1947. "The marine algae of Kangaroo Island. I. A general account of the algal ecology," Trans. Roy. Soc. S. Australia, **71** (2) : 228–52, 5 plates, 5 figures.

WOMERSLEY, H. B. S., and EDMONDS, S. J. 1952. "Marine coastal zonation in Southern Australia in relation to a general scheme of classification," Jour. Ecology, **40** (1) : 84–90, 1 fig.
The authors disagree with the Stephensonian terminology in some details.

YONGE, C. M. 1948. "Bottom fauna of the sea," Research, **13** : 589–95, 3 figures.
Excellent nontechnical review.

The listing of extralimital reports is far from comprehensive; it should be considered a sampling of the literature. Gislén (1930) presents a comprehensive bibliography up to 1930, and Fischer-Piette, in Vol. VII of the Société Biogéographique (pp. 421–34), supplements this up to 1940. Omissions, however, occur in both these listings. Many important papers are listed, and some abstracted, in the various reports of the Committee on Marine Ecology of the National Research Council. It would be easier, perhaps, to list those marine-shore and shallow-water areas which have not been the subject of ecological investigations (as opposed to studies of the natural history of particular animals). We have not encountered papers dealing with Patagonia, Kamchatka, and Easter Island, but would not be surprised to have some turn up as soon as this is read. The large and significant Russian literature is practically a void in all these various bibliographies, although Russian biologists, under the leadership of S. A. Zernoff, were among the first to adopt Petersen's methods. There are detailed studies of the Black Sea, Caspian Sea, and the arctic waters in this literature, most of which was summarized up to 1947 by Zenkevich in volume 2 of his *Fauna and biological productivity of the sea*, Soviet Science, Leningrad, 1947, 588 pages, 327 figures.

Zernoff, incidentally, is the author of a work titled *General Hydrobiology* (2d ed. 1949), the only book of its kind in any language, and one which deserves translation. As far as we know, this branch of Russian science has, at least up to now, been free of eulogistic apothegms to that well-known "Coryphaeus of science" and the confusions of dialectical materialism.

GENERAL INDEX

This alphabetical index comprises an index to scientific names and a subject index as well. Important references to natural history, physiological processes, etc., are grouped together. Thus a reader searching for information on sex-reversal, autotomy, breeding habits, etc., has only to look up these subjects alphabetically. Where there is reference to more than one page number, the figure in **bold face** type refers to the main account. Scientific generic and specific names are in *italics*.

David R. Malcolm

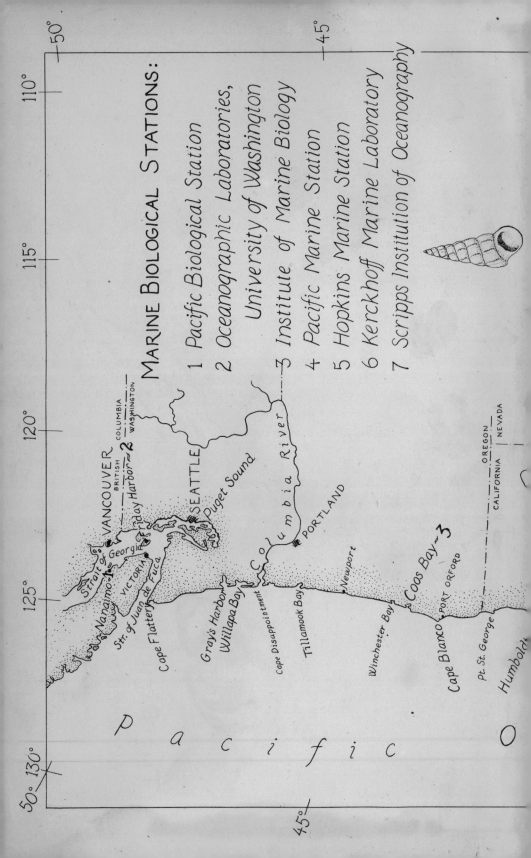

MARINE BIOLOGICAL STATIONS:

1 Pacific Biological Station
2 Oceanographic Laboratories,
    University of Washington
3 Institute of Marine Biology
4 Pacific Marine Station
5 Hopkins Marine Station
6 Kerckhoff Marine Laboratory
7 Scripps Institution of Oceanography